Robert Sheets
   2404 ~~Ohio~~ Ave. #~~4~~
       ~~Cinci~~ ~~Oh~~ 452~~
   381 - 6621

Hydrology and Quality of
Water Resources

Hydrology and Quality of Water Resources

Mark J. Hammer
Professor of Civil Engineering

Kenneth A. Mac Kichan
Professional Engineer

JOHN WILEY & SONS
New York • Chichester • Brisbane • Toronto • Singapore

CONSULTING EDITORS

Alfred S. Harrison
Chief, Technical Engineering Branch
Missouri River Division, Corps of Engineers

Gary L. Hergenrader
Professor of Zoology, School of Life Sciences
University of Nebraska

To Audrey and Lois

Library of Congress Cataloging in Publication Data:

Hammer, Mark J   1931-
  Hydrology and quality of water resources.

  Includes indexes.
  1. Water resources development. 2. Water
quality management. 3. Hydrology. 4. Water—Law
and legislation—United States. I. MacKichan, Kenneth
Allen, 1911-   joint author. II. Title.
TC405.H36   551.48   80-209
ISBN 0-471-02681-6

Printed in the United States of America

10 9 8 7 6 5 4

Preface

This book provides a comprehensive overview of water resources considering both quantity and quality aspects. Following the introduction, hydrology and water quality for groundwater, flowing waters, and impounded waters are presented. The final chapter integrates these individual subjects in a discussion on water resources management.

This textbook incorporates, for the first time, all of the important elements of hydrology and quality of water resources under one cover. Existing publications reflect the traditional fragmented views. Hydrology is treated as a separate subject disregarding water quality, and often without discussing the hydrology of impounded waters. In stressing quality in flowing waters, books on pollution control usually neglect eutrophication and mention groundwater only briefly. Limnology texts, which include the hydrology and quality of impounded waters, are rarely read by engineering and technology students. Because of a lack of revision, most existing textbooks on water resources do not reflect the evolution of recent years. On the other hand, new books frequently stress systems analysis with little or no discussion of the quantity and quality of water. Hopefully, this work presents the balance needed to portray the scope of water resources today.

Hydrology and Quality of Water Resources is also a companion to *Water and Waste-Water Technology*, available in either English units or SI metric. Following introductory chapters on the fundamentals of chemistry, biology, and hydraulics, *Water and Waste-Water Technology* proceeds with a comprehensive coverage of wastewater collection and treatment, water processing and distribution, water reuse and land disposal, and operation of systems. In combination, these two books encompass the basic knowledge needed for civil engineers, water resource planners, natural resource managers, public health technologists, and environmental scientists. The emphasis on art and practice makes them valuable for engineering colleges, technological institutes, and continuing education programs.

Mark J. Hammer
Kenneth A. Mac Kichan

Acknowledgments

The review recommendations of two technical consultants were incorporated during the development and writing of this textbook. Drawing on 15 years of experience as Chief of Hydraulics and Hydrology with the Missouri River Basin Division of the Corps of Engineers, Mr. Al Harrison critiqued all of the chapters on water quantity and hydrology of groundwater, flowing waters, and impounded waters. Dr. Gary Hergenrader reviewed all the sections on water quality. His teaching and research knowledge in water biology and lake eutrophication were beneficial in criticism of the chapters on flowing and impounded waters. We are deeply indebted to these consulting editors for their valuable contributions and critiques.

Mrs. Mary Lou Wegener provided the essential ingredient of typing the manuscript in a professional manner greatly appreciated by the authors. Mrs. Audrey Hammer assisted in assembling the manuscript and proofreading the final draft.

M. J. H.
K. A. M.

Contents

Chapter 1

Introduction

1-1 The Hydrologic Cycle

The hydrologic cycle describes the endless movement of water from the earth to the atmosphere through evaporation and transpiration, and return by precipitation (Figure 1-1). Fresh water evaporating from the ocean and transported over land by maritime air masses adds to atmospheric moisture derived from inland lakes and streams. This water, distilled by energy from the sun, returns to the earth as rain and snow. Condensation of atmospheric water vapor results from cooling of moist air by being forced aloft by mountains or a colder air mass. Runoff from rainfall and snowmelt may flow in streams toward the ocean or inland lakes, infiltrate the ground, reevaporate, or be taken up and transpired by plants. In contrast to swift surface flows, groundwater percolates slowly downgrade to reappear as streamflow or seepage into lakes at a lower elevation. Lakes can either collect or contribute to the quantity of underground water. Along ocean shorelines, where inland aquifers connect to the sea, groundwater flows outward preventing saltwater intrusion under coastal plains.

While nourishing terrestrial ecosystems, the natural water cycle also weathers and erodes the earth's surface. Intense rains wash off soil and swift runoff carves channels that converge to create floods of muddy water leaving higher elevations. The flatter slopes below slow the water and sediments are deposited in valleys forming plains bordering the river channel. River transportation, water power, and fertile plains for farming attract human settlements to these valleys. Meanwhile, the natural processes of the hydrologic cycle continue. Floods overflow channels inundating farmsteads and towns on the plains, and during droughts river transportation and water power are adversely affected. Although on the average the components of the hydrologic cycle are in balance, local weather variations cause droughts in a given area during one year and floods another. Water resources planning and management must account for these perturbations.

1-2 Water Quantity

The conflict between man and nature became more serious as river settlements grew to cities. Also, waterwheels were being abandoned for the new technology of reaction turbines in electric power generation. After private and local enterprises built the first small river projects, the federal government undertook harnessing of interstate rivers.

1

2

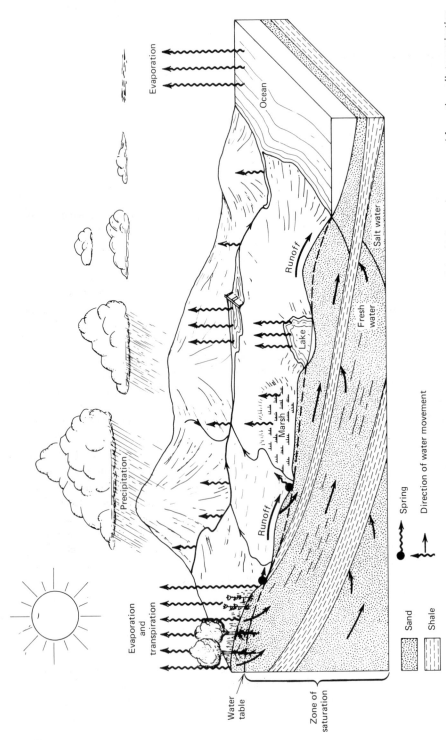

Figure 1-1 The principal flows in the hydrologic cycle are evaporation of water from oceans, inland lakes and streams, and from the soil; transpiration of water from plants; horizontal transportation of atmospheric water as vapor or liquid and ice crystals in clouds; precipitation; condensed water vapor falling back to earth; and, runoff, which is the water flowing on and under the surface back to the oceans. (Adapted from P. B. Jones, G. D. Walker, R. W. Harden, and L. L. Daniels, *The Development of the Science of Hydrology*, Texas Water Commission Circular 63-03, 1963.)

Large dams were built to impound water for hydroelectric power and flood control. Levees constructed along river banks provided further protection against overflow onto flood plains. Navigation was improved by straightening and deepening river channels, damming rivers into a series of pools and locks, and releasing stored water to maintain sufficient depth of flow for boats and barges. In the western states, reservoirs held water to provide a reliable supply for irrigation of agricultural lands. Reservoirs also served municipal and industrial supplies, and enhanced fisheries and recreation. Almost all of the major U. S. rivers were dammed and regulated between 1930 and 1960.

- Soil and water conservation practices in farming started in earnest after the 1930s drought. Today, small watershed projects including terraced fields, farm ponds, and grassed waterways are being promoted for wildlife habitat and to reduce peak flood flows and improve agricultural lands. Even though many large reservoir-canal programs for irrigation and flood control are still under consideration, few are expected to be constructed because of poor economic return or adverse environmental impact. Groundwater irrigation has risen dramatically since the mid 1950s resulting from improved pumping and sprinkler systems and a healthy agricultural economy. In some regions like Nebraska, application of groundwater is competing with the development of large surface-water irrigation districts. The era of reclaiming the west by construction of large federally funded reservoirs is coming to a close—the future is in better management of available water resources stressing quantity conservation.

Migration of people to the favorable climate of southern California and Arizona during the 1940s and 50s imposed serious water shortages on these regions; also, uncultivated lands only lacked water to become highly productive. The solution was to import water, through man-made rivers, from reservoirs collecting snowmelt in mountainous regions. The largest undertaking was the 1960s California State Water Project of 16 reservoirs, 1 000 km of aqueduct, and eight power plants. From northern mountainous regions, water flows parallel to the Pacific Coast supplying cities and irrigation canals all the way to the southern part of the state. This massive water transfer allows use of nearly all surface water available in California.

Groundwater is the source for the majority of towns and farmsteads in the United States. In the past, usage was limited to domestic needs and livestock watering. Now, withdrawal for irrigation accounts for the major consumption in many regions. In some, the supply is replenished by infiltration, but in others groundwater is being mined since withdrawal exceeds recharge. This problem is serious since water law in most states is not constituted to prevent long-term depletion. Quantity control of groundwater is a serious problem defying easy solution.

1-3 Water Quality

As part of a general concern for the environment, water quality became the important water resources issue in the 1970s. Obvious pollution, existing for decades, had been ignored to pursue water-quantity ventures. Suddenly, the situation appeared to be worse and it was. Population growth and urbanization overloaded municipal treatment plants and domestic wastewaters were discharged with little or no treatment. Most industries in the 1940s and 1950s under pressure to expand production for war materials, and later to meet the high demand for consumer products, dumped their wastes raw in nearby rivers and lakes. Manufacturing plants within cities discharged to municipal sewers but treatment plants, having been built in the 1930s, were incapable of handling industrial wastes. Raising of cattle and hogs on dispersed farmsteads was being replaced by large confined feeding operations. Many of these were sited on lots adjacent to streams so the rainfall washed away the manure. Mining and petroleum operations were also major polluters. After strip mining, unrestored wasteland created acid mine drainage and erosion problems. Brine wastewaters from oil wells were simply discharged to surface watercourses. The quantity of wastes from all of these activities exceeded the self-purification capacity of many rivers and streams.

Changes in technology created new, and sometimes exotic, waterborne wastes, either discharged from manufacturing operations, or appearing in wastewater as a result of using the products. Being common in domestic and food-processing wastewaters, biodegradable organic matter had been the contaminant of concern, and dissolved oxygen concentration the principal indicator of pollution of surface waters. These were no longer adequate parameters for measuring the character of complex industrial wastes that frequently contributed nonbiodegradable substances or compounds poisonous at extremely low levels. Fish kills from causes other than lack of oxygen were frequently attributed to toxic industrial wastes. The prevailing methods of wastewater treatment were not adequate for removing heavy metals, synthetic organics, or other refractory compounds.

Technical changes that affected water quality can be illustrated by the use of synthetic detergents as a substitute for soap in washing clothes. While their improved cleaning action prompted wide acceptance, they contributed two detrimental contaminants to municipal wastewater. The first was the ABS detergent molecule resistant to biological degradation. Aeration basins in treatment plants foamed, and unesthetic suds floated on turbulent reaches of rivers. In addition to being a photogenic pollutant, the presence of ABS was used as an indicator of pollution in groundwater, as well as, surface watercourses. Although not a health hazard, ABS helped to foster pollution control before being replaced by LAS, the biodegradable substitute that eliminated nearly all foaming problems. The second critical ingredient in synthetic detergents was the phosphate used in builders, which acted as a chemical buffer to improve cleaning action. With the advent of detergents the phosphorus content of domestic wastewater tripled, and accelerated the eutrophication of impounded waters by supplying phosphorus, which is the growth-limiting element in most natural lakes. Furthermore, only one-third or less of the phosphate in municipal wastewater was removed by biological processing. Thus, this conventional treatment was not protecting downstream lakes from excessive enrichment that produces algal blooms, extensive beds of aquatic plants, and ultimate loss of desired fish species. A substitute for phosphate builders was sought but not found. The only feasible solution was chemical precipitation of the phosphate in the treatment of wastewaters flowing into lakes. Although technically reliable, chemical addition is costly and, therefore, not universally applied in wastewater treatment.

Implementation of the water quality program required federal and state legislation to pass pollution control laws, establish stream and effluent standards, research new treatment processes, institute water quality planning, and provide cost-sharing funds to construct municipal plants. Regulations to abate pollution of surface waters now exist; however, legislation to protect groundwater is fragmented and still incomplete. Although significant progress was made in the 1970s, upgrading of treatment facilities is continuing and expected to be maintained at a strong pace during the 1980s. Areawide planning studies, undertaken to assess regional water pollution, revealed the significance of diffuse sources. Runoff from rainfall and spring snowmelt often created serious degradation, particularly deoxygenation and high turbidity. Control of land drainage is much more difficult than handling point sources that can be piped to a treatment plant. Rainfall also adversely affects wastewater processing in large cities with combined sewers, and no ready solution exists for sewer overflow containing raw wastes during heavy storms.

The most recent aspect of water resources given renewed attention was the quality of public drinking water by passage of a federal act in 1974. Rather than construction of treatment plants, this legislation is primarily concerned with placing all public water supplies under quality control, establishing uniform standards, improving the monitoring of supplies, and protecting groundwater sources. Since many cities withdraw river water contaminated by upstream waste sources, pollution control and water supply are physically connected. The same is true of groundwater contamination and well supplies, for instance, infiltration from fertilized farmland and increased nitrate content in wells of rural towns. The obvious associations between waste disposal, land use, and water quality are now receiving renewed attention. Water quality is, and will continue to be, a critical component of water resources.

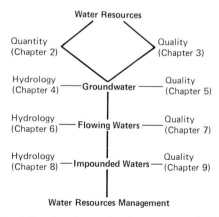

Figure 1-2 Flow diagram relating the phases of water resources with the organization of chapters in this book.

1-4 Water Resources Management

Water resources management now incorporates both quantity and quality. Flowing waters are no longer viewed solely as energy for power or a resource to be dammed for irrigation; their character must also be maintained for public water supplies, recreation, and wildlife. Usefulness of impounded water is diminished by eutrophication, Evaluating corrective measures for lake fertilization involves understanding the interrelated physical, chemical, and biological features. Similarly, both hydrology and quality are essential for managing groundwater resources. The organization of this book, as depicted in Figure 1-2, reflects the elements that define water resources. The major subjects of groundwater, flowing waters, and impounded waters are presented in paired chapters—one on quantity or hydrology, and the other on quality. Hopefully, this approach will help to broaden the traditional views of water resources.

Chapter 2
Water Quantity

Availability of fresh water is a major factor controlling habitation of a region. Water for drinking, irrigation, industry, navigation, hydropower, and fishing all influence development and economic growth. Whereas humid climates have supported substantial human populations for centuries, many semiarid regions are not productive without man-made water resource projects. Dams collect flood flows for agriculture and industrial applications; and aqueducts convey mountain snowmelt to the plains for irrigated farming and urban use. The purpose of this chapter is to define water quantity in terms of use, availability, and water law.

2-1 Water Use

The term water use means to withdraw, either from groundwater or a surface supply, and convey to the place of application. Withdrawal is not synonymous with consumption since water may be used and returned without significant loss. For example, many industries take water for cooling and release the warm water with only a small volumetric reduction due to evaporation. Consumptive use refers to the portion of water lost because of evaporation, transpiration, incorporation into products, or otherwise removed. Nonwithdrawal (in-channel) applications include: Navigation, recreation, fishing, freshwater discharge to estuarine areas for controlling salinity, and flow for dilution of wastewater effluents.

Estimated use of water in the United States is published every five years by the U. S. Geological Survey with the following data reported for 1975.[1] Total water withdrawal (excluding hydroelectric power) was about 34 percent of the average streamflow with 7.9 percent consumption of the basic supply. Approximately 7 200 litres per person per day were withdrawn for the four principal uses: public supply (domestic, commercial, and industrial); rural (domestic and livestock); irrigation; and self-supplied industrial uses. Water use for public and agricultural supplies are detailed in Table 2-1.

The quantity for public supplies averaged 640 litres per person per day, ranging from 450 l/person·d in humid climates to 1 000 l/person·d in western regions. Commerce and industry used about one third of the public supplies, which were two thirds from surface water and one third groundwater. Climatological factors of lawn watering, water-chilled air conditioning, and swimming pools are major influences causing regional variations. The estimated consumptive use of 35 percent of the withdrawal for municipal supplies is attributed primarily to landscape irrigation. Individual domestic

Table 2-1   Water Use in the United States, Million Cubic Metres per Day

Supply	Public Supplies		Rural Use		Irrigation		
	Withdrawn	C. U.[a]	Withdrawn	C. U.	Total	Lost[b]	C. U.
Surface water	72	—	3.8	—	320	—	—
Groundwater	42	—	15	—	210	—	—
Total water	114	25	19	13	530	87	300

Source. C. R. Murray and E. B. Reeves, *Estimated Use of Water in the United States in 1975*, U. S. Geological Survey Circular 765, 1977.

[a] Consumptive use (evaporation and transpiration).
[b] Conveyance losses (evaporation and seepage).

systems serve 46 million people in rural areas with 95 percent drawing groundwater. Approximately one half of livestock watering is surface water. The per capita rate for domestic use averages 250 1/person·d.

The quantity of water withdrawn for irrigation in the United States during 1975 was estimated at 200×10^9 m^3 for application on 22×10^6 ha, a mean of 900 mm for the year. While reliable estimates for consumption and conveyance losses are sometimes difficult to obtain, many irrigation districts have data from detailed record keeping. Consumptive use in the fields, evaporation plus transpiration, averaged 57 percent and conveyance losses (evaporation and seepage from canals) were 16 percent, which adds to a total depletion of three quarters of the applied water. Besides being a quantity problem, high losses by evaporation result in diminished quality of the return flows. Tailwater draining from fields has a considerably increased salt content. Irrigation with reclaimed wastewater, measured at 0.5×10^9 m^3 for 1975, was only one quarter of 1 percent of the total irrigation demand; essentially all of this was applied in the four states of California, Colorado, Arizona, and Texas.

More water is withdrawn for industries than any other use category. The amount of self-supplied industrial water in 1975 was estimated as 330×10^9 m^3 (910×10^6 m^3/d) of which 29 percent was saline as listed in Table 2-2. About 85 percent of the industrial water was withdrawn in eastern United States. Of the total, 93 percent supplied to self-supported industry was for cooling. The relative amounts of groundwater and surface water were 5 percent and 95 percent, respectively, with reclaimed wastewater being less than one tenth of 1 percent. For freshwater uses, consumption was about 1.5 percent by thermoelectric plants and 11 percent by other industries, resulting in a total of approximately 3.6 percent by all industries.

Electric utilities use vast amounts of water, about 80 percent of all industrial uses, with 99 percent of the total withdrawn for condensing spent steam from generators. After passing through the condensors, disposal of the cooling water varies with local conditions. Where water is expensive or scarce, cooling towers or ponds are employed

Table 2-2 Self-Supported Industrial Water Use, Million Cubic Metres per Day

Supply	Thermoelectric Power	Other Industries	Total	Consumptive Use
Surface water (fresh)	490	110	600	22
Surface water (saline)	240	20	260	3
Groundwater (fresh)	5	36	41	1
Groundwater (saline)	<1	4	4	—
Reclaimed wastewater	<1	1	1	—
	735	171	906	26

Source. C. R. Murray and E. B. Reeves, *Estimated Use of Water in the United States in 1975*, U. S. Geological Survey Circular 765, 1977.

for repeated reuse. Prevention of thermal pollution in the receiving water is another factor requiring the installation of cooling towers. As reuse becomes more prevalent, the quantity consumed by steam plants is expected to increase. For example, about 1 percent of the water withdrawn in 1975 was consumed as compared to 0.5 percent in 1970. Application of saline water also rose from 28 percent in 1970 to 33 percent currently. Future exploitation of salt water is anticipated as the number of inland sites with adequate freshwater supplies decreases and more electric plants are located along coastlines.

The estimated withdrawal for all uses (excluding hydroelectric power) increased 11.5 percent in the five-year period between 1970 and 1975. The percentages applied to various categories in 1975 are shown in Figure 2-1. Industry accounts for 58 percent

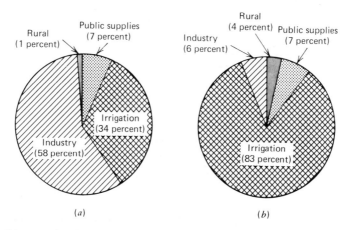

(a)   (b)

Figure 2-1 Diagrams showing the relative proportioning by category of (a) water withdrawn (excluding hydropower) and (b) fresh water consumed in 1975. (From C. R. Murray and E. B. Reeves, *Estimated Use of Water in the United States in 1975*, U. S. Geological Survey Circular 765, 1977.)

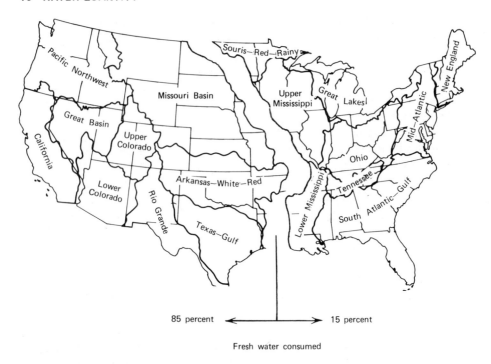

Fresh water consumed

Figure 2-2 A map showing the division of freshwater consumption between the nine water re-source regions in western United States and the nine eastern regions. (Data from C. R. Murray and E. B. Reeves, *Estimated Use of Water in the United States in 1975*, U. S. Geological Survey Circular 765, 1977.)

of the water withdrawn, while irrigation results in 83 percent of the consumption. Influences of climate and extensive irrigation in the western states is reflected in supply and consumption data. The per capita withdrawal for all uses in western regions is double the value for eastern river basins; 11 400 l/person·d compared to 5 700 l/person·d. Geographically, the nine western water-resource regions consumed 85 percent of the fresh water lost by use, as illustrated in Figure 2-2. This translates into per capita consumption values of 4 900 l/person·d in the west and 370 l/person·d in the east. Withdrawals by self-supplied industries in the 48 conterminous states is illustrated in Figure 2-3. Use in the eastern states was about 85 percent of the total, and the percentage of withdrawn water consumed was 3 percent. These data reflect the humid climate and industrial urban society in the eastern portion of the nation.

Nonwithdrawal uses depend on water running freely in a defined channel or stored in a natural or man-made lake. Major commercial practices on flow-controlled rivers are navigation and hydroelectric power. Propagation of fish and wildlife require minimum streamflow and maintenance of wetlands. Protecting the natural environment of lakes and streams conflicts quantitatively with consumptive uses and qualitatively with domestic, industrial, and agricultural applications that result in discharge of contaminated waters. Providing for nonwithdrawal uses is often a formidable management task.

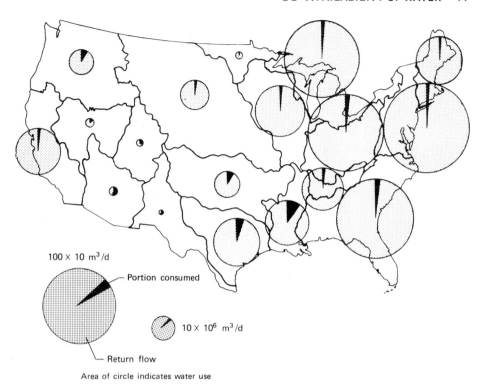

100 × 10 m³/d

— Portion consumed

10 × 10⁶ m³/d

— Return flow

Area of circle indicates water use

Figure 2-3 Plan showing self-supplied industrial water withdrawals for water resource regions in the conterminous United States. (From C. R. Murray and E. B. Reeves, *Estimated Use of Water in the United States in 1975*, U. S. Geological Circular 765, 1977.)

2-2   Availability of Water

The trends in population and water withdrawals from 1950 through 1975 are graphed in Figure 2-4. The rates of increase are steady, except for the somewhat irregular trend in irrigation. Only a slight decrease in the growth of use per capita is detectable in the last five-year period. In the future, greater slowing is anticipated as additional fresh-water surface supplies diminish, thus causing a shift to groundwater or saline sources. Even though water appears to be in oversupply based on average conditions, the abundance has to be evaluated with reference to its distribution. Demand for water must be met by the local supply, or from a source within reach for transporting to the deficient area. While the quantity may be much the same year after year in some regions, unpredictable variations are a more common occurrence. Cumulative withdrawals during dry periods can decrease streamflow and mine groundwater. Historically, storage in reservoirs and artificial underground recharge have been the management solutions selected. Importation from regions with excess natural supplies is also practiced in some areas, notably the aqueducts conveying water to southern California.

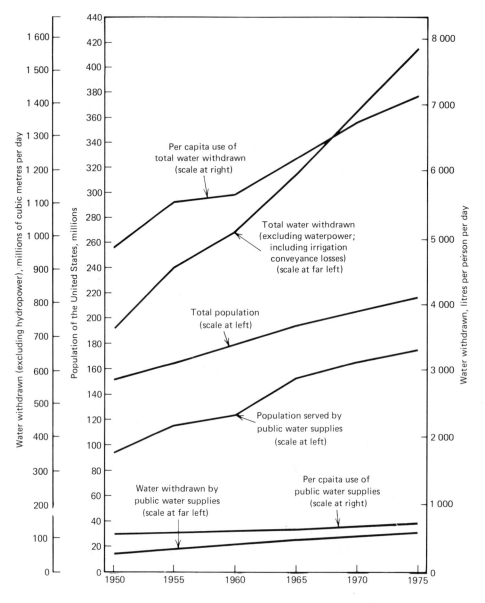

Figure 2-4 Trends in population and withdrawals of water in the United States plotted for the period of 1950 through 1975. (From C. R. Murray and E. B. Reeves, *Estimated Use of Water in the United States in 1975,* U. S. Geological Circular 765, 1977.)

Table 2-3 compares average runoff and annual low streamflow with cumulative water withdrawals in 1975. For each river-basin region (Figure 2-2), the drainage area is listed first followed by average runoff, which is the mean annual water yield for the regional area. The annual flow exceeded in 90 percent of the years in column 4 is, statistically speaking, the quantity of flow equaled or exceeded 9 out of every 10 years on the average. Total groundwater plus surface water withdrawals for 1975 are in column 5. Fresh surface water use and freshwater consumption are given in the last two columns. These data reveal abundant water supplies in eastern regions and the Pacific Northwest, since the annual low flows are greater than recorded water use. However, in the Missouri Basin, Texas-Gulf, Rio Grande, Lower Colorado, Great Basin, and California regions, the flows exceeded in 90 percent of the years are less than the cumulative water withdrawals indicating that these areas are most susceptible to water shortages. Texas-Gulf and Rio Grande cumulative water withdrawals from groundwater plus surface supplies equal a large percentage of runoff and are greater than the 1-in-10-year low streamflow; also, one third to two thirds of the water withdrawn is consumed. In the Upper Colorado region, river water is accessible for irrigation resulting in nearly 45 percent consumption of the surface water being withdrawn. Both water withdrawals and consumption in the Lower Colorado exceed the amount of water originating in the region; this is made possible by augmentation of the supply by inflow from the Upper Colorado region, importation of surface water, repeated withdrawals of the same water, and mining of groundwater. Large groundwater extractions are characteristic of the Texas-Gulf, Rio Grande, Arkansas-White-Red, Lower Colorado, and California basins. These regions contrast with others where fresh surface water withdrawals approach total withdrawals in magnitude.

The two factors limiting the usefulness of Table 2-3 data are cumulative withdrawal values represent an unspecified reuse of the same water through repeated withdrawal and return by different users, and the numerical data represent regional averages that can conceal local water shortages. Despite these qualifications of the data, future problems in the nine western regions are strongly suggested since withdrawals for 1975 were greater than 80 percent of the existing dependable supply and consumption was about 40 percent of supply. Water shortages lead to reuse permitting the gross withdrawal to exceed annual flow; this recycling in turn increases consumption. The large amount currently being lost in the use cycle forewarns of quality degradation in addition to diminishing quantity. Increase in the concentration of dissolved solids from repeated reuse can impair the remaining water to an unacceptable level, particularly in dry climates where evaporation reduces the quantity without extracting any salts. Essential nonwithdrawal uses can suffer from both insufficient volume and poor quality of the flow remaining.

Serious shortages are anticipated in areas where groundwater is being mined, that is, where the withdrawal rate exceeds natural or artificial recharge. Modern pumping and irrigation equipment allows extraction of previously untapped underground water in semiarid and arid regions. Often, the aquifers are deep and recharge very slowly from infiltration of limited precipitation and lateral seepage from nearby elevated plains or mountains. A classic example is the Salt River Valley in central Arizona where thou-

Table 2-3 Estimated Water Supply Compared with Cumulative Water Withdrawals by Region During 1975 in the United States (Excluding Use for Hydroelectric Power Generation)

Region	(1) Area (1 000 km²)	(2) Average Runoff (mm per year)	(3) Average Runoff (10⁶ m³/d)	(4) Annual Flow Exceeded in 90 Percent of Years (10⁶ m³/d)	(5) Withdrawals, Groundwater Plus Surface Water (10⁶ m³/d)	(6) Fresh Surface Water Withdrawn (10⁶ m³/d)	(7) Fresh Water Consumed (10⁶ m³/d)
New England	153	610	250	190	53	17	1.7
Mid-Atlantic	264	460	320	260	200	83	6.0
South Atlantic-Gulf	699	380	750	490	160	91	14.0
Great Lakes	326	300	280	200	140	130	4.2
Ohio	422	400	470	280	140	130	4.5

Tennessee	106	530	160	110	42	38	1.1
Upper Mississippi	492	180	250	140	72	61	3.0
Lower Mississippi	249	430	300	140	61	42	21
Souris-Red-Rainy	153	56	23	8	2	1	.3
Missouri Basin	1 334	56	200	110	130	95	57
Arkansas—White—Red	686	150	280	140	57	23	34
Texas-Gulf	453	99	120	42	83	37	30
Rio Grande	352	20	19	8	20	11	13
Upper Colorado	285	64	49	30	16	15	6.4
Lower Colorado	355	13	12	4	32	13	24
Great Basin	479	25	29	11	26	20	14
Pacific-Northwest	702	400	790	560	120	98	24
California	311	230	230	110	190	83	14

Source. C. R. Murray and E. B. Reeves, *Estimated Use of Water in the United States in 1975*, U. S. Geological Survey Circular 765, 1977.

sands of hectares of agricultural land are irrigated from nonrenewable groundwater from more than 100 m below the surface. Decline in the water table caused by over-draft has been continuous over the past 30 years. Agriculture and urban centers are relying on completion of the Central Arizona Project, currently under construction, to divert Colorado River water from behind Parker Dam to the Phoenix and Tucson areas. Another example is the High Plains of western Texas developed by irrigated agriculture drawing from the underground storage of ancient water. A dropping water table is resulting from mining this water. Without importing a substantial quantity of surface flow in the future, which appears unlikely, the southern regions of the High Plains will have to abandon its present form of agriculture. Conservation is prolonging the life of the supply but cannot maintain it indefinitely. Many other irrigated agricultural projects in dry climates throughout the world are faced with diminishing groundwater supplies.

Water for expanding populations in humid regions with abundant supply, like the eastern United States, is usually available by implementing quantity and quality management. Storage reservoirs, interbasin transfer, and conjunctive use of groundwater and surface sources are alternatives commonly considered conservation measures. Quality depends on adequate treatment of point sources and land management to reduce pollution from runoff. Consequently, solutions to water problems relate to distribution of the quantity available and instituting pollution control.

Increasing the water use in semiarid regions is definitely limited; in fact, availability of water is usually the controlling factor for expansion of agriculture and industry to support population growth. Because of high evaporation losses and rising salinity, increasing reservoir storage can become counterproductive; the Colorado River appears to have reached this point. A long-term groundwater resource requires recharge to replenish the quantity withdrawn. In arid regions, natural recharge is limited by inadequate precipitation making this extremely difficult. Deserts converted to farmland by deep-well irrigation are likely to return to deserts when the supply is depleted. Quality problems are complex for several reasons: high consumption increases the dissolved solids content; the diffuse sources of pollution are extremely difficult, and in some cases impossible to control; and the common contaminants are dissolved salts that cannot be economically removed by treatment. Since water is the key to continued economic growth, withdrawals are expected to rise to an ultimate limit of exploitation. Management practices can optimize and regulate quantity-quality factors for maximum benefits from a fixed base of water resources, while minimizing losses during periods of drought. Obviously, management cannot generate more water than nature provides. Futuristic ideas, such as artificial induction of precipitation, have restricted applications.

2-3 Water Law

Consumptive rights to surface waters are governed by two allocation systems, riparianism and prior appropriation. Riparian doctrine is found in all eastern states except Mississippi, while prior appropriation prevails in the west. Colorado was the first state to adopt a pure appropriation system totally abrogating riparian rights. California, on the other hand, recognizes both riparianism and appropriation, except for the limitation requiring that all uses of water be reasonably beneficial.

Riparian Doctrine

This principle of law provides landowners certain rights to a watercourse adjoining their land. Under the original natural-flow doctrine, each riparian proprietor was entitled to the streamflow through his or her land without having it perceptibly retarded, diminished, or polluted by others. The only water uses permitted were those necessary to sustain life, such as bathing, drinking, other household purposes, and watering animals. Artificial applications like irrigation, manufacturing, and mining operations were allowed only if they produced no noticeable interference with the natural flow. In the early days of the industrial revolution, the natural flow rule insured the passage of water downstream from one water-powered mill or factory to the next.

As demands beyond simple direct needs increased, the concept of reasonable use was introduced to allow for beneficial applications of unclaimed flow. Each riparian proprietor under this new principle was entitled to consumptive use provided it did not unreasonably interfere with legitimate rights of others. Reasonableness must be resolved on a case-by-case basis. Even though some reduction in surface flow results, diversion for irrigation is normally considered as proper riparian use. Impoundments also generally comply with the law as long as no damage is caused to others. For instance, water may not be stored for long periods without some release to maintain a prescribed low flow. Public water supplies in most states have a priority over industrial and agricultural uses, even though municipalities are nonriparian.

The following quotation from the National Water Commission (page 3)[2] summarizes the English legacy of water law and riparian rights.

The English Legacy The water law concepts adopted early in the history of this country were patterned after the law in England. England recognized a public interest in those waters which were affected by the ebb and flow of the tide, because the public customarily used these waters for navigation and fishing. All other waters—the fresh water inland lakes and streams above tidewater—were classified as private waters, in which there were no public rights. The English Crown owned the navigable (public) waters and their beds, and held the same in trust for public use. Private waters were owned and controlled by those who owned riparian land, which was that land located adjacent to the stream or upon which the stream flowed. Each owner of riparian land owned the bed of the stream which crossed his land, and was entitled to have the stream continue to flow in its natural condition by or upon his land, and could make certain uses of the water while it was upon his land, so long as the stream remained undiminished in quantity and quality when it left his land.

Riparian rights also attached to navigable waters, but these rights were more restricted than in private waters, because they were subordinate to the public's right of navigation and fishing, and because the beds and tidelands were owned by the Crown.

While the above principles of English law found early favor in the United States, it will be seen that some of those principles were revised or modified, and some were rejected. The departures from the English law were not too surprising, since the physical characteristics of England, as a small country with abundant rainfall, were quite different from much of the United States, a large country with arid and humid regions, with large inland lakes, and with many rivers that flowed hundreds of miles before reaching tidewater.

Riparian Rights. The Eastern States rather uniformly adopted the basic principles of the English system of riparian rights as they applied to surface waters. However, rights of riparian use were liberalized. Riparian owners were entitled to make reasonable uses of the water for any purpose for which their land was naturally adapted, even though it caused some diminution in the quantity or quality of the water in the stream. Under the "natural flow" doctrine as it originally developed in England, such a diminution was not allowed, but the "reasonable use" relaxation of the rule permitted those uses which did not "unreasonably" interfere with the rights of other riparians.

Another departure from the English law related to the distinction between public (navigable) and private (nonnavigable) waters. This departure evolved as a consequence of Federal jurisdiction over interstate waterways.

. . . . . . all of the Eastern States adopted the new measure of navigability announced by the Supreme Court (in 1876), and declared that all navigable inland waters within their respective borders were subject to public use for navigation and fishing. As a result, riparian rights on nonnavigable waters are more extensive than on navigable waters, because public rights of use extend to all natural waterways physically capable of supporting navigation, whether coastal or inland. The Western States also followed the expanded test of navigability for the purpose of recognizing public rights of use in all waters that were navigable in fact, but western water law doctrines, as will be seen in the next section, differed markedly from riparian concepts.

Prior Appropriation

Priority and beneficial use are fundamental elements of water law west of the Mississippi River. The first appropriator in time is first in right and is entitled to satisfy his water needs before a subsequent appropriator may take any. If the first person only claims a portion of the flow, someone else may take possession of another part with equal protection under the law. The purpose of appropriation must be worthwhile and wastage minimized since water rights are derived from beneficial use, rather than land ownership. Allocations are fixed in terms of a definite quantity of water and associated with a proposed use. Currently, appropriation rights operate within a comprehensive statutory and administrative framework. In most states, permits are issued pursuant to some form of adjudicative process, and the controlling agency may deny or modify permit applications to protect existing water users or the public interest. However, this doctrine does not always protect public water uses. For example, western courts have often refused to recognize streamflows for recreational purposes as beneficial uses subject to appropriation.

The following is an overview by the Commission (page 5)[2] on the law of appropriation.

Early water uses in the West were initiated by miners and farmers, who often were trespassers on the public domain, and who found it necessary to divert water from the streams to the point of use. There were few courts and no established water law doctrines to govern these uses, and so the water users operated in accordance with local rules and customs, which they developed to control water use practices in their respective areas—in much the same manner that miners developed rules applicable to local mining districts.

When water-use conflicts reached the courts, the decisions rendered usually were in accordance with the local rules and customs, and the doctrine of riparian rights was rejected as unsuited to the needs of the arid regions of the West. Development and settlement were dependent upon successful farming and mining, and these in turn were dependent upon use of water from the watercourses. Under the riparian right doctrine, the water would be left in the stream for use of riparian owners (which usually was the Federal Government in the West), and settlement of the area would not have been possible. So the courts decreed that riparian rights would not be recognized, and that water could be withdrawn from the stream by anyone who could put it to a beneficial use. For its part, Congress consented to the withdrawal and use of water in accordance with the customs and laws of the respective States. The law of appropriation was born.

The barest essence of the law of appropriation is that a water right is acquired by diverting water from a natural watercourse and applying it to a beneficial use. The water right carries a priority date, which is the date that the first act was done to initiate the right, and the consequence of the priority date is that the water right will have a superior call upon the watercourse over all rights subsequently initiated. When a stream becomes over appropriated, so that the call upon the stream is in excess of the water in it, then the owner of the oldest water right is first entitled to his full delivery of water, and then the next oldest right is fully satisfied, and so on down the line until the water supply is exhausted—and those with the most recently acquired rights get no water at all.

Combination of Riparian and Appropriation Rights

It would be misleading to suggest that the States can be neatly classified as appropriation or riparian. It is true that riparian law was applied in the East and appropriation law developed in the West, but it is not true—as commonly assumed—that there are 19 appropriation States (from North Dakota to Texas, and States situated west thereof) and 31 riparian States (those remaining). Some Western States (such as Texas, California, and Hawaii), have always recognized certain riparian water rights, and some "pure" appropriation States which have emphatically and repeatedly rejected the entire regime of riparian rights (such as Utah, Nevada, and Idaho), have consistently applied some riparian concepts, such as reliction and accretion. Moreover, the Eastern States are moving toward more comprehensive controls of water use, and all of the States are developing more uniform approaches to common problems, as is illustrated by water quality controls. (National Water Commission, page 5.)[2]

Four common methods for modifying and alleviating the rigidity of the riparian scheme are special legislation to accommodate a beneficial use for the public good; purchase, sale, and lease among parties who make voluntary arrangements for use of water or flowage rights; condemnation by governmental subdivisions, and by giving the power of eminent domain to corporations; and, prescription, which is a method of acquiring water rights from a riparian owner based on long, continued use. Courts justify a transfer of an owner's property to a wrongful user on the grounds that persons having causes of action should be compelled to seek judicial relief within a reasonable time or forever be precluded from a remedy.[3] For example, in Wisconsin the statute controlling acquisition of water rights by prescription is the 20-year statute of limitations applicable to actions for recovery of possession of real estate.

Prior appropriation has also been clarified by state administration of water rights based on appropriation, adjudication, and distribution. Anyone intending to appropriate surface water is required by statute to make application to ensure there is unallocated water and the purposed use is beneficial. Statutory adjudication procedures have been enacted to coordinate and integrate the decree to water users disputing their respective priorities. Previously, when private lawsuits arose, the parties involved were limited and the scope of the case too narrow to provide for a comprehensive adjudication of all the rights from a common source. Another important feature of centralized water administration is the distribution of water. Nearly all western states have statutory procedures for the appointment of water commissioners to assure the proper distribution of water in accordance with recorded and decree rights.

Groundwater Law

Rules for withdrawal of groundwater have four major doctrinal approaches: ownership, reasonable use, correlative rights, and prior appropriation. According to the absolute ownership doctrine, landowners can extract an unlimited amount of groundwater either to apply on their overlying land or export it to other areas, regardless of injury to adjacent landowners. Often criticized for failing to account for drawdown and movement of groundwater, this rule imposes liability only for waste or malicious injury to another. Reasonable use (the American rule) allows landowners to extract as much as they need, regardless of the adverse effect to others, as long as the water is employed on their overlying land for any beneficial use including domestic purposes, agriculture, mining, or manufacturing. By limiting application of the groundwater to the owner's overlying land, this rule is really only a modification of the absolute ownership doctrine. Both favor large users with deep wells and high-capacity pumps. The correlating rights principle allows each owner over a common aquifer equal and corresponding right to beneficial water use on his or her overlying land. These coequal rights require prorating of groundwater among users when the available supply is not sufficient to meet the overall demand. While improving equity, this principle of law is very difficult to apply in different hydrogeological conditions and water use patterns. Prior appropriation, the basis for groundwater codes in several western states, does not give landowners any proprietary right to underlying water. Instead, it is owned by the state with individuals having the right to beneficial use upon application in a priority system. During periods of water shortage, the earlier appropriations have first rights.

At present, groundwater law in most states is not only difficult to interpret, but lacks the necessary statutes to protect its quantity and quality. Consider the following excerpts from National Water Commission reports.[2,4]

Ground water is sometimes thought to be all water under the ground, but this is accurate neither from the standpoint of law nor of hydrology. Soil moisture and suspended water, usually located in a zone of aeration above the ground water table, is not ground water. Hydrologically speaking, ground water is water found in saturated pores and other interstices of subsurface rock formations. However, for legal purposes, ground water is commonly divided into two classes, namely: (1) underground streams which flow in known and definite underground channels; and (2) percolating waters, which ooze, seep, or flow beneath the surface of the earth in no known or identifiable natural channels. These legal distinctions are often at variance with scientific truth, since no such distinction actually exist in many areas.

The law relating to underground streams is essentially the same as that which applies to surface waters, while legal concepts relating to percolating water are quite different. All ground water is presumed in law to be percolating water, and anyone contending otherwise must prove that the water is part of an underground stream, and must also prove the location and bounds of the underground stream.

The English view of ground water, which was announced by the courts much later than the rules governing riparian rights in surface water, was that the owner of the land owned all of the water within or under it, because it was deemed to be part of the soil. The consequence was that a landowner had no liability for any use he made of ground water though his use damaged others.

The same rule was initially applied by many of the States in this country, but was soon modified to limit the landowner to a reasonable use because it became evident that ground water moved in subterranean aquifers and use of, or interference with, such water could affect other landowners.

As more knowledge was acquired with respect to the subterranean migration of water and its interconnection with surface watercourses, further doctrines were developed. When a number of persons owned land overlying an aquifer, withdrawal of water by one would affect all, and many States pronounced a doctrine of correlative rights whereby each landowner was held to have rights in the common pool in proportion to his land overlying the pool. Some States applied the appropriation doctrine to ground water so that rights could only be acquired by withdrawing the water and applying it to a beneficial use. Where appropriation procedures require filing an application, obtaining an approval thereof, perfecting the right and obtaining a certificate of appropriation, the same basic procedures must be followed to obtain a ground water right.

Ground water law has not yet developed satisfactory answers to a number of vexing problems in management and administration of underground basins, reservoirs, or aquifers. One difficulty is in determining the extent to which the owner of a ground water right has, or should have, a right to maintenance of artesian pressures of underground water levels. Another is the extent to which ground water basins should be "mined" or depleted, or even exhausted, and the extent to which this does or does not unlawfully interfere with the earlier rights in the basin. A third is the extent to which ground water and surface water supplies can be integrated for management purposes, so that interconnecting sources of supply can be utilized for a fair administration of existing rights, and so that the total water supply can be used to better advantage in providing for optimal use. (Reference 2, page 7.)

In many States, ground water law, like riparian surface water law, is inadequate to allocate the resource among competing users and is unresponsive to the problem of excessive use. The first defect results from the vagueness of the rules of allocation ("reasonable use") and the second from the failure of the legal system to perceive that ground water is often a common-pool resource in which there is little incentive to save an exhaustible supply for use tomorrow. Any user who seeks to save is subject to having his savings captured by another pumper from the same aquifer. It is the Commission's recommendation that a new legal system to govern ground water should be instituted in States where better management of ground water is needed.

Laws should be enacted authorizing the establishment of water management agencies with power to manage surface and ground water supplies conjunctively, to coordinate surface and ground water withdrawals, to control the rate at which an aquifer is depleted (through pump charges or quotas on withdrawals), to replenish aquifers by artificial recharge techniques, and to protect aquifers from pollution.

Apart from pollution control guidelines comparable to those which apply to surface water, the Commission does not believe that Federal regulation of ground water is desirable, but it does hold that the adequacy of the ground water management system is relevant to the need for Federal projects to supply supplementary water to overdrawn basins, and recommends that a description and evaluation of such ground water management systems be incorporated into reports to Congress on proposed projects for supplying additional water to such basins. (Reference 4, page 61.)

State Water Laws

A compilation of water laws for the 50 states are presented by the National Water Comission[2]. A summary-digest of the water law in each state follows a general introduction covering development and organization of laws for both surface waters and groundwater. Also, the final report of the Commission emphasizes the management of water resources with comments directed toward state and federal water laws.[4]

References

1. Murray, C. R., and Reeves, E. B., "Estimated Use of Water in the United States in 1975," *Geological Survey Circular 765*, U. S. Geological Survey, Washington, D.C., 1977.

2. *A Summary-Digest of State Water Laws*, National Water Commission, U. S. Government Printing Office, May 1973.

3. Harnsberger, R. S., "Prescriptive Water Rights in Wisconsin," *Wisconsin Law Review*, Vol. 1961, No. 1, January 1961.

4. *New Directions in U. S. Water Policy—Summary, Conclusions and Recommendations from the Final Report*, National Water Commission, U. S. Government Printing Office, June 1973.

Problems

2-1 Distinguish between the terms water use (withdrawal) and consumption.

2-2 What are the average values for the total water withdrawn and domestic water use in the United States in units of litres per person per day?

2-3 Based on the data given in Table 2-1, calculate the consumptive use as a percentage of the total water withdrawn for each of the three categories listed.

2-4 Confirm all of the withdrawal and consumption percentages shown in Figure 2-1 using the numerical data given in Table 2-1 and 2-2.

2-5 What are the major differences between eastern and western United States relative to water use and consumption?

2-6 Answer these questions using Figure 2-4. (a) After reading values for population and total water withdrawn for the year 1975, confirm the plotted value of 7 200 1/person for water use. (b) Calculate the average annual percentage increase in total water withdrawn and per capita use between 1965 and 1975.

2-7 Answer the following based on the information given in Table 2-3. (a) Compare the data in columns (4), (5), and (6) for the Mid-Atlantic and California regions. Which region is most susceptible to a water shortage? Why? (b) For the Lower Colorado, compute water consumption as a percentage of total withdrawals. How can consumption exceed the average runoff in the region?

2-8 What problems are related to (a) increased groundwater withdrawal in semi-arid regions, (b) repeated reuse of surface waters.

2-9 State in one sentence the riparian doctrine. Why have eastern states adopted and maintained riparian rights?

2-10 State in one sentence the doctrine of prior appropriation. Why did western states adopt this water law rather than the doctrine of riparian rights?

2-11 Under the law of reasonable use, who owns groundwater and what are the limits in its use?

2-12 What is the legal definition of groundwater?

2-13 According to the National Water Commission, what appears to be the greatest inadequacy of groundwater law in many states?

Chapter 3
Water Quality

Domestic and industrial water supplies, agricultural irrigation, propagation of fish and wildlife, shellfish culture, water-based recreation, and esthetic enjoyment are the principle uses of water founded on quality. Other applications less related to chemical character are hydropower, navigation, and assimilation of wastes. The function of this chapter is to define water quality. Second, government regulations are presented and the general concept of water quality management is outlined.

3-1 Quality for Public Water Supplies

Drinking water must be free of contaminants considered health hazards—pathogens, toxins, and carcinogens. Furthermore, esthetic factors like temperature, appearance, taste and odor, and chemical balance are important to consumers. The original standards, established in 1914 by the U.S. Public Health Service, were to protect the health of the traveling public. Although enforceable only on interstate carriers, they were widely adopted and led to the current standards established under the Environmental Protection Agency. Now, all public water systems having 15 service connections or serving 25 people daily for a total of 60 days per year must comply with the regulations; thus, both resident populations and the traveling public are included.

The interim drinking water standards for the United States are given in Table 3-1, and World Health Organization drinking water standards summarized in Table 3-2.

Table 3-1   Interim Drinking Water Standards of the United States Environmental Protection Agency

---

Primary Standards for Maximum Contaminant Levels
(Approval Limits for Health)

Microbiological Contaminants

When 10-ml portions of water are tested by the multiple-tube fermentation method, not more than 10 percent in any month shall show the presence of coliform bacteria. No more than three portions from one sample shall contain coliforms where less than 20 samples are tested per month; in larger systems, no more than three portions may be positive in 5 percent of the samples analyzed. (If the portions tested are 100 ml, not more than 60 percent shall show presence of coliforms.) When the membrane filter technique is used with 100-ml portions, the arithmetic mean coliform density shall not

24

Table 3-1 Continued

exceed 1 per 100 ml. The maximum density in one sample is 4 per 100 ml for less than 20 samples per month, or 5 percent of the samples where more than 20 samples are tested per month.

Inorganic Chemicals in Milligrams per Litre

Arsenic	0.05
Barium	1.0
Cadmium	0.010
Chromium	0.05
Lead	0.05
Mercury	0.002
Nitrate (as N)	10.0
Selenium	0.01
Silver	0.05

Recommended and approval limits in milligrams per litre for fluoride are based on the annual average of the maximum daily air temperatures.

Temperature °C	Recommended Optimum	Approval Limit
12.0 and below	1.2	2.4
12.1 to 14.6	1.1	2.2
14.7 to 17.6	1.0	2.0
17.7 to 21.4	0.9	1.8
21.5 to 26.2	0.8	1.6
26.3 to 32.5	0.7	1.4

Organic Chemicals in Milligrams per Litre

Chlorinated hydrocarbons

Endrin	0.0002
Lindane	0.004
Methoxychlor	0.1
Toxaphene	0.005

Chlorophenoxys

2,4-D	0.1
2,4,5-TP (Silvex)	0.01

Radionuclides in Picocuries per Litre

Natural

Gross alpha activity	15
Radium-226 + radium-228	5

Man-made

Gross beta activity	50
Tritium	20 000
Strontium-90	8

Table 3-1 Continued

Turbidity

The monthly average shall not exceed 1 turbidity unit (TU). (With state approval 5 TUs may be allowed provided it does not interfere with disinfection, maintenance of chlorine residual, or bacteriological testing.) The maximum two-day average is 5 TUs.

Secondary Standards for Recommended Contaminant Levels
(Limits for Esthetics)

Chloride	250 mg/l
Color	15 color units
Copper	1 mg/l
Corrosivity	(Non-corrosive)
Foaming agents	0.5 mg/l
Hydrogen sulfide	0.05 mg/l
Iron	0.3 mg/l
Manganese	0.05 mg/l
Odor	3 threshold odor number
pH	6.5 - 8.5
Sulfate	250 mg/l
Total dissolved solids	500 mg/l
Zinc	5 mg/l

For bacterial quality, treated water is tested at various points in the distribution system for coliform bacteria with a minimum of approximately one sample each month per 1000 population. Direct testing for pathogens is not feasible because of the complexity and difficulty of the laboratory analyses. Since large numbers of coliforms are excreted in human feces, the presence of these nonpathogenic bacteria indicates the possibility of fecal pollution and presence of microbes or viruses causing enteric diseases. The safety of processed water meeting the criterion of one coliform organism per 100 ml is based on the statisical improbability of ingesting any pathogens.

Presence of chemicals in excess of the maximum contaminant levels for human health constitutes grounds for rejection of the water supply. Arsenic, barium, cadmium, chromium, lead, mercury, selenium, and silver are poisons that affect the internal organs of the human body. In arriving at specific limits, the total environmental exposure of man to a specific toxin is considered. The lowest practical level is selected to minimize the amount of toxicant contributed by water particularly when other sources including milk, food, and air are known to represent the major exposure of man. Nitrate nitrogen in excess of 10 mg/l can cause fatal poisoning in infants, whereas adults can ingest at least double this concentration without an adverse reaction. To prevent cases of infantile methemoglobinemia, the population in areas containing high nitrate water should be warned about the potential dangers of using it for infant feeding. Concentrations of fluoride above the approval limits produce objectionable dental fluorosis. The optimum levels for reduction of dental caries with no

Table 3-2 **International Standards for Drinking Water**

Standards of Bacterial Quality for Water in the Distribution System
1. Coliform bacteria should be absent in 95 percent of the 100-ml samples examined throughout any year.
2. No sample should contain *Escherichia coli* in 100 ml.
3. No sample should contain more than 10 coliform organisms per 100 ml.
4. Coliform organisms should not be detectable in 100 ml of any two consecutive samples.

Toxic Chemical Substances and Their Upper Limits of Concentration

Arsenic (as As)	0.05 mg/l
Cadmium (as Cd)	0.01 mg/l
Cynanide (as CN)	0.05 mg/l
Lead (as Pb)	0.1 mg/l
Mercury (total as Hg)	0.001 mg/l
Selenium (as Se)	0.01 mg/l

Levels of Radioactivity as Maximum Permissible Concentrations

Gross alpha activity	3 pCi/l
Gross beta activity	30 pCi/l

Specific Chemical Substances That May Affect Health

Fluoride	The recommended control limits are in the range of 0.6 to 1.7 mg/l F depending on climatic temperature.
Nitrate	Concentration in excess of 45 mg/l (as NO_3) is a health hazard to infants and possibly older children.
PAH	Polynuclear aromatic hydrocarbons concentration should not exceed 0.2 μg/l.

Substances and Characteristics Affecting the Acceptibility of Water for Domestic Use

Substance or characteristic	Undesirable effect that may be produced	Highest desirable level	Maximum permissible level
Color	Discoloration	5 units	50 units
Odor	Odors	Unobjectionable	Unobjectionable
Taste	Tastes	Unobjectionable	Unobjectionable
Suspended matter	Turbidity	5 units	25 units
Total solids	Taste, gastro-intestinal irritation	500 mg/l	1 500 mg/l
pH range	Taste, corrosion	7.0 to 8.5	6.5 to 9.2
Anionic detergents	Taste, foaming	0.2 mg/l	1.0 mg/l
Mineral oil	Taste and odor after chlorination	0.01 mg/l	0.30 mg/l

27

Table 3-2 Continued

Substance or characteristic	Undesirable effect that may be produced	Highest desirable level	Maximum permissible level
Phenolic compounds (as phenol)	Taste, particularly in chlorinated water	0.001 mg/l	0.002 mg/l
Total hardness (as $CaCO_3$)	Excessive scale formation	100 mg/l	500 mg/l
Calcium (as Ca)	Scale formation	75 mg/l	200 mg/l
Chloride (as Cl)	Taste, corrosion in hot-water systems	200 mg/l	600 mg/l
Copper (as Cu)	Astringent taste, discoloration	0.05 mg/l	1.5 mg/l
Iron (as Fe)	Taste, discoloration, deposits and growth of iron bacteria	0.1 mg/l	1.0 mg/l
Magnesium (as Mg)	Hardness, taste, gastrointestinal irritation	30 to 150 mg/l based on sulfate content	150 mg/l
Manganese (as Mn)	Taste, discoloration, deposits, turbidity	0.05 mg/l	0.5 mg/l
Sulfate (as SO_4)	Gastrointestinal irritation when magnesium or sodium are present	200 mg/l	400 mg/l
Zinc (as Zn)	Astringent taste, opalescence and sand-like deposits	5.0 mg/l	15 mg/l

Source. International Standards for Drinking-Water, Third Edition, World Health Organization, Geneva, 1971.

esthetically significant mottling range from 1.2 to 0.7 mg/l for the temperature listed in Table 3-1. Turbidity is limited to one (nephelometric) turbidity unit unless a higher concentration can be demonstrated not to interfere with disinfection, maintenance of a chlorine residual, or bacteriological testing. Besides, greater than one unit is often related to inadequate treatment facilities or improper operation.

The WHO standards (Table 3-2) differ only slightly from the primary standards of EPA with the exception of a few items: The U.S. standards do not include cyanide and phenol, while WHO does not list barium and silver. Both sets of standards segregate esthetic parameters from health-related contaminants. Instead of being dangerous to human health, excess concentrations of these substances make drinking water less palatable and usable; however, they do not constitute grounds for rejection of the water supply unless their concentrations are extraordinary. High salt content (total dissolved solids, chloride, sulfate) have taste and laxative properties; odors can be caused by undefined organics or inorganic ions like copper; zinc is a gastrointestinal irritant; scale or corrosion of pipe and tank interiors results from chemical imbalance; iron and manganese cause brownish-colored stains on procelain and in laundry; and, visual impurities (color, foaming) are unesthetic.

A proposed addition to the interium primary regulations is a maximum contaminant level of 0.10 mg/l for total trihalomethanes, primarily chloroform and bromodichloromethane, which may have an adverse effect on human health by increasing the risk of human cancer. These halogenated substances are formed during disinfection by the reaction of chlorine with certain inorganic compounds like humic acids that naturally occur in surface waters.

3-2 Quality of Surface Waters

All surface waters should be capable of supporting aquatic life and be esthetically pleasing. Additionally, if needed as a public source, the water must be treatable by conventional processes to yield a potable supply meeting the drinking water standards. Many impoundments and rivers are also maintained at a quality suitable for swimming, water skiing, and boating. Surface waters throughout the nation are classified according to intended uses that dictate the specific physical, chemical, and biological quality standards, thus, insuring the most beneficial uses will not be deterred by pollution. Table 3-3 lists the six most common classifications for surface waters accompanied by dissolved oxygen, solids, and coliform criteria. Other parameters specified for a particular watercourse may include pH, toxic substances, tastes and odors, temperature, color, and radioactivity.

Establishing a lower limit for dissolved oxygen protects propagation of fish and other aquatic life, as well as enhancing recreation and reducing the possibility of odors resulting from decompostion of waste organics. Cold-water fish require stringent limitations, 6 mg/l with a minimum of 7 mg/l at spawning times, and warm-water species being more tolerant need a 4 to 5 mg/l limit. Dissolved solids are restricted because high concentrations interfere with agricultural, domestic, and industrial water uses. The strictest coliform standard applies to shellfish harvesting, since the meat may be eaten without being cooked. The next most stringent is for contract recreation where persons are likely to ingest water while bathing or water skiing.

Toxic pollutants (heavy metals, inorganic nitrogen, pesticides, and other trace organic compounds) cause diseases, behavioral abnormalities, and physiological malfunctions in both aquatic life and man; therefore, they must be carefully monitored and tightly controlled. Bioassays are the best method for determining safe concentrations of toxicants for aquatic organisms. Test species, typically fish, are exposed to various levels of poison concentrations for a specified time span of 96 h or less in a laboratory unit. The median tolerance limit (TLm) is the concentration that kills 50 percent of the test organisms. The maximum allowable toxicant concentration in surface waters is usually between 0.1 and 0.01 of the TLm value. This factor of safety

Table 3-3 Beneficial Uses and Quality Standards for Surface Waters

Water Use	Dissolved Oxygen Minimum Allowable (mg/l)	Solids Allowable		Coliforms Maximum Allowable per 100 ml
		Dissolved (mg/l)	Other	
Public water supply	4.0	500 to 750	No floating solids or settleable solids that form deposits	2000 fecal 10,000 total
Water contact recreation	4.0 to 5.0	None	Same as above	Mean of 1000 (200 fecal) with not more than 10 percent samples exceeding 2000 (400 fecal)
Fish propagation and wildlife	4.0 to 6.0 depending on warm or cold water fishes, fresh water or saltwater	None	Same as above	Mean of 5000

Industrial water supply	3.0 to 5.0 depending on use	750 to 1 500	Same as above	Generally none specified
Agricultural water supply	3.0 to 5.0 based on application	750 to 1 500 based on use and climate	Same as above	Generally none specified
Shellfish harvesting	4.0 to 6.0 depending on local conditions	None	Same as above	Mean of 70 with no more than 10 percent of samples exceeding 230

Source. M. J. Hammer, *Water and Waste-Water Technology, SI Version,* John Wiley and Sons, Inc., 1977.

is to account for long-term exposure and other materials already present in the receiving water that can create additional physiological stresses. The allowable pH range is usually 6.5 to 8.5 for protection of fish life and to control undesirable chemical reactions, such as dissolution of metal ions in acid waters. Many substances increase in toxicity with changes in the hydrogen ion content. For example, the ammonium ion is shifted to the much more poisonous form of unionized ammonia as the pH of water rises above neutrality. Temperature standards usually recommend an upper limit of 32°C with a maximum permissible rise above the naturally existing temperature of 3°C in streams and 2°C in lakes. In addition to making fish more susceptible to infection, rising temperature often increases the toxicity of substances by increasing their solubility or changing their ionic character; the ammonium ion can shift to free ammonia with the warming of water.

Organic matter, poisons, dissolved salts, and suspended solids contaminate both flowing and impounded waters. Nutrient salts, however, are particularly detrimental to lakes, estuaries, and slow-moving rivers by stimulating excessive plant growth, both weeds and algae. Removal of phosphates from wastewaters is practiced to protect many natural lakes including the Great Lakes, but nitrogen removal beyond about 50 percent is not feasible. Therefore, permits for municipalities and industries discharging to lakes, or streams that flow into lakes, commonly limit the phosphate concentration to 1.0 mg/l of phosphorus by chemical precipitation in addition to biological processing. This removal amounts to about 90 percent phosphorus reduction, which is technically possible and economically feasible in regions where natural lakes are endangered. Reduction in agricultural land drainage is, of course, not practical beyond the benefits resulting from good land management. Significant phosphorus reduction in major rivers is not a realistic expectation because of both uncontrolled land drainage and reluctance to pay for phosphate precipitation in wastewater treatment. Consequently, reservoirs on rivers have significant deterioration of water quality from nutrient enrichment with anaerobiosis of the bottom waters being the common result.

Contaminants difficult to remove by ordinary water processing are referred to as refractory pollutants, and many of these are dangerous to human health. For instance, nitrate and fluoride ions are unaffected by chemical oxidation and precipitation reactions. In addition, most of the other inorganic and organic chemicals listed in the primary drinking water standards (Table 3-1) are only sparingly removed by the common sequence of coagulation, sedimentation, filtration, and disinfection applied to surface water treatment. Absorption on granular activated carbon can substantially reduce soluble organics and excess lime additions precipitate heavy metals, but these operations are costly and not universally applied in municipal treatment. Rather than completely purifying surface waters, normally accepted processing is restricted to turbidity removal using aluminum sulfate or iron salt coagulants, disinfection with chlorine, reduction of tastes and odors by applying low dosages of powdered activated carbon, and stabilization by addition of acids or alkalis. In the case of hard river waters, lime softening may be applied to all or a portion of the flow. Where gross pollution exists, pretreatment can consist of percolation through infiltration galleries excavated in naturally permeable soils, or biological filtration through coarse media beds contained in tanks.

Quality criteria for public water sources, established and enforced, are essential for meeting the approval limits for health and avoiding the probability of forced abandonment of a water supply. Although renovating highly polluted waters is technically possible, feasibility relies on applying processes proven to be effective by demonstration and within reasonable economic limits. Safety is also an important factor—a higher quality raw supply insures a better finished water.

3-3 Principal Legislation in the United States

National Safe Drinking Water Act (Public Law 93-523)

Under this 1974 legislation, the Environmental Protection Agency has the primary responsibility of establishing national standards, and the states are responsible for enforcing the standards and otherwise supervising public water supply systems and sources of drinking water. The major provisions of this Act are as follows:

1. Establishment of primary regulations for the protection of public health. Individual states must adopt standards at least equal to the federal regulations in protecting public health.
2. Formation of secondary regulations relating to the taste, odor, and appearance of drinking water, which are optional and only enforced by individual states.
3. Creation of measures to protect underground drinking water sources.
4. Initiation of research and studies regarding health, economic, and technological problems of drinking water supplies. Specifically required are studies of viruses in drinking water and contamination of cancer-causing chemicals.
5. Conducting surveys of the quality and availability of rural water supplies.
6. Providing aid to the states to improve drinking water programs through technical assistance, training of personnel, and grant support.
7. Institution of laws to allow citizen suits against any party believed to be in violation of the Act.
8. Establishment of guidelines for record keeping, inspections, issuance of regulations, and judicial review.
9. Formation of a 15-member National Drinking Water Advisory Council to advise the EPA Administrator on scientific and other responsibilities under the Act.
10. Requirement of standards for bottled drinking water by the Secretary of Health and Human Services.
11. Authorization of appropriations to fund the programs.

This Act is oriented toward consumer protection by encompassing virtually all water supplies accessible to the public and defining the responsibilities of utility owners including monitoring, sampling, testing, and record keeping. The law also requires a water supplier to give public notice for failure to comply with a maximum contaminant level, required treatment, specified monitoring, or applicable testing procedures. Public notice must also announce an approved variance from the standards, and any failure to meet or comply with the stipulations of the variance.

Federal Water Pollution Control Act Amendments of 1972 (Public Law 92-500)

The objective of Public Law 92-500 is to "restore and maintain the chemical, physical, and biological integrity of the Nation's waters." Two goals and eight policies are contained in the Act. The first is an interim goal of water quality providing for the protection and propagation of fish, shellfish, and wildlife and for recreation in and on the water be achieved by July 1, 1983. The second goal is to eliminate the discharge of pollutants into navigable waters by 1985. The policies delineated are to:

1. Prohibit the discharge of toxic pollutants in dangerous amounts.
2. Provide federal financial assistance for construction of publicly owned treatment works.
3. Develop and implement areawide waste-treatment management planning.
4. Mount a major research and demonstration effort in wastewater treatment technology.
5. Recognize, preserve, and protect the primary responsibilities and roles of the States to prevent, reduce, and eliminate pollution.
6. Insure, where possible, that foreign nations act to prevent, reduce, and eliminate pollution in international waters.
7. Provide for, encourage, and assist public participation in executing the Act.
8. Pursue procedures that prevent needless duplication and unnecessary delays in implementing these policies at all levels of government.

The Act provides for achieving these goals and objectives in phases with accompaning requirements and deadlines. Phase I requires industries to install best practicable treatment and municipalities to implement secondary treatment by 1977. For phase II, industries are to install best available technology that is economically achievable, and publicly owned treatment works are to achieve best practicable technology, including water reclamation and confined disposal of pollutants by July 1, 1983. These goals were legislated as targets, not policies or requirements. As a result, phase II for eliminating the discharge of pollutants currently appears to be unrealistic and may never be reached; even the first goal may not be fully achievable owing to a combination of economical, technological, social, and environmental constraints.

The National Commission on Water Quality was established by Section 315 of Public Law 92-500 to determine if midcourse corrections in this Act were needed. The first evaluation by the National Commission on the impacts of water pollution control were submitted to Congress in 1976.[3] The Commission agreed that secondary treatment for all municipalities is technologically achievable with a stable construction grants program assuring 75 percent federal financing but the 1977 completion date would have to be delayed 5 to 10 years. For industries, time extensions and waivers are needed to achieve the 1977 best practicable treatment, which was deemed by the Commission to be both technologically and economically realistic. In general, the 1977 discharge requirements, except for toxic pollutants and new sources of discharge, may be delayed up to the 1983 deadline based on reasonable cause. The Commission goes on to recommend that Congress postpone the 1983 requirements for municipal, agricultural, and industrial discharges with the following recommendation: "No later than 1985 a Commission similar to the National Commission on Water Quality shall evaluate progress toward these goals and make appropriate recommendations, at which time Congress may consider whether uniform application of more stringent effluent limitations than the 1977 requirements is justified and desirable." Another key midcourse correction recommended was: "Decentralize regulatory and administrative functions of the national program by selective certification of states, based on satisfactory state plans and programs to control both point and nonpoint sources (including irrigated agriculture)."

National Pollutant Discharge Elimination System (NPDES)

The permit program to control discharge of pollutants into surface waters is specified in Section 402 of Public Law 92-500. The Environmental Protection Agency is required to establish national effluent limitations and performance standards for sources of water pollution, including factories, power plants, wastewater treatment plants, and animal feedlots. Effluent limits may allow discharge of a specified amount of a pollutant or prohibit emission completely. Toxins that can be contained at an industrial site are often included in the latter. Secondary treatment of municipal wastewater is generally viewed as producing an effluent with less than 30 mg/l BOD and 30 mg/l suspended solids. However, the variation and complexity of manufacturing wastes require separate evaluation for each industry. After public review and comment, the EPA publishes national performance standards that set effluent limits based on the best practicable technology. Anyone discharging pollutants into surface waters must apply for an NPDES permit from the state agency approved by EPA. States also have the legal authority to enforce the program and levy penalties for noncompliance. All information regarding application, findings, discharge criteria, monitoring data, and compliance reports must be accessible to the public. Citizens are given the right to bring civil suit under the Act against any person who is alleged to be in violation of an effluent standard or limitation.

A municipal wastewater ordinance is essential for ensuring proper operation of a treatment plant and meeting effluent standards. Of particular importance is monitoring and restricting industrial discharges into the sewer system. Being a biological process, secondary treatment can be upset by toxic and hydrocarbon wastes resulting in poor removal of organics and passage of the industrial pollutants. Furthermore, even the effluent of a functioning biological treatment plant can contain detrimental amounts of health-related contaminants, such as heavy metal ions and chlorinated hydrocarbons. Thus, refractory contaminants must be prohibited from sewers by an enforceable municipal permit system as a necessary adjunct to the NPDES.

Areawide Waste Treatment Management (Section 208, Public Law 92-500)
The components of 208 water-quality planning include:
1. A description of planning area.
2. Assessment of existing and potential water quality problems.
3. Inventory of municipal and industrial sources of pollutants, and a summary of existing and projected land use patterns.
4. Evaluation of water quality problems caused by nonpoint (diffuse) sources of pollutants.
5. Needs for urban and industrial storm water systems.
6. Target abatement schedules for pollutant sources.
7. Description of existing or needed state and local regulatory programs.
8. Assessment of environmental, social, and economic impact of carrying out the plan.

   This legislation led to designation of the specific agencies responsible for water quality and related land management. Previously, very few areawide plans existed and most river basins were left uncontrolled owing to the lack of coordination, or non-existence, of agencies involved with water pollution control. A second important feature of Section 208 is the inclusion of diffuse sources of contamination. In contrast to pipe discharges (point sources) that are relatively easy to monitor and control, runoff from agricultural activities, urban storm water, and watershed drainage from other diffuse sources cannot be managed through a permit system and effluent standards. Land use patterns, although not regulated under this law, can be recommended to reduce the quantities of diffuse contaminants entering surface waters. For example, soil and water conservation practices of contour plowing, construction of retention ponds, grassed waterways, and reuse of irrigation tailwater can be encouraged, perhaps through economic incentives. Third, the final plan must be economical and implementable, not as unattainable as the original Public Law 92-500 goal of eliminating the discharge of (all) pollutants.

Groundwater Quality Control
Comprehensive federal statutes to control and protect groundwater quality do not exist; nevertheless, some degree of authority is specified in various acts. Although directed toward surface waterways, Public Law 92-500 does provide guidelines for preventing and abating pollution of groundwater through monitoring, planning, and developing criteria for subsurface disposal of wastes. The National Environmental Policy Act of 1969 (Public Law 91-190) requires all federal agencies to prepare environmental impact statements on major federal or federally regulated actions that significantly affect the quality of the environment, including potential groundwater contamination. This process of review and evaluation prior to construction is a deterent against willful pollution from a federally funded project.

   The Safe Drinking Water Act regulates underground injection of pollutants that may endanger drinking water sources (Section 1421) by establishing a permit system incorporating inspection, monitoring, record keeping, and reporting requirements. The precise coverage of the Law has not been legally determined. Currently, the sources included are both deep and shallow waste disposal wells, oil-field brine injection and secondary recovery wells, and engineering projects such as seawater barriers, solution mining, and natural gas storage. Based on a broader interpretation, underground injection could encompass all liquid or solid contaminants that flow or move when put below the ground surface, which would include landfills and surface impoundments. The Act does not restrain subsurface disposal of wastes from an individual residential dwelling. Under Section 1424(e), the EPA Administrator can act to protect the recharge zone of a aquifer that is the sole or principal source of drinking water for an area.

3-4 Summary of Water Quality Management

Water quality for beneficial uses (water supply, recreation, and aquatic life) is degraded by waste disposal. The perfect situation is where a community can use a pristine upstream supply and discharge its waste below. This is rarely possible, however, since someone else who must reuse the water usually lives downstream. Therefore, pollution control measures are instituted by legislative prodding to protect the water environment for the benefit of the downstream majority. Figure 3-1 is a composite diagram to help illustrate the concepts of water quality management.

Point sources originating from municipal, industrial, and agricultural activities are all treatable but, because of economical and other practical considerations, not to the original water supply quality. For example, municipal use followed by biologica' secondary treatment usually adds 300 mg/l total solids, 30 mg/l suspended solids, 2(mg/l inorganic nitrogen, 7 mg/l phosphorus, and thousands of enteric bacteria and viruses per millilitre, plus heavy metals and nonbiodegradable organics. The metals and organics from manufacturing are best controlled at the industrial sites, hence the need for a *sewer use ordinance*. Where deemed necessary, phosphates can be chemically precipitated and an additional portion of the suspended solids removed by granular-media filtration. Effective reduction of bacteria and viruses requires chemical flocculation, filtration, and chlorination-dechlorination, which is a costly series of processes. Removal of dissolved salts and a significant reduction in inorganic nitrogen are not feasible, and therefore must rely on dilution and assimilation in a natural watercourse. Wastewater containing biodegradable organics from industries, such as food processing, are usually treated in a manner similar to municipal wastewater, but toxic and hazardous substances are often contained in evaporation ponds or disposed of by deep-well injection. *Effluent standards* are the primary method for assuring water quality in rivers and lakes receiving wastewaters.

Pollution from diffuse sources—agricultural and urban runoff, and mine drainage—can be controlled to only a limited extent by land management practices. Financial incentives for soil and water conservation in agriculture and restoration of mining areas are beneficial in many regions. Yet turbid runoff during heavy rain storms cannot be realistically prevented. Rainfall from streets and grassed areas in cities is collected and conveyed to a stream or lake without treatment. Cities with combined sewers attempt to process both storm and sanitary wastewaters except during heavy

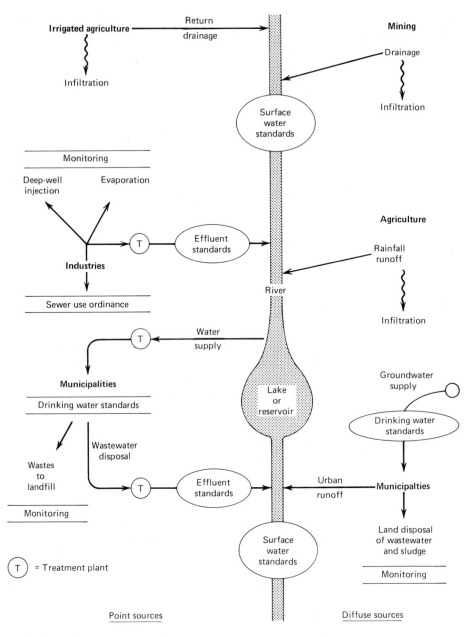

Figure 3-1 A diagram illustrating principal sources of pollution and points where water quality standards are applied.

storms when excess flow bypasses treatment. Fortunately, the unavoidable contamination caused by diffuse sources is rarely related to a health hazard. The most frequent problems are soil turbidity reducing water transparency, phosphate fertilizing river reservoirs, and significant nitrate increases often during periods of low flow. *Surface water standards* are the criteria for judging the seriousness of background pollutants in combination with point discharges.

Groundwater quality has been ignored until recently when occurrences of contamination in well water supplies attracted attention. Legislation is directed toward *monitoring* to insure proper design and operation of waste disposal wells, evaporation ponds, landfills, and surface spreading of wastes. The most common diffuse groundwater contaminants are nitrate and dissolved salts primarily from cultivated agriculture. In some areas, subsurface disposal of wastewaters and mining operations can also be major contributors. These contaminants create serious regional problems since nitrate is related to health and neither nitrate nor dissolved salts are economical to remove in municipal water treatment. In contrast to stream pollution, the recovery of groundwater quality takes a very long time, and restorative actions are very rarely feasible.

Drinking water standards, rather than being directed toward preventing contamination, define potable waters for public supplies. Unsatisfactory quality of water in a piping system only proves that the customers have already ingested impure water. Therefore, monitoring the sources of surface and groundwater supplies is essential to anticipating and preventing quality problems.

References

1. *The Safe Drinking Water Act, Public Law 93-523*, 93rd Congress, S. 433, December 16, 1974.

2. *The Federal Water Pollution Control Act, Public Law 92-500*, 92nd Congress, S. 2770, October 18, 1972.

3. *Report to the Congress by the National Commission on Water Quality*, March 18, 1976, Superintendent of Documents, U.S. Government Printing Office, Washington, D.C. 20402.

Problems

3-1 Why are bacterial standards for drinking water based on the presence of nonpathogenic coliform bacteria?

3-2 Why is nitrate considered a primary, health-related contaminant in a public water supply?

3-3 What is the limit for total solids in drinking water based on (a) United States and (b) international standards? Why is a maximum level recommended?

3-4 List the generally accepted minimum dissolved oxygen levels specified for surface waters.

3-5 Define the meaning of median tolerance limit, and describe the application of TLm values to water quality standards.

3-6 Define the term refractory pollutant. Referring to the Secondary Standards for Recommended Contaminant Levels listed in Table 3-1, select six you consider to be refractory substances.

3-7 Eleven major provisions of the National Safe Drinking Water Act are listed in the beginning of Section 3-3. Which two do you feel are the most important for consumer protection and why?

3-8 What were the two goals of the Federal Water Pollution Control Act Amendments? Are they being realized on schedule? Refer to the midcourse corrections.

3-9 How has the National Pollutant Discharge Elimination System helped to ensure success in meeting surface water quality standards?

3-10 Which of the current water laws protect the quality of groundwater?

Chapter 4
Hydrology of Groundwater

Groundwater is the source of drinking water for approximately one half the population of the United States, with 29 percent through public supplies and 19 percent from individual household wells as depicted in Figure 4-1a. For towns and farms, groundwater is not only the least expensive but may be the only available source. Based on application, irrigation is the biggest user, withdrawing about two thirds of the total supply, domestic supplies are second, and self-supplied industry third (Figure 4-1b). Groundwater exploitation is expected to continue led by irrigation use. Total withdrawal is projected to increase to about one and one-half times the present usage in the next 30 years. In view of this present and future development, the hydrology of groundwater is essential in water resources education. This chapter presents the basic

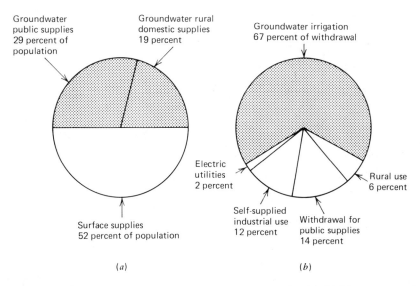

Figure 4-1 Groundwater is extensively used in the United States for (a) drinking water, serving approximately one half of the population, and (b) for agricultural irrigation, which accounts for two thirds of the total groundwater withdrawal. (From *The Report to Congress, Waste Disposal Practices and Their Effects on Ground Water*, U. S. Environmental Protection Agency, January 1977.)

concepts on the physical regime of groundwater. Stress is placed on flow to wells and the fundamentals of well construction and safe yield.

4-1 Occurrence of Groundwater

Groundwater originates as infiltration from precipitation, streamflow, lakes, and reservoirs. Figure 4-2a illustrates the subsurface distribution of water. After entering the ground, it flows vertically down through the zone of aeration by gravity. This percolation leaves behind thin layers of water coating the soil grains, referred to as soil moisture, and enters the zone of saturation. Just above this, continuous films of pore water are held by capillary action. (Capillarity can be demonstrated by immersing the lower end of a glass tube into a vessel containing water. Liquid climbs to the height of capillary rise that is governed primarily by the diameter of the tube; the smaller the diameter the greater the rise.) The amount of water in the suspended zone depends on climatic conditions, grain size of the soil, and depth of the aerated zone. Sands and

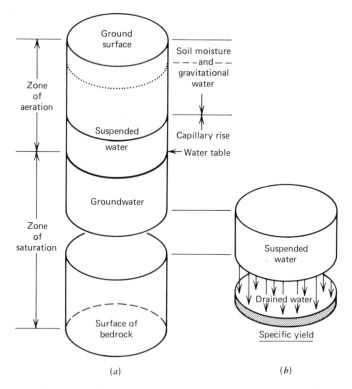

Figure 4-2 (a) Distribution of subsurface water between the zones of aeration and saturation. (b) The concept of specific yield, which is defined as the quantity of water available per unit volume of aquifer.

gravels drain readily and hold little moisture, while fine-grained soils may be saturated for a considerable distance above the water table.

The water table (phreatic surface) is the level of free water in an observation well extending into the saturated zone. The water below this depth, which saturates the porous soil or fissured rock, is defined as groundwater. Its horizontal movement is controlled by the hydraulic gradient, flowing downgrade with little vertical mixing. The water table may fluctuate with seasonal supply and demand.

A permeable geologic formation has sufficiently large pores or fissures to allow transmission of groundwater. Porosity of a soil or rock is an expression of the void space calculated as follows:

$$n = \frac{V_v}{V} \tag{4-1}$$

where n = porosity
$\quad V_v$ = volume of voids
$\quad V$ = total volume

If Equation 4-1 is expressed as a percentage ($n \times 100$), the resultant is often referred to as the percentage of voids. Porosity of sands and gravels ranges from 0.2 to 0.4 depending on grain size and distribution, degree of cementation and compaction. Values for permeable rock vary with texture and the size of interstices; common ranges are 0.1 to 0.2 for sandstones and 0.01 to 0.1 for shale and limestone. When groundwater drains from a porous stratum, some water is retained in the voids reducing the yield to less than the volume of voids. The quantity removed is the specific yield or effective porosity (Figure 4-2b); the amount retained is the specific retention. Specific yield for alluvial sand and gravel deposits ranges from 90 to 95 percent. For example, if a coarse sand has a porosity of 0.40 and specific yield of 90 percent, the volume draining from one cubic metre would be $0.40 \times 0.90 = 0.36$ m^3 of water.

Aquifers are permeable geologic strata that convey groundwater. Most are sufficiently large to be visualized as storage reservoirs that discharge by gravity flow, or well extraction, and recharge by infiltration, Figure 4-3. Aquifers are classed as unconfined or confined depending on the presence of a water table. The upper boundary of an unconfined aquifer is the water table. The name unconfined is appropriate since the surface of the groundwater can move up and down to change the zone occupied by the aquifer. The water table rises with recharge, and drops during dry weather when stored groundwater discharges to surface flows or is withdrawn by pumping. A well in an unconfined aquifer is referred to as a water-table well.

A perched water table is a special case of an unconfined aquifer where groundwater lies on a relatively impermeable stratum of small areal extent above the main body of groundwater. Wells tapping perched aquifers yield only temporary or small quantities of water.

Confined aquifers, also known as artesian or pressure aquifers, exist where groundwater is confined by relatively impermeable strata, Figure 4-3. Water in an artesian well rises to the piezometric level. (A simple piezometer is a tube rising from a con-

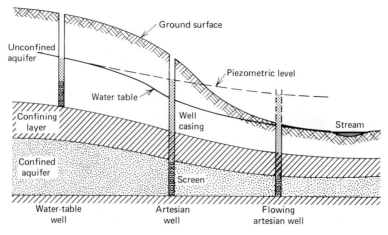

Figure 4-3 A profile of unconfined and confined aquifers illustrating water-table and artesian wells.

tainer of water under pressure. The height of water in the tube indicates the pressure of the confined water; for each 1.0 kPa of pressure the water rises 0.102 m.) Originally, the term artesian referred to a well with flowing water, but presently it applies to any well penetrating a confined aquifer.

Common aquifers are valley fills composed of sand, gravel, and silt adjacent to streams; granular deposits along coastal plains; alluvium and loess of high plains; waterborne deposits from glaciation (glacial drift); terrains of volcanic origin; fractured limestore or dolomite rock; and poorly cemented sandstones.

4-2 Permeability

The ability of a porous medium to transmit water is called permeability. The quantity of flow through a dense rock may be so small as to pass unnoticed because evaporation prevents accumulation of water on the open face. In contrast, granular layers in a valley wall may drain groundwater rapidly enough to create small waterfalls. The law for flow through soils is named after Henri Darcy who demonstrated experimentally that the rate of flow is proportional to the gradient. He used a laboratory apparatus consisting of a sand filter contained between two screens in a column that was placed in a receiving vessel, as sketched in Figure 4-4a. The quantity of flow through the sand filter was found to be proportional to the difference in hydraulic head at the ends of the column $(H + L)$ and inversely proportional to the length of the column (L). This is expressed mathematically as follows:

$$Q = \frac{KA}{L}(H + L) \tag{4-2}$$

where Q = rate of water flow through the sand filter

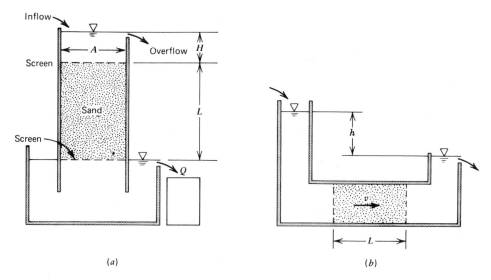

Figure 4-4 Illustrations defining the terms used in two expressions of Darcy's law for flow through a porous medium: (a) Darcy's filtration apparatus for the relationship expressed in Equation 4-2, and (b) a sketch showing the parameters of Equation 4-3.

A = cross-sectional area of the filter
L = length of the filter in the direction of flow
H = height of water above the sand
K = coefficient depending on the properties of the sand

Darcy's law, as the basic principle defining the flow of groundwater, is presently written as follows:

$$v = Ki \qquad (4\text{-}3)$$

where v = discharge velocity (Q/A), millimetres per second (metres per day)
K = coefficient of permeability, millimetres per second (metres per day)
i = hydraulic gradient (h/L), metres per metre

Figure 4-4b illustrates the parameters of this formula. The discharge velocity v is calculated as Q/A, which is an observed experimental value and not the actual velocity of flow through the pores of the soil. Thus, this equation defines the coefficient of permeability K as the constant of proportionality between the superficial velocity v and the hydraulic gradient i. The coefficient K, often referred to as simply the permeability, is primarily a characteristic of the porous medium. Even though it is affected by fluid characteristics, the variations in density and viscosity of groundwater are negligible for practical considerations. Typical values for the coefficient of permeability are: 0.01 to 1.0 mm/s for clean sand and gravel mixtures, 10 mm/s for clean sands, and 100 to 1 000 mm/s for clean gravels.

Darcy's law is valid for laminar flow; a condition where the velocity is sufficiently slow to allow each water particle to travel along a definite path without interference from other moving particles. This is the state of almost all natural groundwater movement. Turbulent flow results when particles follow irregular paths, crossing and recrossing at random. For instance, rapid flow through a fissured rock aquifer containing solution openings.

Laboratory permeability tests on soil samples are performed using either a constant-head or falling-head permeameter. An apparatus with a constant hydraulic head (Figure 4-4a) is reliable for highly permeable materials, such as clean sands and gravels. Results are calculated by Equation 4-2. For low permeability materials, the falling-head permeameter employs a tall standpipe of small diameter attached on top of the cylinder containing the soil sample. This inlet tube allows convenient application of greater water pressure on the sample, and can be calibrated to measure the small amount of water passing through the sample. The drop in water level is observed with respect to time and K computed as follows:

$$ K = \frac{aL}{At} \log_e \left(\frac{h_0}{h_1} \right) \tag{4-4} $$

where K = coefficient of permeability

a = cross-sectional area of the standpipe

L = length of the sample

A = cross-sectional area of the sample

t = time interval

h_0 = initial hydraulic head (height difference between the original water level in the standpipe and water level in the vessel on the discharge side of the sample)

h_1 = final hydraulic head

$\log_e$ = Napierian logarithm

The results of permeability tests on alluvial deposits are often misleading because of the difficulty in obtaining representative samples. Undisturbed removal of sands and gravels is impractical and placement in a permeameter is not likely to represent the actual field condition. Furthermore, many natural deposits are stratified with differing horizontal and vertical permeabilities. In the horizontal direction, the average permeability may be almost as great as the rate of the most porous stratum, whereas in the vertical direction the average is likely to be as small as the least permeable layer. The ratio of the average coefficients of permeability in horizontal and vertical directions in stratified soil deposits may be as low as 2 to 1 or over 10 to 1.

Field measurements of permeability include tracer studies, infiltration tests, and pumping tests with wells. In tracer analysis, a dyelike sodium fluorescein is injected at one point and then measured as it appears in time sequence at a downstream location. This technique has serious limitations related to detection of the dye at low concentrations, possible reactions with the soil, and dispersion of the dye. An infiltration test can be conducted if the water table is near the ground surface. Water is poured into a cylindrical hole and the rate of fall in water level related to permeability by means of a

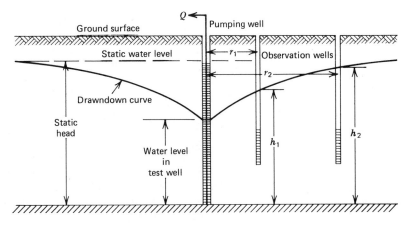

Figure 4-5 Flow of water toward a well during a pumping test in an unconfined coarse-grained aquifer. The dimensions shown apply to Equation 4-5.

suitable equation. This method has limited application to deep aquifers tapped for water supplies.

Pumping from a test well is the most reliable method for estimating permeability of a coarse-grained aquifer below the water table. While pumping the main well, free water levels are measured in piezometer tubes (observation wells) located at various distances from the central well, as shown schematically in Figure 4-5. The observation wells are usually drilled along two straight lines, one oriented in the direction of natural groundwater movement and the other at right angles to it. Once a steady state of flow under constant pumping has been established and water levels in all wells are nearly stationary, the coefficient of permeability is calculated from the appropriate well hydraulics equation. For testing an unconfined aquifer, Equation 4-5 is appropriate. The equations for computing K from a test well in a confined aquifer is given in Section 4-5.

$$K = \frac{Q}{\pi(h_2{}^2 - h_1{}^2)} \log_e\left(\frac{r_2}{r_1}\right) \tag{4-5}$$

where K = coefficient of permeability, millimetres per second
  Q = pump discharge, litres per second
  h = water level in observation well, metres
  r = distance from test well to observation well, metres

Example 4-1

A sample of sandstone cored from an aquifer is tested in a falling-head permeameter. The specimen has a diameter of 50 mm and length of 80 mm. The inside diameter of the standpipe is 2.0 mm. During a time interval of 6 min, the hydraulic head on the sample decreased from 100 to 50 cm. Compute the value of K for this test run.

Solution

Substituting into Equation 4-4,

$$K = \frac{\pi(1.0 \text{ mm})^2(80 \text{ mm})}{\pi(25 \text{ mm})^2(6 \times 60 \text{ s})} \log_e\left(\frac{100 \text{ cm}}{50 \text{ cm}}\right) = 2.4 \times 10^{-4} \text{mm/s}$$

Example 4-2

A pumping test was conducted to estimate the in situ permeability of an unconfined sand aquifer underlaid by impervious bedrock. The test well penetrated the entire 20 m depth of the aquifer. The two observation wells located at distances of 15 m and 100 m from the main well were drilled to a depth of 15 m. Before testing, the static water level in all wells was 15 m above the bedrock datum (5 m below the ground surface). After pumping for several days at a rate of 70 l/s, the drawdown in the test well measured 6.0 m and the water levels in the two observation wells at 15 and 100 m stabilized at 11.4 and 13.1 m, respectively, above the bedrock datum.

Make a profile sketch of the test conditions, and compute the coefficient of permeability.

Solution

The diagram of test conditions should be similar to the profile in Figure 4-5.

Apply Equation 4-5 to calculate the permeability.

$$K = \frac{70 \text{ l/s}}{\pi[(13.1 \text{ m})^2 - (11.4 \text{ m})^2]} \log_e\left(\frac{100 \text{ m}}{15 \text{ m}}\right) = 1.0 \text{ mm/s}$$

4-3 General Equations for Groundwater Flow

The indefinite form of Darcy's law is

$$v = K\frac{\partial h}{\partial s} \tag{4-6}$$

where v = velocity of flow
K = coefficient of permeability
∂h = head loss along direction of flow
∂s = distance along direction of flow
$\dfrac{\partial h^*}{\partial s}$ = hydraulic gradient

For an aquifer having permeabilities that vary with direction of flow, the velocity components may be expressed in rectangular coordinates with K_x, K_y, and K_z representing the coefficients of permeability in the x, y, and z directions. Using Equation 4-6, the respective velocities of flow become

$$v_x = K_x\frac{\partial h}{\partial x} \qquad v_y = K_y\frac{\partial h}{\partial y} \qquad v_z = K_z\frac{\partial h}{\partial z} \tag{4-7}$$

*A partial derivative is the rate of change of a function with respect to its variables; in this case, the change in hydraulic head with respect to change in distance.

To simplify groundwater flow equations, aquifers are assumed to be homogenous (hydraulically isotropic) with the same permeability in all directions. Therefore, the velocities become

$$v_x = K\frac{\partial h}{\partial x} \quad v_y = K\frac{\partial h}{\partial y} \quad v_z = K\frac{\partial h}{\partial z} \tag{4-8}$$

Velocity potential ϕ is a scalar function of space and time such that its negative derivative with respect to any direction gives the velocity in that direction, hence

$$\phi = -Kh \tag{4-9}$$

By definition a velocity potential exists for groundwater flow, which implies ideal or frictionless flow (irrotational flow). Substituting ϕ, Equation 4-8 becomes

$$v_x = -\frac{\partial \phi}{\partial x} \quad v_y = -\frac{\partial \phi}{\partial y} \quad v_z = -\frac{\partial \phi}{\partial z} \tag{4-10}$$

Steady Flow
Figure 4-6 shows a rectangular element of an aquifer with side lengths of dx, dy, and dz in the x, y, and z directions. The total quantity of water entering the element per unit of time is

$$v_x dz dy + v_y dx dz + v_z dy dx \tag{4-11}$$

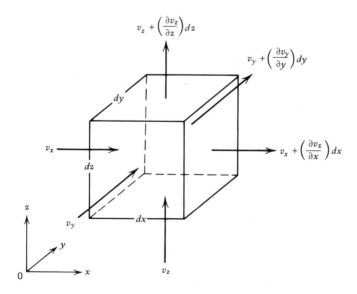

Figure 4-6 An imaginary element of an aquifer showing velocities of flow entering and leaving the element in rectangular coordinates.

The quantity leaving is

$$v_x dz dy + \frac{\partial v_x}{\partial x} dx dz dy + v_y dx dz + \frac{\partial v_y}{\partial y} dy dx dz + v_z dy dx + \frac{\partial v_z}{\partial z} dz dy dx \qquad (4\text{-}12)$$

Assuming water is incompressible, the quantity of water entering the element is equal to the amount leaving under steady flow. Therefore, the terms of Equation 4-11 equal those of Equation 4-12. The resulting continuity equation is

$$\frac{\partial v_x}{\partial x} + \frac{\partial v_y}{\partial y} + \frac{\partial v_z}{\partial z} = 0 \qquad (4\text{-}13)$$

Since neither water nor soil are completely incompressible, groundwater flow does not strictly satisfy the continuity condition. However, for solution of practical problems this fact is relatively insignificant and disregarded.

When the velocity potentials of irrotational flow given in Equation 4-10 are substituted into Equation 4-13, the following expression known as Laplace's equation results.

$$\frac{\partial^2 \phi}{\partial x^2} + \frac{\partial^2 \phi}{\partial y^2} + \frac{\partial^2 \phi}{\partial z^2} = 0 \qquad (4\text{-}14)$$

Replacing ϕ by $-Kh$ results in

$$\frac{\partial^2 h}{\partial x^2} + \frac{\partial^2 h}{\partial y^2} + \frac{\partial^2 h}{\partial z^2} = 0 \qquad (4\text{-}15)$$

which is the partial differential equation for steady flow of water in homogenous, incompressible, isotropic porous media.

Unsteady Flow

Equations for unsteady flow must take into account storage of water in an aquifer since inflow and outflow are not equal. In short, portions of the aquifer are either being dewatered or recharged.

For a confined aquifer, the coefficient of storage S is a function of hydraulic pressure in the aquifer. Refer to Figure 4-7a. When the piezometric surface is lowered a unit distance, the quantity of water released from the column by the pressure change is defined as the coefficient of storage. An artesian aquifer is considered to be elastic, expanding when confining pressure is reduced by pumping. Water is assumed to be compressible while the soil grains (porous media) are rigid. Also, the compressive force is assumed to act in a vertical direction over a large areal extent so that horizontal changes are negligible. Incorporating these concepts in the continuity equation (Equation 4-13) and rewriting in the form of Equation 4-15, the partial differential equation for unsteady flow of water in a confined aquifer is

$$\frac{\partial^2 h}{\partial x^2} + \frac{\partial^2 h}{\partial y^2} + \frac{\partial^2 h}{\partial z^2} = \frac{S}{Kb} \frac{\partial h}{\partial t} \qquad (4\text{-}16)$$

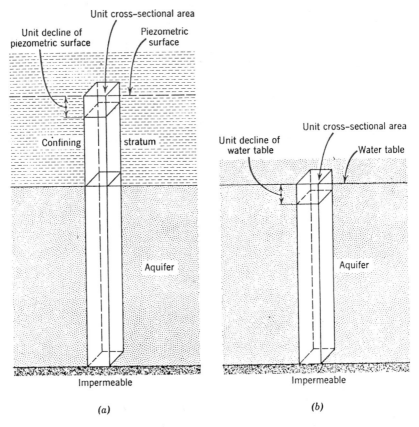

Figure 4-7 Illustrations defining coefficient of storage S for (a) confined and (b) unconfined aquifers. S is a dimensionless number equal to the quantity of water released for each unit of surface area per unit change in pressure head on the aquifer. (From D. K. Todd, *Ground Water Hydrology*, John Wiley & Sons, Inc., 1959.)

where S = dimensionless coefficient of storage
K = coefficient of permeability
b = confined aquifer thickness
h = piezometric head
t = time

The corresponding equation for unsteady flow in an unconfined aquifer is nonlinear making direct solution impossible. Consequently, the mathematics of this condition are not presented. By approximation, however, Equation 4-16 can be applied where the variation in saturated thickness of an unconfined aquifer is relatively small. The storage coefficient for an unconfined aquifer is defined as specific yield (Figures 4-7b and 4-2b).

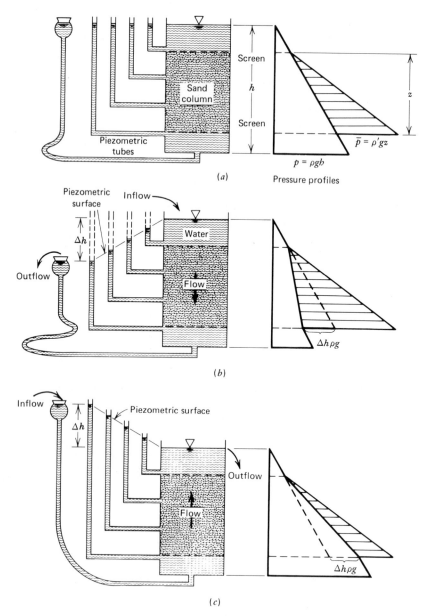

Figure 4-8 Diagrams illustrating the meaning of porewater and intergranular pressures in groundwater flow.

52

4-4 Groundwater Pressures

The stresses acting within a saturated aquifer are transmitted both by grain to grain contact of the porous media and hydraulically through the water that fills the pores. The former is called intergranular pressure and the latter porewater or groundwater pressure. The distribution between intergranular and groundwater pressures are illustrated under no-flow conditions in Figure 4-8a. Static pressure in the water above the sand, in the pore water of the sand column, and below the filter increases linearly with depth, such that

$$p = \rho g h = \gamma h = 9.79h \qquad (4\text{-}17)$$

where p = pressure in the pore water, kilopascals

ρ = specific density of water, kilograms per cubic metre (998 kg/m^3 at 20°C)

g = acceleration of gravity, metres per second squared (9.807 m/s^2)

h = depth below free water surface, metres

$\gamma = \rho g$ = 9.79 = specific weight of water, kilonewtons per cubic metre (998 kg/m^3 × 9.807 m/s^2 = 9 790 N/m)

Since the vessel is open on top, this apparatus represents an unconfined aquifer with the water surface above the sand being the static water level. And under conditions of no flow, the piezometric surfaces of the tubes penetrating the sand filter are level with that water surface.

Intergranular pressure in the submerged sand bed with no water flow is determined by the equation

$$\bar{p} = (\rho_{\text{sat}} - \rho)10^{-3}gz = \rho'10^{-3}gz \qquad (4\text{-}18)$$

where $\bar{p}$ = intergranular pressure, kN/m^2

ρ_{sat} = specific density of saturated soil, kilograms per cubic metre

ρ = specific density of water, kilograms per cubic metre (998 kg/m^3 at 20°C)

ρ' = submerged density of soil, kilograms per cubic metre

g = acceleration of gravity (9.807 m/s^2)

z = depth below the ground surface, metres

In the pressure diagram on the right side of Figure 4-8a, the change in width of the unshaded area represents the distribution of porewater pressure with depth. The shaded area is intergranular pressure with depth.

Groundwater flow through an aquifer shifts the distribution of pressures between intergranular and porewater stresses. Visualize maintaining the free water surface at the top of the container holding the sand filter by continuously replenishing the supply and lower the reservoir attached to the bottom by a flexible tube. The new pressure distributions with water discharging from the bottom of the column, after establishing steady flow through the sand bed, are sketched in Figure 4-8b. The increase in intergranular pressure resulting from the flow of water through the voids is

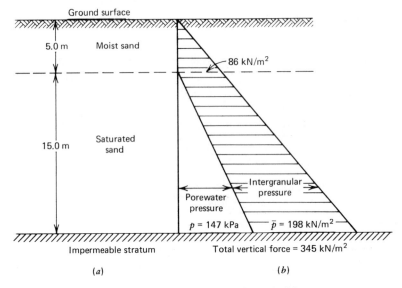

Figure 4-9 Aquifer profile and pressure distributions for Example 4-3.

known as seepage pressure. It is caused by the frictional drag of the flowing water on the soil grains. The amount of the pressure transferred from the pore water to grain to grain contact at the bottom of the sand layer equals $\Delta h \rho g$, which is the loss of head through the bed. Assuming an ideal homogeneous sand, the piezometric surface through the sand column shows an uniform reduction.

Figure 4-8c illustrates upflow through the sand filter, which increases the porewater pressure with corresponding reduction of intergranular pressure. The critical hydraulic gradient occurs when upflow is sufficiently great to reduce the intergranular pressure to zero. This phenomenon is known as the quick condition, and in this case being a sand bed it would be referred to as quicksand.

Example 4-3

Compute the porewater pressure and the vertical intergranular pressure distributions for the soil profile in Figure 4-9a. The sand above the water table has a moist density of 1 760 kg/m^3, below the water table the saturated density is 1 940 kg/m^3

Solution

The porewater pressure increases linearly from zero at the water table to the following value calculated at the base of the aquifer using Equation 4-17:

$$p = 15.0 \text{ m} \times 9.79 \text{ kPa/m} = 147 \text{ kPa}$$

This groundwater pressure is exerted equally in all directions.

The vertical intergranular pressure at the water table is the force resulting from the weight of 5.0 m of moist sand.

$\bar{p}$ = 5.0 m × 1 760 kg/m³ × 9.807 m/s² × 10^{-3} = 86 kN/m²

The vertical stress from the submerged sand using Equation 4-18 is

$\bar{p}$ = (1 760 kg/m³ - 998 kg/m³)10^{-3} × 9.807 m/s² × 15.0 m = 112 kN/m²

Therefore, the total intergranular pressure at the bottom of the aquifer is

86 kN/m² + 112 kN/m² = 198 kN/m²

This value is the vertical grain to grain pressure. The horizontal intergranular pressure depends on the relative density of the sand and the natural processes that formed the deposit. The coefficient of earth pressure at rest for a sand ranges from about 0.4 to 0.5, thus, the horizontal pressure is probably between 80 and 100 kN/m².

The pressure distributions are shown in Figure 4-9b. The total vertical force on the underlying impermeable stratum is

147 kN/m²(kPa) + 198 kN/m² = 345 kN/m²

4-5 Flow Nets

The graphical representation of flow through soil, known as a flow net, is useful for visualizing groundwater movement. Figure 4-10 is a cross-sectional drawing of a sheet pile penetrating halfway into a surface aquifer, which is underlain by an impermeable stratum. Water is standing at a depth h on the left side of the wall, while on the right side the surface is exposed to the atmosphere. Thus, groundwater passes through the aquifer under the sheeting from left to right in two-dimensional flow. The paths followed by particles of percolating water are called flow lines, which are drawn as solid curved lines in Figure 4-10. If a model of this section was constructed between glass

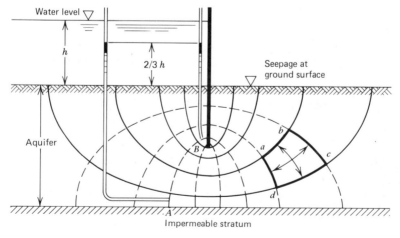

Figure 4-10 Flow net for groundwater passing under a sheet pile wall penetrating into an aquifer. The solid lines are flow lines, and the dashed ones are equipotential lines.

plates, flow lines could be observed by injecting small amounts of dye immediately under the aquifer surface at several points on the left side.

The dashed lines in Figure 4-10, called equipotential lines, connect points of equal piezometric head on the flow lines. Since each flow path starts on the left under a pressure head of h and terminates on the right at atmospheric pressure, the head loss h resulting from frictional resistance to flow is distributed along the flow line. Therefore, a point exists on every flow line where the remaining potential (pressure head) is the same. A trace through these points is an equipotential line, as illustrated by line AB at a head of $2/3h$. Hydraulic gradients are maximum along paths normal to equipotential lines and flow follows paths of greatest gradient; therefore, in isotropic soil all crossings of equipotential and flow lines must be at right angles.

The figures enclosed by adjacent pairs of flow lines and equipotential lines resemble squares, like $abcd$ in Figure 4-10. All four corners of each figure form right angles and the mean distances between opposite faces are equal. Although this shape is actually curvilinear, repeated subdividing would create figures approaching true squares. For two-dimensional flow through homogeneous soil, a flow net contains square figures for continuity and to satisfy Darcy's law. With this geometry of a flow net, together with the permeability and head loss, the total flow in the section can be computed directly using the following equation:

$$Q = \left(\frac{n_e}{n_f}\right) Kh_L \tag{4-19}$$

where Q = quantity of flow
K = coefficient of permeability
h_L = head loss
n_f = the number of arbitrary flow channels
n_e = the number of corresponding equipotential intervals

For example, in Figure 4-10, n_e/n_f is $4.5/9.0 = 0.50$.

The hydraulic boundary conditions in a flow net must represent steady flow. Referring to Figure 4-10, both the entrance and exit surfaces of the aquifer are equipotential lines. The sides of the sheet wall and the base of the aquifer represent the upper-

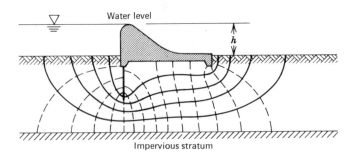

Figure 4-11 Flow net under a dam with a cutoff extending into the porous foundation soil.

most (shortest) flow line and the lowest (longest) flow line, respectively. To satisfy these boundary conditions, all flow lines are perpendicular to the aquifer surface and all equipotentials are perpendicular to the sheeting and impervious base.

The simple flow net illustrated in Figure 4-11 also represents two-dimensional flow through homogeneous media under steady state. Anisotropic soils and analysis of groundwater flow by other methods are not considered in this discussion, except to mention radial flow because of its importance in well hydraulics.

A three-dimensional view of flow toward a well in an unconfined aquifer is illustrated in Figure 4-12. Assuming an ideal aquifer with a horizontal water table, the plan view of radial flow shows the flow lines radiating from the center of the well and the equipotential lines as concentric circles. The free water surface in the horizontal view has a logarithmic shape with its focus at the axis of the well.

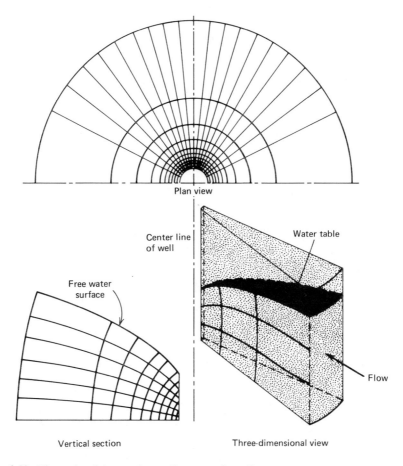

Figure 4-12 Views of radial groundwater flow toward a well.

4-6 Steady Flow to Wells

The distribution and movement of groundwater near a pumping well depends on the characteristics of the aquifer and construction of the well. When pumping is started, drawdown of the water table forms a cone of depression. Water flows radially through the aquifer and converges on the well with steadily increasing velocity. Based on Darcy's law, the hydraulic gradient must also increase as groundwater approaches the well, thus, the drawdown curve has a continually steeper slope toward the well. The size and shape of the cone of depression for a particular well depends on withdrawal rate, duration of pumping, slope of the water table, sources of recharge, and aquifer characteristics.

The fundamental equations from Section 4-3 and Darcy's law can be applied to derive formulas defining radial flow to wells. Steady flow assumes uniform withdrawal, a stable drawdown curve, laminar groundwater flow, and a homogeneous isotropic aquifer. Figure 4-13 illustrates this condition for a well completely penetrating an unconfined aquifer. The flow is assumed to be horizontal and uniform in every vertical section, and the velocity of flow proportional to the tangent of the hydraulic gradient. Hence, referring to Figure 4-13,

$$Q = 2\pi r K h \frac{dh}{dr} \tag{4-20}$$

Integrating between the boundary conditions at the well ($h = h_w$ and $r = r_w$) and at the edge of the cone of depression ($h = h_0$ and $r = r_0$) the equation for well discharge becomes

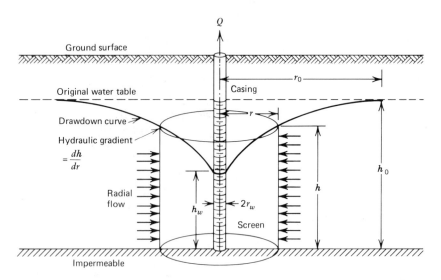

Figure 4-13 Steady radial flow to a well penetrating an ideal unconfined aquifer (Equations 4-20, 4-21, and 4-22).

$$Q = \pi K \frac{h_0{}^2 - h_w{}^2}{\log_e(r_0/r_w)} \tag{4-21}$$

where Q = well discharge, litres per second
$\quad\quad K$ = coefficient of permeability, millimetres per second
$\quad\quad h_0$ = saturated thickness of aquifer before pumping, metres
$\quad\quad r_0$ = radius of the cone of depression, metres
$\quad\quad h_w$ = depth of water in well while pumping, metres
$\quad\quad r_w$ = radius of well, metres

Since vertical flow components assumed to be negligible do actually exist, this equation fails to describe accurately the drawdown curve near the well. However, predictions of well discharge Q and permeability K using this equation are accurate for a natural aquifer that approaches ideal conditions. In practice, the selection of the radius of influence r_0 must be estimated, which is not usually a significant source of error since the change in Q is small for a wide variation in r_0. Data from observation wells in the drawdown area can also be substituted into Equation 4-21 by replacing h_w at r_w with h_1 at r_1 and h_0 at r_0 with h_2 at r_2 (Figure 4-5). Using field measurements from observation wells, rather than the pumping well, improves the accuracy of computations.

Permeability of an aquifer surrounding a well can be determined in the field by conducting a pumping test. Observation wells are needed to record drawdown at various distances from the test well (Figure 4-5). After establishing equilibrium conditions under continuous well discharge, permeability can be calculated as follows:

$$K = \frac{Q}{\pi(h_2{}^2 - h_1{}^2)} \log_e\left(\frac{r_2}{r_1}\right) \tag{4-22}$$

where h = water levels in observation wells during pumping, metres
$\quad\quad r$ = radial distances to observation wells ($r_2 > r_1$), metres

Radial flow in an ideal confined (artesian) aquifer penetrated completely by a well follows theoretical steady flow (Equation 4-15), since the flow is two-dimensional and horizontal everywhere. Using plain polar coordinates, steady radial flow as depicted in Figure 4-14 is

$$Q = Av = 2\pi r b K \frac{dh}{dr} \tag{4-23}$$

Rearranging and integrating between the boundary limits of $h = h_w$ at $r = r_w$ and $h = h_0$ at $r = r_0$,

$$Q = 2\pi K b \frac{h_0 - h_w}{\log_e(r_0/r_w)} \tag{4-24}$$

where Q = well discharge, litres per second
$\quad\quad K$ = coefficient of permeability, millimetres per second
$\quad\quad b$ = thickness of aquifer, metres

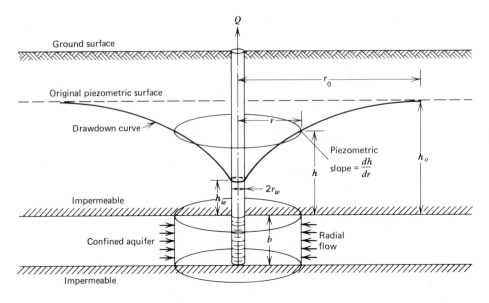

Figure 4-14 Steady radial flow to a well completely penetrating an ideal confined aquifer (Equations 4-23, 4-24, and 4-25).

h_0 = piezometric head above given datum, metres
r_0 = radius of cone of depression, metres
h_w = depth of water in well above datum, metres
r_w = radius of well, metres

Values for r_0 and h_0 may be estimated, or drawdown data from observation wells in the area of the cone of depression can be used. Piezometric surface observations at two different distances from a well pumped at a constant rate allow calculation of the coefficient of permeability by

$$K = \frac{Q}{2\pi b\,(h_2 - h_1)}\, \log_e\!\left(\frac{r_2}{r_1}\right) \tag{4-25}$$

where h = piezometric head in observation well during pumping, metres
r = radial distance to observation well, metres

In order to apply this equation, continuous pumping must be conducted at an uniform rate for sufficient time to approach steady-state drawdown. The observation wells should be located close enough to the test well to produce measurable water level changes.

The previous equations assumed an initially horizontal water table with no groundwater movement prior to pumping. Wells may penetrate an aquifer with flowing groundwater as depicted in Figure 4-15 where a confined stratum carries uniform flow resulting in a sloping piezometric surface. Although the area of influence and the cone of depression are distorted, most natural slopes are relatively flat and the radial flow

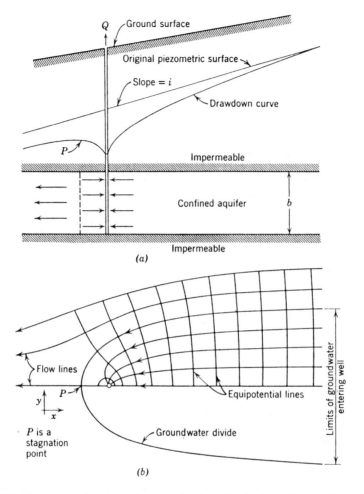

Figure 4-15 Flow to a well penetrating a confined aquifer having a sloping plane piezometric surface. (a) Vertical section; (b) plan view. (From D. K. Todd, *Ground Water Hydrology*, John Wiley & Sons, Inc., 1959.)

equations are still applicable without serious error. However, for a steep piezometric slope, calculations for permeability require averaging hydraulic gradients on each side of the well and lying along a line parallel to the natural flow direction. For an unconfined aquifer, the gradient formula is

$$K = \frac{2Q}{\pi r(h_u + h_d)(i_u + i_d)} \tag{4-26}$$

where K = coefficient of permeability
Q = well discharge
r = distance upstream and downstream to the observed h and i measurements

h_u = upstream water level (piezometric surface)
h_d = downstream water level (piezometric surface)
i_u = upstream hydraulic gradient (piezometric slope)
i_d = downstream hydraulic gradient (piezometric slope)

For a confined aquifer the expression is

$$K = \frac{2Q}{\pi r(2b)\,(i_u + i_d)} \tag{4-27}$$

where b = thickness of aquifer

A common municipal installation is a field with several wells withdrawing ground-water from the same aquifer. During pumping, the areas of influence are likely to over-lap causing a composite depression of the water table. Drawdown at any point in the area of influence is equal to the sum of the drawdowns caused by individual wells. Therefore,

$$D_T = D_a + D_b + D_c + \cdots\cdots + D_n \tag{4-28}$$

where D_T = total drawdown at a given point
D_a to D_n = drawdowns at the point caused by discharge of wells, $a,b,c,\ldots,n$, respectively

Figure 4-16 is a profile of three identical wells pumping at the same rate from a confined aquifer. The individual and composite drawdown curves are sketched for $Q_1 = Q_2 = Q_3$.

Recharge, well penetration, and boundary conditions have significant effect on discharge-drawdown characteristics. Vertical recharge may result from rainfall or excess irrigation water, for example, a water-table well in a permeable sand. A stream

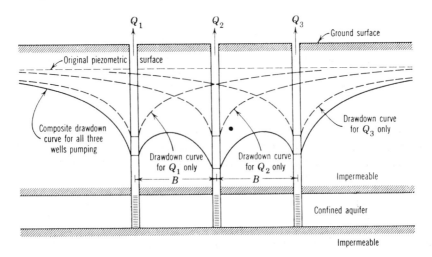

Figure 4-16 Individual and composite drawdown curves for three wells in a line. (From D. K. Todd, *Ground Water Hydrology*, John Wiley & Sons, Inc., 1959.)

bed, connected hydraulically to an aquifer, can be a major source of recharge to a nearby well. Complete penetration of the well into the aquifer was assumed for the flow equations presented in this section. Partial penetration results when drilling is stopped upon reaching a satisfactory aquifer without extending the well to an impervious bottom. The derivation of the flow equations also assumed an aquifer of infinite extent. Relatively few natural formations are large enough to conform to this assumption since most have definite geologic and hydraulic boundaries. These can be detected by pumping tests and accounted for in detailed analyses. The complex problems of recharge, well penetration, and boundary conditions are discussed by others.[1,2,3]

Well loss refers to drawdown in a well resulting from flow through the screen and inside the casing to the pump intake. Being turbulent flow,

$$\text{Well loss} = CQ^n \tag{4-29}$$

where C = constant depending on radius, construction, and condition of the well
Q = well discharge
n = exponential constant greater than 1.0

Thus, the drawdown inside a well casing equals the drawdown in the aquifer $(h_0 - h_w)$ plus the well loss CQ^n. Values for C and n can be derived from a step-drawdown pumping test comparing piezometric level outside the intake screen with water levels in the well casing.

Well losses can be minimized by using a porous screen with a large diameter to reduce entrance velocity. For instance, doubling the radius of a well doubles the intake area with a corresponding reduction in entrance velocity resulting in a friction loss of less than one third, assuming n is equal to 2. In typical construction, well loss is negligible at low pumping rates; however, at high discharges the loss can be a significant portion of the total drawdown. Screen size should be compatible with the porosity of the surrounding aquifer and the design rate of pumping.

Example 4-4

A well with a diameter of 0.6 m is constructed in a confined aquifer as illustrated in Figure 4-14. The sand aquifer has a uniform thickness of 15 m overlain by a surface clay layer with a depth of 35 m. A pumping test is conducted to determine the permeability of the aquifer. The initial piezometric surface was 15.0 m below the ground-surface datum in the test well and all observation wells. After pumping at a rate of 13.0 l/s for several days, water levels in the wells stabilized with the following drawdowns: 6.4 m in the test well, 3.7 in the observation well 10 m from the test well, and 2.4 m in a second observation well at a distance of 30 m.

Calculate the coefficient of permeability for the aquifer. Then, using this K value, estimate the well discharge with the drawdown in the well lowered to the surface of the confined aquifer.

Solution

Assume a datum at the top of the aquifer as in Figure 4-14. Then

$$h_0 = 35.0 - 15.0 = 20.0 \text{ m}, h_w = 20.0 - 6.4 = 13.6 \text{ m}$$

$h_1 = 20.0 - 3.7 = 16.3$ m, $h_2 = 20.0 - 2.4 = 17.6$ m

Substituting into Equation 4-25,

$$K = \frac{13.0 \text{ l/s}}{2\pi(15.0 \text{ m})(17.6 \text{ m} - 16.3 \text{ m})} \log_e \left(\frac{30 \text{ m}}{10 \text{ m}}\right) = 0.12 \text{ mm/s}$$

With the drawdown in the well at the surface of the sand aquifer, h_0 equals 20.0 m and h_w equals 0.0 m. The radius of the well is 0.3 m, and distance to the edge of the cone of depression is assumed to be 200 m. The estimated well discharge at maximum drawdown is computed as follows applying Equation 4-24:

$$Q = 2\pi(0.12 \text{ mm/s})15.0 \text{ m} \frac{20.0 \text{ m} - 0.0 \text{ m}}{\log_e (200 \text{ m}/0.3 \text{ m})} = 35 \text{ l/s}$$

Or, based on Equation 4-24, well discharge Q is directly proportional to drawdown $h_0 - h_w$; therefore,

$$Q \text{ at } 20.0 \text{ m} = \frac{13.0 \text{ l/s}}{6.4 \text{ m}} \times 20.0 \text{ m} = 40 \text{ l/s}$$

4-7 Unsteady Flow to Wells

Pumping a well to equilibrium drawdown is not often practical. Even though a substantial cone of depression usually forms within a few hours, the rate of decline decreases and the area of influence may slowly expand for several days. As long as the volume of the dewatered aquifer is enlarging, water is being drawn from storage and a steady state of flow cannot exist. As a result, several techniques have been developed to conduct pumping tests during the phase of unsteady flow in confined aquifers. Nonequilibrium equations introduce the coefficient of transmissibility and coefficient of storage as two additional field parameters, commonly referred to as formation constants. As the physical indexes of aquifer characteristics, they can be used for theoretical prediction of future yield of groundwater in storage.

The coefficient of transmissibility T is defined mathematically as

$$T = Kb \qquad\qquad\qquad (4\text{-}30)$$

where T = coefficient of transmissibility, cubic metres per day per metre
  K = coefficient of permeability, metres per day
  b = thickness of the confined aquifer, metres

Thus, this single term represents the water transmitting capability of the entire thickness of an aquifer under an unit hydraulic gradient. Any consistent units can be used in this formula; those given in Equation 4-30 define the coefficient of transmissibility as the rate of groundwater flow in cubic metres per day through a vertical strip of the aquifer one metre wide and having a height equal to the thickness of the aquifer when the hydraulic gradient is 1.00. After field determination of T, the average coefficient of permeability of the aquifer can be calculated using Equation 4-30 and converted to the common units of millimetres per second (1.00 m/d = 0.0116 mm/s).

The coefficient of storage characterizes the ability of an aquifer to release stored water as the piezometric head declines. As discussed in Section 4-3 and illustrated in Figure 4-7, this dimensionless coefficient is defined as the volume of stored water released from a column of the aquifer of unit cross-sectional area during a decline in the piezometric surface of unity.

The differential equation applying to unsteady flow is Equation 4-16. Substituting T for Kb and writing in plain polar coordinates, the form becomes

$$\frac{\partial^2 h}{\partial r^2} + \frac{1}{r}\frac{\partial h}{\partial r} = \frac{S}{T}\frac{\partial h}{\partial t} \qquad (4\text{-}31)$$

Theis[4] solved Equation 4-31 for an ideal confined aquifer (a homogeneous and isotropic porous medium of infinite areal extent) based on the comparison between groundwater flow and heat conduction. This analogy also assumes the well completely penetrates the aquifer drawing groundwater from the full thickness, water removed from storage is discharged instantaneously lowering the piezometric head, and the aquifer receives no recharge. The Theis formula is

$$Z_r = \frac{Q}{4\pi T} \int_u^\infty \frac{e^{-u}\,du}{u} \qquad (4\text{-}32)$$

where Z_r = drawdown in an observation well at r distance from the well being pumped, metres

Q = constant well discharge, cubic metres per day

T = coefficient of transmissibility, cubic metres per day per metre

u = dimensionless constant, Equation 4-33

The constant pumping rate Q is expressed in cubic metres per day rather than litres per second so the units of the equation are consistent.

The term u is dimensionless and given by

$$u = \frac{r^2 S}{4Tt} \qquad (4\text{-}33)$$

where r = distance from pumping well to the observation well, metres

S = coefficient of storage, dimensionless

T = coefficient of transmissibility, cubic metres per day per metre

t = time since the start of pumping, days

The integral in Equation 4-32 is commonly written as $W(u)$ and is read as "the well function of u." It is not directly integrable, but can be expanded as the convergent series

$$W(u) = -0.5772 - \log_e u + u - \frac{u^2}{2\cdot 2!} + \frac{u^3}{3\cdot 3!} - \frac{u^4}{4\cdot 4!} + \ldots \qquad (4\text{-}34)$$

The magnitudes of $W(u)$ for various values of u are given in Table 4-1.

These equations can be rearranged to solve for the desired formation constants of T and S as follows:

Table 4-1   Values of $W(u)$ Corresponding to Values of u in Equation 4-34

u	1.0	2.0	3.0	4.0	5.0	6.0	7.0	8.0	9.0
$\times 1$	0.219	0.049	0.013	0.0038	0.0011	0.00036	0.00012	0.000038	0.000012
$\times 10^{-1}$	1.82	1.22	0.91	0.70	0.56	0.45	0.37	0.31	0.26
$\times 10^{-2}$	4.04	3.35	2.96	2.68	2.47	2.30	2.15	2.03	1.92
$\times 10^{-3}$	6.33	5.64	5.23	4.95	4.73	4.54	4.39	4.26	4.14
$\times 10^{-4}$	8.63	7.94	7.53	7.25	7.02	6.84	6.69	6.55	6.44
$\times 10^{-5}$	10.94	10.24	9.84	9.55	9.33	9.14	8.99	8.86	8.74
$\times 10^{-6}$	13.24	12.55	12.14	11.85	11.63	11.45	11.29	11.16	11.04
$\times 10^{-7}$	15.54	14.85	14.44	14.15	13.93	13.75	13.60	13.46	13.34
$\times 10^{-8}$	17.84	17.15	16.74	16.46	16.23	16.05	15.90	15.76	15.65
$\times 10^{-9}$	20.15	19.45	19.05	18.76	18.54	18.35	18.20	18.07	17.95
$\times 10^{-10}$	22.45	21.76	21.35	21.06	20.84	20.66	20.50	20.37	20.25
$\times 10^{-11}$	24.75	24.06	23.65	23.36	23.14	22.96	22.81	22.67	22.55
$\times 10^{-12}$	27.05	26.36	25.96	25.67	25.44	25.26	25.11	24.97	24.86
$\times 10^{-13}$	29.36	28.66	28.26	27.97	27.75	27.56	27.41	27.28	27.16
$\times 10^{-14}$	31.66	30.97	30.56	30.27	30.05	29.87	29.71	29.58	29.46
$\times 10^{-15}$	33.96	33.27	32.86	32.58	32.35	32.17	32.02	31.88	31.76

Source. L. K. Wenzel, "Methods for Determining Permeability of Water-Bearing Materials with Special Reference to Discharging-Well Methods," U. S. Geological Survey Water-Supply Paper 887, 1942.

$$T = \frac{Q}{4\pi Z} [W(u)] \tag{4-35}$$

$$S = \frac{4Ttu}{r^2} \tag{4-36}$$

where T = coefficient of transmissibility, cubic metres per day per metre

Z = drawdown in an observation well at r distance from the well being pumped, metres

$W(u)$ = the well function of u, dimensionless

S = coefficient of storage, dimensionless

t = time since the start of pumping, days

u = dimensionless term

r = distance from pumping well to the observation well, metres

A nonequilibrium pumping test provides the necessary data. While the test well is pumped at a constant discharge Q, drawdown measurements Z in the observation well at distance r are recorded with regard to time t. However, direct mathematical solution of unsteady flow equations is extremely difficult. The only practical solutions are by the approximate graphical methods of Theis and Chow.

Specific capacity defined as the yield (well discharge) per unit of drawdown is another parameter commonly calculated from nonequilibrium testing. It is a measure of the effectiveness of a well. Rearranging Equation 4-35, specific capacity is

$$\frac{Q}{Z} = \frac{4\pi T}{W(u)} \tag{4-37}$$

Based on this formula the units of Q/Z are the same as T, cubic metres per day per metre; however, specific capacity may also be expressed in litres per second per metre. Theoretically, yield and specific capacity are directly proportional providing the confined aquifer is not dewatered. Doubling the drawdown doubles the well yield. In fact, this is not true since actual pumping tests commonly show a decreasing specific capacity with increasing drawdown. Furthermore, the value also decreases with duration of pumping.

Theis Method of Solution[1,2]
Field data from a nonequilibrium pumping test are listed in Table 4-2. Using these drawdown-time values, the coefficients of transmissibility T and storage S can be computed based on a graphical method of superposition to determine $W(u)$ and u. First, a type curve of $W(u)$ versus u is plotted on logarithmic paper as shown in Figure 4-17 using values from Table 4-1. Next, drawdowns and corresponding times since the start of test pumping from Table 4-2 are plotted on transparent (thin) logarithmic paper in Figure 4-18 to the same scale as the type curve.

Observed drawdown-time data, for an ideal confined aquifer, correspond to a portion of the type curve having the same rate of change of curvature. To find the proper location, the drawdown curve is superimposed on the type curve keeping the coordinate axes of the two curves parallel. By observing the type curve through the plotted

Table 4-2 Data from Nonequilibrium Pumping Test: t Is Time Since the Start of Pumping, and Z Is the Corresponding Drawdown in an Observation Well Located 60 m from Well Pumped at 2 700 m³/d

t (min)	Z (m)	t (min)	Z (m)
0	0.00	24	0.72
1	0.20	30	0.76
2	0.30	40	0.81
3	0.37	50	0.85
4	0.41	60	0.88
5	0.45	80	0.93
6	0.48	100	0.96
8	0.53	120	1.00
10	0.57	150	1.04
12	0.60	180	1.07
14	0.63	210	1.10
18	0.67	240	1.12

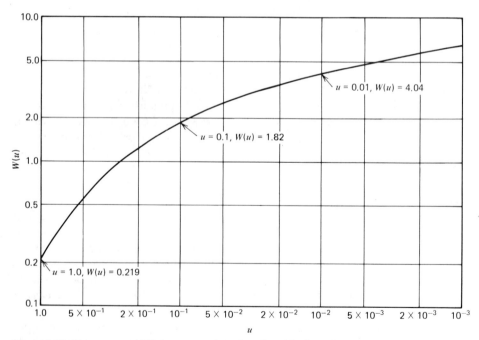

Figure 4-17 Type curve of $W(u)$ versus u plotted on logarithmic scales for solving the Theis nonequalibrium equation graphically. Values of $W(u)$ and u are from Table 4-1, and Equations 4-32 through 4-36 include $W(u)$ or u parameters. (Note that the horizontal scale of u decreases to the right, thus reversing the usual logarithmic cycle.)

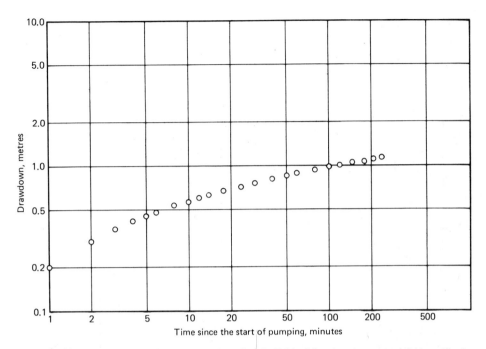

Figure 4-18 A plot of drawdown versus time data in Table 4-2 using the same scale logarithmic cycles as those of the type curve in Figure 4-17. (Note that the horizontal scale however increases to the right in this diagram.)

data, the drawdown-time curve is adjusted so the plotted points lie on a segment of the underlying type curve. After achieving this best fit position, as shown in Figure 4-19, an arbitrary match point is selected on the curve. This point defines the relative positioning of the plotted data and type curve. In Figure 4-19, the coordinates of the match point on the type curve are $W(u) = 4.04$ and $u = 0.01$, and those on the plotted drawdown data are $Z = 0.70$ m and $t = 23$ min.

The coefficient of transmissibility at $Q = 2\ 700$ m^3/d, $Z = 0.70$ m, and $W(u)$ of 4.04 substituted into Equation 4-35 is

$$T = \frac{2\ 700\ \text{m}^3/\text{d}}{4\pi \times 0.70\ \text{m}}\ (4.04) = 1\ 240\ \text{m}^3/\text{d}\cdot\text{m}$$

From Equation 4-36, the coefficient of storage is

$$S = \frac{4 \times 1\ 240\ \text{m}^3/\text{d}\cdot\text{m} \times 23/1\ 440\ \text{d} \times 0.01}{(60\ \text{m})^2}$$
$$= 0.000\ 22$$

and, the specific capacity of the well applying Equation 4-37 is

$$\frac{Q}{Z} = \frac{4\pi \times 1\ 240}{4.04} = 3\ 900\ \text{m}^3/\text{d}\cdot\text{m} = 45\ 1/\text{s}\cdot\text{m}$$

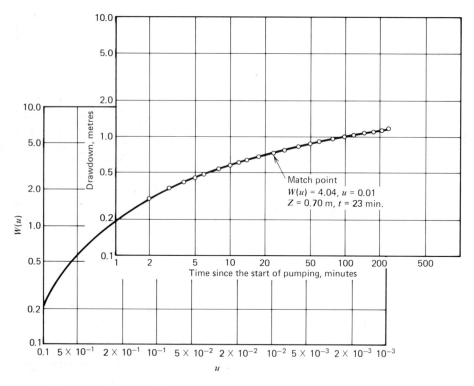

Figure 4-19 The drawdown-time data (Figure 4-18) superimposed on the type curve (Figure 4-17) to determine a match point.

Chow Method of Solution[5,3]

Based on the Theis nonequilibrium equations (Equations 4-32, 4-33, and 4-34) Chow[5] determined the relationship

$$\frac{Z}{dz/d \log_{10}t} = \frac{W(u) \times e^{u}}{2.3} \tag{4-38}$$

where Z = drawdown in observation well, metres
t = time since the start of pumping, days
$W(u)$ = well function of u, dimensionless

He referred to both of the terms in this equation as $F(u)$. When equated to the left side of Equation 4-38,

$$F(u) = \frac{Z}{dz/d \log_{10}t} \tag{4-39}$$

This term can be evaluated from a semilogarithmic plot of drawdown-time data from a pumping test. From the right side of Equation 4-38, $F(u)$ is related to $W(u)$ and u as follows:

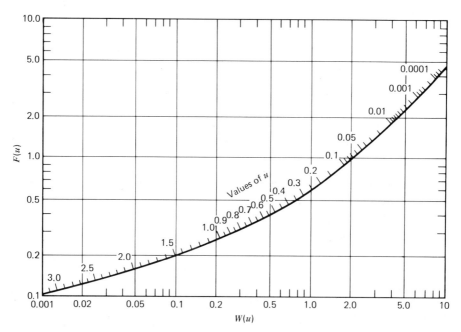

Figure 4-20 Relation among $F(u)$, $W(u)$, and u expressed by Equation 4-39. (From V. T. Chow, "On the Determination of Transmissibility and Storage Coefficients From Pumping Test Data," *Transactions, American Geophysical Union*, Vol. 33, 1952, copyrighted by American Geophysical Union.)

$$F(u) = \frac{W(u) \times e^u}{2.3} \qquad (4\text{-}40)$$

A graphical solution of this formula is given in Figure 4-20. Thus, values of $W(u)$ and u are available from a known $F(u)$ that has been determined by graphical solution of Equation 4-39. Finally, coefficients of transmissibility and storage are calculated from Equations 4-35 and 4-36.

The following computations illustrate the Chow technique applying the same data used in the previous Theis solution. The observation well data from Table 4-2 are plotted on semilogarithmic paper in Figure 4-21 with the drawdown Z on the linear y-axis and time since the start of pumping t on the logarithmic scale. An arbitrary point is selected on the plotted curve and ordinate values of t and Z noted; for example, 30 min and 0.76 m. Next, a line is drawn tangent to the curve at the chosen point; its slope is equal to $dz/d \log_{10} t$. For convenience, the slope may be measured by taking the drawdown difference for one logarithmic cycle of time. On Figure 4-21, the value at log time 100 is 0.97 m and at log time 10 is 0.57 m, therefore, the slope equals $0.97 - 0.57 = 0.40$ m. Using Equation 4-39,

$$F(u) = \frac{0.76 \text{ m}}{0.97 \text{ m} - 0.57 \text{ m}} = \frac{0.76}{0.40} = 1.9$$

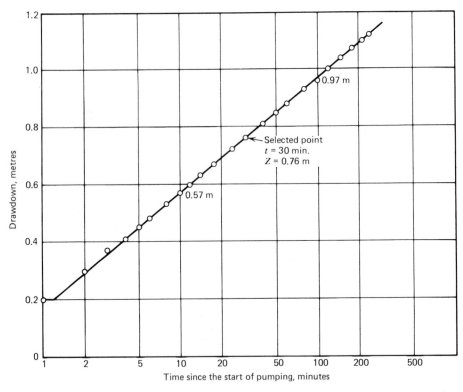

Figure 4-21 A plot of drawdown versus time data listed in Table 4-2 on semilogarithmic paper for the Chow method of solution.

Entering Figure 4-20 with an $F(u)$ value of 1.9, $W(u) = 4.4$ and $u = 0.007$.

Finally, the coefficients are calculated applying Equations 4-35 and 4-36 as follows:

$$T = \frac{2\ 700\ \text{m}^3/\text{d}}{4\pi \times 0.76\ \text{m}}\ (4.4) = 1\ 240\ \text{m}^3/\text{d} \cdot \text{m}$$

$$S = \frac{4 \times 1\ 240\ \text{m}^3/\text{d} \cdot \text{m} \times 30/1\ 440\ \text{d} \times 0.007}{(60\ \text{m})^2} = 0.000\ 20$$

4-8 Well Construction

Wells to extract groundwater vary from shallow dug holes to deep shafts bored by rotary drilling. In shallow unconsolidated formations, small-diameter wells may be driven or jetted for setting a screened point attached to the end of connected lengths of pipe. These are suitable for domestic supplies or temporary wells. For municipal or industrial applications, the construction of a typical high-capacity well, screened in an unconsolidated soil profile, is illustrated in Figure 4-22. In a consolidated rock aquifer, the lower portion of the well is usually an open borehole without a casing or screen.

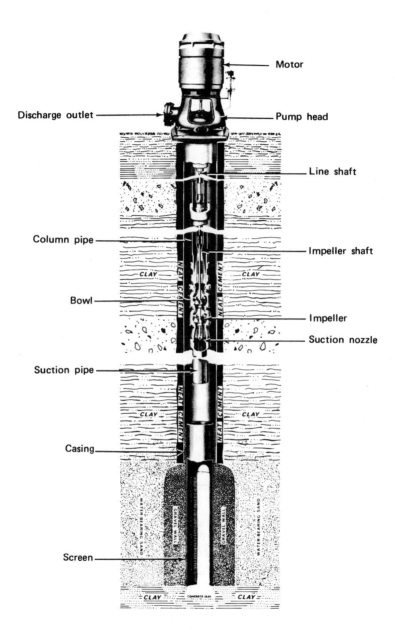

Figure 4-22 A gravel-packed water well screened in a confined sand aquifer and equipped with a two-stage vertical turbine pump. (Courtesy of Layne-Western Company, Inc.)

The basic principles of design are performance—highest yield with lowest drawdown—and long service life at reasonable first and operating costs. The major components in design are the well diameter and depth, length and type of screen, gravel pack, and pumping equipment.

Well drilling is commonly performed by either cable-tool percussion or the hydraulic rotary method. The latter consists of drilling a borehole by means of a rotating bit and removing the cuttings by continuous circulation of a drilling fluid. The bit is attached to the lower end of a string of drill pipe held by the rotary table of a drilling machine, which is usually mounted on the rear of a truck under a mast used to lift the lengths of pipe. The drilling fluid is a viscous, dense mud formed by mixing bentonite clay with water. The mud is pumped down through the drill pipe and out nozzles in the bit. As it flows upward in the borehole, cuttings are carried in suspension to the ground surface to be settled out by gravity, so the mud can be recycled. The drilling fluid also holds the sides of the hole open by hydraulic pressure and caking of mud on the wall. After installation of the well screen, this clogging of the water-bearing formation may be corrected by hydraulic cleaning.

Cable-tool percussion drilling is performed by repeated lifting and dropping of a heavy string of drill tools. The attached cable extends out of the borehole, over a pulley at the top of the drill-rig mast, and down to a power-driven wheel that provides 30 to 60 strokes per minute. From top to bottom, a string of drill tools consists of a cable socket, a set of jars, drill stem, and bit; the total weight may be several thousand kilograms. The drill bit (1 to 3 m in length) crushes hard rock and loosens unconsolidated materials in a water slurry at the bottom of the borehole. The drill stem (2 to 10 m) gives added weight increasing impact of the bit. A set of jars consists of a pair of narrow connected lengths used to free a stuck bit. By slackening and tightening the cable, the jars provide an upward hammering action to loosen a wedged bit. The socket at the top of the string allows the tools to rotate slightly with respect to the cable. After advancing the hole by crushing the soil or rock, the drill string is removed and a bailer used to dip out the accumulated solids. A bailer is a long tube with a valve at the bottom and a ring at the top to attach a rope or cable. They range from 3 to 10 m in length with volumetric capacities up to several hundred litres. When lowered into the borehole, the check valve allows sludge to enter but prevents the cuttings from falling back out. After filling, the bailer is hoisted to the surface and emptied. Water is added as necessary to maintain an adequate volume of slurry in the hole.

Casing is constructed of pipe or corrosion-resistant tubular steel with individual sections connected by threaded or welded joints. Casing may be installed as a single wall using pipe lengths of the same diameter or double wall formed by telescoping cylindrical sections halfway through one another. After drilling the borehole, the casing is set in position and sealed in place by forcing cement grout between the casing and the drilled hole. Temporary casing, penetrating near surface strata, may be withdrawn as grout is placed around the inserted well casing. Figure 4-23a illustrates typical construction where the borehole is cased and sealed through an unconsolidated surface stratum and fractured rock layer. In this case, the aquifer is water-bearing rock and no screen is needed.

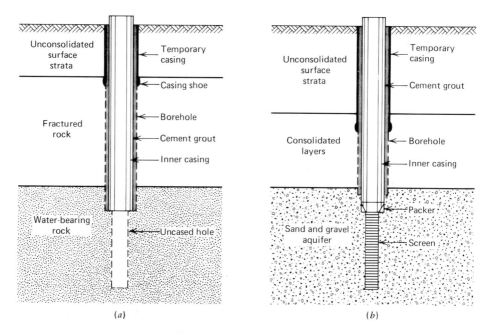

Figure 4-23 Examples of well construction in (*a*) a consolidated aquifer not requiring a screen and (*b*) an unconsolidated sand and gravel formation.

The well screen in an unconsolidated aquifer allows water to enter the casing while precluding the sand and gravel (Figure 4-23*b*). One of the most common ways for placing a screen in this type of formation is by the pullback method. Casing is sunk to the full depth, the screen is lowered inside, and the pipe is then pulled back a sufficient distance to expose the screen to the water-bearing layer. If a gravel pack is needed, the double casing technique can be employed as follows: after sinking the outer casing to full depth, the inner pipe with well screen is gravel packed inside and the outer casing is lifted to leave a gravel-packed screen in the aquifer. When the pullback method is impractical, a screen is set in an open borehole below the casing after it has been cemented into position. The sand and gravel surrounding the screen may be hydraulically surged to develop a natural gravel wall or gravel may be artificially placed around the telescoped screen. After placing a gravel pack, the screen is sealed to the bottom of the casing by an expanded lead packer (Figure 4-23*b*). The screen length is normally 70 to 80 percent of the aquifer thickness, and the openings depend on gradation of the sand and gravel in the stratum. Thus, to a large extent, natural characteristics of an aquifer determine these dimensions leaving the diameter as a major variable. Experience has shown the velocity of groundwater entering a screen should be equal to 0.03 m/s or less for negligible friction losses and minimum encrustation or corrosion of the screen.[6]

After completing construction, a well is developed by vigorous hydraulic action through pumping, surging, or jetting. Mechanical surging is done by operating a plunger up and down in the casing like a piston in a cylinder. A heavy bailer can be used to produce the surging action, but it is less efficient. Air surging is accomplished by lowering an air pipe into the screen area and purging with compressed air. In high-velocity jetting, a tool is slowly rotated inside the screen shooting water out through the openings. The purposes of well development are (1) to correct any damage or clogging of the water-bearing formation that may have occurred as a side effect of drilling, (2) to increase the porosity and permeability of the natural formation surrounding the screen, and (3) to stabilize the aquifer so that the water is free of sand. The net effect is to increase the specific yield.

The screen and its envelope of gravel are primary considerations in well design. High efficiency screens have the greatest possible open area while maintaining structural strength. The slot openings should be shaped to minimize plugging by sand and gravel from the aquifer. Two popular types of screens are shown in Figure 4-24. Sometimes perforated or slotted pipe is installed; however, it is hydraulically less efficient than spiral-wound and shutter screens. Openings are dictated by the grain size distribution

(a)

(b)

Figure 4-24 Two types of screens common in high-capacity wells are (a) the shutter screen (courtesy of Layne & Bowler, Inc.) and (b) the spiral-wound screen (courtesy of Johnson Division, UOP Inc.).

Figure 4-25 A naturally developed well has coarser sand and gravel surrounding the screen than the undisturbed aquifer. In order to improve water flow into the well, this gradation is formed by washing fines through the screen openings during development and then extracting them from the well. (Courtesy of Johnson Division, UOP Inc.)

of the aquifer sand and gravel, or gradation of the gravel pack, and whether the gravel wall is naturally developed or artificially packed.

A natural gravel-packed well is formed by developing the well after setting the screen in the borehole. The slot size of the screen is selected to allow 40 to 50 percent of the sand surrounding the screen to pass through the openings. Development removes this finer portion of the granular material from around the well screen and leaves the coarser grains as a natural gravel pack as pictured in Figure 4-25. An artificially gravel-packed well has an envelope of specially graded gravel around the well screen. This provides a zone of high permeability and prevents sand in the aquifer from entering the well after development to clean and flush the gravel and adjacent aquifer. This construction is depicted in Figure 4-22 by a gravel pack surrounding a shutter screen.

Artificial gravel packing is common in fine, uniform sand formations, thick highly stratified aquifers, and loosely cemented sandstones.

A popular deep well pump is a multistage vertical turbine (Figure 4-22) with the following four major components: a drive motor that is mounted at ground level (or is submerged below the pump), a discharge pipe column, pump bowls with enclosed impellers, and suction pipe. The pumping units are bottom-suction centrifugal impellers mounted on a vertical shaft submerged below the water level in the well casing. The desired discharge and pumping head determine the size and number of pump bowls and speed of impeller rotation. A turbine pump may be equipped with a submersible electric motor mounted under and coupled to the impeller shaft. This places the sealed motor underwater directly below the pump intake. The principal advantage of a submersible pump is elimination of the long drive shaft and bearing assemblies necessary to transmit torque from a motor mounted at the ground surface.

This presentation has been an overview of well construction to describe the common elements of high-capacity wells. Particular installation techniques are based on regional practices and local conditions. Along with the absence of construction detail, topics of maintenance, corrosion, disinfection, and sanitary protection are not discussed. For those interested, a popular book is *Ground Water and Wells*[6] (440 pages). Data on pumps and motors are available in literature from manufacturers.

4-9 Groundwater Fluctuations and Aquifer Recharge

Natural groundwater reservoirs exist in a state of long-term equilibrium with recharge balancing discharge. Groundwater level variations relate to wet and dry years with the amount of infiltration from rainfall producing fluctuations over long time periods. Where stream channels have direct contact with unconfined aquifers, the water levels vary with streamflow. During seasons of limited rainfall over a region, streamflow is primarily the drainage of groundwater from storage in the basin. Unconfined aquifers with water tables near the ground surface often exhibit small diurnal fluctuations attributed to evaporation and transpiration. Small, abrupt, water level variations are caused by changes in atmospheric pressure.

The natural equilibrium of groundwater systems can be altered by (1) increased discharge from wells, most notably for irrigation, (2) recharge from infiltration of imported surface water applied to fields or by seepage from reservoirs and canals, (3) discharge to man-made drains, and (4) changes in land use that affect the amount of recharge an aquifer receives. In many areas, water level fluctuations resulting from human activities dominate and mask natural variations.

Many regions in the United States have observation wells for measuring and recording water level fluctuations. These data can be used to correlate the effects of withdrawal and recharge to predict future trends. Figure 4-26 is a record for an observation well penetrating a stratified formation of sand and gravel layers interbedded with silt and clay, providing a combination of unconfined and confined aquifers. The sharp water level declines in summer and fall are caused by irrigation withdrawals during the crop growing season. Rapid recharge occurs in the spring from both rainfall and infiltration from irrigation canals that import surface water. The predevelopment water level in this area was approximately 30 m (100 ft) below the ground surface. In the early 1940s, substantial quantities of surface water were diverted for irrigation from the North Platte River located approximately 50 km north of the observation well. Infiltration and deep percolation of water from the distribution system and water applied to crops raised the water table from 3 m to 30 m above the predevelopment elevation beneath an area of approximately 2 000 km². Installation of wells for irrigation with groundwater has increased steadily in the past 20 years providing conjunctive use of groundwater and surface water for agriculture in the region. Although seasonal pumping lowers the water table about 4 m, long-term depletion has not occurred since withdrawal for irrigation is balanced by recharge from imported surface water and local rainfall. Many of the small, water level fluctuations in Figure 4-26 are responses to changes in barometric pressure.

The observation well record in Figure 4-27 illustrates overdraft, or mining, of groundwater. Abstraction for irrigation exceeds the water supply to the basin with a resulting gradual depletion of groundwater in storage. A rapid rise in sprinkler irrigators coupled with the dry climate (450 mm precipitation) permanently lowers the water level after each seasonal fluctuation. The land under irrigation in the area has increased approximately fivefold between 1964 and 1976. The unconfined aquifer consists of sand and gravel strata interbedded with layers of fine-textured sediment. The hydrologic cycle for the region was in balance until about 1960, since then the overdraft has steadily increased because of rising consumptive use.

4-10 Safe Yield

The equilibrium of a groundwater reservoir is disrupted when wells are pumped. Some groundwater is always mined since a portion of the supply must come from storage. In many cases, loss of stored water is the major initial source increasing in amount with well drawdown. After sufficient pumping time, the drawdown cone reaches areas of recharge so that further well discharge is drawn in part from more distant sources, such as surface impoundments and streams. This infiltration decreases streamflow and stored surface waters. Ultimately, if pumping exceeds the available unappropriated water supply, or capacity of the water to recharge the aquifer, the quantity of groundwater in storage continues to deplete resulting in overdraft. That amount available as a renewable resource has a limit referred to as the safe yield. In other words, the maximum quantity of water that can be abstracted from an underground reservoir while maintaining an unimpaired supply is the safe yield.

Safe yield not only depends on the available water supply but also economics, water quality, and water rights. Economic considerations may govern safe yield when the cost of pumping groundwater becomes excessive. Damage results if the investment for deepening of wells and installing larger pumps prohibits further development or abandonment of groundwater supplies. Agricultural economics based on crop prices and

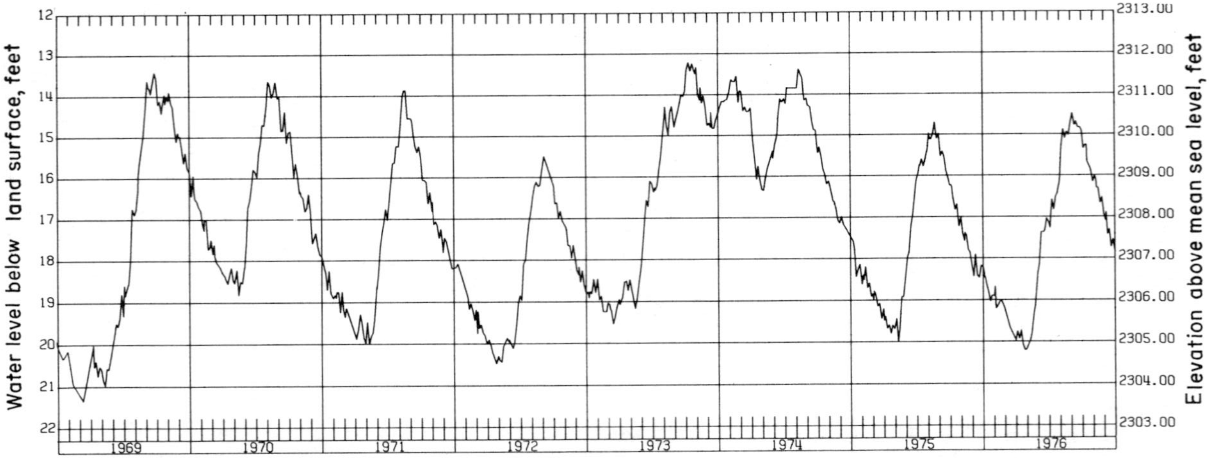

Figure 4-26 Water level fluctuations in an observation well showing seasonal variations due to irrigation withdrawal. Recharge from infiltration of surface water balances the consumptive use with no apparent long-term rise or fall of the water table. (Holdrege recorder well, Phelps County, Nebraska. Courtesy of the Conservation and Survey Division, University of Nebraska—Lincoln.)

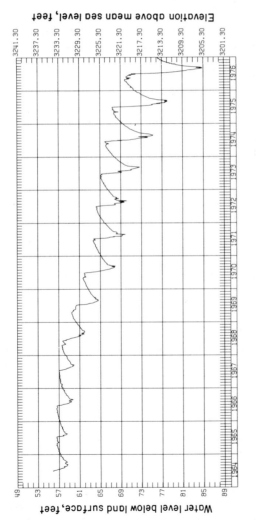

Figure 4-27 Declining water levels resulting from the overdraft of groundwater for consumptive use by irrigation. (Imperial recorder well, Chase County, Nebraska. Courtesy of the Conservation and Survey Division, University of Nebraska–Lincoln.)

government farm subsidies may set an economic limit for pumping groundwater and establish a safe yield contingent upon maximum pumping lifts. Safe yield may also be defined by a lowering of the water level that produces a groundwater of inferior quality. This can occur as a result of saltwater intrusion of a coastal aquifer, upflow of saline water from a deeper stratum, or recharge by poor quality water from an adjacent area. Legal considerations may limit safe yield as a result of interference with prior water rights within a region. They may apply to either reducing the water levels or artesian pressures in nearby wells, or diminishing of streamflow by reducing seepage and increasing infiltration.

Artificial recharge of groundwater can be used to augment the natural replenishment of underground storage, to reduce overdraft, conserve surface runoff, and increase available groundwater supplies. The common methods are water spreading, basin infiltration, and recharge through wells. Water spreading structures range from shallow diked ponds to ditches. A common problem is silt deposition sealing the bottom reducing infiltration rates. The partial solution is recharge of settled water through deep excavated basins that penetrate less permeable surface strata. These also reduce evaporation losses. By the most direct method, water can be recharged underground through specially designed wells. Recharge rates are usually less than pumping rates because of clogging around the screen. To improve efficiency, the wells can be gravel packed and sealed with concrete at the top of the aquifer to prevent upward movement of the water outside the casing. Where coastal aquifers connect to the ocean underwater, recharge wells are used to form a freshwater barrier to prevent saltwater intrusion. The theoretical well recharge formulas for unconfined and confined aquifers are Equations 4-21 and 4-22, respectively, where Q is the rate of recharge rather than discharge. All of these recharge techniques are practiced by the Orange County Water District in southern California as described in Section 5-8 under the heading *Increased Dissolved Solids from Groundwater Recharge*.

References

1. Todd, D. K., *Ground Water Hydrology*, John Wiley and Sons, Inc., New York, 1967.

2. Briggs, G. F., Chapter 8, Developing Groundwater Resources, *Handbook of Water Resources and Pollution Control*, edited by H. W. Gehm and J. I. Bregman, Van Nostrand Reinhold Co., New York, 1976.

3. Todd, D. K., Section 13, Groundwater, *Handbook of Applied Hydrology, A Compendium of Water-Resources*, V. T. Chow, editor-in-chief, McGraw-Hill Book Co., New York, 1964.

4. Theis, C. V., "The Relation Between the Lowering of the Piezometric Surface and the Rate and Duration of Discharge of a Well Using Ground-Water Storage," *Transactions, American Geophysical Union*, (Currently EOS), Vol. 16, 1935, pp. 519-524.

5. Chow, Ven Te, "On the Determination of Transmissibility and Storage Coefficients From Pumping Test Data," *Transactions, American Geophysical Union* (Currently EOS), Vol. 33, 1952, pp. 397-404.

6. *Ground Water and Wells*, Johnson Division, Universal Oil Products Co., St. Paul, Minnesota, 1972.

Problems

4-1 Define the term water table. How can its elevation in the ground be measured?

4-2 Why is "effective porosity" a suitable descriptive synonym for the term specific yield?

4-3 Describe the difference between a water-table well and an artesian well.

4-4 A glass cylinder with an internal diameter of 50 mm, having a screen at the bottom to support a column of sand, was used as a falling-head permeameter. The length of the sand sample was 100 mm. The water level in the tube at the start of the test was 400 mm above the tailwater level and dropped 100 mm in one minute, while the tailwater elevation remained unchanged. What is the calculated permeability? (*Answer* 0.48 mm/s)

4-5 A core of sandstone 100 mm in diameter and 50 mm thick was tested in a falling-head permeameter. The hydraulic head in the standpipe, which had an internal cross-sectional area of 12 mm^2, fell from 800 mm to 600 mm in 65 s. Compute the coefficient of permeability.

4-6 For what type of media does the equation for steady flow, Equation 4-15, apply? What are the additional qualifications applied to the unsteady flow equation, Equation 4-16?

4-7 Define coefficient of storage.

4-8 Compute the porewater and vertical intergranular pressure distributions for the following soil profile: ground surface to water table, at a depth of 10.0 m, is a moist sand and gravel with a specific weight of 15.6 kN/m^3. Below the water table, the aquifer is saturated at a specific weight of 19.5 kN/m^3 extending to bedrock 30 m below the ground surface.

4-9 Sketch a flow net for groundwater passing under a sheet pile wall penetrating an unconfined aquifer to three quarters depth. The profile is like Figure 4-10, except the cutoff penetration is 75 percent rather than 50 percent. What is the n_e/n_f value? (*Answer* 0.35)

4-10 For the dam illustrated in Figure 4-11, calculate the seepage based on a head loss of 12 m and coefficient of permeability equal to 1.0 μm/s. (*Answer* 350 l/d per metre of dam length)

4-11 Sketch flow nets for the diagrams in Figure 4-28. What are the n_e/n_f values?

4-12 A pumping test was conducted in an unconfined aquifer using a test well penetrating to the underlying impervious stratum. Two observation wells were located at distances of 20 m and 120 m from the main well. Before starting, the static water levels in all three wells were 15.0 m above the underlying impervious stratum. Upon reaching equilibrium conditions after several hours of pumping the test well at a steady rate of 35 l/s, the water level drawdowns were measured as 3.04 m and 0.80 m in the observation wells at distances of 20 m and 120 m, respectively.

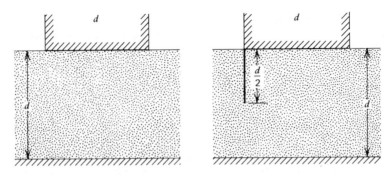

Figure 4-28 Problem 4-11 diagrams for drawing flow nets.

Compute the field coefficient of permeability. (*Answer* 0.34 mm/s)

4-13 A pumping test was conducted to estimate the in situ permeability of a sand and gravel aquifer bounded top and bottom by impervious glacial till. The confined aquifer, 10 m thick, was overlain by 10 m of till, and the well extended to the bottom of the aquifer at a depth of 20 m below the ground surface. Two observation wells penetrated the aquifer at distances of 15 m and 100 m from the main well. Before testing, the piezometric surfaces in all wells were 15 m above a datum plane through the bottom of the well. After pumping at a rate of 70 l/s to drawdown equilibrium, the water levels in the two observation wells were 11.4 m and 13.1 m above the datum. Compute the coefficient of permeability. (*Answer* 1.2 mm/s)

4-14 Verify Equation 4-26 using the relationship in Equation 4-20.

4-15 Define well loss and describe how it can be determined by field testing.

4-16 What assumptions were made in deriving the equations for unsteady flow. Consider both the general formula Equation 4-16 and the Theis formula Equation 4-32. Why is the Theis formula applied to both confined and unconfined aquifers?

4-17 Field data from a nonequilibrium pumping test are listed in the following table. The t is time since the start of pumping and Z is the corresponding drawdown in an observation well located 30.5 m from the well being pumped at an uniform rate of 30 l/s. Determine the coefficients of transmissibility and storage using both the Theis and Chow methods. (*Answer* $T = 110$ to 140 m³/d·m)

t (h)	Z (m)	t (h)	Z (m)
1.0	0.18	8.0	1.58
2.0	0.43	10.0	1.89
3.0	0.73	12.0	2.29
4.0	0.88	18.0	2.77
5.0	1.01	24.0	3.20
6.0	1.22	30.0	3.60

4-18 Field data from a nonequilibrium pumping test are listed in the following table. The t is time since the start of pumping and Z is the corresponding drawdown in an observation well located 245 m from the well being pumped at an uniform rate of 45 l/s. Determine the coefficients of transmissibility and storage using both the Theis and Chow methods.

t (min)	Z (m)	t (min)	Z (m)
10	0.02	140	0.50
20	0.08	160	0.57
30	0.13	200	0.60
40	0.19	240	0.66
50	0.23	280	0.70
60	0.27	320	0.74
80	0.34	360	0.78
100	0.40	400	0.82
120	0.46	440	0.85

4-19 Describe the process of cable-tool percussion drilling.

4-20 How is a gravel pack placed around a well screen?

4-21 What is a natural gravel-packed well, and how is it formed?

4-22 List the major components of a multistage vertical-turbine well pump.

4-23 Explain the reason for the water level fluctuations in Figure 4-26.

4-24 Why is the elevation of the water table declining in the region represented by the observation well record in Figure 4-27?

4-25 Define the meaning of safe yield for a groundwater basin.

4-26 Review the discussion of the Orange County Water District in Section 5-8. Describe the purposes and methods used for artificial recharge of groundwater.

Chapter 5
Groundwater Quality

Approximately one-half the population of the United States depends on groundwater as a source of drinking water with about 30 percent delivered by community systems and another 20 percent from domestic wells. Furthermore, industrial plants, office buildings, restaurants, recreational areas, and schools that serve millions of people rely on groundwater supplies. Over one-third of the nation has an underground supply capable of yielding sufficient quantity at suitable quality for individual domestic wells. This accessibility, where surface water is not available, allows inhabitation of many regions that would otherwise be unoccupied.

Future demand is expected to increase dramatically since groundwater in many areas is the only high quality, economical source available. While public agencies have stressed the obvious pollution of streams and lakes, subsurface degradation has generally been ignored. Almost every known instance of groundwater contamination has been discovered only after drinking supply has been affected.

This chapter discusses the nature of groundwater quality, sources of contamination, and technical difficulties of monitoring, controlling, and correcting pollution.

5-1   Groundwater Contamination

Numerous natural and man-made products are stored and spread on, or beneath, the land surface where they are susceptible to percolation. Depending on the relative liquid density and natural flow pattern of the water already contained in the aquifer, seepage containing contaminants can move vertically or horizontally. The rate of movement is a function of both the type of pollutant and the local hydrogeology.

Figure 5-1 summarizes the common sources and routes leading to contamination of groundwater. Industrial and urban waste disposal practices are of principal concern. Absorption fields, following household septic tanks, percolate large volumes of effluent, while sanitary sewers with poor jointing can leak wastewaters into porous soils. Industrial waste impoundments, landfills, and storage piles are potential problems, with the degree of contamination ranging from a slight degradation to damaging concentrations of toxic heavy metals, organic compounds, or radioactive materials. Properly constructed disposal wells for injecting industrial wastewaters into deep saline aquifers rarely cause pollution. In oil fields, the primary problem is improper plugging of abandoned wells and, to a lesser degree, inadequate operation of produc-

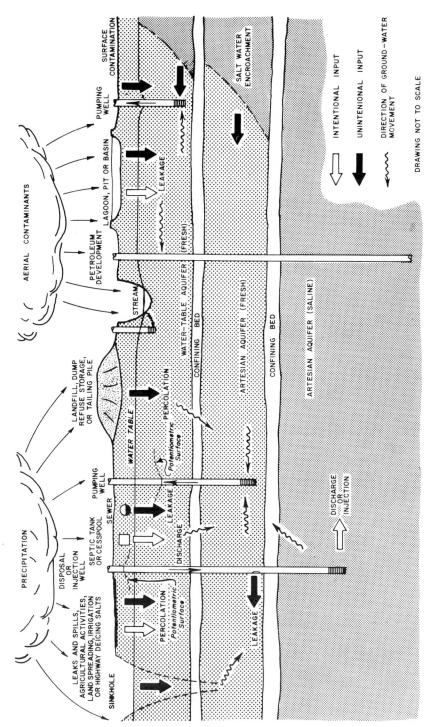

Figure 5-1 Typical routes of groundwater contamination. (From *Groundwater Pollution Problems in the Southeastern United States*, EPA-600/3-77-012, January 1977.)

tion and disposal wells. Agricultural activities, owning to their great areal extent, tend to cause buildup of contaminants such as nitrates and dissolved salts over an entire region, rather than the relative local effects of most point sources.

Pollution attenuates with time and distance travelled through chemical adsorption and hydrological dispersion and dilution. The rate of attenuation is related to the type of contaminant, site geology, topography, climate, and subsurface hydrology. Adsorption of ions and molecules from water is much greater in fine-grained soils (clays and silts) than porous sands and gravels. Water percolating through unsaturated soil strata can remain unchanged, lose solutes, or gain dissolved substances. Multivalent ions—heavy metals and orthophosphate—are readily extracted by adsorption on clay minerals, whereas monovalent ions like boron, chloride, and nitrate generally pass

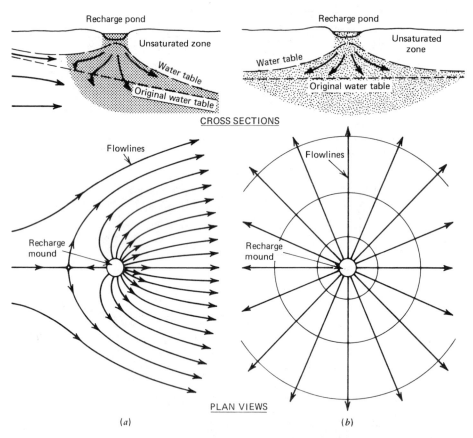

Figure 5-2 Percolation of contaminants from a recharge pond to an underlying aquifer with a (a) sloping water table and (b) level water table. (The distribution of contamination illustrated is for polluted water with the same density as the groundwater.) (Adapted from M. Deutsch, *Ground-Water Contamination and Legal Controls in Michigan*, U. S. Geological Survey Water-Supply Paper 1691, 1963.)

unaffected through even a fine-grained soil. In contrast, organic substances are often reduced by a combination of physical, chemical, and biological activities in the upper soil profile.

The amount of water, either from precipitation or the wastewater itself, is a primary factor in carrying pollutants down through a soil profile. Surface water passes downward through the unsaturated zone and disperses in an aquifer in a definite pattern depending on site conditions. Figure 5-2 illustrates idealized flow from a recharge pond overlying an unconfined aquifer. A recharge mound forms on the water table and flows laterally outward. On a sloping water table, inflow extends a short distance upstream, but the bulk of recharge spreads in a downgradient direction within clearly defined boundaries. Thus, contaminated water moves by a definite route and is not, as is often imagined, subject to dilution by the entire body of groundwater underlying a disposal site. Dispersion is influenced both physically by soil porosity and hydraulically by the rate of water movement.

Polluted water moving through an aquifer forms a bulb or plume extending along the flow path from the source. It either attenuates within the aquifer, discharges to a well, or occasionally seeps from the ground to enter a surface watercourse. Although dispersal in the direction of flow tends to reduce the concentration of a pollutant, intermixing with natural groundwater is often limited and the plume may not fan out. For example, the contaminant may be a light-density fluid like petroleum, or in the case of a rock aquifer the flow may be directed and controlled by the fracture pattern. A well near a recharge source acts as a hydraulic collector reducing dispersion of pollutants. The sketch in Figure 5-3 shows convergence of contaminants from a shallow disposal well and surface water to a nearby pumping well.

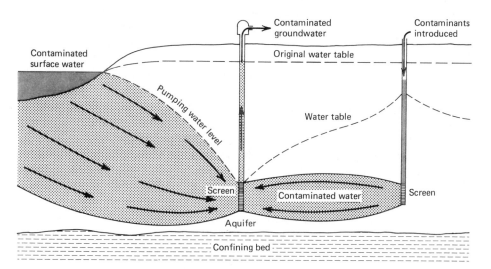

Figure 5-3 Movement of contaminants from a recharge or drainage well and surface watercourse to a nearby pumping well. (From *Groundwater Pollution Problems in the Southeastern United States*, EPA-600/3-77-012, January 1977.)

5-2   Effects of Pollution

Degradation is reflected by undesirable amounts of inorganic chemicals, organic compounds, or biological indicators that render the water unfit for beneficial uses. Toxic substances are perhaps the most serious problem in water intended for domestic and agricultural consumption. Examples are arsenic as a poison that affects human health and excess boron, which is detrimental to agricultural crops. For drinking water, the absence of human pathogens is an equally important criterion. Since coliform bacteria are excreted in large numbers in feces of man and animals, their presence in water indicates fecal wastes and potential presence of disease-producing microorganisms.

The inorganic chemical content of irrigation water is of great concern to agriculture in arid climates. Quality criteria most often applied relate to total dissolved solids, chloride, sodium, boron, and bicarbonate. Even though low salinity is most desirable for irrigation, in many regions the only water available contains several thousand milligrams per litre of salts. High evaporation rates and lack of adequate flushing can cause salt accumulation in the root zone with a resulting decrease in crop yields. Water reuse and recycling for irrigation is a frequent source of salt buildup in both surface supplies and groundwaters.

Organic chemical contamination is most often caused by petroleum products, phenolic compounds, and pesticides. Gasoline and other hydrocarbons, resulting from leaking tanks, pipeline breaks, or spills on the land surface, create objectionable odors and tastes. Phenols present in oil refinery or chemical manufacturing wastes are detectable in water at concentrations of a few micrograms per litre. When contaminated by petroleum derivatives or phenols, drinking-water wells are often abandoned because of the obnoxious and persistent nature of these compounds. Pesticides can be flushed into groundwater with excess irrigation or rainfall and, if resistant to degradation, they may reappear in irrigation or domestic wells near the cultivated area.

Health problems related to pollution are worthy of emphasis since groundwater is the domestic source for the majority of households. The most common hazards are infant methemoglobinemia caused by high nitrate concentration; dental fluorosis resulting from excess fluoride ion; potential carcinogenic effect of organic chemicals; serious illnesses caused by arsenic, cadmium, or lead; and infectious hepatitis attributed to pathogenic enteric viruses. Results of a national inventory of waterborne disease outbreaks related to untreated groundwater sources for the period 1946 through 1970 are shown in Table 5-1. Contamination at the land surface and overflow or seepage of wastewater into improperly constructed wells were the major identified causes of disease outbreaks.

The persistence of contamination is a very serious aspect of groundwater degradation. The contrast with surface-water pollution can be visualized by comparing the residence time of days for water in a river to the average residence time of groundwater in the order of decades to hundreds of years. Consequently, a pollutant that is not readily decayed or adsorbed underground can remain as a degrading influence for an indefinite period. Groundwater has been contaminated in local areas in all parts of the United States and on a regional basis in some heavily populated and industrialized

Table 5-1 Incidence of Waterborne Disease in the United States, 1946-1970, Due to Source Contamination of Untreated Groundwater

Cause	Private		Public		All Systems	
	Outbreaks	Cases	Outbreaks	Cases	Outbreaks	Cases
Improper construction or location of well or spring						
Surface contamination nearby	21	640	1	2 500	22	3 140
Overflow or seepage of sewage	49	2 779	4	531	53	3 310
Seepage from abandoned well	1	50	–	–	1	50
Source of contamination not determined	8	235	1	400	9	635
Flooding	4	66	3	4 400	7	4 466
Contamination through creviced limestone or fissured rock	10	555	1	70	11	625
Chemical or pesticide contamination	4	17	–	–	4	17
Data insufficient to classify	46	2 001	3	16 350	49	18 351
Total:	143	6 343	13	24 251	156	30 594

Source. G. F. Craun and L. J. McCabe, "Review of the Causes of Waterborne-Disease Outbreaks," *Journal American Water Works Association,* Vol. 65, January 1973. Reprinted with permission of the American Water Works Association, copyrighted 1973.

areas precluding the development of water wells resulting in serious local economic problems.[1] Control is best achieved by regulating the source of pollution rather than relying on remedial corrections.

5-3 Natural Pollution

Underground sources, while generally more mineralized than surface water, are uniform in quality from season to season and often constant in temperature. As a result of filtering through the unsaturated zone, groundwater is normally free of microorganisms and suspended solids. The principal natural chemicals found are dissolved salts, iron and manganese, fluoride, arsenic, radionuclides, and trace metals.

Natural quality varies widely from region to region based on geologic and climatic conditions. Both the mineral and physical composition of the soil strata and the length of contact time with seeping water influence the concentration of dissolved salts. In arid zones with limited recharge, the slow movement results in highly mineralized, poor quality water. Excessive evapotranspiration rates can cause capillary rise depositing salts near the land surface. As a result, many areas in western United States have naturally occurring contamination of sodium chloride. Weathering sedimentary rock often releases calcium and magnesium creating excessive hardness. In terms of treatability, dissolved salts resulting from sodium chloride and calcium bicarbonate have distinctly different characters. Carbonate hardness can be readily reduced by chemical treatment whereas removal of sodium chloride is not feasible for municipal practice. (Reverse osmosis, although technically possible, is very costly.) Also, excess chlorides are the major problem in irrigation water, not calcium and magnesium bicarbonates.

Dissolved iron and manganese naturally occur in the aquifers of many regions. Although tolerated by most consumers in small amounts, the brown oxides of these metals create unesthetic color and staining problems. Reduced iron can also promote bacterial growths in distribution systems imparting foul odors to the water. The only permanent solution to iron and manganese problems is removal by treatment, which can be accomplished by conventional processes.

Fluoride is a constituent of mineral fluorite found in sedimentary rocks and is present in nearly all igneous and metamorphic rocks, principally in apatite, mica, and amphiboles. In low concentrations, fluoride is beneficial and reduces the incidence of dental caries. At slightly higher concentrations, above 1.5 mg/l, detrimental dental fluorosis (mottling of teeth) increases, and at very high concentrations fluorides are toxic to humans and cause bone damage. Only a few areas have natural fluoride ion greater than the upper recommended limit of 1.5 mg/l. In the United States, more high fluoride groundwater is present in the northwest with major aquifers yielding levels above the approval limit but much lower than a toxic level.[2] Unfortunately, removal of the fluoride ion by water treatment is costly and not commonly practiced. A few communities have been able to seek alternate sources of water to solve their problem without special treatment. More commonly, fluoride compounds are added to well water in order to meet the optimum limit for a public supply.

Arsenic, present as native arsenic or arsenopyrite, can be a significant problem in aquifers of volcanic deposits. Concentrations higher than the recommended limit have been identified in isolated areas in northwestern United States.[2] These aquifers are avoided for public water supplies.

Natural radioactive substances, while present in most rocks, are at very low levels of activity. Since accumulations of excess radium and strontium constitute a health hazard, these two nuclides have approval limits established for drinking water. Geological formations containing radioactive minerals often contain large amounts of organic matter in the form of lignite or phosphates occurring as phosphatized bone and shell material. For example, a study of 420 wells in the phosphate-producing area of southern Florida showed that 68 percent of them contained groundwater with radium-226 levels higher than the recommended limit of 3 picocuries per litre.[3]

Small amounts of metals such as selenium, cadmium, lead, copper, and zinc are found in rocks and unconsolidated deposits. Groundwater generally only contains traces of these metallic elements, and their presence is rarely a water quality problem.

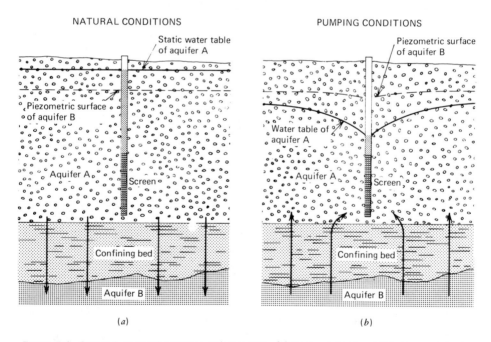

Figure 5-4 Reversal of aquifer leakage by pumping. (a) Under natural conditions, groundwater percolates from the upper to lower aquifer. (b) When water is withdrawn from the overlying stratum, the deeper groundwater flows up through the confining layer to the upper aquifer. (From M. Deutsch, *Ground-Water Contamination and Legal Controls in Michigan,* U. S. Geological Survey Water-Supply Paper 1691, 1963.)

Changes in water quality resulting from withdrawal of groundwater or channelization of rivers, although induced by human activities, are not considered groundwater contamination in the usual meaning. Thus, the following concepts are presented under the heading of natural pollution. Figure 5-4 illustrates the reversal of underground flows due to pumpage from one aquifer and, hence, the possibility of degrading the groundwater quality by interaquifer flow. Under natural conditions, the water table of aquifer A is higher than the potentiometric surface of aquifer B; therefore, groundwater tends to move downward through the semipermeable zone separating the two strata. Pumping however interchanges the relative positions of the two water levels, and results in a greater pressure in aquifer B causing water to migrate upward into aquifer A. If, as is often the case, the lower aquifer is more saline, this change in flow pattern increases the salt content of the upper stratum. Increases in iron and manganese, which have been observed with a lowering of the water table by overpumping, have also been attributed to interaquifer flow. Figure 5-5 illustrates how underlying saline groundwater can rise due to deepening of a river channel that results in a lowering of the water table. This intrusion of saline water occurs because of the reduced pressure of overlying fresh water near the channel.

Lateral intrusion of salty water into freshwater aquifers in coastal areas is caused by pumping from wells that induce the influx of saline water. Strict controls over diversion of groundwater in the coastal plain states of the Northeast have been effective in eliminating saltwater intrusion as a critical problem in this region. Meanwhile,

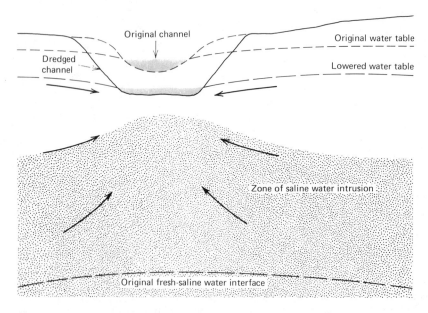

Figure 5-5 Migration of saline water caused by lowering of water levels in an effluent stream and streamside aquifer hydraulically connected to an underlying saline-water aquifer. (From M. Deutsch, *Ground-Water Contamination and Legal Controls in Michigan*, U. S. Geological Survey Water-Supply Paper 1691, 1963.)

encroachment in the Gulf coast area has affected a number of important and heavily pumped groundwater areas of major urban centers. California has had serious problems in many of its coastal basins. To reverse the movement of intruding salinity, freshwater injection wells have been installed in selected areas. The intention of the barrier, formed by the line of wells parallel to the ocean shore, is to reverse the hydraulic gradient in the aquifer so flow moves toward the sea again.

5-4   Sources of Contamination from Domestic Wastes

The most serious widespread source of contamination is subsurface disposal of domestic wastewater from individual household systems (septic tank-absorption fields and cesspools). The most popular disposal system is a septic tank for retaining and digesting large solids followed by a percolation bed as sketched in Figure 5-6. The tank has cleaning ports to periodically remove accumulated sludge. The absorption field usually consists of perforated pipe laid in gravel-lined trenches. Organics decompose in the aerobic environment of the bed, which is ventilated to the house plumbing stack, and the water seeps down into the soil profile. If a water-supply well is nearby and the soil permeable, seepage reaching the water table can be withdrawn with the groundwater. The typical cesspool is a stone-lined sump excavated into the ground to receive household wastewater directly. Large solids settle to the bottom and water seeps out through the walls. Plugging problems in cesspools, which occur except in very coarse soils, led to developing the septic tank. The pit privy is an outhouse built over a shallow trench used as a receptacle for human waste. Groundwater pollution from such a shallow pit is extremely rare.

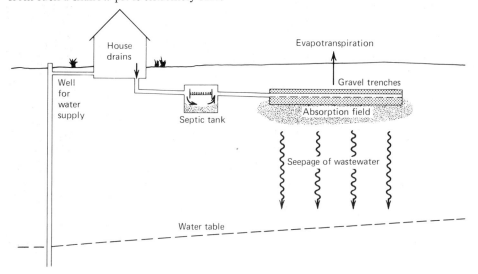

Figure 5-6 A typical household system for disposal of wastewater on the building site. The septic tank reduces plugging of the percolation bed by removing large solids. The absorption field permits biological decomposition of waste organics and seepage of the water.

Approximately 30 percent of the population in the United States, representing about 20 million single housing units, dispose of their domestic waste through individual on-site systems.[1] Almost 7 million of these housing units use septic tanks or cesspools. Contamination may be local, for instance, where a well is polluted by disposal sites in the vicinity. Such instances have been experienced throughout the country. A regional problem is created when many individual disposal units pollute extensive aquifers that supply water over a broad area, such as one or more counties. The density of seepage disposal systems in an area is the principal factor with geology, depth to water, and climate affecting the nature and degree of contamination. The potential for pollution in a region is suggested by the relative density of household disposal systems as shown in Figure 5-7 in three density ranges of less than 3.8 units per square kilometre, between 3.8 and 15.4 and more than 15.4 units/km^2.

Site acceptability for a percolation system is commonly based on the ability of the local soil to absorb water at a rate fast enough to handle the anticipated quanitiy of effluent. A percolation test is used to determine the suitability of the soil and area required for an absorption field. However, a high infiltration rate does not correlate with the capacity of a soil to absorb contaminants. For this reason, the most frequently reported cases of contamination are in highly permeable soils. Where recycling of the wastewater effluent is sufficiently rapid, nearby wells are a potential source of disease-producing microorganisms, particularly hepatitis viruses. The most common pollutants, however, are mobile substances like detergents or ions such as chloride and nitrate. Being a health hazard, nitrate is of major concern. Normally, ammonia nitrogen is biologically oxidized to nitrate in the tile field and then flushed into the ground.

Several cases of groundwater pollution on a regional scope have been documented in the northeastern and southeastern regions of the United States; note the darkened areas in Figure 5-7. From an investigation in southern Nassau County, New York, the two chief sources of nitrate contamination of major aquifers in a 470 km^2 area were absorption field infiltration and leachate from chemical fertilizers.[5] Nitrate nitrogen content in the shallow glacial aquifer averaged 7 mg/l and in several places exceeded 22 mg/l. Enriched water also penetrated to a considerable depth into an underlying unconsolidated artesian aquifer, which was revealed by nitrate nitrogen levels of 10 to 21 mg/l from 16 public supply wells screened in this deeper zone. Further analyses revealed detergent widely distributed in the groundwater of the shallow glacial aquifer.

Correction of regional problems is extremely difficult owing to the high cost of replacing household disposal systems and persistence of the contamination long after the seepage beds have been replaced. The common remedial action is installation of public sewers to collect and treat the wastewater at a central facility. Where piping systems are not economically feasible, prevention has normally been attempted by low density zoning prescribed by the local government, although increased regulation of septic tank siting is being proposed by some state agencies.

Sanitary sewers are intended to provide watertight containment of wastes being conveyed. Exfiltration can be a local problem in the case of cracked pipe or poor jointing; the latter is often related to the past practice of using inflexible cement-mortar connections.

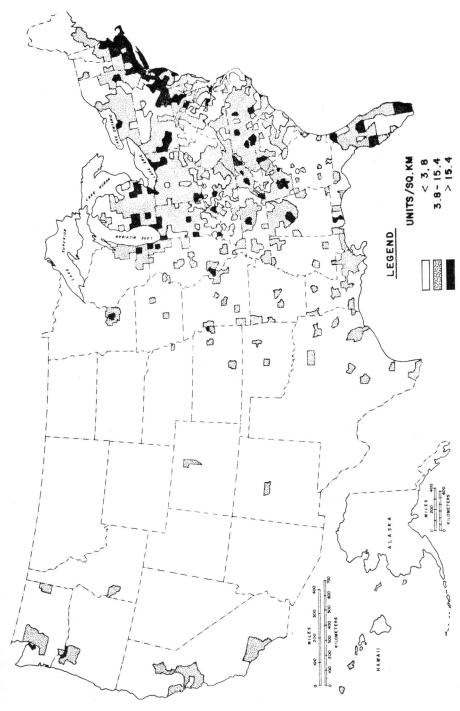

Figure 5-7 Density of housing units using on-site domestic wastewater disposal systems. (Data were taken from the 1970 U. S. Census of Housing and mapped by county.)

Wastewater effluent from secondary treatment (biological processing to reduce the organic contaminants to less than 30 mg/l) is not likely to seriously degrade groundwater quality upon discharge to a surface watercourse. Seepage into a dry stream bed, which is likely to occur in an arid climate, infiltrates dissolved salts. Of particular concern is the nitrate ion and perhaps chloride. Despite this, natural percolation of treated effluent is generally not viewed with concern since adequate dilution by rainfall, except in a semiarid climate, reduces significant buildup of salts contributed by the wastewater. Where infiltration takes place into a known water supply aquifer, a higher degree of treatment prior to discharge may be specified, for example, chemical coagulation followed by granular-media filtration and disinfection.

Land disposal of wastewaters, which is discussed extensively in other books,[6,7] has been practiced historically in arid regions where irrigation water is scarce. In these areas, groundwater is often not accessible or is naturally saline making it unsuitable for use, thus, contamination is not a primary concern. Where the quality of infiltration is a major consideration, the ideal site is a moderately permeable soil with a deep water table supporting a perennial grass. The dosage of biologically treated effluent applied should not exceed the amount of nitrogen assimilated by the forage crop. Percolation of nitrate usually occurs in the case of a permeable soil, high water table, seasonal crop, or overdosing. Other pollutants frequently encountered are sodium chloride, refractory trace organics and inorganics, and pathogenic viruses. Land disposal of digested wastewater sludges, by surface spreading or shallow subsurface incorporation, can cause similar contamination. If the site does not support a continuous grass cover, the soil must be relatively impervious to prevent nitrate formed in the decomposition of the organics from being driven into the ground by rainfall infiltration. The practice of intermittent cropping, where the site is alternately used for sludge disposal on grass and planting corn or grain, results in leaching of inorganic nitrogen after plowing.

Burial of solid wastes can result in degradation of subsurface water through the generation of leachate caused by water percolating through the refuse fill. Contamination problems are more likely to occur in humid areas where the entering moisture exceeds the absorption capacity of the disposal area. Leachate is highly mineralized water containing such constituents as chloride, iron, lead, copper, sodium, nitrate, ammonia, and a variety of organic chemicals. Where manufacturing wastes are included, hazardous constituents like cyanide, cadmium, and chlorinated hydrocarbons are often present; the particular composition depends on the industries using the landfill.

The organic matter in refuse slowly decomposes by aerobic and anaerobic biological activities producing soluble compounds and gases. By infiltration of surface water to the layers of waste, dissolved substances percolate to the groundwater. Leachate often contains a wide variety of elements and compounds; the significant indicators from landfills containing municipal refuse include BOD, COD, iron, chloride, and inorganic nitrogen. Well-documented case histories have shown that leachate can cause contamination after extended periods of time, even 20 years after the site is abandoned.[5]

Landfills or dumps in the past have invariably been located on land considered to have little value for other uses—marshlands, abandoned sand and gravel pits, old strip mines, and limestone sinkholes, all of which are susceptible to groundwater pollution problems. Many existing landfills in the Northeast were originally designed as "reclamation" projects to fill marshes or abandoned pits for future land development. Often they were operated by private profit-making organizations contracting with communities and industries for disposing of their solid wastes.[5] Control procedures for reducing potential groundwater contamination were not instituted.

Modern sanitary landfills are designed to reduce environmental impact by managing leachate production; hence, present problems bear little relationship to concerns associated with existing or abandoned dumps. Key factors are proper siting and reduction of infiltration by considering steepness of the surface slope, selection of a relatively impervious cover, and type of surface vegetation. Regulations normally require separating the base of the refuse from the water table using a compacted clayey fill. Also under consideration, but usually costly, are pretreatment techniques to reduce the volume of solid wastes, detoxification of hazardous wastes, and installation of liners to collect leachate for treatment.

5-5 Industrial and Commercial Sources

Industries produce huge volumes of wastewater from manufacturing and processing operations, cooling uses, and sanitary facilities. The latter are generally segregated and treated as domestic wastewater prior to discharge in a surface watercourse. Nonprocess water is often cleaned and recycled, or discharged without treatment when uncontaminated. Process wastes, not economically reclaimable, are disposed of in liquid or sludge form. On a dry weight basis, the industrial wastes of all types generated is almost twice as much as that produced by residential and commercial sources. Preliminary data from nationwide industrial surveys revealed over 90 percent of all hazardous wastes being disposed of on the land, mainly because it is the cheapest waste management option. A similar percentage of the nonhazardous portion of trade wastes is probably disposed of on land, as opposed to undergoing treatment or recovery. The manufacturing of chemical and allied products produces wastewater potentially more hazardous than the other industrial categories of primary metals, petroleum and coal products, and paper and allied products. Table 5-2 lists common contaminants in industrial wastewaters.

The practices of handling nonreclaimable industrial wastewaters and sludges, in order of frequency of application, are discharge to impoundments, burial in landfill, and injection in deep saline aquifers. Impoundments (lagoons, basins, pits, and ponds) are a serious source of contamination because of their large number and potential for leaking hazardous substances. Since the stored wastewater tends to percolate into the underlying aquifer (Figure 5-2), mobile substances are likely to be carried into the groundwater either by accident or design to reduce the liquid in storage. In some heavily industrialized sections of the nation, regional problems of groundwater contamination have developed where the areal extent and toxic nature of the contaminants have ruled out the use of groundwater from shallow aquifers.[1]

Table 5-2 Industrial Wastewater Parameters Having or Indicating Significant Groundwater Contamination or Potential

PAPER AND ALLIED PRODUCTS

Pulp and Paper Industry

COD	Phenols	Nutrients (nitrogen
TOC	Sulfite	and phosphorus)
pH	Color	Total dissolved solids
Ammonia	Heavy metals	

PETROLEUM AND COAL PRODUCTS

Petroleum Refining Industry

Ammonia	Chloride	Nitrogen
Chromium	Color	Odor
COD	Copper	Total phosphorus
pH	Cyanide	Sulfate
Phenols	Iron	TOC
Sulfide	Lead	Turbidity
Total dissolved solids	Mercaptans	Zinc

PRIMARY METALS

Steel Industries

pH	Cyanide	Tin
Chloride	Phenols	Chromium
Sulfate	Iron	Zinc
Ammonia		

CHEMICALS AND ALLIED PRODUCTS

Organic Chemicals Industry

COD	TOC	Phenols
pH	Total phosphorus	Cyanide
Total dissolved solids	Heavy metals	Total nitrogen

Inorganic Chemicals, Alkalies, and Chlorine Industry

Acidity/alkalinity	Chlorinated benzenoids and	Chromium
Total dissolved solids	polynuclear aromatics	Lead
Chloride	Phenols	Titanium
Sulfate	Fluoride	Iron
COD	Total phosphorus	Aluminum
TOC	Cyanide	Boron
	Mercury	Arsenic

Plastic Materials and Synthetics Industry

COD	Phosphorus	Ammonia
pH	Nitrate	Cyanide
Phenols	Organic nitrogen	Zinc

Table 5-2 Continued

Total dissolved solids	Chlorinated benzenoids and	Mercaptans
Sulfate	polynuclear aromatics	
	Nitrogen Fertilizer Industry	
Ammonia	Sulfate	COD
Chloride	Organic nitrogen	Iron
Chromium	compounds	pH
Total dissolved solids	Zinc	Phosphate
Nitrate	Calcium	Sodium
	Phosphate Fertilizer Industry	
Calcium	Acidity	Mercury
Dissolved solids	Aluminum	Nitrogen
Fluoride	Arsenic	Sulfate
pH	Iron	Uranium
Phosphorus		

Source: The Report to Congress, Waste Disposal Practices and Their Effects on Ground Water, U. S. Environmental Protection Agency, January 1977.

Solid wastes and sludges from industries are often incorporated with municipal refuse for burial in sanitary landfills. In addition, manufacturing plants may operate burial grounds on their own property—a practice without government regulation in most regions. The environmental problems of landfills are discussed in Section 5-4.

Injection into deep wells is environmentally acceptable and often an economical method for disposal of hazardous wastewaters. Pollution control laws rule out injection into freshwater aquifers, although some states have not yet banned disposal of storm runoff and excess irrigation water in shallow wells. For concentrates of toxic chemicals, the boreholes usually penetrate saline aquifers over a thousand feet deep. Ideally, in addition to adequate porosity to receive the flow, the stratum should be overlain by impervious layers to prevent upward migration into potable water zones.

Production of crude oil is usually accompanied by withdrawal of water having a high chloride content. In an old well, the yield of brine can exceed oil production, with a typical ratio of salt water to oil being 2 or 3 to 1. The common method of handling oil-field brines prior to 1970 was discharge to unlined pits, which lead to pollution of both groundwater and surface watercourses. Banning of unlined basins led to construction of lined evaporation impoundments and the use of brine disposal wells. Abandoned production wells, not cased or cemented for brine disposal, should be modified to prevent undetected ruptures beneath the surface allowing seepage into freshwater aquifers. One technique is to place an encased injection tubing inside the existing borehole. A fluid confined under pressure in the casing, surrounding the tubing, allows leak detection by a drop in fluid pressure. However, even with properly installed disposal wells, potential problems exist because of abandoned and inade-

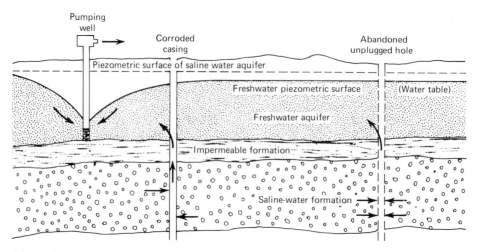

Figure 5-8 Improperly constructed wells, uncased holes, and abandoned wells left unplugged can provide vertical openings between different geological strata leading to contamination of fresh-water aquifers with saline water. (From *Ground Water Pollution in the South Central States*, EPA-R2-73-268, June 1973.)

quately plugged borings from early oil explorations. These vertical openings connecting freshwater aquifers to deeper saline strata allow possible transfer of salt water under sufficient pressure from brine injection as graphically shown in Figure 5-8.

All forms of mining create wastes and changes in hydrogeological conditions that contribute to degradation of groundwater. Patterns of water movement, responsible for the distribution of contaminants, are highly variable and almost entirely founded on the mining practice and local conditions of geology, drainage, and hydrology. With both surface and underground mining, refuse piles and slurry lagoons are probably the major potential sources of pollution. The open pits from stripping ore near the ground surface provide a path for water to reach aquifers. Although some restoration can be accomplished by backfilling and grading, these actions do not ensure protection of freshwater strata. Infiltration can selectively move through a fill material that is more permeable than the undisturbed rock. The primary mechanisms characteristic of underground mining are mine tunnels and shafts influencing water movement; unplugged wells and test borings interconnecting different water-bearing strata; and, dewatering to keep the mines from flooding. Dewatering lowers the hydrostatic head of the fresh water to the extent that upwelling of deeper mineralized water takes place, thus, contaminating shallow potable-water aquifers.

Principal impurities from mine wastes are acidity, dissolved solids, metals, radio-active materials, color, and turbidity. While many of these are not toxic, they are desirable for esthetic reasons. The most prevalent problem is acid drainage from coal mining, which results from leaching of pyrites and subsequent oxidation to form sulfuric acid. Dissolution of metals, such as iron, copper, zinc, cadmium, and manganese, in acidic water often aggravates the difficulty. Even though formation of acid is not anticipated in western coal mining, stripping of alkaline rock is expected to make reclamation difficult. High soil alkalinity inhibits regrowth of vegetation on spoil banks and, in the absence of this protective cover, uncontrolled weathering will continue to transport alkaline wastes into the surrounding environment. If the coal seams separate fresh water from deeper saline strata, removal of the overburden soil and coal layers can cause a loss of the perched fresh water and intrusion of saline water (Figure 5-5).

Mining metals has the potential for creating serious predicaments caused both by the nature of some ores and recently developed mining procedures.[1] A serious problem of waste disposal results from uranium tailings high in dissolved toxins including selenium, molybdenum, arsenic, and radioactive materials. Solution mining is being used to extract copper by first fracturing the underground rock in situ and then leaching the copper by introducing sulfuric acid through pipes extending into the deposit. After removing the copper from the extracting fluid, large quantities of acidic wastewater laden with heavy metals and other impurities must be disposed. Despite the potential dangers, solution mining is being considered for extraction of uranium.

Procedures for abatement of groundwater pollution from mining can be divided into the following two broad categories. The first consists of methods to control infiltration of surface and groundwater into the mine; and, the second is treatment to reduce levels of contaminants in the waste. All are very costly processes and have not been applied to any significant degree. The least controllable practice is dewatering of a mine prior to and during operation. One effect is exposure of mineralized rocks to oxidation forming impurities that then leach into the groundwater. Another is the possible migration of poorer quality water into the mining area after the mine is abandoned and dewatering stopped.

Accidental spills of liquid wastes, toxic fluids, gasoline, and oil risk migration through the unsaturated soil zone to groundwater. Hydrocarbons are, by far, the most prevalent contaminants reported in spills and leaky or ruptured buried pipelines and storage tanks. When a large quantity of oil or gasoline percolates down to the water table, the plume tends to float as sketched in Figure 5-9. Hydrocarbons in groundwater persist for decades creating foul taste at trace levels in water pumped from the aquifer. Most recorded cases of accidental contamination could have been prevented by good management through providing barriers, preventing indiscriminate dumping, and promptly cleaning up spills.

Large amounts of sodium and calcium chloride are used for road maintenance during winter months in northern latitudes; several states apply greater than a hundred thousand tons on highways per year. Contamination results from salt-laden roadway runoff and infiltration from storage piles. Because of the large amounts of salt spread and stored in the Northeast, waters from many sand and gravel aquifers have shown a rise in sodium chloride concentrations. In Maine, 100 randomly selected wells adjacent to major highways were sampled over a three-year period. While natural chloride contents are normally less than 20 mg/l, the average April concentration for chloride ion from these aquifers was 171 mg/l.[1] Complaints regarding individual wells are

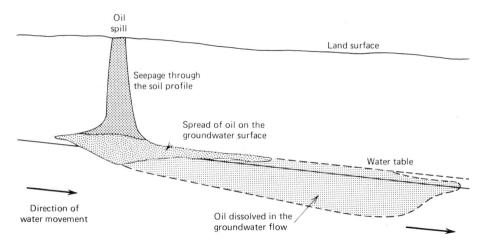

Figure 5-9 Movement of contamination in groundwater resulting from a spill of hydrocarbons. (Adapted from *Evaluation and Treatment of Oil Spill Accidents on Land*, Water and Petroleum Study Group, Federal Ministry of the Interior, Germany, 1970.)

so common in New England that several states have established annual budgets to allow for replacement of affected wells. Despite this, no adequate substitute for highway deicing salts appears acceptable. Several states have programs to reduce the quantities of salt spread for winter storms, and highway departments are enclosing many salt storage piles for protection against precipitation.

5-6 Agricultural Sources

A portion of the rainfall, or irrigation water applied, on agricultural land filters through the surface soils carrying with it dissolved substances. Due to evapotranspiration, the concentration of dissolved salts in the percolate from irrigation is two or three times greater than in the applied water. In permeable soils, excess water rids the root zone of salt deposits by carrying dissolved minerals (particularly chloride, sulfate, and sodium ions) to groundwater.

The practice of irrigation usually involves applying more water than is consumed by evapotranspiration and direct percolation to groundwater. This practice results in either overland runoff, or subsurface seepage, to surface watercourses from which the irrigation return flows are reused in subsequent irrigation cycles. In arid climates, this process unavoidably increases the concentration of dissolved minerals with each water reuse. Groundwater quality in the southwestern and south central states, has deteriorated from infiltration of irrigation return flows and the buildup of salts is expected to continue for the foreseeable future.

Fertilizers and pesticides can migrate into the groundwater under cultivated land, except in the case of clayey soils that inhibit infiltration. While some pesticides are persistent, many do not pose a threat since they are readily degraded in the soil environment. Also, these chemicals are only applied in limited quantities, which reduces the probability of leaking into the groundwater. The most troublesome health-related pollutant from agriculture is the nitrate ion, which is readily carried by water percolating down through unsaturated soil and groundwater flow in the saturated zone. Irrigation and application of inorganic-nitrogen fertilizer appear to have contributed to the rapid rise in nitrate levels in many agricultural areas; nevertheless, increases are also being observed under areas of unirrigated arable lands where organic soil conditioners are applied. Apparently, infiltration of the nitrate ion under cultivated land with well-drained soils cannot be prevented without abandoning fertilization and converting the vegetation back to natural grasses.

The use of synthetic fertilizers has dramatically increased during the past 30 years, since it is one of the few ways the agriculturist can influence the natural processes governing plant growth. Applications of inorganic nitrogen are often in excess of the amounts removed by the crop in order to stimulate greater yields. Based on studies of Coastal Plain soils in North Carolina, approximately one half of the applied nitrogen fertilizer was not used by the crop.[3] In poorly drained soils with high water tables, much of the leached nitrate was lost as gaseous nitrogen through denitrification, while drain pipes installed under moderately well-drained soils collected about one half of the nitrate. Obviously, the amount of fertilizer applied, soil permeability, and rate of water infiltration are all key factors influencing the movement of nitrate to groundwater.

The problem of rising nitrate levels in groundwaters is occurring in many regions of arable land. Changes in water management and farming practice might reduce the rate of increase in these regions, but intensive agriculture is a necessity for food production. Serious problems are occurring where small towns in rural areas use groundwater as a drinking water source and where former cultivated areas are urbanized and wells installed for domestic supplies. To make the predicament worse, feasible treatment for removal of nitrate from drinking water has not yet been perfected.

Cattle feedlots are also potential sources of nitrate and dissolved salts. However, transmission of these or other contaminants is related to local conditions of soil, drainage, rainfall, and surface conditions in the lots. Nitrification-denitrification appears to take place in the mixture of manure and surface soils reducing the risk of nitrogen infiltration. Burial of agricultural solid wastes including crop residues, dead animals, and manure can produce leachates, but these are often small landfills that must be viewed locally.

5-7 Prevention and Control

Prevention is the key to groundwater quality management—after contamination, remedial actions are largely ineffective and natural purification requires decades. Knowledge of potential sources and a comprehensive understanding of the hydro-

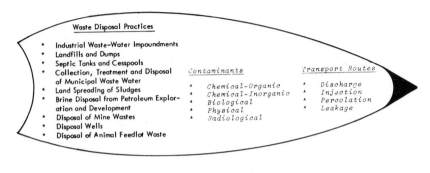

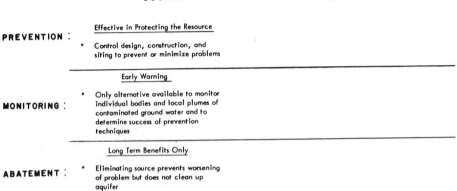

Figure 5-10 The hydrologic system controlling groundwater contamination and its constraints on methodologies for prevention, monitoring, and abatement. (From *The Report to Congress, Waste*

geology of a region are both essential to preventing pollution. Figure 5-10 summarizes the recommended procedure from source identification through environmental impact, and the methodologies of prevention, monitoring, and abatement. The system includes establishing the source, defining the groundwater regime, the points of contaminant discharge, and potential impact on water uses.

The nature of a groundwater system determines the techniques available to prevent, monitor, and abate degradation. Prevention is directed toward the source by proper design, construction, and siting. Monitoring is intended as an early warning to determine the success of prevention techniques and protect the environment if the system contaminates groundwater. Abatement action is to stop further damage eliminating the source. If these controls fail or are not effectively employed and contamination reaches the point of discharge, condemnation of the water supply or expensive treatment are the aftereffect alternatives.

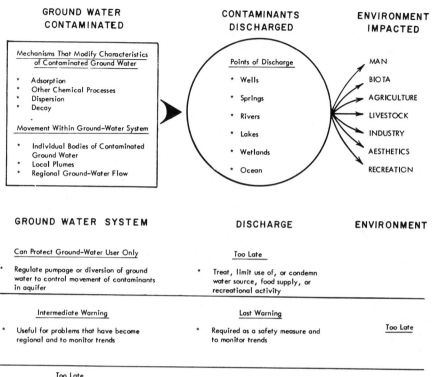

GROUND WATER CONTAMINATED

Mechanisms That Modify Characteristics of Contaminated Ground Water

* Adsorption
* Other Chemical Processes
* Dispersion
* Decay

Movement Within Ground-Water System

* Individual Bodies of Contaminated Ground Water
* Local Plumes
* Regional Ground-Water Flow

CONTAMINANTS DISCHARGED

Points of Discharge

* Wells
* Springs
* Rivers
* Lakes
* Wetlands
* Ocean

ENVIRONMENT IMPACTED

MAN
BIOTA
AGRICULTURE
LIVESTOCK
INDUSTRY
AESTHETICS
RECREATION

GROUND WATER SYSTEM

Can Protect Ground-Water User Only

* Regulate pumpage or diversion of ground water to control movement of contaminants in aquifer

Intermediate Warning

* Useful for problems that have become regional and to monitor trends

Too Late

* Clean-up of most aquifers is not technically or economically feasible

DISCHARGE

Too Late

* Treat, limit use of, or condemn water source, food supply, or recreational activity

Last Warning

* Required as a safety measure and to monitor trends

ENVIRONMENT

Too Late

Disposal Practices and their Effects on Ground Water, U. S. Environmental Protection Agency, 1977.)

5-8 Case Studies

Incidences of groundwater pollution related to solid waste disposal are local in scope, such as leachate from a landfill. Similarly, small leakages of wastewater are often confined to a small area. Regional problems pose much more difficult questions since management of the sources may be neither politically or technically feasible. The most serious of these in the future are likely to be: increase in dissolved salts from irrigation return flows, seawater intrusion, and disturbance of saline aquifers; buildup of nitrate in domestic supplies drawn from beneath agricultural land under fertilized cultivation; and, contamination related to exploration for energy sources including brine disposal from petroleum and gas wells, acid mine drainage and saltwater seepage from coal mines, and potential release of toxins from extraction of uranium and storage of spent radioactive wastes from nuclear power plants. The following case studies direct attention to the serious nature of some of these pollution problems.

Nitrate Infiltration from Agricultural Practices in the United Kingdom

Work carried out by the Water Research Centre[8, 9] shows that increasing concentrations of nitrate have been recorded in groundwater from the main aquifers within the United Kingdom over the last few years. (*The European Standard*, 2nd Ed., recommends nitrate-nitrogen concentrations less than 11.3 mg/l for drinking water. An upper limit of 22.6 mg/l is, however, considered to be acceptable providing local health authorities are informed so that problems arising with infants may be readily recognized.) An extensive field exploration program, prompted by concerned governmental agencies, was undertaken by the Water Research Centre to determine the extent of pollution of main aquifers and their overlying unsaturated zones; relationships between rock types, climatic variations, land use practices, and fertilizer applications with the rates of accumulation and movement of nitrogen compounds within the unsaturated zones; and relationships between hydrogeological factors and the rates of accumulation and lateral dispersion of nitrogen within the saturated zone.

Borings were located in outcrop areas of chalk (fissured carbonate rock) and sandstone aquifers with an unsaturated zone of at least 20 m in depth. To ensure minimal contamination, dry augering and drive coring techniques were employed to advance the borehole and obtain samples. The interstitial water centrifuged from undisturbed specimens was tested for nitrate and other ions as detailed in the technical reports.[8, 9]

Thirty-seven sites selected in England and Wales included land use types ranging from unfertilized long-term grassland to fertilized arable land. Typical nitrate profiles in the unsaturated zone beneath these two land practices are shown in Figure 5-11. Measurements beneath unfertilized grassland consistently showed interstitial nitrate-nitrogen values below 6 mg/l (Figure 5-11a). In contrast, levels exceed the lower recommended limit for nitrate in the pore water infiltrating when land is cultivated and fertilized to yield cereal crops. The relatively smooth profile in Figure 5-11b is from a field in which cereal was cropped almost continuously for 18 years with uniform fertilizer application from 1957 to 1974.

Profiles under fertilized arable land with long intervals of grass between planting cereals also had amounts greater than 11.3 mg/l in the pore waters of the unsaturated zone. An example from the chalk of Hampshire, given in Figure 5-12, exhibits the broad variations with depth of nitrate concentrations typical beneath this farming practice. Apparently nitrogen accumulations in the grass are released after plowing to create peaks in the profile. This postulate is supported by the distribution of tritium (a natural isotope of hydrogen) in the chalk revealing that nitrate percolates downward at about one metre per year. Prior to 1949 the Hampshire site was permanent grassland; the leading edge of the high-nitrate interstitial water was measured about 35 m below the ground surface 26 years later in 1975.

Excess fertilization can leach nitrate into groundwater but, even with appropriate applications, nitrate levels are high under cultivated land. Organic residues remaining in a field after harvest are susceptible to mineralization and nitrification by bacteria. During the nongrowing season in northern Europe, rainfall infiltration transports this nitrate into the soil profile. Percolate under grassland generally contains only a few milligrams per litre resulting from year-round uptake by the grass and denitrification in

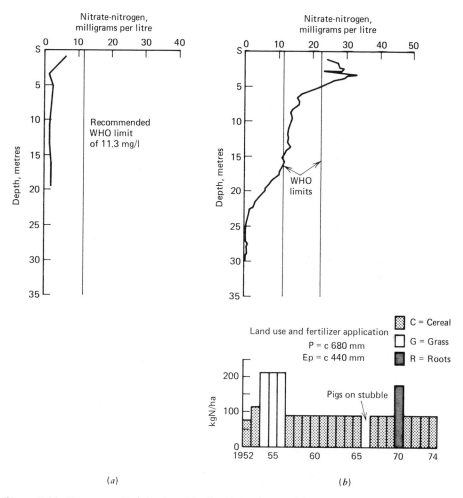

Figure 5-11 Nitrate profiles developed in the Chalk beneath (*a*) unfertilized long-term grassland and (*b*) fertilized arable land with temporary rotations to grassland. The bar graph under profile (*b*) shows the fertilizer application rates in kilograms of nitrogen per hectare and the crops grown each year from 1952 through 1975. *P* is the mean annual rainfall and *Ep* is the estimated evapotranspiration. (From C. P. Young and E. M. Gray, *Nitrate in Groundwater*, TR 69, Water Research Centre, United Kingdom, January 1975.)

the organically rich surface soil. In all cropland, plowing destroys naturally developed soil strata and aerates the lower zones assisting in formation of nitrate. This increases leaching losses during the autumn and winter if the field is cultivated after summer harvest. Plowing of established grassland makes large quantities of accumulated soil organic matter available for mineralization. Rationally relating this to Figure 5-12, the major peaks in pore water are due to large releases of nitrate accompanying plowing of grasslands.

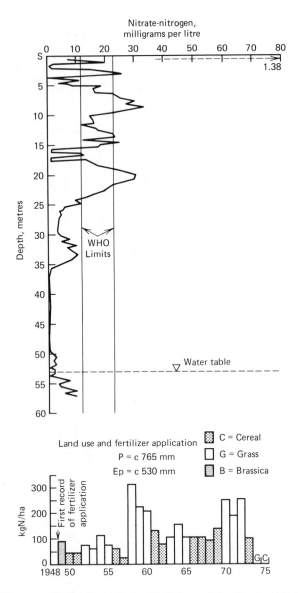

Figure 5-12 Nitrate profile developed in the Chalk beneath fertilized arable land with crop rotation between cereal and grass, as shown by the bar graph of land use and fertilizer application. (From C. P. Young, E. S. Hall, and D. B. Oakes, *Nitrate in Groundwater—Studies on the Chalk near Winchester, Hampshire*, TR 31, Water Research Centre, United Kingdom, September 1976.)

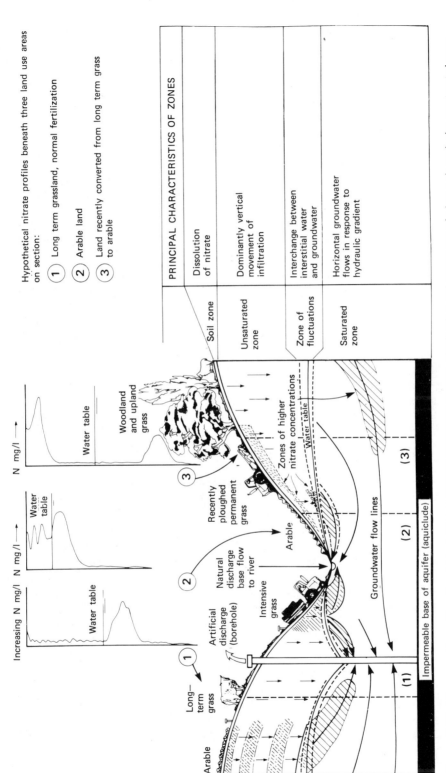

Hypothetical nitrate profiles beneath three land use areas on section:

1️ Long term grassland, normal fertilization
2️ Arable land
3️ Land recently converted from long term grass to arable

PRINCIPAL CHARACTERISTICS OF ZONES	
Soil zone	Dissolution of nitrate
Unsaturated zone	Dominantly vertical movement of infiltration
Zone of fluctuations	Interchange between interstitial water and groundwater
Saturated zone	Horizontal groundwater flows in response to hydraulic gradient

Figure 5-13 Diagrammatic section of a groundwater catchment illustrating possible distribution and movement of nitrate through the unsaturated zone and below the water table. (From C. P. Young and E. M. Gray, *Nitrate in Groundwater*, TR 69, Water Research Centre, United Kingdom, January 1975.)

Boreholes were extended below the water table to collect groundwater samples from the saturated zone. Abrupt changes in nitrate concentration often occurred across the water table resulting from the transition between vertical percolation and horizontal transport. In certain cases, nitrate within the saturated zone varied with depth. At locations with minimum groundwater movement, traverses across the water table showed little or no change in nitrate content, suggesting that interstitial solutions were in equilibrium with the slow-moving groundwater.

Figure 5-13 summarizes the findings of these underground studies on the accumulation and movement of nitrate. Sketches for (1) long-term grassland, (2) arable land, and (3) land recently converted from long-term grass to cultivated crops illustrate interstitial nitrate profiles in the unsaturated zone and concentrations in the saturated zone as influenced by postulated groundwater movements. The surface zone of the soil profile is where dissolution of nitrate takes place along with microbial transformations of nitrogen in organic residues and denitrification. In the unsaturated zone, vertical flow carries dissolved substances to the water table, often migrating downward in a pattern established by land use cycles. Where interstitial water in unsaturated rock mixes with groundwater, sharp changes in nitrate concentrations are possible. Horizontal groundwater movements are in response to hydraulic gradients in the saturated zone, and water layers of different qualities remain distinct because of slow vertical dispersion. Convergence of flow lines to discharge points leads to mixing of waters of differing qualities and age.

As demonstrated by this study, replacement of permanent pasture with cultivated agriculture and use of artificial fertilizer for better yields of cereal crops during the past 30 years has resulted in an increased concentration of nitrogen in groundwater. The nitrate content in interstitial water, migrating downward in the unsaturated zone, commonly exceeds the recommended limit for drinking water; consequently, as this water mixes with storage in the saturated zone, well water will continue to degrade in quality. Unless the land use over porous aquifers is returned to permanent grassland, this is the future trend. However, predicting levels of anticipated nitrate at specific locations is difficult owing to complex hydrogeology.

Assuming the maximum allowable nitrate levels are reached in some regions, the prospect of an easy economical solution is indeterminate. Seeking a new uncontaminated source, either surface water or groundwater, within the region may be one solution. The alternative is treatment by ion exchange—a process still in the developmental stage.[10] Even though technically possible, the feasibility of removing nitrate by ion exchange is likely to be very costly for municipal supplies—particularly, for small communities sited in rural areas.

Brine Contamination from Petroleum Production[11,1]

This case of contamination, resulting from imporper disposal of oil field brine, happened in the flood plain of the Red River in southwestern Arkansas. In 1967, an irrigation well in the alluvial aquifer had to be shutdown when the chloride concentration reached 1100 mg/l. Although most of the test holes and wells in the adjacent oil field had been abandoned, several were still pumping oil and brine. An estimated one-half million cubic metres of salt water had been disposed of first in an evaporation pit and later in a disposal well near the same location. Resulting from the initial pollution survey, an abandoned oil well for subsurface injection was substituted for the pit that seeped brine directly into the alluvium. Later, observations revealed brine escaping through the corroded casing of the abandoned oil well and again entering the aquifer. The final solution was construction of a proper disposal well, which is functioning today.

The extent of pollution, shown by a section through the site in Figure 5-14, was defined by installing 28 observation wells in the area. The soil profile consisted of a 4 m surface stratum of clayey soil topping sand and gravel alluvium extending to a depth of about 12 m, which was underlain by shale. Lateral and vertical distribution of the chloride is shown by the lines of equal concentration sketched through the section. Elongation of the plume toward the south is caused by groundwater flow in that direction. Having a greater density, the brine tends to sink to the base of the aquifer increasing salt content with depth. A submerged layer of water in excess of 500 mg/l salt has spread over the shale stratum covering an area of about 2.6 km². Based on an estimated rate of groundwater flow, the saline water will start discharging to the Red River, 7.2 km down slope, in approximately 250 years.

The initial monetary losses incurred were the irrigation well valued at $4 000 and 48 hectares of one year's rice crop worth $36 000. Assuming 2.6 km² of irrigable land is removed from production, future annual losses would amount to approximately $50 000 depending on the crop grown.

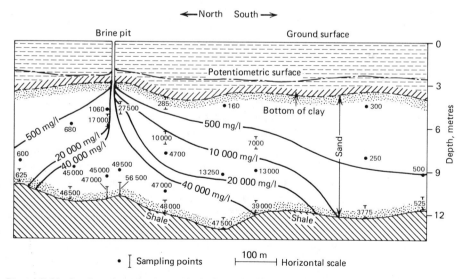

Figure 5-14 Section through the geological strata showing concentrations of chloride in the groundwater of a site contaminated by seepage from a brine disposal pit. (From J. S. Fryberger, "Investigation and Rehabilitation of a Brine-Contaminated Aquifer," *Ground Water*, Vol. 13, March-April 1975. Copyright 1972, Water Well Journal Publishing Company. All rights reserved.)

The two broad courses of action available concerning the contaminated part of the aquifer are to attempt corrective measures or simply warn potential groundwater users in the area and await natural recovery. Fryberger[11] evaluated the economics of rehabilitation by containment, accelerated discharge, withdrawal for use, and deep-well disposal.

The estimated cost of constructing an impermeable subsurface wall to contain the contamination was $7 000 000. Artificial recharge to hasten natural flushing by injection of fresh water into the aquifer upstream was approximately $1 300 000. Extracting the brine using strategically located wells and a pipeline for discharge to the Red River was relatively inexpensive at $180 000, but this process would pollute the river in violation of existing regulations. The ways of using salty water included blending for agricultural use, but no one wanted even slightly salty water for irrigation; and desalinization at excessive cost. Disposal through deep-well injection appeared to be technically feasible and the most economically acceptable technique with cost estimates ranging from $290 000 to $450 000 for the required 17-year operation. However, from the calculated negative public benefit-cost ratios, the author considers rehabilitation economically unjustified and goes on to stress the higher priority of funds to seek and prevent groundwater contamination.

Heavy Metal Pollution from Mine Wastes[12]

The Canyon Creek basin, located in the Coeur d'Alene River basin of Idaho, has been a mining area for over 85 years. Prior to 1968, wastes generated by concentrating plants were discharged directly to Canyon Creek. Following the installation of tailings ponds to reduce surface water pollution, this study investigates the increase of heavy metals observed in the groundwater of the canyon basin.

The steep narrow valley, with an area of about 50 km², has a small population supported by the mining industry. In the lower valley, alluvial sediments of unconsolidated sand and gravel with unknown depth cover the bedrock. Spread over this natural alluvium are extensive deposits of coarse wastes from early day mining, which are high in metal content. These jig tailings were generated from simple wooden concentration boxes used to separate heavy grains from light grains in water suspension. Jigging was inefficient and produced tailings with substantial concentrations of zinc, lead, and other metals. As shown in Figure 5-15, two settling ponds for the current mill and mine wastes were construced in the upper portion of the valley area in 1968.

Leakage from the waste ponds raised the water table increasing flow from small springs and created new seepages that discharge throughout most of the year. Concern for water quality led to testing of these discharges as well as both the inflow and outflow of the settling ponds for heavy metals, including cadmium, lead, and zinc. In some cases, the springs and groundwater contained concentrations of these toxins in excess of the health limits for drinking water. Effluent and leakage from the ponds were initially suspected as the source; however, that speculation was soon dismissed by the data. Zinc in the pond water was slightly greater than 1 mg/l while downslope seepages ranged from 6 to 37 mg/l, and Canyon Creek water above the ponds was about 3 mg/l while the downstream increased only to approximately 6 mg/l. The same

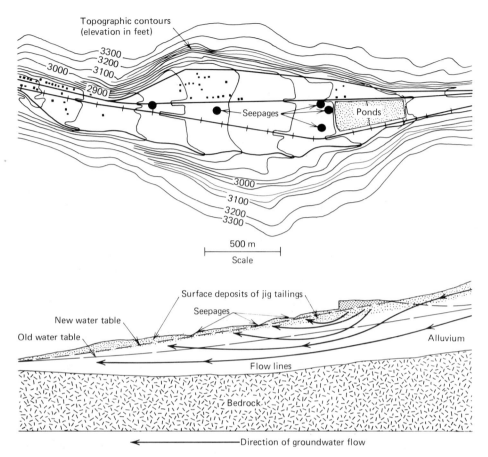

Figure 5-15 Contoured plan and section of Canyon Creek valley showing the location of the settling ponds, direction of groundwater flow, approximate positions of seepages, and descriptive soil profile. (Adapted from L. L. Mink, R. E. Williams, and A. T. Wallace, "Effect of Early Day Mining Operations on Present Day Water Quality," *Ground Water*, Vol. 10, January-February 1972. Copyright 1972, Water Well Journal Publishing Company. All rights reserved.)

relationships existed for concentrations of cadmium and lead—much greater amounts in groundwater seeping from the valley floor than the pond water. The most plausible explanation is based on the following events. First, the rising water table caused by recharge from the ponds saturated old mine tailings containing substantial amounts of heavy metals. Next, groundwater percolating through these deposits turned acid by the solubilization and oxidation of sulfides, which hastened the dissolution of heavy metals. These findings illustrate an unique situation of impurities from old wastes being introduced back into the water environment through inadvertent raising of the water table by instituting ponds to remedy a water pollution problem (Figure 5-15).

Remedial actions included warning the people not to consume the water, primarily because of the lead content, and constructing trenches to lower the water table.

Trenches are expected to reduce the flow from springs and drop the groundwater level below the old jig tailings. Consideration is being given to modifying the settling ponds to reduce groundwater recharge. In their final statement reporting this study, the authors stressed the advisability of thoroughly evaluating an area to accurately delineate the role of a proposed waste disposal facility before construction.[12]

Increased Dissolved Solids from Groundwater Recharge[13]

The Orange County Water District, located south of Los Angeles in the semiarid coastal plain of California, encompasses an area of 816 km² supporting a largely urban population of 1.5 million. Originally, local water was drawn from natural flows of the Santa Ana River and wells in the groundwater basin, which has an areal extent of about 800 km². With increasing consumption, the river supply diminished and demand for groundwater exceeded natural recharge resulting in mining (overdrafting) and gradual lowering of the water table in the basin. Beginning in the early 1940s, water imported from the Colorado River by an aqueduct was available for direct service to cities within the county by purchase from the Metropolitan Water District of Southern California. Yet most of the numerous cities and water agencies within the county continued to withdraw substantial groundwater causing gradual depletion of underground storage. In 1949, the district initiated groundwater recharge by surface spreading of water drawn from the Colorado River aqueduct. At the peak overdraft condition in 1956, traces of seawater were found as far inland as 6 km resulting in increased salinity of water supplies and loss of municipal water wells. Despite this, surface recharging rejuvenated the groundwater basin by 1969.

The California State Water Project provided another source for the Metropolitan Water District with the completion of the aqueduct from northern California in 1973. This is a less reliable supply with upstream users having a high priority during periods of water shortage. (This occurred during the drought conditions of 1977 in California.) Nevertheless, during periods of abundant supply, large quantities can be purchased for recharging the basin in Orange County to meet demand over long-cyclic periods. The need for future water conservation and reuse are still anticipated, since the allotment from the Colorado River will be reduced by one-half in 1985 upon completion of the aqueduct for diversion to Arizona. Currently, about 40 percent of all consumption is imported water directly supplied, mostly from the Colorado River aqueduct, and 60 percent is groundwater. The natural flows of the Santa Ana River combined with local precipitation (a mean of 340 mm annually) yields approximately 25 percent of the total water demand. Thus, a substantial amount of imported water—over one-third of the consumption—must be used to recharge underground storage to prevent excessive mining of the groundwater.

Figure 5-16 shows the boundaries of the Orange County Water District, gives names of the encompassed cities, locates the Santa Ana River, labels groundwater recharge facilities and seawater intrusion barriers, and places the county within California on an inserted diagram.

Groundwater recharge reduces the cost of water by eliminating treatment, the need for pipe networks to convey potable supplies, and reducing the requirement for

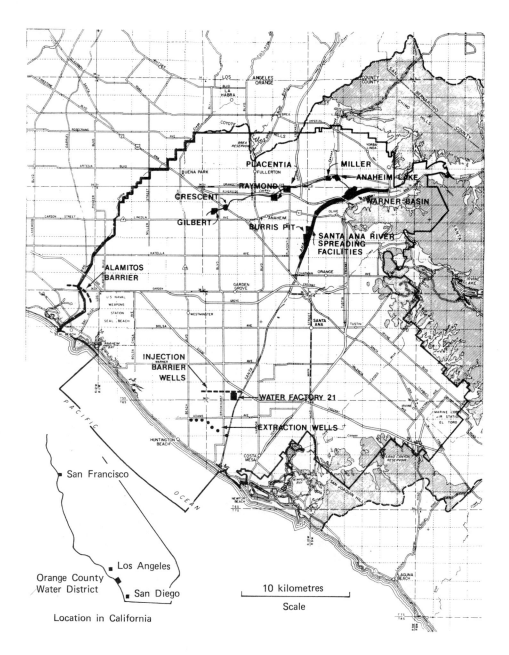

Figure 5-16 A plan showing the groundwater recharge facilities and seawater intrusion barriers of Orange County Water District, California. (From the Annual Report, Orange County Water District, 1976.)

storage reservoirs. The highest rates of percolation are located at inland sites surrounding the upper reaches of the Santa Ana River and its tributaries (Figure 5-16).
The district owns approximately 1 200 ha of land used primarily for groundwater
recharge. About one-third is located in Orange County, with 300 ha situated within
the Santa Ana River and 120 ha nearby that includes two large off-channel impoundments. The spreading facilities are designed to store base flows in the river as the
highest priority with collection of storm flows and imported waters being secondary.

The river is divided into two channels, one primarily for groundwater recharge and
the other doubling for water recharge and storm flow channelization. The 100-m wide
storm channel operates with low height temporary levees that can wash out during
high-velocity storm flows. In the remaining portions of the channel, permanent ponds

Figure 5-17 Aerial view of the Warner Basin adjacent to the Santa Ana River (looking toward the
southwest) in the northeastern area of the Orange County Water District; the location is given on
Figure 5-16. The riverbed serves the dual purposes of providing percolation area and flood control:
The left side of the channel contains temporary L-shaped levees bulldozed into position from the
riverbed; on the right are offstream ponds separated by dikes with concrete structures to control
and measure flow. The large impoundment is the Warner Basin constructed for artifical recharge
by excavating and selling the sand and gravel. River water enters the impoundment by gravity flow
through smaller desilting basins. Sand and gravel operations for expanding the recharge area can
be seen in the picture below the existing basins. (Courtesy of Orange County Water District.)

are constructed to save greater amounts of storm flow without damage. Diversion structures allow flow into the protected conservation basins. A major off-channel facility, viewed in Figure 5-17, is a large complex of desilting and percolation basins with the largest (Warner Basin) having a surface area of 45 ha and a depth of 15 m. Turbid river water is clarified in the desilting ponds prior to entering the main recharge basin to allow for greater infiltration rates and a longer period of operation prior to cleaning. Anaheim Lake, a few kilometres north of this site, and the Warner Basin can receive imported Colorado River water, Northern California State Project water, or natural flows of the Santa Ana River. The master plan for spreading grounds within Orange County optimizes the conservation of both natural runoff and imported waters.

Lowering the water table below sea level, by extensive pumping of the ground-water basin, can cause seawater intrusion along four major areas of the coastline where geologic continuity exists between the ocean and the groundwater basin. Two of these, Talbert and Alamitos, with free access to the ocean have experienced significant historical seawater intrusion; however, based on geologic data, the other gaps appear to be sealed from direct ocean flows by the Newport-Inglewood fault. The Alamitos barrier project, a cooperative effort between Orange County and Los Angeles County, consists of single point injection wells located approximately 3 km inland from the mouth of the San Gabriel River (Figure 5-16). Operation began in 1965 and uses imported water for injection.

The Orange County coastal barrier prevents saltwater encroachment across a 5-km front between Newport Beach and Huntington Beach known as Talbert Gap, which is the mouth of an alluvial fan formed millions of years ago by the Santa Ana River and later buried under clay strata. The hydraulic barrier system, illustrated in Figure 5-18, consists of two separate well fields. First, seven extraction wells approximately 3 km from the coast intercept and return brackish water to the ocean, and a second series of 23 injection wells further inland deliver fresh water to the underground aquifers to form a water mound blocking further passage of seawater.

The injection water is a blended combination of reclaimed wastewater and deep-well water. The wastewater is reclaimed by advanced treatment of secondary effluent in Water Factory 21. Processing of 57 000 m^3/d consists of lime clarification, ammonia stripping, recarbonation, mixed-media filtration, activated carbon adsorption, and chlorination. One-third of this flow is reduced in dissolved solids content by reverse osmosis. Deep wells penetrating aquifers from 300 m to 360 m deep, not subject to seawater intrusion, pump low-salinity water for blending with the treated wastewater. The regulatory limit of 120 mg/l chloride concentration is achieved by mixing approximately equal portions of reclaimed wastewater and deep-well water.

The injection wells have separate casings screened at different depths so that flow to each aquifer can be controlled. Since groundwater quality is influenced by extraction and recharge, both natural and artificial, the district monitors 25 key wells in the basin for the normal dissolved minerals and heavy metals including arsenic, barium, boron, manganese, cadmium, chromium, copper, lead, mercury, and selenium. Problem

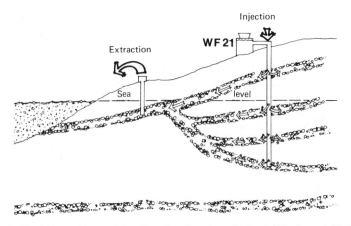

Figure 5-18 Cross section of coastal aquifers showing the scheme at Santa Ana (Talbert Gap) coastal barrier for preventing seawater intrusion by injecting fresh water inland and extracting salt water near the ocean to form a hydraulic barrier. (From the Annual Report, Orange County Water District, 1976.)

constituents appearing in localized areas are nitrates and selenium. The latter is apparently due to natural formations, while the high nitrates are believed to be a result of urban and agricultural land practices. The key long-term problem in the Orange County basin is the buildup in total dissolved solids content.

Over the last 20 years, a continual accumulation of salts in the basin has resulted in increasing salinity of the groundwater; the trend in well water from the city of Anaheim is graphed in Figure 5-19. The major impact on salt balance relates to imported water, which amounts to approximately 75 percent of the supply. Prior to 1973, the primary source of recharge water was the Colorado River with a dissolved solids content between 700 and 750 mg/l; hence, the increase in salinity corresponding to increased recharge of imported water. The decrease of salt content commencing in 1974 corresponds directly with a shift of imported water from the Colorado River to the aqueduct supply from northern California. Between 1974 and 1976, about two-thirds of the water purchased by Orange County for groundwater recharge came from this relatively low-salinity source containing about 250 mg/l of dissolved solids. During 1976, flows of state water combined with natural runoff in the Santa Ana River entered Orange County with an average concentration of 430 mg/l. Potable water piped to consumers by local water agencies is a blend of imported water from the Metropolitan Water District and pumped groundwater. During 1975-1976, the average dissolved solids content was 500 mg/l, also reflecting the greater use of northern California water.

The Orange County District reports the estimated salt balance for the basin each fiscal year. The major inputs are streamflow of the Santa Ana River; imported water for irrigation, domestic supply, and recharge; and the salts applied with fertilizers. Dissolved solids are lost through withdrawal of groundwater, which appears as wastewater sewered to the ocean, and subsurface flow to the Los Angeles basin. Each

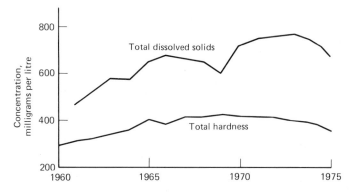

Figure 5-19 Trends in the dissolved solids and hardness in groundwater from a city well in Anaheim, Orange County, California. (Adapted from J. R. Cofer and L. W. Owen, "Solving the Adverse Salt Balance in the Orange County Ground-Water Basin," *Journal American Water Works Association*, Vol. 67, September 1975. Reprinted with permission of the American Water Works Association, copyrighted 1975.)

year, since initiation of the massive recharge program using Colorado River water, the basin has realized a net increase in salt. The 1975-1976 data show an addition of 203 000 tonnes and removal of 129 000 t, leaving a net increase of 74 000 t. This was 38 000 t less than the fiscal year 1974-1975, which is directly attributable to reduced salinity of the imported water.

Several concepts have been evaluated for solving the adverse salt balance.[14] Greater use of northern California water is strongly recommended. Currently, a 50-50 blend yields an acceptable supply of about 500 mg/l; however, the dissolved solids in the Colorado River are expected to increase in the future, perhaps to over 1 000 mg/l. The coupled effects of potential limited availability of northern California water and increasing salinity of Colorado River water can limit any reduction of salt input. Approximately 15 percent of the basin's dissolved solids tonnage is attributable to fertilization practice in citrus and other crops grown in Orange County. Excess application of irrigation water drives salts into the water table. Although a costly option, tile drains can be used to intercept the infiltration for conveying to disposal in the ocean.

Preventing percolation of inadequately treated wastewater by discharge to upstream surface watercourses is of primary concern, since dissolved solids concentrations are in the 1 000 to 1 500 mg/l range. Some processed wastewaters are therefore conveyed to the ocean for disposal. A principal water-quality feature of the basin plan is construction of a 110 000 m³/d sewer to intercept wastewaters entering the Santa Ana River above Orange County. The line extends from western San Bernardino and Riverside Counties to the ocean. Other pipeline projects being studied are collection of dairy wastes and saline irrigation waters. Desalting by reverse osmosis to produce a low salinity water, with the brine discharged to the ocean, is another consideration. Even though the process is technically possible, desalting either wastewater or groundwater is very costly because of the high energy consumption.

References

1. *The Report to Congress, Waste Disposal Practices and Their Effects on Ground Water*, U. S. Environmental Protection Agency, Office of Water Supply, Office of Solid Waste Management Programs, January 1977.

2. *Ground-Water Pollution Problems in the Northwestern United States*, Ecological Research Series, EPA-660/3-75-018, U. S. Environmental Protection Agency, Corvallis, Oregon, May 1975.

3. *Groundwater Pollution Problems in the Southeastern United States*, Ecological Research Series, EPA-600/3-77-012, U. S. Environmental Protection Agency, Ada, Oklahoma, January 1977.

4. *Ground Water Pollution in the South Central States*, Environmental Protection Technology Series, EPA-R2-73-268, U. S. Environmental Protection Agency, Corvallis, Oregon, June 1973.

5. *Ground Water Contamination in the Northeast States*, Environmental Protection Technology Series, EPA-660/2-74-056, U. S. Environmental Protection Agency, Washington, D.C., June 1974.

6. Hammer, M. J., *Water and Waste-Water Technology, SI Version*, John Wiley & Sons, Inc., New York, 1977.

7. Sanks, R. L., and Asano, T., *Land Treatment and Disposal of Municipal and Industrial Wastewater*, Ann Arbor Science Publishers, Inc., Ann Arbor, Michigan, 1976.

8. Young, C. P., Hall, E. S., and Oakes, D. B., *Nitrate in Groundwater—Studies on the Chalk near Winchester, Hampshire*, Technical Report TR31, Resources Division, Water Research Centre, United Kingdom, September 1976.

9. Young, C. P., and Gray, E. M., *Nitrate in Groundwater*, Technical Report TR69, Resources Division, Water Research Centre, United Kingdom, January 1978.

10. Sorg, T. J., "Treatment Technology to Meet the Interim Primary Drinking Water Regulations for Inorganics," *Journal American Water Works Association*, Vol. 70, No. 2, February 1978, pp. 105-112.

11. Fryberger, J. S., "Investigation and Rehabilitation of a Brine-Contaminated Aquifer," *Ground Water*, Vol. 13, No. 2, March-April 1975, pp. 155-160.

12. Mink, L. L., Williams, R. E., and Wallace, A. T., "Effect of Early Day Mining Operations on Present Day Water Quality," *Ground Water*, Vol. 10, No. 1, January-February 1972, pp. 17-26.

13. The Annual Report, Orange County Water District, Fountain Valley, California, 1977.

14. Cofer, J. R., and Langdon, W. O., " Solving the Adverse Salt Balance in Orange County Ground-Water Basin," *Journal American Water Works Association*, Vol. 67, No. 9, September 1975, pp. 481-486.

Problems

5-1   List the sources of groundwater contamination illustrated in Figure 5-1. What are the routes of pollution shown?

5-2   Does percolate from a recharge pond mix with the entire mass of groundwater under the site?

5-3   What are the primary concerns regarding degradation of groundwater for (a) domestic consumption and (b) agricultural use? What are the principal pollutants in each case?

5-4   What are the major causes of outbreaks of waterborne disease resulting from contamination of public groundwater supplies?

5-5   In natural pollution, how does groundwater increase in (a) dissolved solids and (b) fluoride content?

5-6   The groundwater profile of a site consists of a freshwater stratum overlying a formation containing salty water. How can heavy pumping of shallow wells adversely affect water quality?

5-7   Briefly describe the operation of a household wastewater disposal system consisting of a septic tank and absorption field.

5-8   What health-related pollutants are most likely to enter groundwater from a household disposal system as shown in Figure 5-6?

5-9   Name the pollutants most likely to enter groundwater in significant amounts from (a) land disposal of wastewater and (b) burial of municipal solid wastes.

5-10   Approximately what percentage of industrial waste is disposed of on land? What are the three popular methods of handling nonreclaimable wastewaters and sludges?

5-11   What are the acceptable ways to dispose of oil-field brines?

5-12   Describe the hydrogeological conditions associated with underground mining that may contribute to degradation of groundwater.

5-13   Under what site conditions is strip mining of coal in the semiarid western states likely to degrade groundwater quality?

5-14   What is the most common group of contaminates in accidental spills? What characteristics of these compounds make them so damaging?

5-15   Describe the process of salt buildup in agricultural soils caused by irrigation in arid regions. How can groundwater and surface waters be adversely affected?

5-16   Why is nitrate rather than phosphate or pesticides the dominant pollutant related to groundwater contamination from agriculture?

5-17   Why is prevention of contamination the only feasible approach to groundwater quality management? Where is this concept indicated in Figure 5-10?

5-18   What are the functions of groundwater quality monitoring as (a) an early warning, (b) intermediate warning, and (c) last warning?

5-19   Refer to the nitrate infiltration study conducted in the United Kingdom. Describe the technique for obtaining samples of the interstitial water from the chalk and sandstone aquifers.

5-20   Explain why the nitrate profiles in Figure 5-11 are shaped as shown.

5-21   In Figure 5-12, what is the correlation between the changes in the land use and fertilizer application diagram and the pattern of the nitrate profile?

5-22   Review the three nitrogen profiles shown in the upper portion of Figure 5-13 and groundwater movements illustrated in the site profile below. Explain the variations in the nitrate profiles below the water table.

5-23   In the case history of brine contamination, how did the brine waste enter the alluvial aquifer after the evaporation pit was taken out of service?

5-24   Why does the chloride concentration in the groundwater increase with depth as shown in Figure 5-14?

5-25   What method appears to be most economical for rehabilitation of the brine-polluted aquifer? Is this likely to be done?

5-26   In the case of heavy metal pollution of Canyon Creek basin, how were the metal ions from old jig tailings transported into springs and groundwater?

5-27   How was the problem of groundwater contamination in Canyon Creek basin resolved?

5-28   Name the sources of water for Orange County, California.

5-29   What are the major advantages of recharging groundwater with surface waters rather than using imported water and local runoff directly for municipal supplies?

5-30   Viewing Figure 5-17, describe the recharge system employed along the Santa Ana River channel.

5-31   Describe the physical layout and operation of the Santa Ana coastal barrier.

5-32   How does the source of recharge water affect the salinity of the groundwater in Orange County?

5-33   What measures (a) have been taken or (b) are being evaluated to improve the salt balance of the basin?

Chapter 6
Hydrology of
Flowing Waters

Precipitation is the source of all flowing waters, and therefore the opening discussions of this chapter describe the distribution, occurrence, and magnitude of rainfall and snowfall. Data from the measurements of precipitation can be used to estimate flow records in the absence of observed streamflow. Sample calculations are given to illustrate methods of adjusting precipitation records and computing the average rainfall over an area using individual gage measurements.

Since most hydrologic measurements are random samples, statistical techniques are employed to express the enormous amount of data in simple and practical terms for evaluating engineering projects. Instead of isolating the presentation on statistics, the sections following precipitation incorporate discussions on probability and normal distributions with sample computations employing precipitation data. Nonnormal distributions of hydrologic data and linear regressions are illustrated using streamflow records.

Only a portion of precipitation reaches a stream; therefore, Section 6-10 describes the factors affecting runoff—interception, infiltration, and basin characteristics. Infiltration has the greatest effect on amount of runoff and is important in estimating streamflow from precipitation records.

Measuring streamflow to accumulate accurate long-term records is of vital importance for adequate design, evaluation, and operation of water resource projects. The subject of streamflow measurements is subdivided into stream gaging stations, current metering, and indirect techniques such as the slope-area and contracted section methods, and flow over a weir or dam. The subsequent discussion on rating curves for gaging stations includes sample computations at sites with variable energy gradients. Section 6-17 on streamflow-duration curves concludes the discourse on measurements by applying statistical analyses to streamflow records.

Flow records are usually not available at all sites requiring evaluation, thus, methods are needed for extending or computing hydrographs and other flow characteristics at ungaged sites. The unit hydrograph theory can be used to compute the time-discharge relationship of surface runoff from observed rainfall. Where unit graphs cannot be developed owing to a lack of data, synthetic unit hydrographs are prepared by several empirical methods. Section 6-21 illustrates the application of unit hydrograph computations. Finally, flow models of the parametric type that generate records to supplement or substitute for observed flow data are presented.

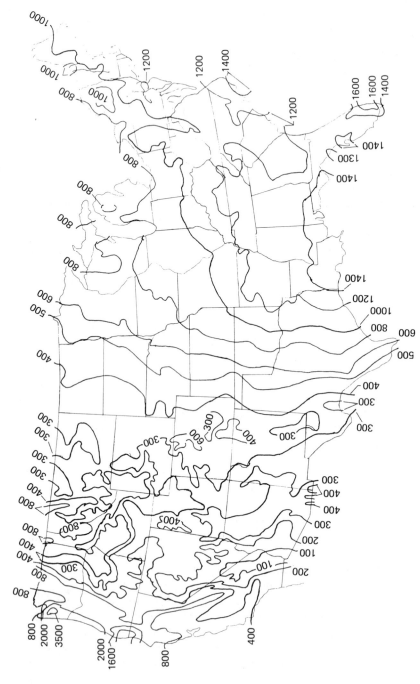

Figure 6-1 Average annual precipitation in millimetres in the conterminous United States. Note the orographic effect along the western side of the Coast Range in Washington and Oregon. (From *Weather Atlas of the United States*, United States Environmental Data Service, 1968.)

Protection from floods is a major concern in water resources management. The text includes sections that describe the probability and frequency of floods; flood routing, which is the timing and shape of a flood wave as it moves downstream; and methods for control of floods.

A stream carves a channel to fit its flow, energy gradient, and sediment load. Section 6-26 is concerned with some of the aftereffects of regulation or diversion of a stream.

6-1 Precipitation

Precipitation is the discharge of water out of the atmosphere and includes rain, snow, hail, and sleet. It is the source of all water flowing in streams and in storage above and below ground. The quantity and variability of streamflow is clearly dependent on the amount, intensity, and distribution of precipitation. If streamflow data are not available, precipitation records can be used to estimate streamflow.

Precipitation occurs when air containing moisture cools sufficiently to cause part of the water vapor to condense on hydroscopic nuclei, which are small particles having an affinity for water. The droplets coalesce until sufficiently large to overcome the frictional resistance of falling. The only known mechanism for cooling air sufficiently to cause available precipitation is pressure reduction when air near the earth's surface ascends to high levels. The rate and quantity of precipitation depends on the rate and amount of cooling and the moisture content of the air.

Lifting of the air can be caused by topographic barriers, thermal convection, or from frontal action and convergence of air currents. Lifting of air over topographic barriers causes orographic precipitation, which is greater on the windward side of the barrier than on the leeward side. For example, precipitation in western Oregon and Washington is orographic as illustrated in Figure 6-1. Orographic precipitation is ordinarily of light intensity. Convective precipitation is caused by unequal heating of the air mass near the earth. The warmed air, and therefore the lightest air, lifts and cools. Convective precipitation ranges from moderate to cloudbursts. Cyclonic precipitation can be caused either by warm air lifting over a wedge of cold air, or be associated with a cyclone. The latter is a large rotating mass of air several hundred kilometres in diameter with a low-pressure area at the center causing air to lift. Cyclonic precipitation is usually light to moderate.

Measuring Precipitation

Precipitation is measured in both nonrecording and recording gages as water depth with respect to time. Snow measurements are reported as depth of snow and as water equivalent. The U. S. Weather Service standard nonrecording precipitation gage, illustrated in Figure 6-2, consists of a 203-mm diameter collector having a knife-sharp edge, a receiver, an overflow chamber, and a measuring stick. Precipitation is caught in the collector and funneled into the receiver, which is a brass tube having a cross-sectional area one-tenth that of the collector. Precipitation accumulated in the receiver is measured with a stick graduated in millimetres. Any overflow from the receiver is

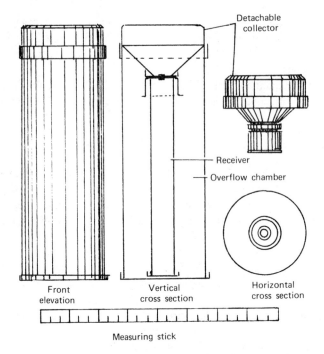

Figure 6-2 A nonrecording precipitation gage consists of a collector, receiver, overflow chamber, and measuring stick. The detachable collector fits on top of the receiving tube, which is located in the overflow chamber. The inside area of the receiver is equal to one-tenth of the collector area.

held in the overflow chamber and poured into the receiver for measuring. If snow is expected, the collector and receiver are removed and the snowfall accumulates in the overflow chamber. The observer commonly takes the overflow chamber into a warm area to melt the snow, and then measures the water equivalent in the receiver with the measuring stick.

Three types of recording precipitation gages are in common use: tipping bucket, float, and weighing. The weighing gage is suitable for measuring rain and snow, whereas the tipping bucket only measures rain and the float gage is not as satisfactory as the weighing gage for measuring snow. A weighing gage is shown in Figure 6-3. Precipitation is caught in the funnel-shaped collector and diverted to a bucket resting on the scale. As the weight of the catch increases, the pen moves across a recorder chart mounted on the drum that is rotated by a timer. Maximum recording capabilities range from 150 to 600 mm, and chart speeds range from a turn per day to a turn per month.

Wind blowing across a precipitation gage affects the quantity of snow collected. Because of an inaccurate catch in a gage, snow may be measured on a snow board laid in a sheltered place on the ground or on old snow. The board should be protected from drifting snow yet far enough away from any obstruction affecting the catch. Depth of snow may be measured with a graduated stick and the collector from the precipitation gage can be used to cut a sample of snow from the board. This is melted

Figure 6-3 A weighing-type recording precipitation gage shown with a detail of the weighing mechanism removed from inside the housing on the left. Precipitation is collected in the cylinder on top and falls into a bucket resting on a scale platform. As the weight of the precipitation increases, the pen on the arm projecting from the weighing mechanism moves across the chart from bottom to top. A timer inside rotates the recorder drum, generally at a rate of one revolution per week. (Courtesy of Belfort Instrument Company.)

and the equivalent water measured in the rain gage receiver. U. S. Weather Service climatic observers report accumulated snow daily. The accumulated snow includes the unmelted previous snow and the current snowfall.

A precipitation gage causes turbulent air currents, thereby causing part of the rainfall to pass the gage, and the amount missed varies directly with wind velocity. Koschmieder[1] compared the catch in an exposed gage with a buried unit that was protected from splash. Figure 6-4 shows that normal upright gage catch is only 30 percent of the true rainfall at a wind speed of 16 m/s. The adverse effect of wind on snow is greater than on rain. By using data of previous investigators, Weiss[2] prepared the graph in Figure 6-5 showing the ratio of snow catch in unshielded and shielded gages is 0.20 at wind speeds of 75 km/h.

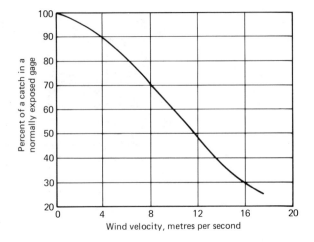

Figure 6-4 Percentage of rain caught in an unshielded gage at wind speeds up to 16 m/s compared to a buried gage protected from splash. (From H. Koschmieder, "Methods and Results of Definite Rain Measurements," *Monthly Weather Review*, 1934.)

Precipitation gages should be protected from wind in all directions. If placed near trees or buildings, overhead obstructions should be at a vertical angle of at least 30° from the gage but not more than 45°. However, suitable areas protected by trees or buildings are not always available, and precipitation gages in exposed sites should be equipped with a windshield. The U. S. Weather Service uses an Alter shield shown in Figure 6-6, nevertheless, even this windshield cannot protect against severe winds. Richards and Larson[3] experimented in a windswept area of Wyoming with gages protected by a wooden slat snow fence having 50 percent open area. The gages were

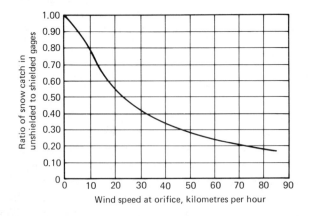

Figure 6-5 Percentage of snow catch in unshielded compared to shielded gages for various wind speeds at the gage orifice up to 85 km/h. (Adapted from L. L. Weiss, "Relative Catches of Snow in Shielded and Unshielded Gages," *Monthly Weather Review*, 1961.)

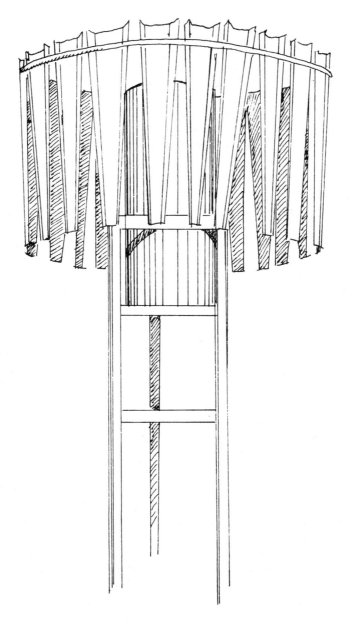

Figure 6-6 The Alter precipitation gage windshield reduces air turbulence over the orifice of a precipitation gage, thus reducing the quantity of water carried past the gage.

placed a distance of five times the height of the fence downwind from the fence. An unprotected gage and another protected by trees, meeting Weather Service installation standards, were used as controls. All units were equipped with Alter shields. The catch in the gages protected by the fence was about the same as in the gage installed among the trees, hence, the fence and trees functioned alike. However, the gage unprotected by the fence caught only 68 percent of that in the unit protected by the trees.

A network of distributed rain gages determines the precipitation falling over the network area. Each gage should be located to obtain an accurate measurement at its location, and the distribution over the area should adequately sample the precipitation, taking into consideration factors like variations in topography. Despite this, gages in networks are seldom spaced close enough to measure high-intensity storms. "Bucket surveys" made by measuring the catch in any vessel exposed during the storm, can be made to estimate the precipitation between regular gages in a network. Typical vessels are buckets, barrels or tanks, tubs, or jars. The survey should be made promptly to avoid loss by evaporation or emptying of containers.

Good judgment is required to interpret observations and reduce inaccuracies caused by poor exposure. For example, the measurement may be greater than the rainfall by including drip from overhead tree limbs. The catch in full containers that possibly overflowed should be qualified as being the observed measure or greater. If the opening of a vessel is not level, the horizontal projection of the opening should be measured before disturbing it. Many containers have sloping sides or irregular shapes. In these, the catch is most easily measured by pouring the contents into a calibrated container and then adjusting the measured volume for the size of opening. Photographs of vessels in their undisturbed locations are helpful in evaluating the effect of surroundings and angle of the opening on the catch.

6-2 Snow Surveys

Snow accumulations shown in Figure 6-7 are important sources of streamflow, especially in the Rocky Mountain area and New England. Consequently, a hydrologist in these regions is often more interested in the water equivalent of accumulated snow than the snowfall of individual storms. Accumulations of importance are generally at headwaters of streams remote from potential observers; therefore, special snow surveys are made in these areas. Snow packs are highly variable due to drifting and nonuniform melting. Although the amount varies seasonally and annually, accumulations follow a rather general pattern for large areas having similar elevations and exposure. Therefore, survey results can be used as an index to runoff by correlating historical survey data with corresponding quantities of spring runoff.[4] Since snow accumulation and total precipitation varies substantially with elevation and aspect, snow surveys are made on permanent courses at fixed measuring sites.

Snow courses are selected during the winter so areas subject to extreme drifting can be identified and avoided, whereas measuring points on the courses are located during the summer to avoid drainageways of meltwater or seeps. They should be on moderately steep slopes with a series of courses extending from a low level in the basin to-

Figure 6-7 Average annual snowfall in the conterminous United States in millimetres. Note the heavy amounts in the Northern Rocky Mountains and New England. (From *Weather Atlas of the United States*, United States Environmental Data Service, 1968.)

ward the headwater. Typically the elevation difference between courses is 150 to 300 m.[4] North-facing slopes accumulate the maximum snow and provide desirable sites; in contrast, winter melting may occur on south and west slopes.

The depth and water equivalent of the snow is measured at each sampling site with a sampler consisting of tubular sections connected with threaded couplings (Figure 6-8). The lower section has a steel cutting bit to facilitate penetrating ice lenses. The tube is pushed into the snow pack with a minimum of turning, employing a driving wrench as necessary to penetrate hard compacted snow or layers of ice. When the sampler reaches the bottom, the depth of the pack is read from graduations on the tube. The water equivalent of the pack is measured by weighing the sampler and contents after withdrawal.

Other methods have been devised to obtain snow pack information, since travel on snow courses is often difficult and time consuming. Markers read from low-flying

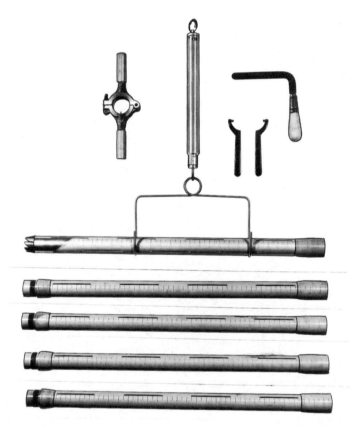

Figure 6-8 The bottom section of a snow sampler is shown resting suspended from a scale in weighing position. The left end is toothed to facilitate cutting through ice layers and sections are graduated to measure the depth of snow. The handle at the left is to turn the sampler as it is pushed into the snow, and the tool at the right is to assist in removing the snow core. (Courtesy of Leupold and Stevens, Inc.)

aircraft have been used, and remote sensing devices are being developed. One such unit, called a snow pillow, is being designed to measure water equivalent by indirectly weighing snowfall.[4] The pillow is a flat fluid container made of metal, rubber, rubber fabric, or neoprene filled with antifreeze and ranging in area from 6 to 37 m^2. A metal unit is 1.3 to 3.8 cm thick when filled, whereas the others are 5 to 10 cm thick. Pressure transducers, electrical converters, or mechanical floats translate the snow load into water equivalent. When equipped for radio transmission, these devices can be programmed to transmit on a schedule.

Gamma emissions, another means of remote sensing, were investigated by Gerdel, Hansen, and Cassidy[5]. The emission source was 40 millicuries of the radioisotope cobalt 60 imbedded in the ground. The gamma emissions, not absorbed by the overlying snow, were measured with a Geiger-Muller tube suspended 4.57 m above the source. Pulses from the tubes were transmitted to a laboratory by radio. Up to 1.4 m water equivalent were measured by this technique.

6-3   Adjusting Precipitation Records

Occasionally, climatic observation stations are moved for convenience of the observer without changing the station's name or noting the change in the record. The records at the various sites may not be equivalent due to differences in elevation or exposure. Therefore, precipitation records should be tested for consistency before use and adjusted if necessary.[6] Example 6-1 illustrates a test and adjustment using a double-mass technique.

Example 6-1

Precipitation records at Flagstaff, Arizona, began in 1915 at a site 2 120 m above mean sea level. The station was moved in 1927 to an elevation of 2 105 m and again in 1944 to an elevation of 2 104 m. Precipitation records available until 1951 are given in Table 6-1. What is the October to April precipitation for the period 1916 to 1951 at the 1944 to 1951 site?

Table 6-1   Seasonal, October to April, Precipitation in Millimetres, at
Flagstaff and Adjacent Stations, 1916-1951, for Example 6-1

Year	Flagstaff		Twelve Control Stations	
	Seasonal (mm)	Cumulative (mm)	Seasonal (mm)	Cumulative (mm)
1951	180	180	100	100
1950	230	410	150	250
1949	400	810	180	430
1948	260	1 070	210	640

Table 6.1 continued

Year	Flagstaff		Twelve Control Stations	
	Seasonal (mm)	Cumulative (mm)	Seasonal (mm)	Cumulative (mm)
1947	150	1 220	100	740
1946	250	1 470	100	840
1945	260	1 730	200	1 040
1944	350	2 080	180	1 220
1943	210	2 290	200	1 420
1942	200	2 490	210	1 630
1941	510	3 000	350	1 980
1940	200	3 200	150	2 130
1939	200	3 400	160	2 290
1938	310	3 710	200	2 490
1937	300	4 010	220	2 710
1936	160	4 170	190	2 900
1935	300	4 470	200	3 100
1934	250	4 720	200	3 300
1933	200	4 920	150	3 450
1932	410	5 330	260	3 710
1931	210	5 540	210	3 920
1930	200	5 740	120	4 040
1929	210	6 050	200	4 240
1928	150	6 200	100	4 340
1927	300	6 500	260	4 600
1926	260	6 760	230	4 830
1925	250	7 010	150	4 980
1924	250	7 260	200	5 180
1923	310	7 570	200	5 380
1922	460	8 030	130	5 510
1921	200	8 230	210	5 720
1920	510	8 740	250	5 970
1919	250	8 990	200	6 170
1918	150	9 140	130	6 300
1917	410	9 550	180	6 480
1916	460	10 010	250	6 730

Solution

Records for 12 nearby stations were selected and each record, when tested for consistency, proved to have year-by-year relationship with the remaining 11. The seasonal precipitation for Flagstaff and the control stations are then accumulated and plotted in Figure 6-9, which shows that changes in gage location affected the records. A

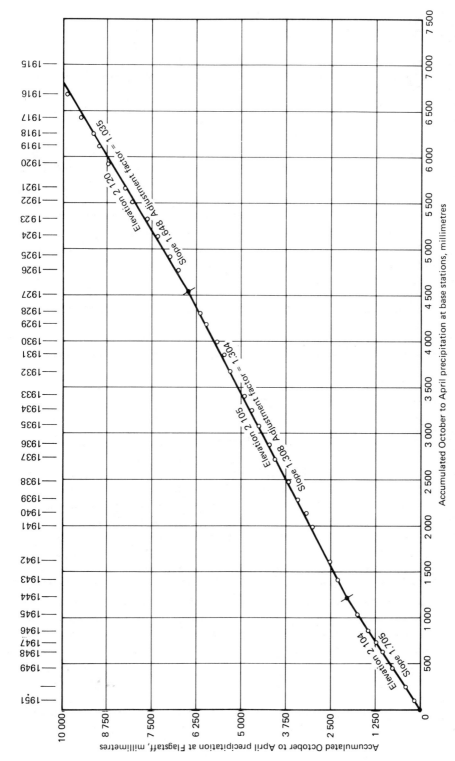

Figure 6-9 Double-mass analysis for adjusting precipitation records for Flagstaff, Arizona, for Example 6-1. (From W. E. Hiatt, *The Analysis of Precipitation Data*, 1953.)

137

broken line drawn through the plotted points changes slope in 1927 and 1944. Slopes of segments of the line are 1.648 for 1916 to 1927, 1.308 for 1927 to 1944, and 1.705 for 1944 to 1951. Adjustment factors equal to the slope during the period 1944-51 divided by the slope during each of the other periods are then calculated as: 1916-26, 1.705/1.648 = 1.035; 1927-43, 1.705/1.308 = 1.304; and, 1944-51, 1.000. The adjusted mean for the period 1916-51 is computed as follows:

Period	Accumulated Precipitation During Period (mm)	Adjustment Factor	Adjusted Accumulated Precipitation (mm)
1944-51	2 080	1.000	2 080
1927-43	4 420	1.304	5 760
1916-26	3 510	1.035	3 630
		Total	11 470

The adjusted average 36-year mean October to April precipitation at the 1916-51 site is 11 470/36 = 318.6 mm.

6-4 Precipitation Over an Area

The solution of a hydrologic problem often requires knowledge of the equivalent uniform depth of precipitation over an area. A simple approximation is to average the depth recorded by all gages in the area. However, if gages are not evenly spaced or the precipitation irregularly distributed, the unweighted average is a poor estimate.

The Thiessen method is a means of weighting the precipitation at gages in proportion to their representative areas. Each gage is assumed to represent all points closer to it than to any other gage. This method is illustrated by Example 6-2.

The isoheytal method, being less rigid than the Thiessen method, permits an analyst to allow for variation in topography or other features that might affect precipitation. Isoheytal lines (lines connecting points of equal precipitation) are located by interpolation between gages, generally by eye, and sketched as smooth curves. Adjustments can be made in locating the isoheytal points between gages for unusual topographic features. The interval between lines depends on the amount of variation of the precipitation and gage density. Example 6-3 applies the isoheytal method.

Example 6-2
Compute mean precipitation for the area shown in Figure 6-10 by the Thiessen method using the precipitation data shown on the diagram.

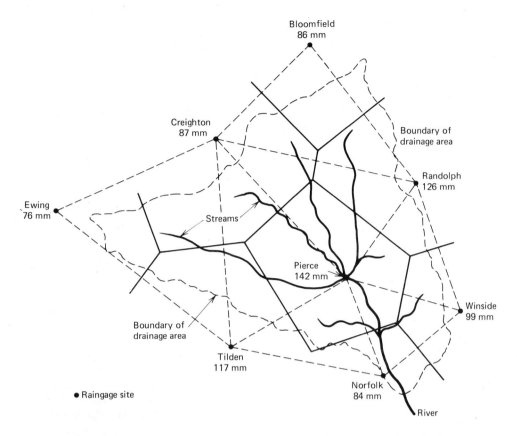

Figure 6-10 The North Fork Elkhorn River drainage basin showing the location of raingage stations, storm rainfall in millimetres, and Thiessen polygons for Example 6-2.

Solution

Connect adjacent gages by lines and construct perpendicular bisectors to each connecting line. Measure the area within each polygon that lies in the drainage basin with a planimeter, or by overlaying the basin with a transparent grid and counting the intersections of the grid falling in each polygon. The areas, or number of intersections, are coefficients for weighting the individual gage reading and calculating the average precipitation as follows:

Station	Observed Precipitation (mm)	Number of Grid Intersections	Product
Norfolk	84	94	7 896
Winside	99	94	9 306

Station	Observed Precipitation (mm)	Number of Grid Intersections	Product
Randolph	126	209	26 334
Bloomfield	86	106	9 116
Creighton	87	303	26 361
Ewing	76	74	5 624
Tilden	117	139	16 263
Pierce	142	434	61 628
		1 453	162 528

Mean precipitation = 162 528/1 453 = 112 mm.

Example 6-3

Find the average precipitation on North Fork Elkhorn River basin by the isoheytal method. The rain gage data are given in Figure 6-11.

Solution

The location of precipitation gages are plotted, and the amount of precipitation noted at each location. Selecting an interval of 10 mm, the isoheytal map is drawn and the area within each isoyhetal measured by planimeter or counting grid intersections. First the area within the basin boundary is measured, followed by each successive smaller area. The average precipitation between isoheytals is usually assumed to be the average of the adjacent isoheytals. However, the map shows that the precipitation between isoheytals 80 and 90 mm and between 90 and 100 mm is greater than average, so the precipitation between these isoheytals was estimated. Mean precipitation is computed as follows:

Isoheytal	Enclosed Area	Incremental Area	Average Precipitation (mm)	Product
130	143	143	135	19 305
120	388	245	125	30 635
110	646	258	115	29 620
100	936	290	105	30 450
90	1 420	484	97	46 948
80	1 455	35	87	3 045
			Total	160 043

Mean precipitation = 160 043 / 1 455 = 112 mm.

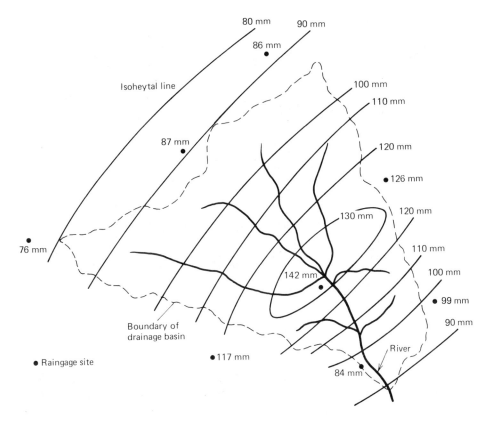

Figure 6-11 North Fork Elkhorn River drainage basin showing the location of raingage stations and isoheytal lines with storm rainfall in millimetres for Example 6-3.

6-5 Intensity, Duration, and Frequency of Precipitation

The designer of drainage structures, such as culverts and storm sewers, needs to know the frequency of occurrence of various size storms in order to select the most economical design and size of structures. Intensity-duration-frequency data are prepared using records from individual recording precipitation stations.

In the United States, the Weather Bureau has compiled intensity-duration-frequency data for many precipitation stations and presented these data in curves similar to Figure 6-12.[7] They give the exceedance probability of the maximum precipitation in a year expressed as the average recurrence interval. The maximum storm precipitation in some years will be exceeded by several storms in other years. If the curves are to be used to design for short recurrence intervals the recurrence intervals should be computed using all storms above a base precipitation. This is called a partial-duration series. Precipitation from the curves in Figure 6-12 can be approximately transformed to the partial-duration series by multiplying by the following factors: 2-year recurrence interval, 1.13; 5-year interval, 1.04; and, 10-year interval, 1.01. The difference between the two series is insignificant for larger recurrence intervals.

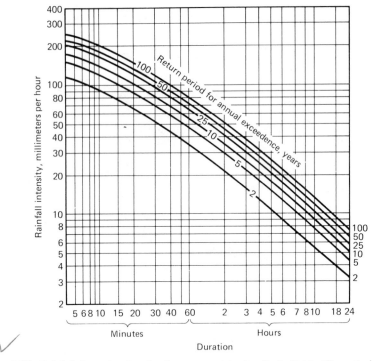

Figure 6-12 Rainfall intensity-duration-frequency data for Springfield, Missouri. (From U. S. Weather Bureau, *Rainfall Intensity-Duration-Frequency Curves*, Technical Paper Number 25, 1955.)

Maps like Figures 6-13 and 6-14 showing the frequency-duration of precipitation have been prepared by several authors.[8,9,10] Durations of 30 minutes to 24 hours and recurrence intervals of 1 to 100 years are based on annual data transformed to partial-duration series. These maps are only applicable to small areas of a few square kilo-metres. For larger areas, the average depth over the entire area must be considered. The area-depth curves in Figure 6-15 relates the point precipitation to the average depth over areas up to 1 000 km^2.

Sometimes protection against the worst possible event is essential, usually where loss of life or essential services are in jeopardy. For instance, dam spillways are designed for these extreme storms. A realistic probability cannot be computed for such events, and an economic loss cannot be attached to failure. The design criterion for such extreme events is a policy decision.

For this situation, the U. S. Weather Bureau[11,12] has compiled data on the probable maximum possible precipitation for storm events in all seasons on the basis of current meteorological theory and available data. Figure 6-16 shows the average all season probable maximum possible precipitation over a 500-km^2 area; other maps are avail-able showing similar information for each month. Depth-area precipitation for areas from 25 to 2 500 km^2 can be estimated for all seasons by multiplying the 24-hour precipitation for a 500-km^2 area (Figure 6-16) by a factor from Table 6-2.

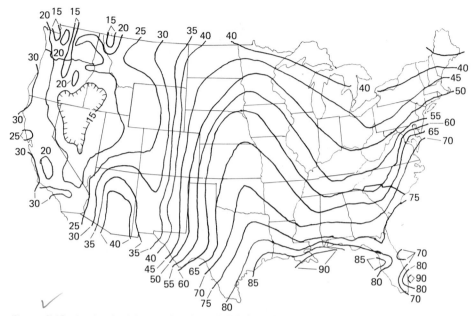

Figure 6-13 An isopluvial map showing rainfall intensity, in millimetres, of a one-hour storm having a return period of 10 years. (From D. M. Hershfield, *Rainfall Frequency Atlas of the United States*, 1961.)

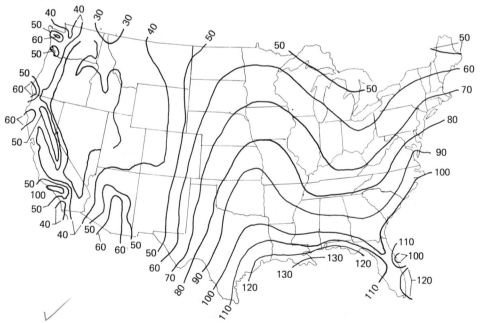

Figure 6-14 An isopluvial map showing rainfall intensity, in millimetres, of a three-hour storm having a recurrence interval of 10 years. (From D. M. Hershfield, *Rainfall Frequency Atlas of the United States*, 1961.)

143

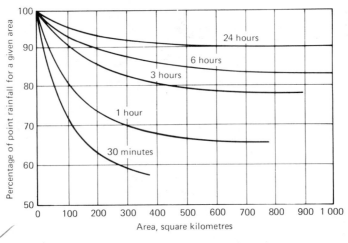

Figure 6-15 Curves to compute depth-area precipitation in millimetres from Figures 6-13 and 6-14. (From D. M. Hershfield, *Rainfall Frequency Atlas of the United States*, U. S. Weather Bureau Technical Paper 40, 1961.)

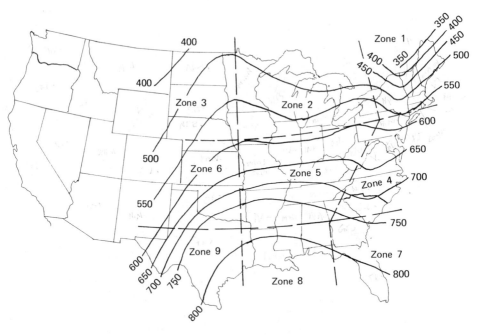

Figure 6-16 Probable maximum-possible precipitation in millimetres in the conterminous United States east of the 105th meridian. (From J. T. Riedal, J. A. Appleby, and R. W. Schloemer, *Seasonal Variation of the Probable Maximum Possible Precipitation East of the 105th Meridian for Areas from 10 to 100 Square Kilometres*, U. S. Weather Bureau Hydrometeorological Report Number 35, 1956.)

144

Table 6-2 Coefficients to Adjust Probable Maximum Possible Precipitation in
Millimetres on 500 Square Kilometres Given in Figure 6-16 to Areas
Ranging from 25 to 2 500 Square Kilometres

Zone	Duration (h)	Drainage Area (km^2)							
		25	50	75	100	250	500	1000	2500
1	6	1.11	1.03	0.97	0.94	0.84	0.75	0.66	0.55
	12	1.23	1.15	1.11	1.08	0.97	0.88	0.80	0.70
	24	1.33	1.26	1.22	1.18	1.08	1.00	0.91	0.82
	48					1.14	1.05	0.97	0.88
2	6	1.17	1.08	1.04	0.99	0.89	0.80	0.73	0.65
	12	1.27	1.19	1.14	1.09	0.98	0.89	0.82	0.74
	24	1.41	1.31	1.25	1.21	1.09	1.00	0.92	0.83
	48					1.19	1.10	1.01	0.81
3	6	1.01	0.98	0.95	0.93	0.86	0.81	0.75	0.64
	12	1.21	1.15	1.12	1.09	1.00	0.93	0.85	0.75
	24	1.33	1.26	1.22	1.18	1.08	1.00	0.93	0.82
	48						1.15	1.07	0.96
4	6	1.11	1.05	1.00	0.98	0.89	0.82	0.76	0.68
	12	1.23	1.17	1.12	1.09	1.00	0.93	0.85	0.77
	24	1.32	1.23	1.19	1.16	1.06	1.00	0.93	0.85
	48						1.18	1.10	1.04	0.97
5	6	1.01	0.95	0.91	0.88	0.78	0.70	0.62	0.55
	12	1.22	1.14	1.10	1.06	0.96	0.88	0.80	0.71
	24	1.31	1.24	1.21	1.17	1.08	1.00	0.93	0.87
	48						1.16	1.08	1.02
6	6	1.12	1.06	1.02	0.99	0.90	0.83	0.76	0.67
	12	1.23	1.17	1.12	1.08	0.98	0.91	0.82	0.74
	24	1.32	1.25	1.21	1.18	1.08	1.00	0.92	0.83
	48						1.16	1.07	0.98
7	6	1.00	0.95	0.90	0.88	0.79	0.73	0.66	0.58
	12	1.19	1.13	1.08	1.05	0.96	0.88	0.82	0.73
	24	1.29	1.23	1.17	1.15	1.06	1.00	0.94	0.84
	48					1.17	1.10	1.05	0.96
8 and 9	6	0.96	0.91	0.87	0.85	0.78	0.72	0.65	0.60
	12	1.07	1.03	1.00	0.98	0.91	0.86	0.81	0.75
	24	1.22	1.18	1.14	1.12	1.04	1.00	0.93	0.88
	48					1.19	1.14	1.08	1.03

Source. Seasonal Variation of the Probable Maximum Possible Precipitation East of the 105th Meridian for Areas from 10 to 100 Square Kilometres, U. S. Weather Bureau, 1956. SI units by the author.

145

6-6 Probability of Hydrologic Events

The ultimate goal of the hydrologist is to make the best possible forecast of events of unknown timing and magnitude in order to formulate decisions to control and manage these natural occurrences. Statistical techniques are used to extract meaningful information, such as the probability of a water supply failure because of a drought, or the probability of a certain area being flooded.

Probability is the relative frequency of a particular event in a long sequence. If certain to occur, the probability is 1.00, and an impossible event has a probability of 0. Suppose a box contains the following balls as listed in Table 6-3: 4 red balls marked 1; 6 red balls marked 2; 10 red balls marked 3; 10 white balls marked 1; 14 white balls marked 2; and 6 white balls marked 3. If they are well mixed, the probability of drawing one ball is the same as drawing any other ball; but the probability of drawing a ball with a certain characteristic is the number of balls having that characteristic divided by the total number that could be drawn. For instance, the chance of drawing a red ball is 20/50 = 0.4, and of drawing a red ball marked 3 is 10/50 = 0.2.

Table 6-3   Two-Way Probability

Color	Marking			Total of Each Color
	1	2	3	
Red	4	6	10	20
White	10	14	6	30
Total	14	20	16	50

In dealing with two events, the probability of either one or the other occurring is the sum of the individual probabilities. Therefore, the probability of drawing either a red ball marked one or a white ball marked two is 4/50 + 14/50 = 18/50 = 0.36. If an event can happen in more than one way, the probability of it happening in only one way must be counted. For instance, the probability of drawing a red ball (any marking) is 20/50 = 0.4, and the probability of drawing a ball marked one (either red or white) is 14/50 = 0.28. However, as shown in Table 6-3, the four red balls marked one have been counted twice, as red balls and as balls marked one. Therefore, the probability of drawing a red ball (any marking) or a ball marked one (either red or white) equals 20/50 + 14/50 − 4/50 = 30/50 = 0.6.

Probability Rules

If an event can succeed in A likely ways and fail in B equally likely ways, the probability of success is:

$$P = \frac{A}{A + B} \tag{6-1}$$

where P = probability

$\quad A$ = number of successes

$\quad B$ = number of failures

The meaning of equally likely ways was demonstrated with the red and white balls. They were well mixed so that one ball was as likely to be drawn as any other without regard to color or marking.

The probability of obtaining a prescribed sequence of events from a collection of independent random events equals the product of the probabilities of the individual events.

$$P = P_1 \times P_2 \times P_3 \ldots \ldots P_n \qquad (6\text{-}2)$$

For example, as illustrated in Figure 6-17, the probability of obtaining three heads in three tosses of a coin equals

$\quad 1/2 \times 1/2 \times 1/2 = 1/8$

The probability of an independent event is the same without regard to the outcome of other events. For instance, the daily flow of a stream depends on the flow the preceding day and perhaps several preceding days. Equation 6-2 cannot be used to compute the probability of a sequence of dependent events such as daily streamflow.

The evaluation of probabilities requires consideration of all possible outcomes of a given chance event. Consider the number of arrangements of digits 1 through 4, which are listed as follows:

1-2-3-4	2-1-3-4	3-4-1-2	4-1-2-3
1-2-4-3	2-1-4-3	3-4-2-1	4-1-3-2
1-3-4-2	2-3-4-1	3-2-1-4	4-2-3-1
1-3-2-4	2-3-1-4	3-2-4-1	4-2-1-3
1-4-3-2	2-4-1-3	3-1-4-2	4-3-2-1
1-4-2-3	2-4-3-1	3-1-2-4	4-3-1-2

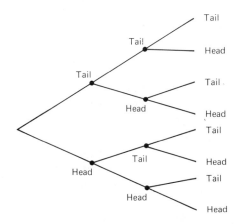

Figure 6-17 Possible combinations of heads and tails by tossing a coin three times.

The number of arrangements is 24. Four choices are available for the first number. After selecting the first digit, three choices are available for the second number. Then, two choices remain for the third number, and finally one for the fourth. The number of arrangements is $4 \times 3 \times 2 \times 1 = 24$. The general equation is:

$$N(N - 1)(N - 2)(N - 3) \ldots \ldots (2)(1) = N! \qquad\qquad (6\text{-}3)$$

where N = the number of events
$\qquad N!$ = N factorial

Values of $N!$ from 1 to 100 are listed in Table 6-4, which gives

$\qquad 4! = 2.400 \times 10 = 24$

Table 6-4   **Factorials of the Number N. The Numerical Value of $N!$ Is the Entry Multiplied by the Power of 10 Given in Parentheses**

N	$N!$	N	$N!$	N	$N!$	N	$N!$
1	1.000	26	4.033(26)	51	1.551(66)	76	1.886(111)
2	2.000	27	1.089(28)	52	8.066(67)	77	1.452(113)
3	6.000	28	3.049(29)	53	4.275(69)	78	1.132(115)
4	2.400(1)	29	8.842(30)	54	2.308(71)	79	8.946(116)
5	1.200(2)	30	2.652(32)	55	1.270(73)	80	7.157(118)
6	7.200(2)	31	8.223(33)	56	7.110(74)	81	5.797(120)
7	5.040(3)	32	2.631(35)	57	4.053(76)	82	4.754(122)
8	4.032(4)	33	8.683(36)	58	2.351(78)	83	3.946(124)
9	3.629(5)	34	2.952(38)	59	1.387(80)	84	3.314(126)
10	3.629(6)	35	1.033(40)	60	8.321(81)	85	2.817(128)
11	3.992(7)	36	3.720(41)	61	5.076(83)	86	2.423(130)
12	4.790(8)	37	1.376(43)	62	3.147(85)	87	2.108(132)
13	6.227(9)	38	5.230(44)	63	1.983(87)	88	1.855(134)
14	8.718(10)	39	2.040(46)	64	1.269(89)	89	1.651(136)
15	1.308(12)	40	2.159(47)	65	8.248(90)	90	1.486(138)
16	2.092(13)	41	3.345(49)	66	5.443(92)	91	1.352(140)
17	3.557(14)	42	1.405(51)	67	3.647(94)	92	1.244(142)
18	6.402(15)	43	6.042(52)	68	2.480(96)	93	1.157(144)
19	1.216(17)	44	2.658(54)	69	1.711(98)	94	1.087(146)
20	2.433(18)	45	1.196(56)	70	1.197(100)	95	1.033(148)
21	5.109(19)	46	5.503(57)	71	8.505(101)	96	9.917(140)
22	1.124(21)	47	2.586(59)	72	6.123(103)	97	9.610(151)
23	2.585(22)	48	1.241(61)	73	4.470(105)	98	9.427(153)
24	6.204(23)	49	6.083(62)	74	3.308(107)	99	9.333(155)
25	1.551(25)	50	3.041(64)	75	2.481(109)	100	9.333(157)

Consider the number of permutations that can be made from N objects if only r objects are used. As an illustration, pairs of the four numbers given in the previous paragraph can be arranged as follows: 1-2, 2-1, 1-3, 3-1, 1-4, 4-1, 2-3, 3-2, 2-4, 4-2, 3-4, and 4-3. Four choices are available for the first number and three for the second, which is $4 \times 3 = 12$ permutations. The general equation is:

$$P_{(N,r)} = N(N - 1)(N - 2)(N - 3) \ldots \ldots (N - r + 1), \text{ or}$$

$$P_{(N,r)} = \frac{N!}{(N - r)!} \tag{6-4}$$

where $P_{(N,r)}$ = the number of permutations of N objects if only r objects are used.

$P_{(N,r)}$ counts all the possible selections of objects as well as all possible arrangements of the selection. A permutation can be made of different arrangements of the same objects. For example, 1-2 and 2-1 are two permutations but only one combination. Therefore:

$$C_{(N,r)} = \frac{P_{(N,r)}}{r!} \tag{6-5}$$

where $C_{(N,r)}$ = the number of combinations of N objects if only r objects are used.

The outcome of a series of independent trials is either success S with a probability of p, or failure F with a probability of $1 - p$. The possible results of three trials are:

Results	Probability
SSS	p^3
SSF, SFS, FSS	$p^2(1 - p)$
FFS, FSF, SFF	$p(1 - p)^2$
FFF	$(1 - p)^3$

The general equation for probability of success is $p^r(1 - p)^{N-r}$. Using Equation 6-5 to compute the number of combinations, the equation for probability of success becomes

$$P_{(N,r)} = \frac{N!}{r!(N - r)!} p^r(1 - p)^{N-r} \tag{6-6}$$

where $P_{(N,r)}$ = the probability of exactly r success in N trials
   p = the probability of a single event

The reciprocal of probability, commonly used in hydrology, is called the return period or recurrence interval. A flood probability of 1/25 or 0.04 is referred to as a 25-year flood, in other words it will likely be equaled or exceeded at average 25-year intervals. However, during any selected period of 25 consecutive years, it may not appear or may occur more than once. The probability of a 25-year flood occurring exactly twice in a 25-year period is calculated in Example 6-4.

Example 6-4
What is the probability of a 25-year flood occurring exactly twice in a 25-year period?

Solution
Use Equation 6-6. The value r is the number of times a 25-year flood will occur and equals 2. The N is the length of period, 25 years. The number of failures, when a 25-year flood did not occur is $N - 2$. The number of combinations of r floods, in 25 years is

$$\frac{N!}{r!(N-r)!} = \frac{25!}{2!(23!)}$$

Using factorials from Table 6-4 the number of combinations is

$$\frac{1.551\,(25)}{2 \times 2.585\,(22)} = 300$$

The probability p of a 25-year flood is 0.04. $1 - p$ is the probability of failure and equals 0.96.

$$P_{(25,2)} = 300\,(0.04)^2\,(0.96)^{23} = 0.188$$

6-7 Normal Distributions of Hydrologic Data

MEAN

The mean or average of several values is their sum divided by the number of values

$$\bar{X} = \frac{\Sigma X}{N} \qquad (6\text{-}7)$$

where $\bar{X}$ = mean of observations
Σ = symbol meaning summation
X = individual observations
N = number of observations

The precipitation plotted in Figure 6-18 was taken from Table 6-5 and the mean is calculated as follows:

$$\text{Mean} = \frac{65\,817}{93} = 708 \text{ mm}$$

Table 6-5 Annual Precipitation in Millimetres, 1884 to 1976 at Lincoln, Nebraska, for Figures 6-18, 6-21, and 6-22 and Example 6-5

Year	Precipi- tation	Year	Precipi- tation	Year	Precipi- tation	Year	Precipi- tation
1884	683						
85	682	1910	795	1935	593	1960	800
86	723	11	624	36	357	61	802

Table 6-5 continued

Year	Precipitation	Year	Precipitation	Year	Precipitation	Year	Precipitation
87	481	12	568	37	491	62	860
88	652	13	666	38	466	63	597
89	572	14	1 016	39	501	64	737
1890	384	1915	935	1940	588	1965	1 057
91	1 034	16	585	41	636	66	500
92	752	17	660	42	732	67	822
93	510	18	565	43	553	68	737
94	486	19	820	44	892	69	774
1895	416	1920	665	1945	831	1970	686
96	966	21	608	46	600	71	937
97	652	22	629	47	845	72	887
98	713	23	735	48	671	73	1 010
99	672	24	556	49	904	74	494
1900	856	1925	637	1950	610	1975	613
01	561	26	666	51	1 033	76	841
02	1 047	27	543	52	812		
03	880	28	706	53	470		
04	704	29	851	54	827		
1905	907	1930	526	1955	473		
06	865	31	822	56	652		
07	693	32	665	57	778		
08	906	33	673	58	861		
09	862	34	484	59	830		

Dispersion about the mean is pictured in the histogram (Figure 6-19). If sufficient records were plotted and the increment size approached zero, the histogram would become a smooth curve called a probability density curve. The curve for most observed data takes a specific mathematical shape called a normal distribution, which has been superimposed on the histogram in Figure 6-19. The dispersion about the mean is measured by the standard deviation, which is also called the root mean square of the departures from the mean. Standard deviation is usually computed by the equation:

$$S = \left[\frac{\Sigma X^2 - (\Sigma X)^2/N}{N - 1} \right]^{0.5} \tag{6-8}$$

where S = standard deviation

Σ = symbol meaning summation

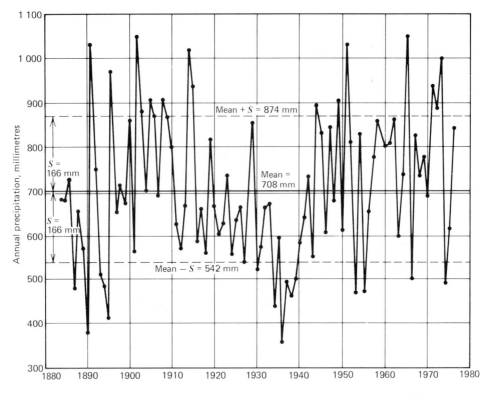

Figure 6-18 Average annual precipitation in millimetres at Lincoln, Nebraska, 1884 to 1976, showing the mean value and standard deviation.

X = an individual observation
N = number of observations

The standard deviation of the precipitation from Table 6-5 is:

$$\left[\frac{49\ 111\ 566\ -\ (65\ 817)^2/93}{93\ -\ 1}\right]^{0.5} = 166\ \text{mm}$$

The area under the normal distribution curve is the probability of an occurrence and equals 1.00. The dispersion about the mean is measured in standard deviation units as illustrated in Figure 6-20. Normal distribution cumulated from the left side of the curve is given in Table 6-6. The k is the number of standard deviation units from the mean. Minus k is to the left of the mean and plus to the right. The cumulative area to the left of $k = -1.00$ (one standard deviation) is 0.1587. The area to the left of $k = +1.00$ is 0.8413. Therefore, the area within one standard deviation on each side of the mean is 0.8413 - 0.1587 = 0.6826 or 68 percent, which is illustrated by the shaded area in Figure 6-20. The left edge of the shaded area is at 708 - 166 = 542 mm, and

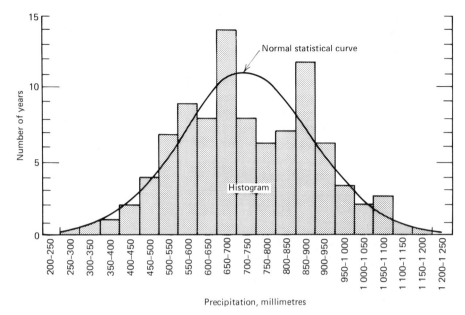

Figure 6-19 Histogram of annual precipitation taken from Table 6-5 with a normal distribution curve fitted to it.

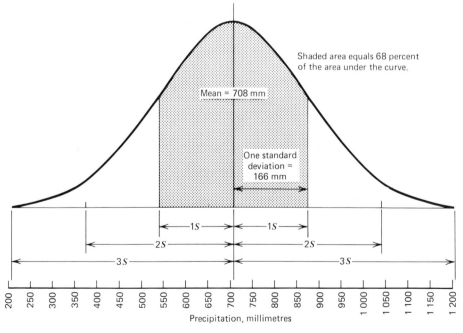

Figure 6-20 A normal distribution curve of precipitation in Table 6-5 showing the mean and bounds of one, two, and three standard deviations from the mean.

153

the right edge is at 708 + 166 = 874 mm. The annual precipitation at Lincoln will be more than 542 but less than 874 mm 68 percent of the time. The probability of the precipitation exceeding 956 mm is calculated in Example 6-5.

Table 6-6   Cumulative Normal Distribution to Be Used in Example 6-5 and Figure 6-20: k Is the Number of Standard Deviation Units from the Mean, X Is the Scale of the Abscissa in Data Units, Area Is the Cumulative Area from the Left Side of the Curve Taking the Entire Area as One, $\bar{X}$ Is the Mean, and S Is the Standard Deviation

k	X	Area	k	X	Area
-3.00	$\bar{X} - 3.00S$	0.0013	0.25	$\bar{X} + 0.25S$	0.5987
-2.75	$\bar{X} - 2.75S$	0.0030	0.50	$\bar{X} + 0.50S$	0.6915
-2.50	$\bar{X} - 2.50S$	0.0062	0.75	$\bar{X} + 0.75S$	0.7734
-2.25	$\bar{X} - 2.25S$	0.0122	1.00	$\bar{X} + 1.00S$	0.8413
-2.00	$\bar{X} - 2.00S$	0.0228	1.25	$\bar{X} + 1.25S$	0.8944
-1.75	$\bar{X} - 1.75S$	0.0401	1.50	$\bar{X} + 1.50S$	0.9332
-1.50	$\bar{X} - 1.50S$	0.0668	1.75	$\bar{X} + 1.75S$	0.9599
-1.25	$\bar{X} - 1.25S$	0.1056	2.00	$\bar{X} + 2.00S$	0.9772
-1.00	$\bar{X} - 1.00S$	0.1587	2.25	$\bar{X} + 2.25S$	0.9878
-0.75	$\bar{X} - 0.75S$	0.2266	2.50	$\bar{X} + 2.50S$	0.9938
-0.50	$\bar{X} - 0.50S$	0.3085	2.75	$\bar{X} + 2.75S$	0.9970
-0.25	$\bar{X} - 0.25S$	0.4013	3.00	$\bar{X} + 3.00S$	0.9987
0.0	$\bar{X}$	0.5000			

Cumulative probability curves can be used to show probability either equal to or less than, or equal to or greater than, an indicated amount depending on whether the interest is in excessive or deficient values. The curves are usually plotted on paper having a normal probability scale. If the data are normally distributed, the curve approximates a straight line.

Cumulative probability of the annual precipitation at Lincoln is computed in Table 6-7 and plotted in Figure 6-21. Probability equals the cumulated occurrences divided by the total number of occurrences. The normal cumulative distribution is also shown as a straight line drawn through the mean (708) and one standard deviation each side of the mean (542 and 874). The close fit of the plotted points indicates that the annual precipitation at this station is distributed normally.

Example 6-5

What is the probability of the annual precipitation at Lincoln exceeding 956 mm?

Solution

Figure 6-21 shows the data are normally distributed so Table 6-6 is applicable. The

Table 6-7 **Precipitation Data from Table 6-5 Organized for Computation of the Cumulative Frequency Curve Shown in Figure 6-21**

Precipitation Class	Tally	Number of Occurrences	Cumulative Occurrences	Probability
325-374	L	1	93	1.00
375-424	II	2	92	0.99
425-474	IIII	4	90	0.97
475-524	JHT II	7	86	0.92
525-574	JHT IIII	9	79	0.85
575-624	JHT III	8	70	0.75
625-674	JHT JHT IIII	14	62	0.67
675-724	JHT III	8	48	0.52
725-774	JHT I	6	40	0.43
775-824	JHT II	7	34	0.37
825-874	JHT JHT II	12	27	0.29
875-924	JHT I	6	15	0.16
925-974	III	3	9	0.10
975-1024	II	2	6	0.064
1025-1074	IIII	4	4	0.043

ratio of the shaded area in Figure 6-22 to the total area is the probability that 956 mm will be exceeded. The distance k is measured in standard deviation units:

$$k = (956 - 708)/166 = +1.50$$

From Table 6-6, the unshaded area for $k = +1.50$ is 0.9332 and the area of the shaded area is 1.0000 - 0.9332 or 0.0668. The chance that the annual precipitation will exceed 956 mm in any year is about 7 percent which agrees with Figure 6-21.

6-8 Nonnormal Distributions of Data

The density distribution for many hydrologic data is not normal. The distribution can be checked for normalcy by plotting a cumulative probability curve on normal probability paper as in Figure 6-21. Unless the curve approximates a straight line, a normal distribution should not be used; it may be possible, however, to modify the measuring units so the distribution is nearly normal. Figure 6-23 shows that the distribution of floods do not have the normal bell-shaped curve. However, the data can be transformed by plotting the common logarithm of the discharge so that the distribution density curve is approximately normal as shown in Figure 6-24. This is then called a log normal distribution and the standard deviation is in logarithmic units.

Several other distributions are used in hydrology. One of the most common is the logarithmic Pearson type III. This distribution has the advantage of providing a skew

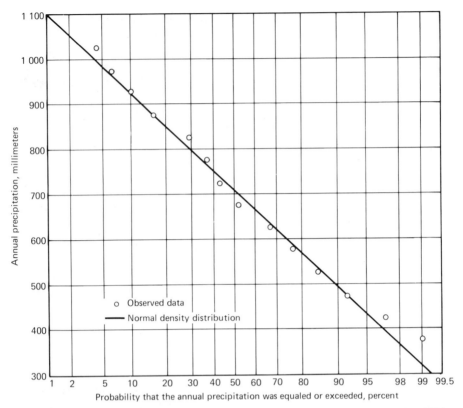

Figure 6-21 Cumulative probability of annual precipitation at Lincoln, Nebraska, for 1884 to 1976. The close fit of the observed data to the normal density distribution show that the annual precipitation is normally distributed.

adjustment. The skew statistic is a measure of nonsymmetry and if the skew is zero the log Pearson distribution is identical to the log normal distribution. Skewed data are illustrated in Figure 6-23.

The Gumbel distribution, also commonly used, is an extreme value distribution having a fixed skew of 1.139. The mean has a recurrence interval of 2.33 years (probability of 0.43). A plotting paper has been designed for this distribution. Events are ranked in order of magnitude beginning with the greatest and plotting positions are calculated as follows:

$$\text{Plotting position} = \frac{n+1}{m} \tag{6-9}$$

where n = total number of events
m = the rank of an event

The plotting position is the recurrence interval.

The probability of extreme events, such as floods or droughts, are usually computed

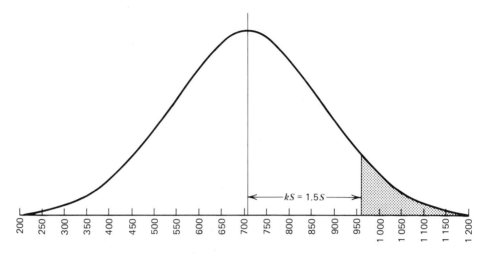

Figure 6-22 Computation of probability of annual precipitation at Lincoln exceeding 956 millimetres for Example 6-5.

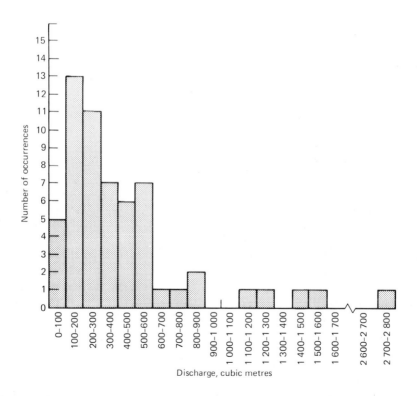

Figure 6-23 Histogram of annual floods on the Elkhorn River at Waterloo, Nebraska, 1899-1975, showing that the floods are not normally distributed.

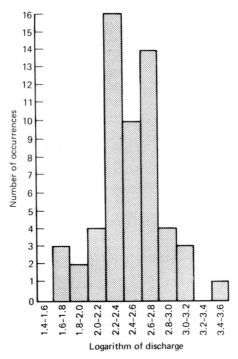

Figure 6-24 Histogram of logarithms of annual floods on the Elkhorn River at Waterloo, Nebraska, 1899-1975, showing that the logarithmic values of the flows in cubic metres are normally distributed.

from annual events, that is, from the most extreme in each year. A collection of annual events is called an annual series. A second or even a third extreme can occur that exceeds the annual event in some other years. Events having a return period of less than 10 years (probability more than 0.1) based on the annual series will occur more frequently than indicated because the second or third events in some years were greater than the annual events in other years and have been omitted from consideration. If events that occur frequently (probability more than 0.1) are important, a partial-duration series should be used. The partial-duration series includes all events that are more extreme than a base that has been selected to include at least one event each year. Langbein[13] derived the theoretical relationship between the recurrence intervals for annual and partial-duration series given in Table 6-8. A recent study shows that the relation between annual and partial-duration series varies from region to region but that the theoretical recurrence interval taken from Table 6-8 is slightly small.[14]

Example 6-6
Compute intensity-frequency curves of 30- and 60-minutes precipitation at Lincoln from data given in Table 6-9, using the Gumbel method.

Table 6-8   Relationship Between Recurrence Intervals By
the Partial-Duration Series and the Annual
Series; a Flood Having a Recurrence Interval
of 1.16 in the Annual Series Will Have a
Partial-Duration Recurrence Interval of 0.5

Recurrence Interval in Years by Partial-Duration Series	Recurrence Interval in Years by Annual Series
0.50	1.16
1.00	1.58
1.45	2.00
2.00	2.54
5.00	5.52
10.00	10.50
20.00	20.50
50.00	50.50
100.00	100.50

Source. W. B. Langbein, "Annual Floods and Partial-Duration
Series", *Transactions of the American Geophysical Union,* Vol.
30, pp. 879-881, 1949.

Table 6-9   Maximum Annual 30- and 60-Minute Precipitation in Millimetres, 1955-
1976 at Lincoln, Nebraska, for Example 6-6

Year	30-Minute Precipitation			60-Minute Precipitation		
	(mm)	Rank	Plotting Position	(mm)	Rank	Plotting Position
1955	38.1	1	22			
1956	37.0	2	11	43.7	5	4.20
1957	31.5	9	2.44	51.8	2	10.5
1958	27.4	12	1.83	53.3	1	21
1959	17.7	20	1.10	20.7	18	1.17
1960	27.7	11	2.00	30.7	12	1.75
1961	32.5	7.5	2.93	36.6	10	2.10
1962	20.3	15.5	1.42	37.6	6.5	3.23
1963	35.3	5	4.40	37.0	8.5	2.47
1964						
1965	36.3	3	7.33	43.9	4	5.25
1966	33.5	6	3.67	37.0	8.5	2.47
1967	32.5	7.5	2.93	48.3	3	7.00

Table 6-9   **continued**

	30-Minute Precipitation			60-Minute Precipitation		
Year	(mm)	Rank	Plotting Position	(mm)	Rank	Plotting Position
1968	18.8	18	1.22	30.0	13.5	1.56
1969	19.7	17	1.29	25.2	15	1.40
1970	35.6	4	5.50	36.3	11	1.91
1971	21.8	14	1.57	30.0	13.5	1.56
1972	22.9	13	1.69	24.6	16	1.31
1973	20.3	15.5	1.42	22.1	17	1.24
1974	30.5	10	2.20	37.6	6.5	3.23
1975	18.5	19	1.16	19.1	19	1.11
1976	15.5	21	1.05	16.5	20	1.05

Solution

List the precipitation in chronological order and rank the data beginning with the highest precipitation as 1. If precipitation is the same in two or more years give them the same rank, for instance, 30-minute precipitation in 1961 and 1967 was 32.5 mm, rank them 7.5 rather than 7 and 8. Compute the plotting position with Equation 6-9. Plot on Gumbel paper with a linear ordinate scale as in Figure 6-25. Paper with a log ordinate scale can be used if the range in data is more than one log cycle. The missing record for 1964 will not affect the validity of the results because the period does not have to be continuous.

6-9   Linear Regressions

In hydrology, measuring the association between two or more variables may be desirable. If two associated variables are plotted on a graph, one placed on the X axis and the other on the Y axis, they form a path across the paper. The independent or causal variable is plotted on the X axis. If the association is not perfect, the points depart from the indicated line. The greater the departure the less perfect the association. The departures are known as scatter, and the graph is called a scatter diagram.

If the trend is a straight line, the relationship is linear and has the equation:

$$Y = a + bX \tag{6-10}$$

Hydrologic data can often be transformed to a straight line by using logarithms of the variables. If a linear relationship cannot be assumed, a more complicated analysis is required. The equation defines any number of lines depending on the values of a and b. The method of least squares is used to select the line that fits the data best. The principle of least squares states that the best line for fitting a series of observations is the one for which the sum of the squares of the departures is minimum. A departure is the difference between the observed value and the line. Because X is the independent

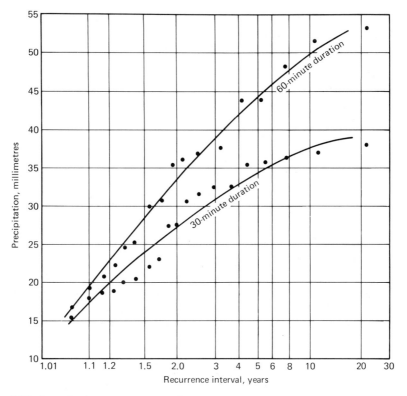

Figure 6-25 Intensity-frequency curves of 30- and 60-minute precipitation for Example 6-6.

variable, the departures of Y are used. If the departures of X were used, the line would likely be different.

The least squares line may be computed using two normal equations

$$\Sigma Y = Na + b\Sigma X \qquad \qquad (6\text{-}11)$$

$$\Sigma XY = a\Sigma X + b\Sigma X^2 \qquad \qquad (6\text{-}12)$$

$b = $ slope

where N = the number of X and Y pairs

$a = $ y-intercept.

The above simultaneous equations can be solved

$$b = \frac{\Sigma XY - \dfrac{\Sigma X \Sigma Y}{N}}{\Sigma X^2 - \dfrac{(\Sigma X)^2}{N}} \qquad \qquad (6\text{-}13)$$

$$a = \frac{\Sigma Y - b\Sigma X}{N} \qquad \qquad (6\text{-}14)$$

$$S_{y \cdot x}^2 = \frac{N-1}{N-2}(S_y^2 - b^2 S_x^2) \qquad \qquad (6\text{-}15)$$

where $S_{y \cdot x}$ = the standard error of estimate of Y with respect to X
     S_y = standard deviation of Y from Equation 6-8
     S_x = standard deviation of X from Equation 6-8

The standard deviation, Equation 6-8, measures the scatter about the mean whereas the standard error of estimate measures the scatter about the regression line and it is the quadratic mean of the deviation from the line.

$$r = \left(1 - \frac{S_{y \cdot x}^2}{S_y^2}\right)^{0.5} \tag{6-16}$$

where r = the correlation coefficient which is a measure of the scatter explained by the regression line. If $r = 1$, the correlation is perfect and all the points plot on the regression line. If $r = 0$, the two variables, X and Y, are not related.

    Statistical methods can be applied to many kinds of meteorological and hydrological data, such as precipitation, temperature, floods, droughts, and water quality. Available data are frequently a sample of a much larger population and the validity of conclusions drawn from the data depends on the quality of the sample; therefore, the method of choosing a sample is important. If every individual in the population is equally likely to be chosen, the sample is said to be random. For example, water quality samples collected only during fair weather because of other pressing work during floods, are not random because the flood samples were systematically omitted. Measurements made regularly on a specified day are likely not random. Statistical techniques assume a random sample of independent individuals. Nonrandom and dependent samples require special techniques and should be recognized and considered when the data are evaluated.

    Years of nonnormal streamflow or precipitation tend to follow each other. A nonrepresentative period of record causes a sampling error. For instance, Figure 6-18 shows the estimated mean precipitation at Lincoln would have been considerably different if records had been taken only for either of the periods 1890 to 1910 or 1920 to 1940. Short-term records should be compared with surrounding long-term records for indication of a possible sampling error.

6-10   Factors Affecting Runoff

Part of the precipitation reaching a stream is evaporated or transpired. The remainder becomes runoff but can take many different routes over a long time span to reach a stream. The route and timing depend on the character of the drainage basin and precipitation intensity. Each path affects the rate and amount of runoff in a different way.

Interception
If the ground is covered with vegetation, the first drops of precipitation striking the plant leaves are retained, spreading over the leaf surface in a thin layer. This process and the water stored are called interception. If rain continues after the leaves can

hold no more water, additional precipitation accumulates in droplets and falls to the next lower leaves. Eventually, the storage capacity of all leaves is reached and drops fall to the earth. The amount reaching the earth is called throughfall. Interception is greatest at the beginning of a storm and gradually decreases until interception storage is satisfied. Then it continues at a constant and fairly low rate due to evaporation from the surface of wet leaves. After rainfall has ceased evaporation continues until the interception storage is depleted. The amount of leaf surface, which depends on the stage of development and health of the plant or tree, is the greatest single factor affecting interception. Wind reduces interception by shaking water off the leaves. Also, some rain falls on the trunks of trees or stems of plants and runs to the ground. The water reaching the ground, called stemflow, is largely dependent on the roughness of the trunks and stems. Stemflow from smooth surfaces is greater than from rough surfaces.

Many investigators have measured interception; however, results vary widely due to different methods and plants used. The following reports illustrate the wide range of findings. Leonard[15], measuring interception by hardwood trees in New Hampshire, found no throughfall for storms less than 0.8 mm, and no stemflow for storms less than 1.3 mm. He devised the following relationships from his data:

$$\text{Throughfall} = 0.8904P - 0.030 \text{ mm} \tag{6-17}$$

$$\text{Stemflow} = 0.0562P - 0.0024 \text{ mm} \tag{6-18}$$

$$\begin{aligned} \text{Net precipitation} &= \text{throughfall} + \text{stemflow} \\ &= 0.9547P - 0.034 \text{ mm} \end{aligned} \tag{6-19}$$

Where P = precipitation, millimetres

Helvey[16] reported throughfall and stemflow on three stands of eastern pine in western North Carolina, which were 10, 35, and 60 years of age. He developed the following equations:

$$\text{Throughfall on the 10-year stand} = 0.85P - 1.3 \text{ mm} \tag{6-20}$$

$$\text{Throughfall on the 35-year stand} = 0.85P - 1.0 \text{ mm} \tag{6-21}$$

$$\text{Throughfall on the 60-year stand} = 0.83P - 1.3 \text{ mm} \tag{6-22}$$

$$\text{Stemflow on the 10-year stand} = 0.09P \text{ mm} \tag{6-23}$$

$$\text{Stemflow on the 35-year stand} = 0.06P - 0.25 \text{ mm} \tag{6-24}$$

$$\text{Stemflow on the 60-year stand} = 0.03P - 0.25 \text{ mm} \tag{6-25}$$

where P = precipitation, millimetres

Burgy and Pomeroy[17] used laboratory test plots containing grasses representative of northern California rangeland cover. Their significant finding is that after interception storage capacity has been filled, evaporation is about equal to and offsets transpiration. Scatterfield and Haupt[18] studied disposition of snow caught by conifer crowns during the warm winter of 1966-1967 and 1967-1968 in northern Idaho. About one third of the snow falling in 22 storms was caught; however, more than 80 percent of the snow caught ultimately reached the ground. Only a small part was lost by evaporation.

Depression storage is the water trapped on the surface of the earth in natural depressions or those incidental to human activities, such as ruts and furrows. Water purposely stored in man-made structures, like terraces or detention reservoirs, is not included. Since retained water is evaporated or infiltrated, it does not contribute directly to channel flow during rainy periods. Depression storage can be estimated by comparing stream runoff hydrographs with measured rainfall time graphs. However, designers usually assume values or include depression storage with infiltration in sewer design. Tholin and Keifer[19] assumed depression storage of 1.6 mm on impervious areas and 6 mm on pervious areas in designing a storm sewer system for Chicago.

Infiltration

Infiltration as applied to hydrology is the flow of water into the ground through pores and small openings, whereas the term percolation connotes flow through porous soil. Yet, for practical purposes, the two function together and cannot be separated. After infiltrating, percolation water supplies the evapotranspiration requirements of terrestrial plants, flow to wells, seeps directly to streams as interflow or seeps to the water table where it remains in long-term storage, and is withdrawn from wells or contributes to the base flow of streams.

Factors affecting infiltration are soil characteristics, antecedent moisture conditions, intensity of rain, season of year, crops or other vegetation on the land, frozen ground, clogged soil structure, and most important in urban areas is the percentage of impervious areas, such as rooftops, streets, and parking lots. Infiltration capacity is the maximum rate a soil can absorb falling rain or melting snow under a given condition. Soils composed of large or uniform grains have a greater infiltration capacity than those having small or unsorted grains. Infiltration capacity does not remain constant for a given area, but fluctuates depending on the condition of the soil, season of the year, and presence of vegetation. The maximum rate generally occurs when soil moisture is at field capacity, which is the moisture content that can be permanently retained against the force of gravity by capillarity. Soil conditions producing variations in infiltration in addition to moisture content are cultivation, perforations by earthworms or decayed roots of plants, packing of the soil surface and washing fine material into pores of the soil, and shrinking and swelling of colloidal soil. Vegetation improves infiltration capacity by adding organic matter to the soil, opening the soil structure, and by protecting the soil surface from the impact of intense rains. Overgrazing of pasture and compaction of cropped soil by farm machinery reduces infiltration. Frozen ground greatly reduces infiltration of snowmelt.

Measurements of infiltration rates are usually made in the field on undisturbed soil. One method is to measure water intake with infiltrometers designed as concentric rings or tubes. Another method is to measure the water intake in small sample areas watered by rainfall simulators, and a third way is by measuring the difference between rainfall and surface runoff. The last two techniques include depression storage and interception with infiltration.

The infiltration index Φ is the average rate of infiltration expressed in millimetres per hour, above which the volume of runoff equals the volume of precipitation excess. The index should be computed from precipitation and runoff data for storms of several intensities for different soil moisture and cover conditions. As illustrated in Figure 6-26, infiltration is maximum at the beginning of a storm and then decreases as the storm continues. Therefore, Φ is an average value and assumes too little infiltration at the beginning of the storm and too much near the end.

An infiltration equation proposed by Green and Ampt[20] in 1911 has become recognized as one of the most usable models of the infiltration process. Their model has been expressed as:

$$I = \frac{K(h_w + Z - h_{we})}{Z} \tag{6-26}$$

where I = the infiltration rate, millimetres per minute
   K = hydraulic conductivity of the soil in the wetted zone, millimetres per minute
   h_w = depth of water above soil surfaces, millimetres
   Z = depth of wetted front, millimetres
   h_{we} = pressure head at wetted front, millimetres of water

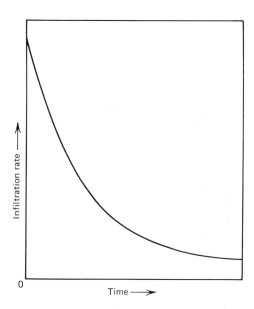

Figure 6-26 An idealized infiltration curve. Infiltration decreases rapidly after the beginning of a storm and eventually approaches a nearly constant rate, which is most important since it affects the amount of runoff more than the early higher rates.

The term on the right is the hydraulic conductivity of the soil multiplied by the hydraulic gradient. The hydraulic conductivity is not maximum at full saturation because of entrapped air; however, it can be assumed to be $0.5K$, at full saturation in the wetted zone.[21] The term h_{we} is approximated by the water entry value or air entry value of the soil.[21] K and h_{we} can be measured in the field with an air entry permeameter. The air entry value is the pressure head of the soil water when air of zero gage pressure enters soil with a continuous water phase. It is negative and is a measure of capillary conductivity. For a detailed description of the permeameter see Bouwer.[21]

Aldabagh and Beer[22] measured K of four soils in Iowa making 5 to 12 tests on each soil type at depths of 0.3 m. The results are tabulated below:

Clarion loam at 0 to 3 percent slope is a well-drained soil and SCS (Soil Conservation Service) hydrologic Class B

$K = 227$ mm/h

Clarion loam on a 3 to 7 percent slope

$K = 150$ mm/h

Webster is poorly drained silt clay loam and SCS hydrologic Class C

$K = 121$ mm/h

Nicollet loam is between Charion and Webster with respect to drainage; it is SCS hydrologic Class B

$K = 141$ mm/h

The cover, condition of the soil, or antecedent conditions were not reported.

Most soils are heterogenous; therefore, several hydraulic conductivity measurements must be made to obtain a good estimate. The Green-Ampt and other models are for the entire infiltration-time curve. The hydrologist is primarily interested in the steady-state infiltration rate that is reached well after the storm begins.

Basin Characteristics

Effectiveness of river systems to collect and convey water is related to topography. Area is the dominate feature affecting the quantity of runoff, whereas other topographic features affect the time distribution. Drainage area, usually expressed in square kilometres, is obtained by outlining and planimetering the boundary on a topographic map. Parts of drainage basins having no apparent surface drainage outlets are noncontributing, and their areas subtracted from the total to obtain the effective drainage area. If a noncontributing area is underlaid by a limestone formation containing sinkholes, it can contribute to the total runoff but the flow is delayed by underground storage and generally does not contribute to the peak. In wetlands and swamps, most of the water is retained and eventually lost by evaporation. When an area without apparent surface drainage has a high infiltration rate, such as the Sand Hills of

Nebraska, precipitation percolates to the water table and emerges as a base flow in a nearby stream.

Stream density has been defined as the total length of all streams divided by the area of the basin. A high density indicates a well-developed drainage system and a quick runoff response to precipitation. A low density yields more overland flow and a slower response.

Stream length is the distance along the longest watercourse from the outlet to the drainage divide. Measurements of stream length are affected by map scale. Large-scale maps result in greater lengths than those of smaller scale because more detail is shown. Length divided by mean velocity of flow is the time of concentration; this is the time required for water to flow from the most distance point of the basin to the outlet.

Channel slope also affects time of concentration. With other factors being constant, channel slope of the principal stream and tributaries has a direct effect on the peak flow. Velocity of the stream varies directly with the square root of the slope, and the time of concentration varies inversely with the velocity. The slope parameter of the channel is computed by dividing the difference in stream elevation at 85 percent and 10 percent of the length, above the point of interest, by the length of channel between these two points.

The concentration of runoff from drainage basins of equal size is greatly influenced by the distribution of the area with respect to distance from the outlet. A compact basin with short streams from all subareas converging near the outlet has a high peak, whereas a basin of equal size with remote subareas has a longer concentration time and lower peak. The effect of drainage basin shape on a runoff hydrograph is illustrated in Figure 6-27.

6-11   Stream Gaging Stations

Streamflow is the discharge that occurs in a natural channel and is the only component of the hydrological cycle that lends itself to measurement of the total. Measurements of all other components are samples of a large population. Furthermore, streamflow is a sensitive indicator of climatic variations, because it is the residual of precipitation after the demands for evapotranspiration have been met. Runoff is streamflow unaffected by storage, diversion, or other works of humans. Streams serve humans in many ways by providing water for drinking, irrigation of crops, removal of wastes, production of power, transporation, and recreation. On the other hand, floods are a serious hazard. Records from gaging stations are needed for design of structures, to manage the water supply, and to reduce flood losses.

A continuous record station has a recorder that makes a graph of the water level, but a few stations have a gage that is read by a gage reader once or twice a day. In contrast, crest-stage stations and low-flow partial-record stations are for the collection of flood and low-flow data, respectively.

Streamflow records are obtained by measuring the water level or stage of the stream and developing a stage-discharge relation or rating using the quantity of flow measured

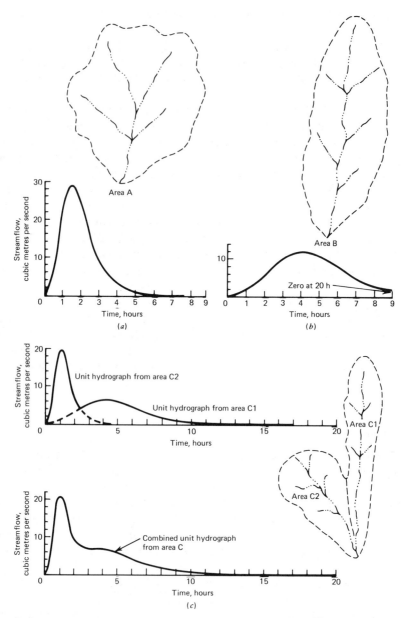

Figure 6-27 Diagrams showing the affect of drainage area shape on runoff hydrographs. (*a*) The hydrograph of an area drained by several short streams that converge near the outlet has a short time of concentration causing a sharp peak soon after rainfall begins. (*b*) The hydrograph of a long narrow basin has a much lower peak and longer time of runoff. (*c*) The hydrograph of a long stream having a short tributary of nearly the same area near the outlet is a combination of (*a*) and (*b*) and may have a double peak. (From *National Engineering Handbook*, Soil Conservation Service, Section 4, Hydrology, 1971.)

by a current meter or other flow-measuring device. After a rating has been developed, measuring is continued periodically to verify the rating and quantify changes. The accuracy and ease of obtaining the record depends on the stability of the rating which depends on the permanence of the control. All gaging stations have a control, a section or reach of the stream that determines the stage-discharge relation. The ideal control should be permanent and cause a unique stage-discharge relation. A rock riffle or a small waterfall has these characteristics; however, a stream bed that is subject to little change will do if a riffle or waterfall is not available. Sand-bed stream reaches or sites where channel instability is obvious should not be selected except when no other site is available. Sites just above tributaries are not suitable because tributaries may cause backwater and are very likely to deposit debris in the channel causing a temporary change in the rating. Low weirs or dams are sometimes built to stabilize the stage-discharge relation.

The discharge is not a unique function of the stage at some sites. Therefore, variables other than stage must be measured continuously to obtain a discharge record. For example, stream slope is sometimes measured by an auxiliary gage downstream. Other desirable characteristics are a good measuring section, a uniform channel, measurable velocities, accessibility during floods, and a suitable structure from which to measure floods. The flow should be perpendicular to the measuring section.

Stage or gage height is the distance of the stream surface above some arbitrary datum. For convenience, the datum or zero of the gage should be below the stream bed to avoid negative readings. The mean sea level elevation of the gage datum is usually determined and should be referenced to permanent marks in the vicinity so the gage can be reestablished to the same datum if it is destroyed.

A vertical graduated staff is the simplest gage, and is frequently used as outside reference at stations equipped with recorders. Staff gages should be attached to permanent structures such as bridge piers or abutments if possible. If attached to less stable structures, they should be set in protected areas where not likely to be destroyed by ice or floating debris. A type A wire-weight gage is also nonrecording. It is usually mounted on a bridge railing or structural member over the main channel. It consists of a drum wound with a single layer of wire cable and a weight attached to the end of the cable which can be lowered to the water surface and cranked back up. The gage is set so when the weight is at the water surface, the gage height is indicated by the combined reading of a veeder counter and a graduated disk. The stage of the check bar should be determined by levels, and the gage disk and counter set to read the height of the check bar with the weight on the bar. A check bar reading should be made each time a stage is read and if it does not agree with the original setting, the gage needs adjusting.

A water-stage recorder is an instrument for producing a graphic or punched tape record of the rise and fall of the water surface with respect to time. It consists of a time element and a gage-height element, which together produce a continuous record of the fluctuations of the stream surface. The time element is controlled by a clock, which is driven by a spring, weight, or electricity. The gage-height element is actuated by a float or a bubble gage.

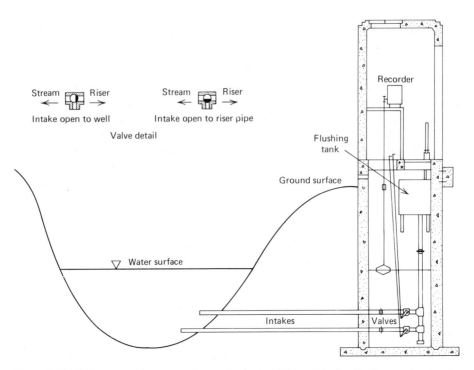

Figure 6-28 A float type of stream gaging station has a stilling well hydraulically connected to the stream by pipes—as the stream rises or falls, the water level in the well follows. The float is attached to one end of a tape that passes over a pulley on the recorder and a counter weight is on the other end. Movement of the tape turns the pulley which moves the recorder pen across the chart. (From T. J. Buchanan and W. P. Somers, *Discharge-Measurements at Gaging Stations*, Surface Water Techniques, Book 1, Chapter 11, U. S. Geological Survey, 1965.)

A float sensor consists of a tape passing over a pulley with a float attached to one end and a counterweight on the other. The float is in a stilling well connected to the stream by pipes as shown in Figure 6-28. As the float follows the rise and fall of the stream the tape turns a pulley that activates a pen. A bubble-gage sensor consists of a gas-purge system, a servomanometer assembly, and a servocontrol unit. Nitrogen fed through a tube bubbles freely into the stream through an orifice at a fixed location (Figure 6-29). The gas pressure in the tube equals the piezometric head on the bubble orifice. The servomanometer, illustrated in Figure 6-30, converts changes in pressure in the gas-purge system to a rotating shaft, which drives the pen across the chart or positions the punches on a digital recorder.

Some recorders are designed so the time element drives the chart or paper tape and the gage height element positions the pen or punch. Other recorders using charts have the reverse arrangement. The important difference is in the range of gage height that can be recorded and the length of time that the instrument will operate without attention. Most stations are equipped with instruments that drive the chart or tape

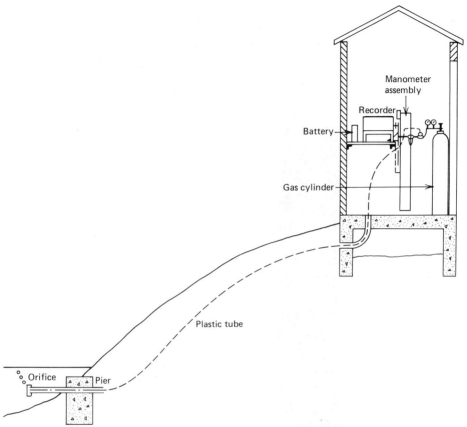

Figure 6-29 A gaging station may use a gas-purge system to measure stream stage. Nitrogen gas, slowly released through a servomanometer in a gage shelter, bubbles freely into the stream. Gas pressure in the tube equals the piezometric head on the orifice. The servomanometer converts pressure changes to a rotating shaft whcih drives a recorder pen. (From T. J. Buchanan and W. P. Somers, *Discharge Measurements at Gaging Stations*, Surface Water Techniques, Book 1, Chapter 11, U. S. Geological Survey, 1965.)

with the time element. These instruments can measure an unlimited range in stage and operate several months. The continuous strip chart recorder shown in Figure 6-31 is of this type. The digital recorder illustrated in Figure 6-32 is a battery-operated slow-speed papertape punch that records a four-digit number on a 16-channel papertape. The digital recorder tape is designed for machine reading and conversion to magnetic tape or punch cards for computer processing. It is not suitable for visual reading.

Telemetering systems can be used if immediate stage information is needed, such as for reservoir operation or flood forecasting. One type of telemetering equipment continually indicates or records the stage at a distant site by use of a pair of self-synchronizing motors, one motor on the transmitter and the other on the receiving unit. This system can transmit stages by wire up to 24 km. Another variation employs

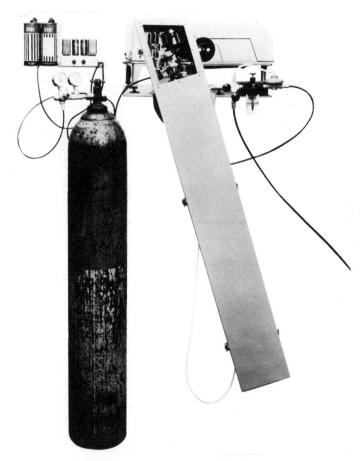

Figure 6-30 A servomanometer drives the strip chart recorder for a gas-purge system for measuring stage as diagrammed in Figure 6-29. (Courtesy of Leupold and Stevens, Inc.)

an impulse sender at the gaging site, which sends electrical impulses over telephone lines. The advantage of the impulse type over the position motor type is that it can transmit for longer distances. The second system codes the instantaneous stage and transmits it over telephone lines or by radio. The distance of transmittal is unlimited. This system responds to a telephone call or it may be interrogated by radio.

The Geostationary Operational Environmental Satellite (GOES) was launched by the National Oceanic and Atmospheric Administration in May 1974. Gage-height records are being transmitted from field radios through a radio transponder on GOES to receiving stations on earth. The transmitting device is attached to a digital recorder. The data from the receiving station are stored by a computer and are available on demand. GOES has the capacity to service 10 000 data collection points.

Crest-stage partial-record stations are equipped with a device that indicates the

Figure 6-31 A strip chart continuous stage recorder. The chain on the pulley attached to the front of the recorder is driven by a servomanometer that turns the pulley and moves the pen across the chart immediately behind the pulley. The pen reverses when reaching either margin of the chart; therefore, the range in stage that the recorder can measure is limitless. The chart is driven by a weight regulated by the timer at the left. (Photograph by Maggie Mac Kichan.)

maximum gage height (Figure 6-33). The gage consists of an iron pipe containing a graduated wooden stick. Powdered cork is placed in a pocket near the lower end of the stick and water enters the pipe through holes in the lower cap. A ring of powdered cork on the stick marks the maximum gage height.

6-12 Measuring of Streamflow by Current Metering

Canals and small streams are sometimes measured with flumes or weirs. However, flows in most natural streams and all large ones are measured by gaging stations calibrated using current metering to establish the stage-discharge rating.

Current meters are manufactured with the cups or vanes on either a vertical or horizontal axis. Vertical-axis meters operate in lower velocity water than horizontal axis meters. Their bearings are well protected from silty water and their rotors can be replaced in the field without adversely affecting their calibration. One rotor serves for the entire range of velocity. Horizontal-axis meters with vane rotors disturb the flow less than vertical-axis cup rotors because the direction of the flow is parallel to the axis. They are less likely to be fouled by debris and bearing friction is less than in vertical-axis meters.

Figure 6-32 The gage-height element of a digital recorder is driven by a float or a servomano-meter. The driving pulley and timer are in the back of the recorder. The two large dials on the front, having pointers at their lower edge, indicate the gage height. The one of the left indicates in feet and the one on the right in hundredths of a foot. An electric motor slowly moves the paper tape upward and, at a preset time interval, punches a record of gage height. Positioned behind the bar located in the center, the punches can be set to operate at 5-, 15-, 30-, or 60-minute intervals. (Photograph by Maggie Mac Kichan.)

The small Price type AA current meter, illustrated in Figure 6-34, is a vertical-axis meter and comes in four models: standard model, low-velocity model, four-vane model for measuring through ice, and a dwarf model. The dwarf model is two-fifths scale of the standard model and is used for shallow depths. The velocity of water is obtained by placing the meter at a point in the stream and counting the revolutions of the rotor during a measured interval of time. The number of revolutions of the rotor is obtained by closure of an electrical circuit with each revolution which produces a click in a headphone set. The time interval is measured with a stopwatch.

Four designs of horizontal-axis meters are the Ott, Neyrpic, Haskell, and Hoff. The Ott meter, a precision instrument made in Germany, has a component head-assembly that registers the velocity projected at right angle to the measuring section for angles up to 45 degrees and velocities less than 2.4 m/s. The Neyrpic meter was developed in France. The Haskell meter was developed in the United States and is used by the Great Lakes Survey. It is well suited to deep swift streams and the range in measurable velocity is increased by varying the pitch of the vanes. The Hoff meter was also developed in the United States and is used to measure flow in pipes.

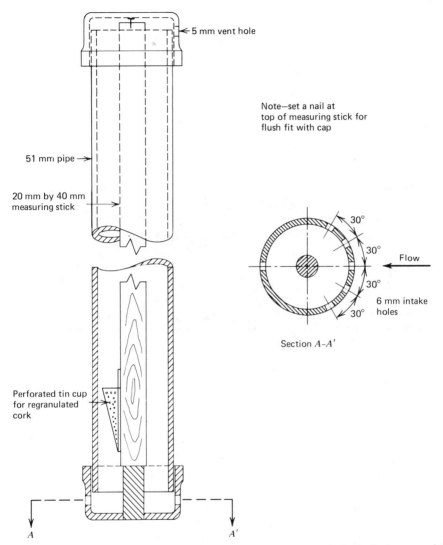

5 mm vent hole

Note—set a nail at top of measuring stick for flush fit with cap

51 mm pipe →

20 mm by 40 mm measuring stick

30°

30°

Flow

30°

6 mm intake holes

30°

Section A–A'

Perforated tin cup for regranulated cork

A A'

Figure 6-33 In this design of crest-stage indicator, water enters the holes in the lower cap (shown in Section A—A') and rises in the pipe. Some of the granulated cork that floats up on the water surface is left clinging to the stick after the water drains out, thus marking the high water level. (From T. J. Buchanan and W. P. Somers, *Discharge Measurements at Gaging Stations*, Surface Water Techniques, Book 1, Chapter 11, U. S. Geological Survey, 1965.)

Each meter must have a calibration or rating that is the relation between the water velocity and the number of revolutions of the rotor in a measured time interval. Formerly each meter had an individual rating. However, recently the cup rotors for the Price meters have been made of plastic, and are near enough alike that a standard rating can be used for many meters.

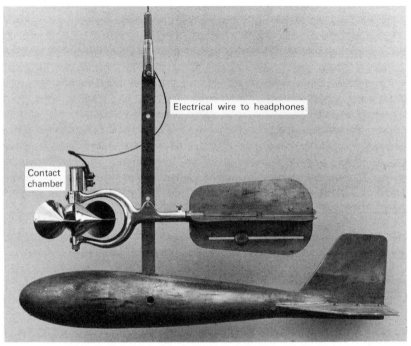

Figure 6-34 A small Price ,current meter suspended above a 13.6-kg Columbus-type sounding weight. The center of the rotor is 152 mm above the bottom of the weight. (Photograph by Maggie Mac Kichan.)

The ideal measuring section has a smooth bottom and fairly uniform depth, the velocity is well distributed across the stream, and the flow is perpendicular to the section. If the stream is wadable, the meter is suspended on a rod used to measure the depth and position of the meter in the vertical. A tagged line or a tape is used to measure the width of the stream and locate the measuring points. The size of meter and its position on the rod depend on the depth of the stream. Types of Price meters and settings are shown for various depths in Table 6-10. If the stream is too deep and

Table 6-10 Type of Price Current Meter and Meter Positions for Various Depths with Rod Suspension

Depth (m)	Meter	Meter Setting Below Water Surface
0.76 and greater	Type AA or type A	0.2 and 0.8 of depth
0.46 to 0.76	Type AA or type A	0.6 of depth
0.09 to 0.46	Dwarf	0.6 of depth

Source. U.S. Geological Survey.

swift to wade, the meter is suspended on a two-conductor cable and is held in the water with a sounding weight. The weights are made in 6.8, 13.6, 23, 34, 45, 68, 91, and 136 kg sizes. All weights are made of lead except the 6.8 kg, which is bronze. Measurements using cable suspension are made from bridges, cableways, or boats. If the weight required is not more than 13.6 kg, the meter may be raised and lowered with a handline. For heavier weights or when measuring from a boat, a sounding reel is used.

The meter is always suspended above the sounding weight as shown in Figure 6-34. The distance from the center of the meter to the bottom of the weight depends on the size of the weight. Soundings are made by setting the meter at the water surface and then lowering it until the weight rests on the stream bed. The distance lowered is measured with a depth indicator, or with a tape if a handline is used. The distance from the meter to the bottom of the weight is added to the measured distance to give the stream depth. Velocity measurements are taken at 0.6 depth, or 0.2 and 0.8 depths, from the water surface depending on the depth of the stream as shown in Table 6-11.

Table 6-11   Velocity-Measurement Method for Various Sounding Weights and Depths

Sounding Weight (kg)	Meter Above Bottom of Weight (mm)	Minimum Depth	
		0.6 depth (m)	0.2 and 0.8 depth (m)
6.8 and 13.6	152	0.37	0.76
23	168	0.43	0.85
23	274	0.67	1.37
34, 45 and 68	305	0.76	1.52
91 and 136	457	1.16[a]	2.29

Source. T. J. Buchanan and W. P. Somers, *Discharge Measurements at Gaging Stations,* Surface Water Techniques, Book 1, Chapter 11, U. S. Geological Survey, 1965.

[a]Use 0.2 method for depths 0.76 to 1.13 m with an estimated coefficient of 0.88.

The size of the weight needed depends on the depth and velocity of the stream. If adequate weight is used, the depth indicator gives the correct depth of the meter. However, if the velocity is high or the stream is carrying much debris, the meter can drift downstream and the depth indicator will register too great a depth, as shown in Figure 6-35. The correction for the downstream drift of the meter has two parts, the air-line correction and the wet-line correction. Air-line corrections for 5, 10, 15, 20, 25 and 30 degree angles and vertical lengths between 5 and 30 m at 5 m intervals are given in Table 6-12. Wet-line corrections for the same angles and wet-line length between 5 and 30 m at 5 m intervals are given in Table 6-13. If discharge measurements are made from a skewed bridge, or if the measuring section is not perpendicular to the thread of

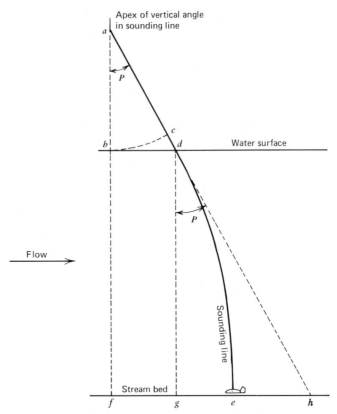

Figure 6-35 If the sounding weight is too light, a current meter is carried downstream causing an error in the sounding. The error is corrected in two parts, by an air-line correction from Table 6-12 and wet-line compensation determined by Table 6-13. (From T. J. Buchanan and W. P. Somers, *Discharge Measurements at Gaging Stations*, Surface Water Techniques, Book 1, Chapter 11, U. S. Geological Survey, 1965.)

the current, a horizontal angle correction is necessary as shown in Figure 6-36. The correction is made by multiplying the measured velocity by the cosine of the angle α.

A current-meter measurement is the summation of the discharge in partial areas. The computation of the discharge in a partial area is illustrated in Figure 6-37 and Equation 6-27.

$$q_3 = v_3 d_3 (b_4 - b_2)/2 \qquad\qquad (6\text{-}27)$$

where b_2 = distance from the initial point to the preceding observation point, metres
      b_4 = distance from the initial point to the following observation point, metres
      d_3 = mean depth of section 3, metres
      v_3 = average velocity in section 3, metres per second
      q_3 = discharge in partial area 3, cubic metres per second

The average velocity in the section is the velocity measured at 0.6 depth or the mean

Table 6-12   Air-line Correction in Metres to Be Substracted from Depth Reading to Correct for Downstream Drift of the Meter as Shown in Figure 6-35

Vertical Length (m)	Vertical Angle of Sounding Line					
	5°	10°	15°	20°	25°	30°
5	0.02	0.08	0.17	0.31	0.50	0.76
10	0.04	0.15	0.35	0.62	0.93	1.50
15	0.06	0.23	0.53	0.96	1.55	2.31
20	0.08	0.31	0.68	1.29	2.08	3.11
25	0.10	0.39	0.88	1.60	2.59	3.87
30	0.14	0.46	1.06	1.92	3.09	4.62

Source. T. J. Buchanan and W. P. Somers, *Discharge Measurement at Gaging Stations,* Surface Water Techniques, Book 1, Chapter 11, U. S. Geological Survey, 1965.

Table 6-13   Wet-line Correction in Metres to Be Subtracted from the Depth Reading to Correct for Downstream Drift as Shown in Figure 6-35

Wet-line Length (m)	Veritcal Angle of Sounding Line					
	5°	10°	15°	20°	25°	30°
5	0.0	0.02	0.05	0.10	0.15	0.23
10	0.01	0.05	0.11	0.20	0.32	0.47
15	0.02	0.07	0.16	0.30	0.48	0.72
20	0.02	0.10	0.22	0.41	0.66	0.95
25	0.03	0.12	0.28	0.51	0.87	1.18
30	0.03	0.15	0.36	0.61	0.96	1.41

Source. T. J. Buchanan and W. P. Somers, *Discharge Measurements at Gaging Stations,* Surface Water Techniques, Book 1, Chapter 1-1, U. S. Geological Survey, 1965.

of the velocities at 0.2 and 0.8 depths. Total discharge equals the sum of partial section discharges.

The observation points should be selected so that no more than 10 percent of the flow is in a single section. Usually about 20 sections are needed for a good measurement. If the depth and velocity are not uniform across the stream, variable width sections can be used. Measurements are made through holes in the ice if it is strong enough to support a man. A Price ice meter is designed to pass through holes made by an ordinary ice drill. The water under the ice is under pressure so when a hole is drilled the water rises into the hole. The depth of the stream is the distance from the bottom of the ice to the stream bed.

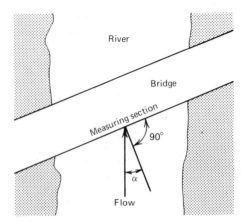

Figure 6-36 If the current is not perpendicular to the measuring section, as when gaging from a skewed bridge, the measured velocity is multiplied by the cosine of the angle α.

6-13   Calculating Streamflow by the Slope-Area Method

During floods, measuring the discharge with a current meter is frequently impossible or impractical. Consequently, peak discharges must be determined by indirect methods, such as slope-area, contracted-opening, flow-over-dam, and flow-through culvert after the passage of the flood. Indirect methods are based on hydraulic equations that relate discharge to the water-surface profile and geometry of the channel. A field survey is made after the flood to determine the location and elevation of high-water marks and the character of the channel.

A slope-area measurement is the most commonly used form of indirect measurement. The Manning equation or any other form of the Chezy equation can be used.

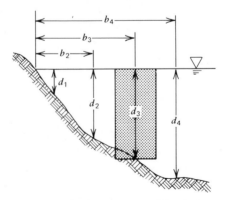

Figure 6-37 In computing the discharge in a partial area of a cross section, b_3 is the distance from the initial point to the center of partial area 3, d_3 is the mean depth, and $(b_4 - b_2)/2$ the width. Therefore, quantity of flow is calculated as shown in Equation 6-27.

The Manning equation is

$$Q = \frac{1.00}{n} A R^{2/3} S^{1/2} \tag{6-28}$$

where Q = quantity of flow, cubic metres per second

$\qquad n$ = coefficient of roughness

$\qquad A$ = cross-sectional area of flow, square metres

$\qquad R$ = hydraulic radius, metres (cross-sectional area divided by the wetted perimeter)

$\qquad S$ = slope of the hydraulic gradient, metres per metre

The Manning equation was developed for conditions of uniform flow in which the water-surface profile and the energy gradient are parallel to the stream bed, and the area, hydraulic radius, and depth remain constant throughout the reach. Natural channels are rarely uniform. However, Manning's equation is considered applicable if the energy gradient is modified to reflect only the losses due to boundary friction. The energy equation for a reach of a nonuniform channel between two sections, as illustrated in Figure 6-38, is

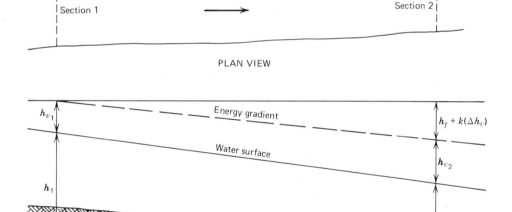

PLAN VIEW

PROFILE VIEW

Figure 6-38 Components of the energy equation in a nonuniform reach with subscript 1 indicating the upper cross section and subscript 2 the lower section. Cross section 2 is smaller than cross section 1, therefore, the velocity and velocity head are greater in section 2. The $k(\Delta h_v)$ is the head loss resulting from acceleration in a contracting reach. (From T. Dalrymple and M. A. Benson, *Measurement of Peak Discharge by the Slope-Area Method*, Techniques of Water Resources Investigations, U. S. Geological Survey, Book 3, Chapter 24, 1967.)

$$h_1 + h_{v_1} = h_2 + h_{v_2} + h_f + k \, \Delta h_v \qquad (6\text{-}29)$$

$$h_v = \alpha \frac{V^2}{2g} \qquad (6\text{-}30)$$

where
h = water surface elevation, metres
h_f = energy loss due to boundary friction in the reach, metres
h_v = velocity head, metres
$\Delta h_v = h_{v_1} - h_{v_2}$ = change in velocity head, metres
$k \, \Delta h_v$ = energy loss due to acceleration or deceleration in the reach, metres
k = a coefficient to correct for acceleration or deceleration
V = mean velocity in the section, metres per second
α = velocity head coefficient to correct for uneven distribution of velocity in cross section
g = acceleration of gravity, 9.80 metres per second squared

Subscripts 1 and 2 refer to the upstream and downstream sections, respectively. Rearranging Equation 6-29,

$$h_f = \Delta h + (1 \pm k)\Delta h_v \qquad (6\text{-}31)$$

where $\Delta h = h_1 - h_2$, the difference in water surface elevation at the two sections

When the flow is decelerating Δh_v is positive and k is positive, and when the flow is accelerating Δh_v is negative and k is negative. The value of k is usually assumed as 0.5 when the flow is decelerating and zero when the flow is accelerating.

The friction slope is

$$S = \frac{h_f}{L} \qquad (6\text{-}32)$$

where L = length of the reach, metres

The equation of flow in an open channel can be expressed as

$$Q = K \, S^{0.5} \qquad (6\text{-}33)$$

where K = channel conveyance, cubic metres per second

If the Equation 6-28 is used

$$K = \frac{1.00}{n} AR^{2/3} \qquad 6\text{-}34)$$

Conveyance of a reach is equal to the geometric mean of the conveyance at the upstream and downstream cross sections, and

$$Q = (K_1 K_2 S)^{0.5} \qquad (6\text{-}35)$$

The velocity head coefficient is

$$\alpha = \frac{\Sigma(K_t^3/A_t^2)}{K_T^3/A_T^2} \qquad (6\text{-}36)$$

Subscripts i and T refer to the subsections of the cross section and the total for the cross section, respectively.

The selections of a suitable reach is probably the most important element of a slope-area measurement. Ideal reaches are usually not found so the best available is selected. Good high-water marks are basic to a reliable slope-area computation, so the presence of quality marks is the first consideration.

The roughness coefficient is a measure of the resistance to flow; therefore, its correct evaluation has a direct effect on the accuracy of the measurement. A reach should be selected that has a roughness coefficient within the experience of the hydrologist or that has been well documented. The character of the bed material, cross-section irregularities, depth of flow, vegetation and alignment of the channel influence resistance to flow.

Basic n values are given in Table 6-14. A gradual change in cross-section shape will not appreciably affect n; however, rock outcrops and scalloped banks may increase n by as much as 0.020. Heavy brush growth on the banks and overhanging trees may increase n by as much as 0.040. Deep narrow channels lined with trees and brush will have an even larger n.

Table 6-14   **Basic Roughness Coefficients for Use in Manning Equation**

Bed Material	Size (mm)	n
Concrete		0.012–0.018
Firm earth		0.025–0.032
Sand	1–2	0.026–0.035
Gravel	2–64	0.028–0.035
Cobbles	64–256	0.030–0.050
Boulders	>256	0.040–0.070

Source. Benson and Dalrymple, *General Field and Office Procedures for Indirect Discharge Measurements,* Techniques of Water-Resources Investigations of the U. S. Geological Survey, Book 3, Chapter A1, 1968.

The geometry of the channel in the reach is also important. Marked changes in the shape of the channel along a reach should be avoided because of the uncertainties regarding the value of the velocity-head coefficient. The channel should be as uniform as possible, but, in any event, the changes in channel conveyance should be fairly uniform from section to section in order to be consistent with the assumption that the mean conveyance is equal to the geometric mean of the conveyance at the end sections. Flow confined within a simple trapezoidal channel is desirable because values of n have been determined for such conditions. However, compound channels can be used if they are properly subdivided. The reach should be contracting rather than expanding if there is a choice. Straight reaches are preferred, but they are seldom found in nature. A minimum of three cross sections is recommended. Computation of a slope-area measurement is illustrated by Example 6-7.

Example 6-7

A slope-area survey has been made of two adjacent reaches of a stream 27 and 36 m in length. The fall of the water surface through the reaches was 0.168 and 0.326 m respectively. The stream was slightly out of its channel so the cross sections were subdivided. Results of the field survey are given in Table 6-15 and Figure 6-39.

Solution

Equations 6-34 and 6-36 are used to compute K and α, respectively, which are entered in Table 6-15.

The friction head is equal to the change in water elevation through the reach adjusted for velocity head; however, the velocity is unknown. Therefore, a value of Q is assumed. The first value of Q can be approximated by ignoring the velocity head. The slope is then the change in elevation divided by the reach length, which gives a slope = 0.00622. Using Equation 6-35 the discharge in the first reach is

$$Q = (438.9 \times 491.3 \times 0.00622)^{0.5} = 36.6 \text{ m}^3/\text{s}$$

The reach is expanding so that A_1 is less than A_2; therefore, the Δh_v will be positive and Q will be greater than 36.6 m³/s. Assume Q is 37.5 m³/s. The final calculations are made on Table 6-16. Compute h_v using Equation 6-30. For the first cross section,

Table 6-15 Cross-Section Data for Slope-area Measurement in Example 6-7

Cross Section	n	$\dfrac{1.0}{n}$	A (m²)	R (m)	$R^{2/3}$ (m)	K	K^3/A^2	α
1	0.080	12.5	0.57	0.21	0.353	2.5	49	
	0.045	22.2	18.9	1.06	1.04	436.4	232 606	
							232 655	
			19.47			438.9	223 031	1.04
2	0.080	12.5	0.93	0.23	0.38	4.4	100	
	0.045	22.2	19.7	1.17	1.11	485.4	294 590	
	0.045	22.2	0.24	0.16	0.29	1.5	64	
							294 754	
			20.87			491.3	272 257	1.08
3	0.080	12.5	1.03	0.19	0.33	4.2	72	
	0.045	22.2	17.9	1.16	1.10	437.1	260 669	
	0.045	22.2	0.30	0.17	0.31	2.1	98	
			19.23			443.4	260 839	
							235 737	1.11

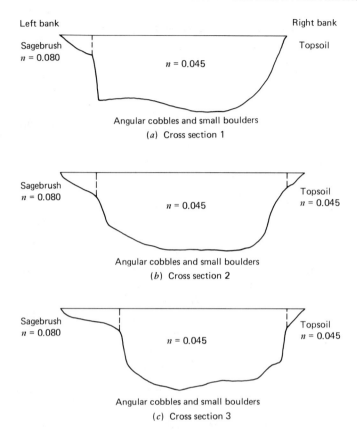

Figure 6-39 Cross sections of the channel for Example 6-7.

$V = 37.5/19.47 = 1.93$ m/s

$$h_v = \frac{1.04(1.93)^2}{2 \times 9.80} = 0.196 \text{ m}$$

and for the second section

$V = 37.5/20.87 = 1.80$ m/s

$$h_v = \frac{1.08(1.80)^2}{2 \times 9.80} = 0.178 \text{ m}$$

Compute h_f from Equation 6-31.
The flow is decelerating; therefore, $k = 0.5$, and

$h_f = 0.168 + 0.5 \times 0.018 = 0.177$

The slope is computed from Equation 6-32 and Q from Equation 6-35.

The computed Q is 37.6 m³/s, so for the second, assume $Q = 37.7$ and repeat the computation.

Table 6-16   Computation of Discharge for Example 6-7

Reach	Q (m³/s)	h (m)			h_v (m)	Δh_v (m)	h_f (m)	S (m/m)	Q (m³/s)
				First Trial					
1-2	37.5	0.168	Section 1	0.196		+0.018	0.177	0.00656	37.6
			Section 2	0.178					
				Second Trial					
1-2	37.7	0.168	Section 1	0.200		+0.019	0.178	0.00657	37.7
			Section 2	0.181					
				First Trial					
2-3	40.0	0.326	Section 2	0.202		−0.043	0.283	0.00786	41.4
			Section 3	0.245					
				Second Trial					
2-3	41.0	0.326	Section 2	0.213		−0.045	0.281	0.00781	41.2
			Section 3	0.258					
				Third Trial					
2-3	41.2	0.326	Section 2	0.215		−0.045	0.281	0.00781	41.2
			Section 3	0.260					

Averaging Discharges

$$\text{Average} = \frac{37.7 + 41.2}{2} = 39.4 \text{ m}^3/\text{s}$$

The computations for the reach between sections 2 and 3 are similar. The flow in the second reach is based on a new set of field measurements and evaluation of the roughness coefficient n; therefore, it is very unlikely that the results will be the same as for the first reach. For the first trial assume $Q = 40$ m³/s and repeat the computations.

The second reach is contracting; therefore, Δh_v is negative and $k = 0$. The reaches are of about equal accuracy so the answer is their average, 39.4 m³/s.

6-14   Determining Streamflow by Other Indirect Methods

The contraction of a stream channel by a roadway crossing creates an abrupt drop in water-surface elevation between an approach section and the contracted section under the bridge. The contracted section formed by the bridge abutments and the channel bed is in a sense a discharge meter which can be used to compute flood flows. The head on the contracted section is defined by high-water marks; the geometry of the channel and bridge as illustrated in Figure 6-40 is defined by field surveys. The drop in water surface between an upstream section and a contracted section is related to the corresponding change in velocity. The discharge equation is derived from the energy and continuity equations for the reach between these two sections.

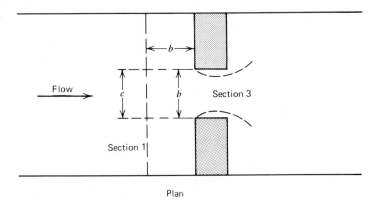

Plan

Figure 6-40 Geometry of a width-contracted section. (From H. F. Matthai, *Measurement of Peak Discharge at Width Contractions by Indirect Methods*, Techniques of Water Resources Investigations of the U. S. Geological Survey, Book 3, Chapter A4, 1968.)

$$Q = CA_3 \left[2g\left(\Delta h + \alpha_1 \frac{V_1^2}{2g} - h_f \right) \right]^{0.5} \tag{6-37}$$

where Q = discharge, cubic metres per second
    C = coefficient of discharge
    A_3 = gross area of section 3; this is the minimum section parallel to the constriction between the abutments and is not necessarily at the downstream side of the bridge, square metres

Δh = difference in elevation of the water surface between section 1 and 3, metres

$\alpha_1 \dfrac{V_1^2}{2g}$ = weighted average velocity head at section 1

where V_1 = average velocity, Q/A_1, metres per second

α_1 = coefficient which takes into account the variation in velocity in that section

h_f = head loss due to friction between section 1 and 3, metres

The head loss is the sum of the losses in the approach section and through the contraction. Both are computed using the Manning equation, Equation 6-28.

The coefficient of discharge is a combination of the coefficient of contraction, energy loss, and velocity head for contracting sections. Geometry of the abutments and channel are the primary factors affecting C. Table 6-17 gives approximate coefficients for the four types of openings shown in Figure 6-41 if the channel-contraction ratio m is greater than 0.70.

Table 6-17   Basic Coefficients for Computation of Flow Through Four Types
of Width Contractions Shown in Figure 6-41 Having a Channel
Contraction Ratio Greater Than 0.70 for Use with Equation 6-37

L/B	Type I	Type II Embankment Slope		Type III	Type IV
		1 to 1	2 to 1		
0.0	0.67	0.71	0.76	0.70	0.67
0.1	—	—	—	—	—
0.2	0.68	—	—	0.72	0.70
0.25	—	0.73	—	—	—
0.3	—	—	—	—	0.72
0.4	0.71	—	—	0.74	0.78
0.5	—	0.75	0.79	—	0.80
0.6	0.74	—	—	0.76	—
0.7	—	0.83	—	—	0.82
0.8	0.77	—	—	0.80	—
0.9	—	—	—	—	—
1.0	0.80	0.80	0.81	0.83	0.85
1.5	0.84	0.83	0.84	0.87	0.88
2.0 and greater	0.86	0.85	0.86	0.88	0.90

Source. H. F. Matthai, *Measurement of Peak Discharge at Width Contractions by Direct Methods*, Techniques of Water-Resources Investigations of the U. S. Geological Survey, Book 3, Chapter A4, 1968.

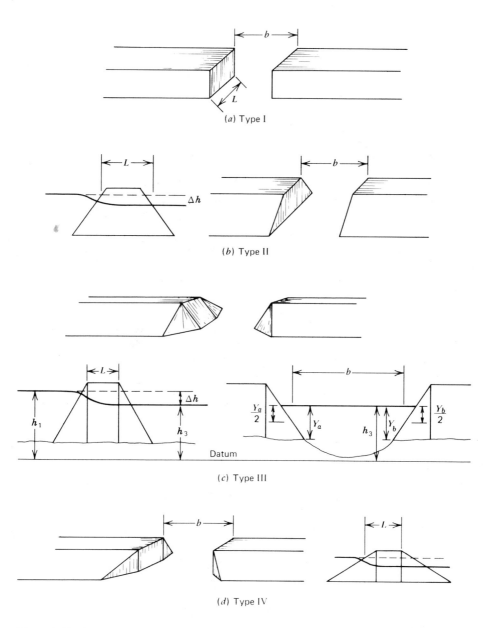

(a) Type I

(b) Type II

(c) Type III

(d) Type IV

Figure 6-41 Geometry of openings for selection of coefficient C for width-contraction computations of discharge. (a) Type I opening has vertical embankments and vertical abutments without wing walls. (b) Type II has sloping embankments and vertical abutments. (c) Type III has sloping embankments and sloping abutments. (d) Type IV has sloping embankments and vertical abutments with wing walls. (From H. F. Matthai, *Measurement of Peak Discharge at Width Contractions by Indirect Methods*, Techniques of Water Resources Investigations of the U. S. Geological Survey, Book 3, Chapter A4, 1968.)

$$m = 1 - \frac{q}{Q} = 1 - \frac{K_q}{K_1} \tag{6-38}$$

where m = channel contraction ratio for a contracted-width measurement

q = the discharge that can pass through the opening without contraction (the width c in Figure 6-40), cubic metres per second

Q = total discharge, cubic metres per second

K_q = conveyance for q, cubic metres per second

K_1 = conveyance for Q, cubic metres per second

The general discharge formula, Equation 6-37, requires a trial-and-error solution.

A weir, dam, or embankment generally forms a control section at which the discharge is related to the upstream water-surface elevation. The peak discharge can usually be determined on the basis of a field survey of high-water marks and the geometry of the structure. The most important elements of a computation of flow over a weir, dam, or embankment are the head h and the discharge coefficient C.[23] The field survey should define the headwater and tailwater elevations from high-water marks on both banks. The head h on the structure is measured at a distance of three or four times h upstream from the crest. If the tailwater elevation is higher than that of the dam or weir, determine tailwater profiles accurately because they may be used in the computation of discharge. The tailwater profiles must extend below the energy recovery zone shown in Figure 6-42.

A detailed description of the crest of the structure is required. The upstream slope, curvature of the crest, width of the crest, its roughness and the slope of the down-

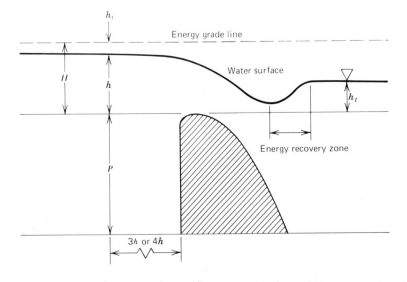

Figure 6-42 Flow over a submerged dam showing the energy recovery zone and tailwater head h_t. (From H. Hulsing, *Measurement of Peak Discharge at Dams by Indirect Method*, Techniques of Water Resources Investigations of the U. S. Geological Survey, Book 3, Chapter A5, 1968.)

stream face are needed to select the discharge coefficient. The height of the dam P is needed to compute the velocity of approach to determine h_v. The number and shape of piers and abutments should be described as well as all gates and other openings. The amount of gate opening should be recorded.

The equation of flow over a weir, dam or embankment is

$$Q = 0.552CbH^{1.5} \tag{6-39}$$

where Q = discharge, cubic metres per second
$\quad\ \ C$ = coefficient of discharge
$\quad\ \ b$ = width of structures normal to the flow excluding width of piers, metres
$\quad\ \ H$ = total energy head at the approach section (h + $V^2/2g$) referred to the crest of the weir or dam, metres
$\quad\ \ V$ = the mean velocity in the approach section, metres per second

Values of C for broad-crested weirs are given in Figure 6-43. Coefficients for dams having curved crests and ogee sections are given by Hulsing[23].

Flow through culverts can also be measured by indirect methods.[24] However, the hydraulics is very complex, depending on the type of flow, subcritical or supercritical, and the geometry of the culverts. Description of this type of measurement is beyond the scope of this book.

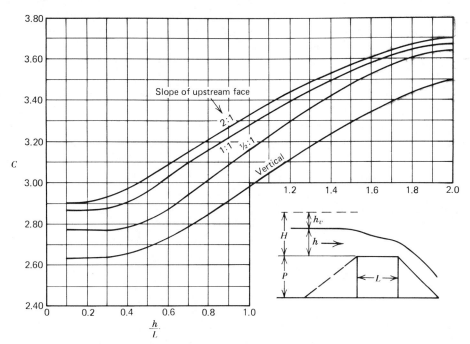

Figure 6-43 Coefficients of discharge for a broad-crested weir with a downstream slope equal to or greater than 1 to 1 and various upstream slopes. (From H. Hulsing, *Measurements of Peak Discharge at Dams by Indirect Methods*, Techniques of Water Resources Investigations of the U. S. Geological Survey, Book 3, Chapter A5, 1968.)

6-15 Computation of Discharge

Discharge measurements and simultaneous gage-height readings are used to prepare a calibration or rating curve for the station. The rating curve is then used to obtain an estimate of the discharge between measurements. If the stage-discharge relation is unique, the rating curve is simple; however, each station has an individual rating. If the rating changes, additional measurements are made until a new rating curve is defined.

A redefined rating curve is needed if the channel geometry or energy gradient changes. The former is the most common. The shifting control method is used if minor changes occur frequently. This method is applied by computing a shift, the difference between the observed gage-height at the time of measurement and the gage-height from the rating curve at the measured discharge. The discharge record is then computed by adjusting the observed gage-height by applying the correction (shift). If the shift is different for subsequent measurements, the shifts during the intervening interval may be varied with time and stage unless the time of occurrence can be identified.

Certain sand channel streams have a very unstable stage-discharge relations. Simons, Richardson, and Albertson[25] made extensive flume experiments and concluded that: "The form of bed roughness in alluvial channels is a function of the sediment characteristics and the characteristic of flow. That is, the bed configuration may change by changing one or more of the following discharge (which affects the depth), slope, temperature, or median diameter or size distribution of the bed material." The major forms of bed roughness that have been identified are illustrated in Figure 6-44. The flow changes from tranquil to rapid between the dune regime and the standing wave regime. However, changing depth or temperature will not change the flow regime from tranquil to rapid unless the slope for a given size of bed material is close to critical.

Critical depth is the depth at which for a given total head $(h + V^2/2g)$ the discharge is a maximum and the slope of the energy gradient is the critical slope. If the energy gradient is greater than critical the water flows at less than critical depth and if the gradient is less than critical the depth is greater than critical. The energy slope of some alluvial streams is so close to critical that a change in stage results in a change in regime. When the regime changes from a dune to standing wave regime, or vice versa, a discontinuity occurs in the rating curve as illustrated in Figure 6-45. The stage where the discontinuity occurs depends on whether the stage is rising or falling. A discontinuous rating is undesirable and should be avoided if possible.

Rating Curves for Gaging Stations

Individual measurements at some gaging stations deviate from the normal rating because the energy gradient at the time of measurement is not normal. Variations in the energy gradient are caused by obstructions in the channel such as a dam or by backwater from a tributary. If the variation in gradient is not too great, the measurement can be adjusted to fit the rating and the reverse adjustment applied when the discharge is computed. The energy gradient is approximated by measuring the dif-

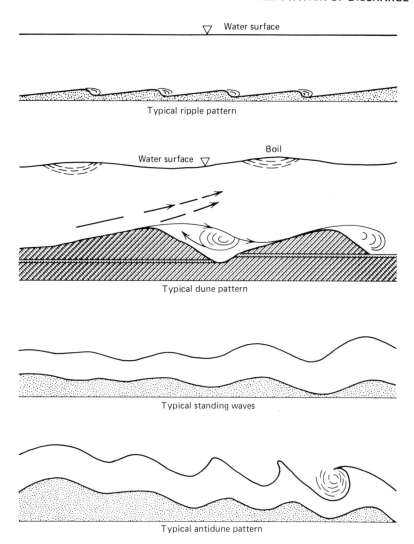

Figure 6-44 The major forms of bed roughness in a sand channel stream. Flow changes from tranquil to subcritical to rapid and finally to supercritcal as the bed form changes from dunes to standing waves. (From D. B. Simons, E. V. Richardson, and M. L. Albertson, "Flume Studies Using Medium Sand (0.45 mm)," *U. S. Geological Survey Water Supply Paper* 1498A, 1961.)

ference in water-surface elevation at the base gage and an auxiliary gage downstream. The gages must have the same datum.

The normal fall method is used to adjust the rating for variations in energy gradient by trial and error. The relation between the discharge at normal fall from the rating curve and the measured discharge is:

$$Q_n/Q_m = (F_n/F_m)^p \qquad (6\text{-}40)$$

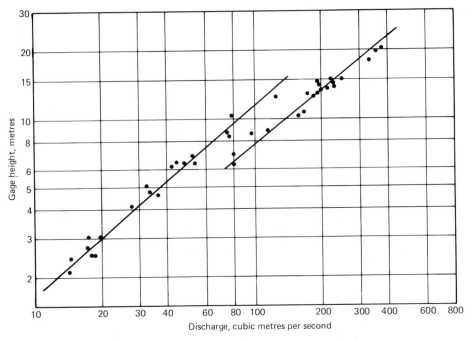

Figure 6-45 A discontinuous rating caused by the flow changing from subcritical to supercritical as a result of the form of bed changing from dunes to standing waves.

where Q = discharge, cubic metres per second
     F = fall, upper gage reading minus lower gage reading, metres
     n = normal conditions
     m = conditions at time of measurement
     p = a constant exponent

The measured discharge and gage height are plotted as shown in Figure 6-46. Assuming that the normal condition has the least backwater, a preliminary rating curve is drawn favoring the measurements farthest to the right. A curve showing the relation between gage height and normal fall is prepared using simultaneous readings on the two gages. A third curve is plotted showing the relation between the ratio of measured discharge to normal discharge and the ratio of measured fall to normal fall, as in Figure 6-47. A new rating curve is prepared using the measured discharge adjusted to normal fall.

The constant fall method is a variation of the normal fall method. A preliminary rating is prepared and the fall is noted by each measurement and a constant fall selected. The constant fall should be within the range of falls experienced. The procedure is the same as for the normal fall method except the constant fall is substituted for normal fall (Figure 6-48). A curve showing the relation between gage height and fall is not needed.

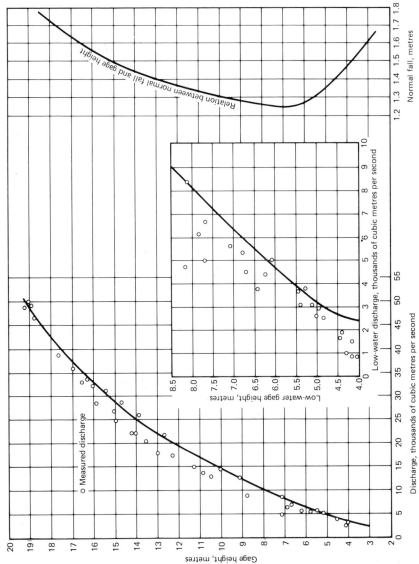

Figure 6-46 Preliminary, normal fall, rating curve for the Ohio River at Metropolis, Illinois, showing the unadjusted discharge and normal fall plotted against gage height. (From D. M. Corbett et al., *U. S. Geological Survey Water Supply Paper* 888, 1962.) SI units by author.

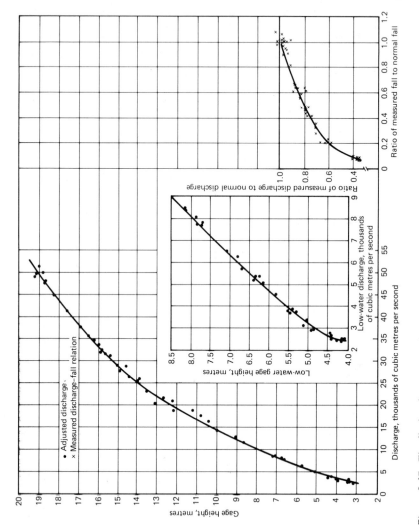

Figure 6-47 The final rating curve and a curve for adjusting the discharge to normal fall for the Ohio River at Metropolis, Illinois. (From D. M. Corbett et al., "Stream Gaging Procedure, A Manual Describing Methods and Practices of the U. S. Geological Survey," *U. S. Geological Survey Water Supply Paper 888,* 1962.) SI units by author.

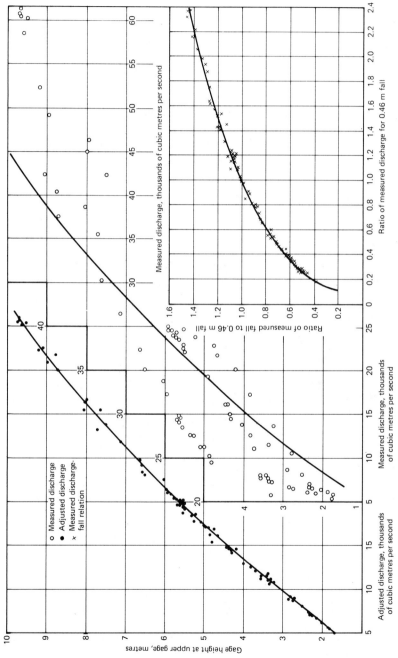

Figure 6-48 Constant fall rating curve for the Tennessee River at Guntersville, Alabama. The middle curve, drawn through the unadjusted measurements, is for a constant fall of 0.46 m. The ordinate of the plotted points at the lower right is the measured discharge divided by the discharge from the middle curve for the observed gage height; the abscissa is the measured fall divided by 0.46. The discharge is adjusted to a constant fall by dividing the measured discharge by the discharge ratio corresponding to the fall ratio. (From D. M. Corbett et al., "Stream Gaging Procedure, A Manual Describing Methods and Practices of the U. S. Geological Survey," *U. S. Geological Survey Water Supply Paper 388*, 1962.) SI units by author.

A flood wave passing down a low-gradient stream may change the energy gradient sufficiently to cause measurements to deviate from the rating.[26] This deviation from the normal is caused by changing discharge and is related to the velocity of the flood wave and the rate of change in gage height. An adjustment can be made without an auxiliary gage. The equation expressing the relation is

$$Q_m/Q_c = \left(1 + \frac{1}{US_e}\frac{dh}{dt}\right)^{0.5} \tag{6-41}$$

where Q_m = measured discharge, cubic metres per second
$\quad\quad\quad Q_c$ = discharge from rating curve, cubic metres per second
$\quad\quad\quad S_e$ = energy gradient at the time of the measurement, metres per metre
$\quad\quad\quad U$ = velocity of the flood wave, metres per second

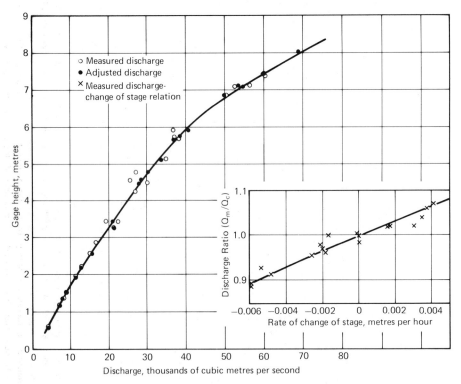

Figure 6-49 A rating curve adjusted for changing discharge. Plot the unadjusted measurements and draw a curve through them so that most of the rising stage measurements are at the right of the curve and falling stage measurements on the left. Second, plot a graph with Q_m/Q_c as the ordinate and the rate of changing stage as the abscissa and draw a curve through the points. Using this relationship, adjust the measured discharge and redraw the rating curve. If the preliminary rating does not fit the adjusted measurements, draw a new rating curve and repeat the process. (From Corbett et al., "Stream Gaging Procedure, A Manual Describing Methods and Practices of the U. S. Geological Survey," *U. S. Geological Survey Water Supply Paper* 888, 1962.) SI units by author.

dh/dt = change in stage during the measurement, positive if the stage is rising and negative if falling, metres per hour

S_e is not known; therefore, the rating is developed by trial and error as demonstrated in Figure 6-49. A preliminary stage-discharge curve is drawn and the dh/dt noted beside each measurement. A relationship is developed between Q_m/Q_c and dh/dt. The measurements are adjusted using this relationship and plotted on the preliminary stage-discharge curve. If they do not fit the preliminary curve, a new one is drawn and the procedure is repeated.

A stage-discharge rating defined by discharge measurements throughout the range of experienced gage height is desirable. However, sometimes the high end of the rating needs to be extended above the measurements. When a stream overflows its banks, the cross-sectional area increases rapidly, which causes the upper end of the rating to flatten. A graphical extension of this part of the rating is unreliable because the degree of flattening is not defined. A more reliable extension can be made by the area-velocity method. Two curves are prepared from discharge measurement notes: one the cross-sectional area versus gage height, and the other velocity versus gage height. The area curve can be developed above the highest discharge measurement from a field survey of the cross section. The velocity curve is extended upward taking into account vegetal cover, the extent of overflow area, and the possibility of backwater from tributaries. The advantage of the area-velocity method is that the area can be defined by surveys and the stage-velocity relation has very little curvature at high stages as shown in Figure 6-50.

Step backwater computations may also be used to define the upper end of a rating. This method requires a field survey and a computer is desirable because several trial computations are needed. A field survey is made much like the slope-area survey, except there are no high-water marks. At least six cross-sections are surveyed beginning at the gage and extending downstream. Additional sections may reduce the trial computations. The cross-section survey should include sufficient detail to compute the area and hydraulic radius of the sections and subsections. Possible subdivision of the sections should be noted and Mannings' n selected. The distance between cross sections should be measured.

The computations are made by assuming a discharge and an elevation at the most downstream section. Step backwater computations are made extending the profile to the gage. Using the same discharge, a second starting elevation is assumed and the step backwater computations repeated. If the two profiles do not converge below the gage, new starting elevations are assumed until two profiles converge. The assumed discharge and the gage height of the assumed profile at the gage are a point on the rating curve. The procedure is repeated for additional assumed discharges until the rating is defined.

Ice in streams also affect the stage-discharge relation. The three kinds of ice that may affect the station rating are surface, frazil, and anchor. If the control is a riffle or dam, the stream may have a complete ice cover above the control but backwater is unlikely if the control is free from ice. When the channel is the control or the control is far from the gage, the channel becomes a closed conduit when the stream is completely covered and the additional friction due to increased wetted perimeter and the slight

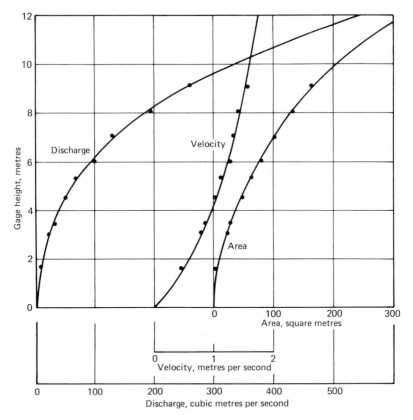

Figure 6-50 Extension of a rating curve by the area-velocity method.

reduction in cross-sectional area causes backwater. The amount of backwater can be determined by making current meter measurements through the ice. The amount of backwater may increase slightly by further reduction in cross-sectional area if the ice thickens, or it may be decreased by the movement of water smoothing the underside of the ice by erosion, thus reducing friction.

Ice crystals (frazil ice) form in swift water during extremely cold periods when there is no ice cover. It does not cause backwater unless lodged on the control or floating downstream and lodging under the surface ice between the gage and control.

Rocks on the bottom of shallow clear streams radiate heat rapidly on cold, clear nights. Anchor ice, a thin sheet, forms on the cooled rocks and causes backwater if formed on the control. However, it usually breaks loose shortly after sunrise. Anchor ice may lodge on the control after it breaks loose causing backwater or by floating downstream and lodging under surface ice between the gage and control. Backwater from frazil or anchor ice cannot be determined satisfactorily from discharge measurements because the backwater is too temporary and may change during the measurement.

Ice corrections to the discharge records are generally made after the record has been computed assuming no backwater. Each type of ice has a distinctive effect on the gage-height record. The open water discharge is estimated from discharge measurements, the appearance of the gage-height record, and temperature records in the vicinity.

6-16 Streamflow Records

Streamflow is expressed in SI units as a rate in cubic metres per second and as a volume in cubic metres, and in U. S. customary units as cubic feet per second and acre feet. In the United States, discharge records are published by the U.S. Geological Survey[27] and stage records by the National Weather Service.[28] The Corps of Engineers and others have streamflow and stage records on file. The National Water Data Exchange[29] (NAWDEX) has a water data source directory containing names and addresses of approximately 300 organizations that have water data available. The NAWDEX catalog contains information on the kinds of data, sites, and periods of record.

Streamflow records are published by water years, October 1 to September 30. Floods are unlikely in most parts of the United States in September and October; therefore, flow and channels are relatively stable, which is an advantage in compiling the records. Discharge is sometimes compiled by climatic years, April 1 to March 31. This sequence of months is suitable for compiling low-flow frequencies.

Although long records are preferred for most uses, manmade changes during a long period may have affected the flow. Changes may be obvious such as major storage or diversion; however, gradually increasing diversions or the effect of groundwater pumping near a stream may go unnoticed. Therefore, records should be tested for consistency before use.

The double-mass curve technique, which is the plot of the cumulation of one variable against the cumulation of a second variable for the same period, can be used, for instance, precipitation at one site versus precipitation at another site as in Example 6-1. The variable that is known to be consistent is known as the control record. The curve is a straight line if the variables are proportional, that is

$$Y = bX \qquad (6\text{-}42)$$

However, if the flow of a stream has changed due to human activities, probably adjacent streams have changed also. Therefore, control records that can be used with assurance are seldom available. Precipitation records can be used as a control for testing streamflow records, but the streamflow-precipitation relationship is not a simple ratio. Instead it usually approximates the form

$$Q = a + bP \qquad (6\text{-}43)$$

where Q = stream discharge
$\quad\ P$ = precipitation
$\quad\ a$ = constant representing infiltration and other initial abstractions
$\quad\ b$ = constant

Therefore, the discharge used for a control record should be computed by Equation 6-43 using P records that have been tested for consistency against other precipitation.

Some precipitation falling in a year infiltrates and appears as streamflow in a later year. Stream discharge computed with Equation 6-43 is more accurate if precipitation is adjusted to the effective precipitation P_e by allowing for carryover at the end of the year. The adjustment is made by using the equation

$$P_e = aP_0 + (1 - a)P_1 \qquad\qquad (6\text{-}44)$$

where P_e = effective precipitation
P_0 = current year precipitation
P_1 = preceding year precipitation
a = constant

The value of a is estimated by trial using the rank correlation technique.

The double-mass technique is used to test streamflow records for consistency but not to adjust them. If the slope of the curve shows an inconsistency and the record is proved to be in error, the records are recomputed. If the inconsistency is due to diversions or return flows, the amount of diversion or return flow is used to adjust the record if that is desired for the intended use.

Example 6-8

Lincoln Creek near Seward, Nebraska, has been gaged since 1954. Test the consistency of the discharge record by the double-mass technique from the data given in Table 6-18. The natural flow of Lincoln Creek has been affected by variable diversions. The same is true of all neighboring streams, therefore, it is necessary to use Equation 6-43 and a precipitation record for the test. Assume that the precipitation measured at York has been tested and found consistent.

Solution

List the observed discharge and precipitation in columns 1, 3, and 5 of Table 6-18. Rank the discharge listed in column 3 beginning with 1 for the greatest and record in column 2. If two values are identical, assign both the average rank if one had been slightly larger and the other slightly smaller. Rank the precipitation in column 5 and record in column 4. Square the difference in ranks (column 2 − column 4) and record in column 6. The sum of column 6 is 449.50. The equation for the rank correlation coefficient is

$$r = 1 - \frac{6\Sigma d^2}{N(N^2 - 1)} \qquad\qquad (6\text{-}45)$$

where r = rank correlation coefficient (This coefficient has the same meaning as the correlation coefficient computed by Equation 6-16.)
Σd^2 = sum of the rank differences squared
N = number of paired observations

Substituting the observed Lincoln Creek and York data in Equation 6-45,

$$r = 1 - \frac{6 \times 449.5}{21(21^2 - 1)} = 1 - \frac{2\,697}{9\,240} = 0.71$$

Assume a equal to 0.9 and use Equation 6-44 to compute P_e and list in column 8 and rank in column 7. Square the difference between column 7 and column 2 and list in column 9. The sum of column 9 is 427.5, and

$$r = 1 - \frac{6 \times 427.5}{21(21^2 - 1)} = 1 - 0.28 = 0.72$$

The correlation has improved by using a equal to 0.9. As a second assumption use a equal to 0.8 and repeat the computations using columns 10, 11, and 12. The sum of the ranks squared equals 421.5

$$r = 1 - \frac{6 \times 421.5}{21(21^2 - 1)} = 1 - 0.27 = 0.73$$

The best results are obtained using a equal to 0.8.

Plot a scatter diagram using P_e from column 11 as the abscissa and measured discharge, column 3, as the ordinate as illustrated in Figure 6-51. Although the points scatter widely, the relationship can be considered linear. Determine the regression line using Equations 6-8 and 6-11 to 6-16.

$$N = 21$$
$$\Sigma Q^2 = 47.475\,3$$
$$\Sigma Q = 27.046$$
$$\Sigma Q P_e = 19\,297.313$$
$$\Sigma P^2 = 9\,619\,662$$
$$\Sigma P_e = 14\,038$$

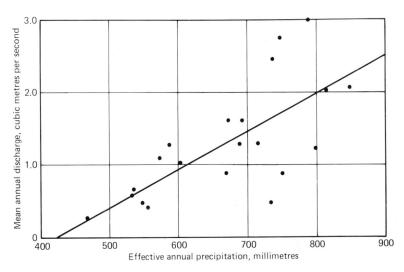

Figure 6-51 Scatter diagram of annual flow of Lincoln Creek at Seward, Nebraska, and effective precipitation, for Example 6-8.

Table 6-18 Computation of Effective Precipitation, in Millimetres, at York, Nebraska, from 1954 to 1976 for Example 6-8: Data in Columns 3, 5, 8, and 11 are Ranked in Columns 2, 4, 7 and 10 Beginning with the Largest; Columns 8 and 11 Are the Effective Precipitation Computed Using Equation 6-44

	Discharge		Observed			First Assumption			Second Assumption		
						Precipitation in Millimetres					
Year	Rank	(m^3/s)	Rank	(mm)	$(Rank\ 2^a$ - $Rank\ 4)^2$	Rank	$0.9P_0$ + $0.1P_1$ (mm)	$(Rank\ 2$ - $Rank\ 7)^2$	Rank	$0.8P_0$ + $0.2P_1$ (mm)	$(Rank\ 2$ - $Rank\ 10)^2$
1	2	3	4	5	6	7	8	9	10	11	12
1953				608							
54	9	1.28	8	740	1	9	727	0	9	714	0
55	17.5	0.481	17	498	0.25	17	522	0.25	18	546	0.25
56	21	0.272	20	457	1	21	461	0	21	465	0
57	1	3.00	2	871	1	2	830	1	4	788	9
58	9	1.28	13	641	16	13	664	16	11	687	4
59	14	0.898	6	777	64	6	763	64	5	750	81

Table 6-18 Continued

Year											
1960	3	2.46	10	726	49	8	731	25	7	736	16
61	7	1.60	11	682	16	11	686	16	10	691	9
62	6	1.61	12	671	36	12	672	36	12	673	36
63	13	1.02	15	586	4	15	594	4	14	603	1
64	12	1.10	16	570	16	16	572	16	16	573	16
65	4	2.06	1	915	9	1	880	9	1	846	9
66	16	0.592	21	435	25	20	483	16	20	531	16
67	2	2.75	3	824	1	5	785	9	6	746	16
68	11	1.22	5	792	36	4	795	49	3	798	64
69	5	2.01	4	821	1	3	818	4	2	815	9
1970	19	0.411	18	487	1	18	520	1	17	553	4
71	9	1.28	14	610	25	14	598	25	15	585	36
72	17.5	0.481	7	765	110.25	7	750	110.25	8	734	90.25
73				261							
74				440							
75	15	0.884	9	728	36	10	699	25	13	670	4
76	20	0.357	19	485	1	19	509	1	19	534	1
Total					449.5			427.5			421.5

[a]This computation is performed by subtracting the rank value in column 4 from the rank number in column 2 and squaring the remainder.

205

From Equation 6-13

$$b = \frac{19\ 297.313 - \dfrac{14\ 038 \times 27.046}{21}}{9\ 619\ 662 - \dfrac{(14\ 038)^2}{21}} = \frac{1\ 217.71}{235\ 593} = 0.005\ 17$$

From Equation 6-14

$$a = \frac{27.046 - 0.005\ 17 \times 14\ 038}{21} = -2.17$$

From Equation 6-8

$$S_y^2 = \frac{47.475\ 3 - \dfrac{(27.046)^2}{21}}{20} = 0.632\ 1$$

$$S_x^2 = \frac{9\ 619\ 662 - \dfrac{(14\ 038)^2}{21}}{20} = 11\ 780$$

From Equation 6-15

$$S_{y \cdot x}^2 = \frac{20}{19}\ [0.632\ 1 - (0.005\ 17)^2 \times 11\ 718] = 0.304$$

From Equation 6-16

$$r = \left(1 - \frac{0.304}{0.632}\right)^{0.5} = 0.72$$

which agrees with the rank correlation coefficient.

Substituting in Equation 6-43

$$Q = 0.005\ 17 P_e - 2.17$$

Plot the equation on the scatter diagram (Figure 6-51), for a visual check of fit.

Compute the annual Q using the regression equation and enter in Table 6-19. Cumulate the measured and computed discharge and plot on Figure 6-52. The mass curve is irregular as expected from the large departures from the regression line. However, the cumulative curve has a constant slope for the period 1954 to 1971. Beginning in 1972, the runoff appears to have declined. Insufficient record has been obtained since 1972 to draw a definite conclusion since records were not obtained in 1973 and 1974. However, runoff of irrigation water has reduced in the last few years. The equality of the cumulated computed discharge and measured discharge in 1976 has no hydrologic significance; they should be identical.

6-17   Streamflow-Duration Curves

A flow-duration curve is a cumulative frequency curve that shows the percent of time that a specified discharge was equaled or exceeded, and expresses the full range of historical flows combined in a single graph. If based on a long period of consistent and

Table 6-19 Computation of Double-Mass Data for Solution of Example 6-8 and Figure 6-51. Effective Precipitation is from Column 11, Table 6-18. Computed discharge Q equals 0.005 $17P_e$ − 2.17

Year	Effective Annual Precipitation (mm)	Measured Discharge		Computed Discharge	
		Annual (m^3/s)	Cumulative (m^3/s)	Annual (m^3/s)	Cumulative (m^3/s)
1954	714	1.28	1.28	1.52	1.52
55	546	0.481	1.761	0.66	2.18
56	465	0.272	2.033	0.24	2.42
57	788	3.00	5.033	1.91	4.33
58	687	1.28	6.313	1.38	5.71
59	750	0.898	7.211	1.71	7.42
1960	736	2.46	9.671	1.64	9.06
61	691	1.60	11.271	1.40	10.46
62	673	1.61	12.881	1.31	11.77
63	603	1.02	13.901	0.95	12.72
64	573	1.10	15.001	0.73	13.45
65	846	2.06	17.061	2.21	15.66
66	531	0.592	17.653	0.58	16.24
67	746	2.75	20.403	1.69	17.93
68	798	1.22	21.623	1.96	19.89
69	815	2.01	23.633	2.05	21.94
1970	553	0.411	24.044	0.69	22.63
71	585	1.28	25.324	0.86	23.49
72	734	0.481	25.805	1.63	25.12
75	670	0.884	26.689	1.30	26.42
76	534	0.357	27.046	0.59	27.01

representative record, it can be used to predict future flows for water power and water supply provided storage and diversions remain unchanged.

Mean daily records are generally used, however, monthly or annual records can be employed depending on the purpose of the curve. Curves prepared from annual and monthly data are less variable. Complete years must be used, but they need not be consecutive. If storage or diversions have changed since records began, the curves should be prepared for each period of consistent record.

The technique for preparing duration data is the same as that demonstrated in Table 6-7 for precipitation. The data are usually plotted on logarithmic normal probability

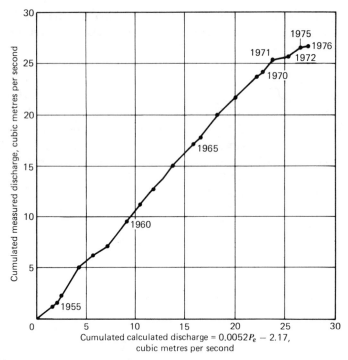

Figure 6-52 Double-mass curve of discharge of Lincoln Creek at Seward, Nebraska, for Example 6-8.

paper. Class intervals should provide from 20 to 30 well-distributed plotting points that include extreme observations.

The slope of the curve indicates the variability of flow as illustrated in Figure 6-53. The Dismal River at Dunning, Nebraska, drains a sand hills area where infiltration rates are high, and low flows are maintained by groundwater seepage, thus, the flow is very uniform. Logan Creek near Uehling, Nebraska, drains a loess covered area having a lower infiltration rate and steeper slopes; therefore, runoff is rapid and its variability high.

Low-Flow Frequency Curves

The adequacy of streamflow to supply requirements for disposal of liquid wastes, municipal and industrial supplies, and to maintain adequate habitat for fish and wildlife is commonly evaluated in terms of low-flow frequencies. In some places, a legal index for water pollution control is keyed to the seven-day 10-year low flow, which may be derived from seasonal or climatic-year records. A seven-day 10-year low flow is the lowest average flow for seven consecutive days that has an average recurrence interval of 10 years.

Low-flow frequency distributions are generally computed using annual series data and are plotted on extreme probability paper using a logarithmic scale for discharge;

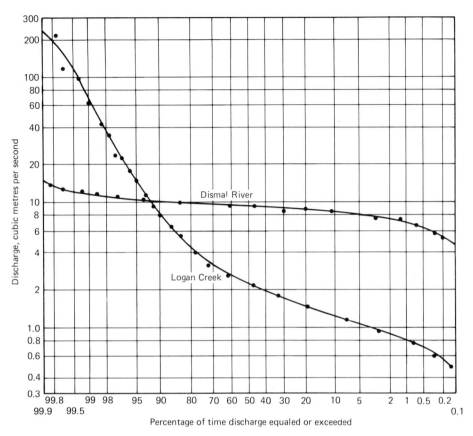

Figure 6-53 Flow-duration curves of daily flow of the Dismal River at Dunning, Nebraska, and Logan Creek at Uehling, Nebraska. The Dismal River drains a sand hills area having a high infiltration rate, while Logan Creek drains loess hills that have a low infiltration causing the flow to be variable.

an annual series is composed of the lowest value in each year of record. Plotting positions can be computed for the Gumbel distribution using Equation 6-9 and ranking the flows beginning at the lowest with one, or by using the log Pearson type III distribution. If the stream is dry in one or more years, zero values are entered in the series and ranked along with the flow data. Spatial variations in the geology of a basin may cause some departures from the usual shape of the curve. Therefore, the fit of the log Pearson distribution at the low end should be verified by plotting some of the observed data using the Gumbel plotting positions. The log Pearson fit can be modified if necessary.

Typical examples of seven-day low-flow curves are shown in Figure 6-54. The curve for the Elkhorn River at Waterloo, Nebraska, is a straight line on a logarithmic scale and typical of a stream unaffected by storage or diversion. The curve for Beaver Creek at Genoa, Nebraska, turns downward at the low end indicating diversions in the basin.

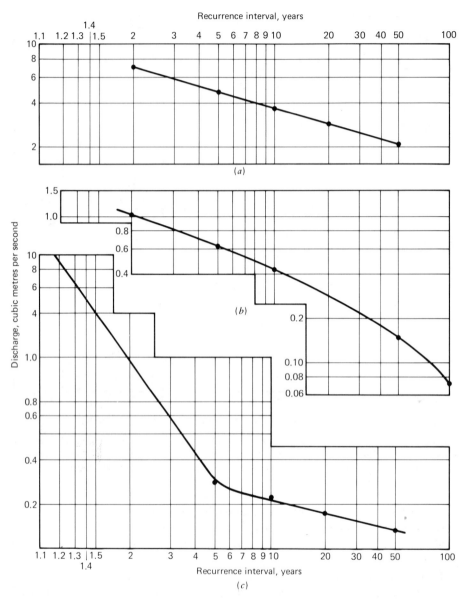

Figure 6-54 Typical 7-day low-flow frequency curves. (*a*) Elkhorn River at Waterloo, Nebraska, is typical of a stream unaffected by diversion or storage and plots as a straight line. (*b*) Beaver Creek at Genoa, Nebraska, is affected by diversion causing the lower end to turn down. (*c*) Suwannee River at White Springs, Florida, is fed by two sources having different flow characteristics causing the lower end to flatten.

The unusual shape of the curve for the Suwannee River at White Springs, Florida, reflects geological differences in the basin.[30] The annual minimum flow of Suwannee River at White Springs consists of two principal parts: a flow ranging from about 22 to zero m³/s from the headwaters in Okefenokee Swamp and an inflow of 0.1 to 3 m³/s from a limestone aquifer in the lower reach of the river. The wide range in shape of the curves in Figure 6-54 emphasizes the risk of extending curves or estimating low flows at ungaged sites without knowledge of the physical character of the basin and the effects of manmade works.

Many streams cannot supply the demands on them without storage. Riggs and Hardison[31] described how low-flow frequency curves can be used to develop a draft storage relationship that has a stated probability of failure. Example 6-9 illustrates the method.

Example 6-9

Determine the combination of flows and storages that the Elkhorn River at Waterloo, Nebraska, can provide with a 0.05 probability of failure (recurrence interval of 20 years). Low-flow frequency curves are available in Figure 6-55.

Solution

Multiply the mean 7-day 20-year low flow from Figure 6-55 by 7 (7 X 2.83 = 19.8 m³/s·d) and plot the product 19.8 as the ordinate and 7 as the abscissa on Figure 6-56.

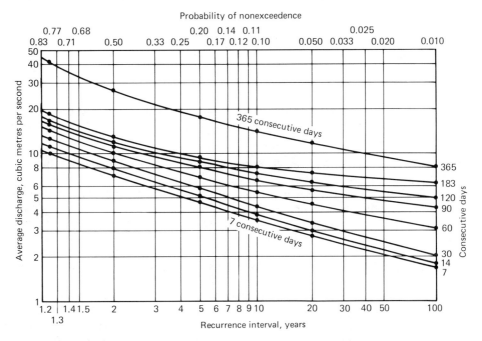

Figure 6-55 Low-flow frequency curves for the Elkhorn River at Waterloo, Nebraska, for the period 1930-1976 based on an annual series for Example 6-9.

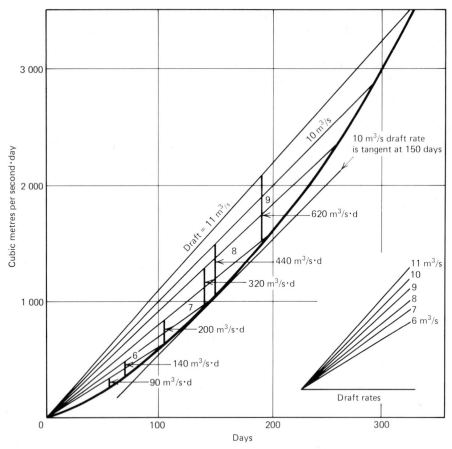

Figure 6-56 Frequency-mass curve with a 0.05 nonexceedence probability for the Elkhorn River at Waterloo, Nebraska, for Example 6-9.

Repeat the computation for each consecutive-day period by multiplying the flow for the 20-year recurrence interval by the number of consecutive days.

The points define a frequency-mass curve of low flows that can be used to define a draft-storage relationship. Compute and plot several draft rates. For example, a draft rate of 10 m³/s for 100 days amounts to 1 000 m³/s·d. The storage required is the maximum difference in ordinates between the straight line representing the draft rate and the mass diagram curves. The difference in ordinates is a maximum where the slope of the draft rate line is tangent to the frequency-mass curve. The 10 m³/s draft rate is tangent at 150 days. Measure the maximum storage for each rate and convert to millions of cubic metres by multiplying by 0.086 4. Plot the results on Figure 6-57.

Storage computed by this method depends on a full reservoir at the beginning of each year since no provisions is made for carryover. If the low-flow period occurs at the beginning of the climatic year, April 1, the analysis must begin at some other date when the reservoir is usually full. The curves in Figure 6-55 were computed from an

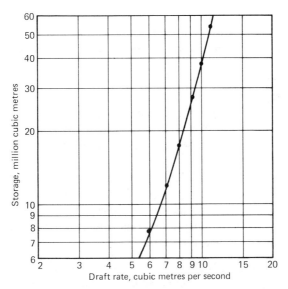

Figure 6-57 Storage-draft-frequency relation with a 0.05 nonexceedence probability for the Elkhorn River at Waterloo, Nebraska, for Example 6-9.

annual series; therefore, if recurrence intervals of less than 10 years are used, the interval of the annual series is adjusted according to Table 6-8.

6-18 Parametric and Statistical Hydrology

Many streams have not been measured and, at best, historical records on others are likely quite short. Parametric methods have been used for many years to calculate records at ungaged sites; whereas statistical methods have recently come into use because of the availability of digital computers, although they too have been known for a long time. These methods range from entirely empirical to entirely statistical and from simple to complex. Usually the complex methods are more reliable; however, they require the use of digital computers to be economically justified.

Parametric hydrology is that field of mathematical hydrology that attempts to model the land phase of the hydrologic cycle by approximating the physical laws governing the various components of the rainfall-runoff system. Hydrologic models contain certain parameters that can be changed to represent various climatic and physical conditions of a drainage basin. The model parameters are adjusted by trial and error until they approximate the observed record well enough to be judged adequate to solve the problem at hand. Parametric methods must be used with caution and judgment and, if possible, verified with local data.

A statistical model generates a long series of events by use of statistical parameters computed from a short historical record. Statistical parameters are the mean, standard deviation, skew, and serial correlation coefficient. The model does not reproduce the specific sequence of events observed; rather, it generates an equal likely sequence of events. If the parameters used in the model are derived during a sequence of exceptionally dry or wet years, the model generates records that are too low or too high, respectively.

Runoff Equations

Empirical formulas have been used for many years to compute flood flows for the design of drainageways, culverts, and small dams; although generally more dependable methods have been available. The Meyer equation is one of the simplest formulas of this type.

$$Q = 176P(A)^{0.5} \qquad\qquad (6\text{-}46)$$

where Q = maximum discharge, cubic metres per second
$\quad\ \ P$ = variable percentage coefficient, called the Meyer coefficient
$\quad\ \ A$ = drainage area, square kilometres

The rational equation, also used for many years for culvert and storm sewer design, has the two independent variables of rainfall intensity and drainage area.

$$Q = 0.278CIA \qquad\qquad (6\text{-}47)$$

where Q = maximum rate of runoff, cubic metres per second
$\quad\ \ C$ = coefficient of runoff based on type and character of surface, Table 6-20
$\quad\ \ I$ = average rainfall intensity, for the period of maximum rainfall of a given frequency of occurrence having a duration equal to the time required for the entire drainage area to contribute flow, millimetres per hour
$\quad\ \ A$ = drainage area, square kilometres

The rational equation is an improvement over earlier empirical formulas and is still applied where information is not available to allow use of more accurate methods. However, satisfactory results are possible only for small watersheds where coefficients are determined from local experience and runoff data from similar watersheds are available for comparison.

A brief description of the rational method follows but for complete instructions consult *Design and Construction of Sanitary and Storm Sewers*. Manuals and Reports of Engineering Practice, No. 37, American Society of Civil Engineers, 1969. The procedure assumes that the maximum rate of runoff is directly related to the rainfall intensity during the time of concentration, which is the time required for the entire basin to contribute to runoff. Average coefficients given in Table 6-20 can be adjusted to reflect antecedent and other conditions affecting runoff. The flood computed by this method has the same recurrence interval as the precipitation obtainable from graphs or maps, such as those shown in Figures 6-12, 6-13, and 6-14.

Soil-Cover Complex Method

The Soil Conservation Service has developed a method of computing direct storm runoff from areas without streamflow records but where detailed data on soils and vege-

Table 6-20   **Average Runoff Coefficients for Use in the Rational Equation**

Description of Area	Runoff Coefficients
Business—Downtown	0.70 to 0.95
Neighborhood	0.50 to 0.70
Residential	
Single-family	0.30 to 0.50
Multiunits, detached	0.40 to 0.60
Multiunits, attached	0.60 to 0.75
Residential (suburban)	0.25 to 0.40
Apartment	0.50 to 0.70
Industrial	
Light	0.50 to 0.80
Heavy	0.60 to 0.90
Parks, cemeteries	0.10 to 0.25
Playgrounds	0.20 to 0.35
Railroad yard	0.20 to 0.35
Unimproved	0.10 to 0.30

Character of Surface	Runoff Coefficients
Pavement	
Asphaltic and concrete	0.70 to 0.95
Brick	0.70 to 0.85
Roofs	0.75 to 0.95
Lawns, sandy soil	
Flat, 2 percent	0.05 to 0.10
Average, 2 to 7 percent	0.10 to 0.15
Steep, 7 percent	0.15 to 0.20
Lawns, heavy soil	
Flat, 2 percent	0.13 to 0.17
Average, 2 to 7 percent	0.18 to 0.22
Steep, 7 percent	0.25 to 0.35

Source. Design and Construction of Sanitary and Storm Sewers, American Society of Civil Engineers, Manuals and Reports on Engineering Practice, No. 37, 1969, p. 51.

tative covers are available. The method was developed from many records of rainfall and runoff and numerous combinations of soils and covers.

The following description was taken from section 4 of the *National Engineering Handbook.*[32] The basis of the method is that runoff equals the excess precipitation, which is the total precipitation less infiltration and other losses. Soils are assigned to hydrologic groups listed in the *National Engineering Handbook* and defined as follows:

A. (Low runoff potential). Soils having high infiltration rates even when thoroughly wetted and consisting chiefly of deep, well to excessively drained sands or gravels. These soils have a high rate of water transmission.

B. Soils having moderate infiltration rates when thoroughly wetted and consisting chiefly of moderately deep to deep, moderately well to well drained soils with moderately fine to moderately coarse textures. These soils have a moderate rate of water transmission.

C. Soils having slow infiltration rates when thoroughly wetted and consisting chiefly of soils with a layer that impedes downward movement of water, or soils with moderately fine to fine texture. These soils have a slow rate of water transmission.

D. (High runoff potential). Soils having very slow infiltration rates when thoroughly wetted and consisting chiefly of clay soils with a high swelling potential, soils with a permanent high water table, soils with a claypan or clay layer at or near the surface, and shallow soils over nearly impervious material. These soils have a very slow rate of water transmission.

Ground cover, soil conditions, and land treatment have an effect on infiltration and an identification number called a curve number is assigned to each combination of soil and cover as given in Table 6-21.

Infiltration is the rate water enters the soil; however, the ability of the soil to transmit water away from the surface affects infiltration. As a storm progresses, slow transmission of the water away from the surface retards infiltration. Consequently, infiltration is greatest near the beginning of a storm and gradually decreases to some steady rate as shown in Figure 6-26. Infiltration capacity to return to prestorm rate, called the antecedent condition, can take several days after precipitation ceases. The Soil Conservation Service procedure adjusts the identification number for antecedent conditions. Condition I is the lowest limit of moisture content and the upper limit of retention, condition II is the average, and condition III is the upper limit of moisture content and the lower limit of retention. Adjustments for antecedent conditions are given in Table 6-22.

The soil-cover complex method was designed to use available rainfall data, mostly from nonrecording stations where only daily amounts are recorded. The empirical rainfall-runoff relationship is

$$Q = \frac{(P - 0.2S)^2}{P + 0.8S} \tag{6-48}$$

where Q = runoff, millimetres of depth
P = total precipitation, millimetres
S = retention including the initial abstraction, which is assumed to be $0.2S$ millimetres, millimetres

Runoff does not begin until rainfall exceeds infiltration. Retention S and precipitation P when runoff begins are listed in Table 6-22 for each curve number. The curve number is a transformation of S to make the curves nearly a straight line.

Table 6-21 Runoff Curve Numbers for Hydrologic Soil-Cover Complexes (Antecedent Moisture Condition II, and $I_a = 0.2S$)

Land Use	Cover Treatment or Practice	Hydrologic Condition	A	B	C	D
Fallow	Straight row	—	77	86	91	94
Row crops	Straight row	Poor	72	81	88	91
	Straight row	Good	67	78	85	89
	Contoured	Poor	70	79	84	88
	Contoured	Good	65	75	82	86
	Contoured and terraced	Poor	66	74	80	82
	Contoured and terraced	Good	62	71	78	81
Small grain	Straight row	Poor	65	76	84	88
	Straight row	Good	63	75	83	87
	Contoured	Poor	63	74	82	85
	Contoured	Good	61	73	81	84
	Contoured and terraced	Poor	61	72	79	82
	Contoured and terraced	Good	59	70	78	81
Close-seeded	Straight row	Poor	66	77	85	89
Legumes[a] or	Straight row	Good	58	72	81	85
rotation	Contoured	Poor	64	75	83	85
meadow	Contoured	Good	55	69	78	83
	Contoured and terraced	Poor	63	73	80	83
	Contoured and terraced	Good	51	67	76	80
Pasture or		Poor	68	79	86	89
range		Fair	49	69	79	84
		Good	39	61	74	80
	Contoured	Poor	47	67	81	88
	Contoured	Fair	25	59	75	83
	Contoured	Good	6	35	70	79
Meadow		Good	30	58	71	78
Woods		Poor	45	66	77	83
		Fair	36	60	73	79
		Good	25	55	70	77
Farmsteads		—	59	74	82	86
Roads (dirt)[b]		—	72	82	87	89
(hard surface)[b]		—	74	84	90	92

Source. National Engineering Handbook, Section 4, Hydrology, Soil Conservation Service, 1971.

[a] Close-drilled or broadcast.
[b] Including right-of-way.

Table 6-22 Curve Numbers and Constants for Antecedent Conditions and Initial Abstractions = 0.2S (Refer to Equation 6-48 and Figure 6-58)

1	2	3	4	5	1	2	3	4	5
Curve Numbers for Conditions			S Values[a] (mm)	Value of P When Runoff Starts[a] (mm)	Curve Numbers for Conditions			S Values[a] (mm)	Value of P When Runoff Starts[a] (mm)
II	I	III			II	I	III		
100	100	100	0	0	60	40	78	169	33.8
99	97	100	2.57	0.5	59	39	77	177	35.3
98	94	99	5.18	1.0	58	38	76	184	36.8
97	91	99	7.85	1.5	57	37	75	192	38.4
96	89	99	10.6	2.0	56	36	75	200	39.9
95	87	98	13.4	2.8	55	35	74	208	41.6
94	85	98	16.2	3.3	54	34	73	216	43.2
93	83	98	19.1	3.8	53	33	72	225	45.0
92	81	97	22.1	4.3	52	32	71	234	47.0
91	80	97	25.1	5.1	51	31	70	244	48.8
90	78	96	28.2	5.6	50	31	70	254	50.8
89	76	96	31.5	6.4	49	30	69	264	52.8
88	75	95	34.5	6.9	48	29	68	274	54.9
87	73	95	37.8	7.6	47	28	67	287	57.4
86	72	94	41.4	8.4	46	27	66	297	59.4
85	70	94	44.7	8.9	45	26	65	310	62.0
84	68	93	48.3	9.6	44	25	64	323	64.5
83	67	93	52.1	10.4	43	25	63	335	67.1
82	66	92	55.9	11.2	42	24	62	351	70.1
81	64	92	59.4	11.9	41	23	61	366	73.2
80	63	91	63.5	12.7	40	22	60	381	76.2
79	62	91	67.6	13.5	39	21	59	396	79.2
78	60	90	71.6	14.2	38	21	58	414	82.8
77	59	89	76.0	15.2	37	20	57	432	86.4
76	58	89	80.3	16.0	36	19	56	452	90.4
75	57	88	84.6	17.0	35	18	55	472	94.5
74	55	88	89.2	17.8	34	18	54	493	98.6
73	54	87	94.0	18.8	33	17	53	516	103
72	53	86	98.8	19.8	32	16	52	538	108
71	52	86	104	20.8	31	16	51	564	113
70	51	85	109	21.8	30	15	50	592	118
69	50	84	114	22.9					
68	48	84	119	23.9	25	12	43	762	152
67	47	83	125	24.9	20	9	37	1016	203

218

Table 6-22 **continued**

1	2	3	4	5	1	2	3	4	5
				Value of					Value of
Curve Numbers				P When	Curve Numbers				P When
for Conditions			S	Runoff	for Conditions			S	Runoff
			Values[a]	Starts[a]				Values[a]	Starts[a]
II	I	III	(mm)	(mm)	II	I	III	(mm)	(mm)
66	46	82	131	26.2	15	6	30	1440	288
65	45	82	137	27.4	10	4	22	2286	457
64	44	81	143	28.4	5	2	13	4826	965
63	43	80	149	29.7	0	0	0	infinity	infinity
62	42	79	156	31.2					
61	41	78	162	32.5					

Source. National Engineering Handbook, Section 4, Hydrology, Soil Conservation Service, 1971. SI units by author.

[a]For Curve number in column 1 for Condition II

$$\text{Curve number } = \frac{25\,400}{S - 254} \tag{6-49}$$

Figure 6-58 can be used for rapid solution of Equation 6-48.

Example 6-10
Determine the runoff from a 150-mm rain on a drainage basin planted with crops in straight rows, hydrologic Class B soils, and antecedent moisture condition II.

Solution
A Class B soil in a straight row crop in good condition has a curve number of 78 from Table 6-21. Class II antecedent conditions require no adjustment. Enter Figure 6-58 at a rainfall of 150 mm, interpolate between curves 75 and 80, reading a runoff of 94 mm depth over the drainage area.

6-19 Unit Hydrographs

A graph showing variations of stage, discharge, velocity, or any other property of water with respect to time is a hydrograph. A discharge hydrograph has three parts: a rising limb, crest segment, and falling limb. Points of inflection separate the crest segment from the rising and falling limbs, as illustrated in Figure 6-59. Hydrologists generally assume that surface runoff ceases at the point of inflection between the crest segment and the falling limb.

A discharge hydrograph has three components depending on the route to the stream. Surface runoff is the water flowing over the surface of the ground to a stream channel

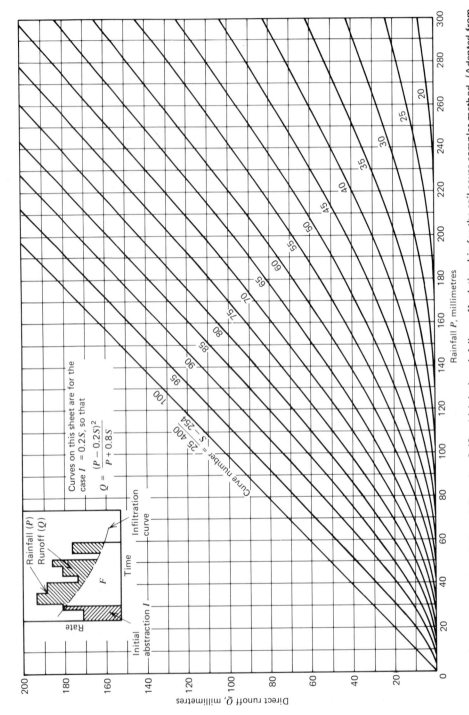

Figure 6-58 Diagram for the solution of Equation 6·48, which is the rainfall-runoff relationship for the soil-cover comples method. (Adapted from *National Engineering Handbook*, Section 4, Hydrology, Soil Conservation Service, 1971.)

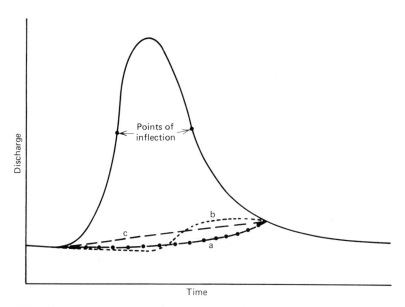

Figure 6-59 The portions of a hydrograph are the rising limb, crest segment, and falling limb. The parts are separated by points of inflection where the hydrograph changes from convex to concave and then concave to convex. Lines *a*, *b*, and *c* illustrate methods of base flow separation.

and includes the precipitation falling directly in the stream. The second component is the precipitation that infiltrates but is obstructed by less permeable soils near the surface thus discharging through the upper layer of soil in a relatively short time; this is called interflow or sometimes subsurface streamflow. The third component is the water that reaches the water table and eventually seeps into a stream, which is referred to as base flow and constitutes all the natural dry-weather flow.

A unit hydrograph represents the surface runoff resulting from 1.0 mm of precipitation in excess of infiltration and other losses, occurring in a unit time. This hydrograph can be used to compute the peak and other rates of surface runoff from an observed rainfall. The basic hypothesis is that, for a given drainage basin, surface runoff from excess rainfall occurring in a unit time produces a hydrograph with a common time base and discharge ordinates in linear proportion to the amount of rainfall excess. That is, a rainfall excess of 10 mm within a unit time produces a hydrograph having ordinates 10 times as great as those of a 1-mm rainfall excess, while the duration of the discharge remains approximately the same. Furthermore, application of a unit hydrograph assumes that the rates of runoff from consecutive units of rainfall excess, having an uniform areal distribution, are proportional to the unit hydrograph; hence, the ordinates of several partial hydrographs, obtained by multiplying the unit hydrograph by rainfall excess in successive units of time, can be superimposed and added to obtain the total hydrograph.

The unit hydrograph theory also assumes a precipitation of uniform rate during the unit time period, thus, the time unit is selected so this assumption is substantially correct. For a drainage area of less than about 200 square kilometres, a unit time about half the lag time from the center of precipitation excess to the peak flow is satisfactory. The minimum unit time for any area is about one third the lag period. In general, a unit time of 12 hours is too great since a uniform rate of rainfall of this duration is unlikely.

The shape of the falling limb of a hydrograph depends on valley storage because outflow is a function of storage.

$$S = kO^x \qquad\qquad\qquad\qquad (6\text{-}50)$$

where S = storage, cubic metres
   k = a function of the relation between capacity of the reservoir and capacity of the outlet
   O = outflow, cubic metres
   x = a function of the relative slopes of stage-discharge and stage-storage curves

The principle of proportionality and superposition, which is the basic assumption, requires a linear storage effect; that is, x equals unity.[33] Although theoretically the unit hydrograph method required a linear storage relationship, the method can be used successfully in most cases since this relationship is close to linear for many streams. As applied to unit hydrographs, the valley acts as a reservoir and the channel acts as an outlet. The value of x is the slope of the line defined by plotting dQ/dt against average Q on log-log paper.

Unit hydrographs are prepared by analyses of observed rainfall data and the resulting runoffs. The ideal hydrograph for analysis is caused by isolated short-duration intense storms, of uniform intensity spread over the entire drainage area. To prepare a unit hydrograph, first the precipitation records are examined to determine the approximate date of suitable storms. Next, the corresponding discharge records are reviewed to select several of the most suitable for further study. For best results, runoff should be 25 mm or more.

The unit hydrograph excludes base flow so it must be separated from the observed hydrograph. The separation is somewhat arbitrary because surface runoff and base flow are indistinguishable. One assumption is that the base flow declines at the same steady rate as prior to the storm until after the peak discharge has passed, and then it

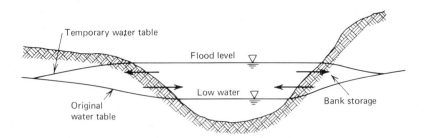

Figure 6-60 Bank storage allows movement of water away from the stream when the stage is rising and toward the stream under a falling stage. The effect is to reduce the base flow to a stream with rising stages and increase it during falling stages.

gradually increases to an arbitrary point on the falling limb as illustrated by line *a* in Figure 6-59. If a stream and an aquifer are hydraulically connected, some water enters bank storage when the stream is rising thus reducing base flow, as illustrated by Figure 6-60. After surface runoff ceases and the stage begins to fall, bank storage is released and base flow increases to a level greater than prior to the storm as depicted by line *b* in Figure 6-59. The simplest assumption is illustrated by line *c*, which is a straight line. Variations in the assumed base flow involve very little water compared to the surface runoff; therefore, the choice of separation does not appreciably affect the results. According to unit hydrograph theory, the time base for direct surface runoff is approximately the same for all unit storms on a given stream, hence, base flow separation should provide a consistent base.

After the base flow has been separated, the volume of runoff is measured in millimetres of depth. A unit hydrograph is then obtained by dividing each ordinate of the observed hydrograph by the volume of surface runoff of that storm. The method is illustrated by Example 6-11.

When less ideal storms are used, the unit hydrograph is likely to be less accurate. If the precipitation is not uniformly distributed over the drainage basin, a mean can be determined by the Theissen, or isoheytal method, or a unit hydrograph may be developed for the conditions of rain on a part of the basin. If the precipitation is variable with time, periods may be selected so precipitation is uniform within each time unit. Under these conditions, plotting graphs of precipitation against time is desirable. If the hydrograph has more than one peak, it must be divided into separate hydrographs for each peak.

Unit hydrographs determined from the selected storm events will be slightly different; consequently, for best results they are combined. Both the peak discharges and times from the beginning of excess precipitation to the peak discharge are averaged. The unit hydrographs are superimposed so the times of peak discharge coincide. The remainder of the unit hydrograph can then be sketched giving weight to all of the superimposed graphs.

Example 6-11

Compute a 1-hour unit hydrograph for Ash Creek near Red Willow, Nebraska, which has a drainage area 47.4 km^2. Runoff from a single-peak 16-mm precipitation is given in Table 6-23.

Solution

The stream was dry immediately before and after the storm so there is no base flow to separate. The total runoff was

$$2.59 \text{ m}^3/\text{s} \times 21 \text{ h} \times 3\,600 \text{ s/h} = 195\,840 \text{ m}^3$$

Converting cubic metres to depth over the drainage area,

$$\frac{195\,840 \times 1\,000}{47.4 \times 1\,000 \times 1\,000} = 4.13 \text{ mm}$$

The measured discharge in Table 6-23 is then divided by 4.13 to obtain the unit hydrograph, as given in the right column.

Table 6-23   Runoff Data for Computation of a 1-Hour Unit
Hydrograph for Ash Creek Near Red Willow,
Nebraska, for July 20, 1966, for Example 6-11

Time (h)	Measured Discharge (m³/s)	Unit Hydrograph (m³/s)
0	0	0
1	2.35	0.57
2	9.77	2.37
3	10.85	2.63
4	9.69	2.35
5	6.77	1.64
6	3.79	0.92
7	2.21	0.54
8	1.78	0.43
9	1.44	0.35
10	1.19	0.29
11	0.99	0.24
12	0.79	0.19
13	0.68	0.16
14	0.57	0.14
15	0.45	0.11
16	0.37	0.09
17	0.28	0.07
18	0.23	0.06
19	0.14	0.03
20	0.06	0.01
21	0	0

Total = 54.40 m³/s

Average = $\dfrac{54.40}{21}$ = 2.59 m³/s

6-20   Synthetic Unit Hydrographs

Hydrographs are often needed for streams where observed data are not available or
not available in sufficient quantity to prepare unit graphs; consequently, methods of
preparing synthetic unit graphs have been developed. Empirical equations were devised
by Snyder[34] using data from Appalachian Highland streams that ranged widely in
drainage area but other characteristics such as slope, soils, and cover were relatively
uniform. Lag time, the time from the center of mass of rainfall excess to the resulting
peak discharge, is the dominate basin characteristic in describing a unit hydrograph;

therefore, the accuracy of the unit graph depends on an accurate lag time evaluation. The Snyder equation for lag time is

$$t_p = C_t (L_{ca}L)^{0.3} \tag{6-51}$$

where t_p = lag time, hours
L_{ca} = distance along the major stream channel to approximately the center of gravity of the basin, kilometres
L = distance along major stream to the basin boundary, kilometres
C_t = coefficient depending on drainage area characteristics

The maximum discharge is given by the equation

$$q_p = C_p/t_p \tag{6-52}$$

where q_p = peak discharge, cubic metres per second per square kilometre
C_p = coefficient depending on units and drainage area characteristics

The length of the hydrograph base is

$$T = 3 + t_p/8 \tag{6-53}$$

where T = length of base, days

This equation was derived from large drainage areas in the Appalachian Highlands where there is a large quantity of interflow (infiltration that penetrates a short distance then flows to the stream rather quickly). Although the unit hydrograph is intended to include only surface runoff, interflow was included by Snyder; thus extending the base time. The base time for smaller drainage areas and excluding interflow is appreciably shorter. The Soil Conservation Service[32] uses the following equation for small drainage areas.

$$T = 5t_p \tag{6-54}$$

where T = length of the unit hydrograph base, hours
t_p = lag time, hours

The Corps of Engineers[35] defined two additional points on the unit hydrograph, the width of the hydrograph at 75 and 50 percent of the peak discharge as illustrated in Figure 6-61.

$$w_{75} = \frac{9.30}{q_p^{1.1}} \tag{6-55}$$

$$w_{50} = \frac{16.5}{q_p^{1.1}} \tag{6-56}$$

where w_{75} = width of the unit hydrograph at 75 percent of the peak discharge, hours
w_{50} = width of the unit hydrograph at 50 percent of the peak discharge, hours
q_p = peak discharge, cubic metres per second per square kilometre

One third of the width is placed to the left and two thirds to the right of the peak.

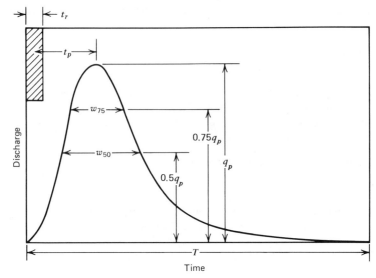

Figure 6-61 Dimensions of the Snyder synthetic unit hydrograph: t_r is the duration of rainfall excess, t_p is the lag time, T is the length of the hydrograph base, q_p is the peak discharge, and w_{75} and w_{50} are defined by Equations 6-55 and 6-56.

The constants in the Snyder equations appear to vary with channel slope, rainfall intensity, and other basin and meteorological conditions. Some values for these constants determined by other investigators are given in Table 6-24. The wide range in values is evidence that constants determined from local observed data are needed for best results.

Table 6-24 Variation in Snyder Constants for Equations 6-51 and 6-52

Region	C_t	C_p	Source
Appalachian Highlands	1.4 to 1.7	3.92 to 4.80	Snyder[34]
Southern California	0.30	6.5	Corps of Engineers[35]
Eastern Gulf of Mexico	6.1	2.18	Corps of Engineers[35]
Texas	0.30 to 1.7	2.18 to 8.56	Hudlow and Clark[36]
Northwestern states	0.23 to 0.53	2.44 to 3.48	Linsley[37]

Adapted for SI units by author.

SCS Dimensionless Unit Hydrograph

The Soil Conservation Service, using many unit hydrographs from drainage areas ranging widely in size and geographic location, defined a dimensionless unit graph.

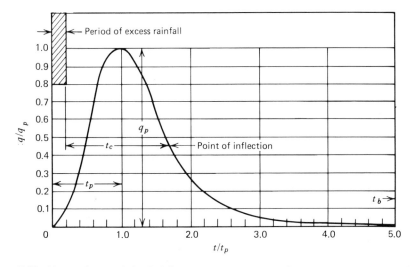

Figure 6-62 Nomenclature of the SCS (Soil Conservation Service) dimensionless unit hydrograph: q_p is the peak discharge, t_p is the time period from the beginning of excess rainfall to peak discharge, t_c is the time of concentration, and t_b is the time length of the hydrograph.

The coordinates are defined by q/q_p and t/t_p as illustrated in Figure 6-62 and Table 6-25.

$$q_p = \frac{0.208AQ}{t_p} \tag{6-57}$$

where q_p = peak discharge, cubic metres per second
A = drainage area, square kilometres
Q = quantity of runoff, millimetres depth
t_p = time to peak discharge, hours

$$t_p = \frac{t_c + 0.133t_c}{1.7} \tag{6-58}$$

where t_c = time of concentration, hours

Time of concentration is the time required for runoff from the most distant point in the basin to reach the outlet. Most hydrologists assume t_c is the time from end of rainfall excess to the point of inflection on the falling limb of the hydrograph which is at t/t_p equals 1.7 as shown in Figure 6-62.

An accurate estimate of t_c is important because q_p is inversely proportional to it. For preliminary work, t_c can be estimated by measuring the length of the stream on a map and estimating the velocity by field inspection; however, hydraulic computations using the Chezy or Manning equations are more accurate. If equations are used, the stream is divided into reaches and the length and slope of each measured. These measurements can be made on maps, but cross sections must be surveyed and rough-

Table 6-25 **Coordinates for the SCS Dimensionless Hydrograph for Figure 6-62**

Time Ratios, t/t_p	Discharge Ratios, q/q_p	Time Ratios, t/t_p	Discharge Ratios, q/q_p
0	0	1.7	0.460
0.1	0.030	1.8	0.390
0.2	0.100	1.9	0.330
0.3	0.190	2.0	0.280
0.4	0.310	2.2	0.207
0.5	0.470	2.4	0.147
0.6	0.660	2.6	0.107
0.7	0.820	2.8	0.077
0.8	0.930	3.0	0.055
0.9	0.990	3.2	0.040
1.0	1.000	3.4	0.029
1.1	0.990	3.6	0.021
1.2	0.930	3.8	0.015
1.3	0.860	4.0	0.011
1.4	0.780	4.5	0.005
1.5	0.680	5.0	0
1.6	0.560		

ness coefficients selected based on field inspection for bankfull or slightly higher stages.

The flow in the upper part of the basin is overland without a defined channel. The velocity of overland flow can be read from Figure 6-63 and the time of travel computed by Equation 6-59. The sum of the time of travel for the reaches and overland flow is the time of concentration t_c.

$$T = \frac{L}{3\,600V} \qquad (6\text{-}59)$$

where T = time of travel through a reach, hours
L = length of reach, metres
V = average velocity in reach, metres per second

The computation of a unit hydrograph from a dimensionless hydrograph is demonstrated in Example 6-12.

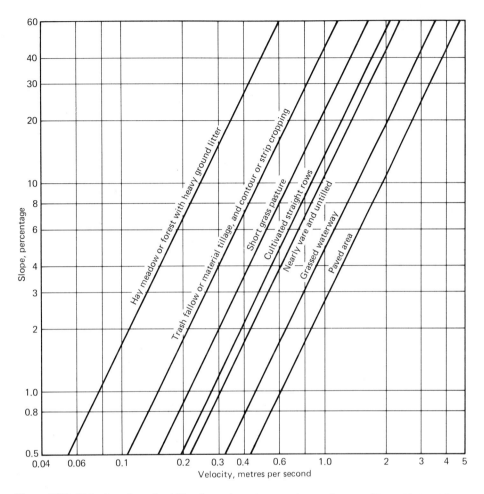

Figure 6-63 Velocity of overland flow for various slopes and ground covers. (From *National Engineering Handbook*, Section 4, Hydrology, Soil Conservation Service, 1971.) SI units by author.

Example 6-12

Compute the unit hydrograph for a drainage area of 12 km² with a time of concentration of 2.3 h using the SCS dimensionless unit hydrograph.

Solution

From Equations 6-57 and 6-58

$$t_p = \frac{2.3 + 0.133 \times 2.3}{1.7} = 1.53 \text{ h}$$

$$q_p = \frac{0.208 \times 12 \times 1}{1.53} = 1.63 \text{ m}^3/\text{s}$$

Computational results for the unit hydrograph are given in Table 6-26.

Table 6-26 Computation of Unit Hydrograph for Example 6-12

Time Ratio, t/t_p	Time $t/t_p \times 1.53$	Discharge Ratio, q/q_p	Discharge, $q/q_p \times 1.63$ (m^3/s)
0	0	0	0
0.1	0.15	0.030	0.049
0.2	0.31	0.100	0.163
0.3	0.46	0.190	0.310
0.4	0.61	0.310	0.505
0.5	0.77	0.470	0.766
0.6	0.92	0.660	1.080
0.7	1.07	0.820	1.340
0.8	1.22	0.930	1.520
0.9	1.38	0.990	1.610
1.0	1.53	1.000	1.630
1.1	1.68	0.990	1.610
1.2	1.84	0.930	1.520
1.3	1.99	0.880	1.430
1.4	2.14	0.780	1.270
1.5	2.30	0.680	1.100
1.6	2.45	0.560	0.913
1.7	2.60	0.460	0.750
1.8	2.75	0.390	0.636
1.9	2.91	0.330	0.538
2.0	3.06	0.280	0.456
2.2	3.37	0.207	0.337
2.4	3.67	0.147	0.240
2.6	3.98	0.107	0.174
2.8	4.28	0.077	0.126
3.0	4.59	0.055	0.090
3.2	4.90	0.040	0.065
3.4	5.20	0.029	0.047
3.6	5.51	0.021	0.034
3.8	5.81	0.015	0.024
4.0	6.12	0.011	0.018
4.5	6.89	0.005	0.008
5.0	7.65	0	0

6-21 Unit Hydrograph Application

A storm hydrograph resulting from rainfall over an extended time can be computed by the unit hydrograph method. If the drainage area is large or irregular in shape, runoff from the principal tributaries can be computed individually and then combined and routed to the outlet. Precipitation is recorded for the same time units as the unit hydrograph and discharge for each time period is calculated. The graphs for individual unit storms are added offsetting them in sequence by one time unit.

The volume of discharge for the storm must be known before the hydrograph can be developed. The soil-cover complex method can be used if sufficient information is available. An alternative is to estimate the infiltration index after examining the drainage area. Subtracting the infiltration index from the precipitation gives the storm runoff expressed in millimetres of depth. Example 6-13 illustrates this method.

Example 6-13

A 200-mm rainfall occurred on the Ash Creek basin in five hours beginning at 0600 h. The rain fell as follows: 6 to 7, 75 mm; 7 to 8, 25 mm; 8 to 9, none; 9 to 10, 60 mm; and 10 to 11, 40 mm. The infiltration index was 25 mm per hour. Compute and plot the storm hydrograph using the 1-hour unit hydrograph from Example 6-11.

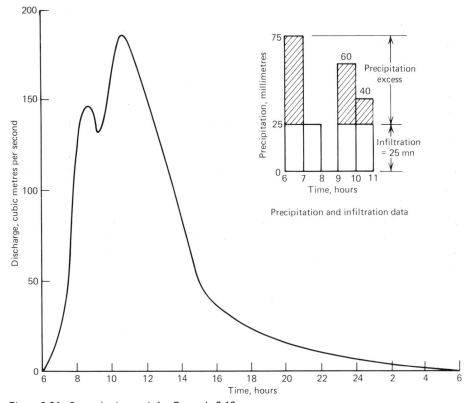

Figure 6-64 Storm hydrograph for Example 6-13.

Solution

Enter the time at hourly intervals in column 1 of Table 6-27 beginning with 0600, which is the time rain began. Enter the 1-hour unit hydrograph from Table 6-23 in column 2 and the rainfall excess during each hour (rainfall less infiltration index) in column 3. The discharge resulting from the rainfall excess between 0600 and 0700 is calculated in column 4 by multiplying column 2 by 50 mm, the rainfall excess. The procedure is repeated for each unit time. Columns 5 and 6 contain zero because no rainfall excess occurred between 0700 and 0900. The rainfall excess between 0900 and

Table 6-27 **Computation of a Storm Hydrograph for Ash Creek near Red Willow, Nebraska, for Example 6-13**

Time (h) 1	One-Hour Unit Hydrograph (m³/s) 2	Rainfall Excess (mm) 3	Surface Runoff (m³/s) 4	5	6	7	8	Total Surface Runoff (m³/s) 9	Base Flow (m³/s) 10	Total Flow (m³/s) 11
6	0	0								0
7	0.57	50	28.5					28.5	0	28.5
8	2.37	0	118.5	0				118.5	0	118.5
9	2.63	0	131.5	0	0			131.5	0	131.5
10	2.35	35	117.5	0	0	20.0		137.5	0	137.5
11	1.64	15	82.0	0	0	83.0	8.6	173.6	0	173.6
12	0.92		46.0	0	0	92.0	35.6	173.6	0	173.6
13	0.54		27.0	0	0	82.2	39.4	148.6	0	148.6
14	0.43		21.5	0	0	57.4	35.2	114.1	0	114.1
15	0.35		17.5	0	0	32.2	24.6	74.3	0	74.3
16	0.29		14.5	0	0	18.9	13.8	47.2	0	47.2
17	0.24		12.0	0	0	15.0	8.1	35.1	0	35.1
18	0.19		9.5	0	0	12.2	6.4	28.1	0	28.1
19	0.16		8.0	0	0	10.2	5.2	23.4	0	23.4
20	0.14		7.0	0	0	8.4	4.4	19.8	0	19.8
21	0.11		5.5	0	0	6.6	3.6	15.7	0	15.7
22	0.09		4.5	0	0	5.6	2.8	12.9	0	12.9
23	0.07		3.5	0	0	4.9	2.4	10.8	0	10.8
24	0.06		3.0	0	0	3.8	2.1	8.9	0	8.9
1	0.03		1.5	0	0	3.2	1.6	6.3	0	6.3
2	0.01		0.5	0	0	2.4	1.4	4.3	0	4.3
3	0		0	0	0	2.1	1.0	3.1	0	3.1
4				0	0	1.1	0.9	2.0	0	2.0
5					0	0.4	0.4	0.8	0	0.8
6						0	0.2	0.2	0	0.2
7							0	0	0	0

1000 was 35 mm; therefore, the surface runoff for that hour is $35 \times 0.57 = 20 \text{ m}^3/\text{s}$, which is entered on the 1000 line in column 7. Repeat the computations for the period between 1000 and 1100 and enter in column 8 beginning at 1100.

Add the hourly surface runoff and enter in column 9. Base flow is entered in column 10; however, Ash Creek is dry most of the time so base flow is assumed to be zero. Add columns 9 and 10 and enter in column 11 to obtain the total flow. The total surface runoff, column 9, is an aid to estimating the base flow; therefore, it is a desirable intermediate step.

The storm hydrograph, column 11, is plotted in Figure 6-64.

6-22   Flow Models

Several similar flow models of the parametric type have been developed; some are proprietary. They are used to generate a flow record that can be used to supplement an observed record or as a substitute if none is available. The models are based on the assumption that the hydrologic cycle is fundamentally the same on all drainage basins and the magnitude of the parameters influencing runoff vary with climate, geology, soils, and topography. Hence, concurrent streamflow and climatic records are required for calibration. The principal data input is daily potential evaporation and hourly precipitation. If snowfall is significant, additional meteorlogical data are needed. Basically, flow models convey precipitation to a stream by various routes taking into account storage, losses, and diversions.

Infiltration rate, by having a direct effect on runoff, is a very important component of a model. Of the many factors affecting infiltration (described in Section 6-3), the level of soil moisture is the most variable. Where soil moisture content is low, as it may be at the beginning of rain, infiltration rate is high. As the rain continues soil moisture is replenished and infiltration decreases. Therefore, models must continuously assess the soil moisture level and adjust the infiltration rate accordingly. After rain ceases moisture content is adjusted in models by using evaporation records to provide the moisture content and the infiltration rate at the beginning of the next rain.

Statistical Models

A statistical model generates a long series of events that does not duplicate the observed record. Instead, it creates a series of equal likely events having the same mean, standard deviation, skew, and serial correlation coefficient as an observed record. Skew as an unstable statistic is not ordinarily used as a parameter unless it is large. The model generates high and low flows in a variety of sequences that provide the designer of a reservoir with more combinations than obtainable from the observed record. Consequently, the dependable yield can be determined with greater assurance. The generated record also provides more data for flood frequency computations provided the parameters were derived from a representative sequence of dry and wet years.

Streamflow observations arranged in order of occurrence are a time series. When the mean and variance of the observations are unchanged with time, the series is stationary.

In using a statistical model, the hydrologist assumes the series is stationary and that the statistics (mean, variance, and serial correlation) calculated from the sample are representative of the entire population. Because the population statistics are unknown, the sample statistics are assumed equal to those of the population. The difference between the sample statistics and those of the population is called the sampling error which directly affects the accuracy of the model. Generally the larger the sample the smaller the sample error.

A time series may or may not consist of observations that are independent of one another. Streamflow records are not completely independent. Experience shows that if most records are close to average, the probability of the next observation being near average is high and that the variability is unlikely to change much. Furthermore, high flows are likely to follow high flows and low flows follow low flows. This persistence is measured by a serial lag coefficient sometimes called the Markov coefficient. The lag interval may be one or several time units. One lag is usually sufficient for a streamflow model. The model equation is

$$Q_i = \bar{Q} + r_1(Q_{i-1} - \bar{Q}) + t_i S (1 - r_1^2)^{0.5} \qquad (6\text{-}61)$$

where Q_i = discharge at time i, cubic metres per second
$\quad \bar{Q}$ = mean Q from Equation 6-7, cubic metres per second
$\quad Q_{i-1}$ = discharge at time i-1 (the time preceding), cubic metres per second
$\quad r_1$ = a lag one Markov coefficient, which is a portion of the departure from the previous flow from the mean
$\quad t_i$ = a random variate at time i from an appropriate distribution with a mean of zero and variance one
$\quad S$ = standard deviation of Q from Equation 6-8

Equation 6-61 yields a normal synthetic flow that preserves the maximum, variance, and first-order correlation coefficient of the observed record.

Statistical streamflow models are assumed stationary, that is, without a time trend. Consequently, streamflow affected by diversions or other man-made changes are adjusted to natural flow before the statistical parameters are calculated. Then, the generated record must be adjusted to current conditions by subtracting the diversion.

Data generated by models can be used to design reservoir capacity using several techniques, such as, the low-flow-frequency mass diagram techniques illustrated by Example 6-9. Several hundred years of records are generated to obtain an adequate number of high and low flow sequences.

Flow at Ungaged Sites by Multiple Regression
Flow at ungaged sites has been estimated by a multiple regression technique using drainage basin and climatic characteristics as independent variables. The regression constant and coefficient are calculated using data from gaged streams. The equation has been transformed to the linear form by expressing the variables in common logarithms. The general equation is

$$\text{Log } Q = a + b_1 \log x_1 + b_2 \log x_2 + \ldots + b_n \log x_n \qquad (6\text{-}62)$$

where Q = the dependent variable, cubic metres per second. It may be the annual or monthly flow, peak flow with any assigned probability, or runoff volume with any assigned probability and duration.

a = regression constant

x = an independent variable representing a drainage basin or climatic characteristic

b = the regression coefficient for x

The independent variable can be any drainage basin or climatic characteristic that affects the dependent variable. Some that have been considered are drainage area, contributing drainage area, stream length, infiltration index or another measure of infiltration, elevation of drainage area, slope of stream channel, orographic effect, percentage of open water surface, percentage of forest, precipitation intensity, annual precipitation, January temperature, and annual evaporation. Zero does not have a logarithm; therefore, any characteristic that has a zero value is adjusted by adding 1 or 0.5. Characters that are expressed by very large numbers such as elevation are adjusted by subtracting a constant. Twenty or more sets of data are needed to obtain reliable values of the regression constant and coefficients by solving Equation 6-62.

Calculation of the equation requires many computations, thus economics dictate the use of a computer. A step-backward regression method is used; that is, the hydrologist specifies the independent variables. Not all of the listed independent variables are needed in some areas, such as, elevation and orographic effects in flat areas. After solving the equation for the constant and coefficients, the computer records the standard error of estimate and the effectiveness of each independent variable. The computer is programmed to drop the least effective independent variable and repeat the process until only one independent variable remains. The hydrologist selects variables to use in the formula giving consideration to improvement in the standard error of estimate of each marginal variable. Application of the equation is easy with a small electronic calculator.

Benson[38] examined characteristics affecting flood peaks in New England using floods from more than 100 streams. The area, slope, orographic factor, percentage of storage, and January temperature were the most significant characteristics. Floods calculated with Equation 6-62 using selected independent variables and having 5- to 100-year recurrence intervals had the following standard errors of estimate:

Independent Variables	Standard Error of Estimate, percentage
Area	59.9 to 65.2
Area and Slope	41.1 to 50.6
Area, slope, and orographic effect	33.0 to 37.7
Area, slope, orographic effect, and surface storage	29.5 to 36.8
Area, slope, orographic effect, surface storage, and January temperature	26.1 to 36.8

Slope factor equals the difference in elevation between 10 percent and 85 percent of the total distance above the gage divided by the distance.

Orographic factor is calculated from the difference between observed peaks and those calculated from Equation 6-62 using area, slope, surface storage, intensity, and January precipitation as independent variables. The factor was computed using floods having a range in recurrence interval and for those areas where precipitation records indicated an orographic effect. Surface storage factor is the water surface area of the basin as a percentage of the total basin plus 0.5. January temperature factor is the number of degree days below freezing.

6-23 Floods

A flood is any relatively high flow overtopping the natural or artificial banks in any reach of a stream. The U. S. Weather Service defines flood stage as the gage height at which overflow of natural banks of a stream begins to cause damage. Since the dawn of civilization, few natural phenomena have been as well recorded as floods. Legends and folklore of people throughout the world are ample evidence that floods were of concern long before recorded history. The earliest known records are those of the Nile River in Egypt where records extending back to 1800 B. C. are carved on cliff walls. An almost continuous record of stage of the Nile has been maintained at Cairo since 620 A. D. In the United States, a few intermittent records of stage extend into the colonial period; however, discharge has been recorded for only about 100 years.

A popular conception is that floods are increasing in magnitude and frequency, yet, all available evidence indicates they are not. Floods are extreme events. As long as floods at a particular site are observed, breaking the record is probable, although it diminishes as the record lengthens. The greatest floods recorded in the United States are plotted in Figure 6-65, with an envelope curve indicating the reasonable limit for estimating maximum floods. The maximum recorded at many sites falls far below the line indicating that a much greater flood than has been experienced could occur on most streams.

Although floods are not increasing, damages amounting to many millions of dollars annually are increasing steadily due to greater exposure to risk as man increases occupancy and obstruction of floodplains. Furthermore, many millions of dollars are being spent and will continue to be spent in the future to control floods. Consequently, knowledge of the magnitude and frequency of floods is important.

A flood has the three important dimensions of height, volume, and maximum discharge. Height is important in defining the extent of the area inundated and the minimum elevation of any structure built in the floodplain. The volume of a flood is needed to design retarding and storage structures, and the peak discharge to design spillways, bridge and culvert openings, levees, and channel modifications.

Flood heights are obtained from stream gage records if available; although height can be calculated by indirect methods. Highwater marks are the only other source of direct measurement. Great care must be used in selecting marks, and those pointed out by local residents are usually unreliable unless a marker was placed shortly after

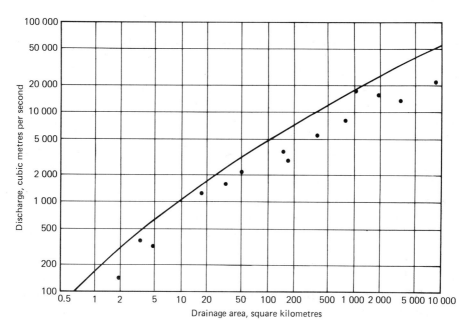

Figure 6-65 An envelope curve indicating the reasonable limit for estimating maximum floods.

the flood. Debris, such as seeds or small bits of vegetation deposited by slow-moving water, are the most reliable. Marks left by swift-running water, especially due to wave action, are inaccurate and those on obstructions that caused velocity head recovery are not reliable. Oil and other spilled material can leave excellent marks; however, they are to be viewed with caution because they may not have been deposited at the maximum height.

The hydrologic design of structures is concerned with future events for which the magnitude and frequency cannot be predicted. Consequently, the hydrologist must rely on the probability that a future height, volume, or rate of flow will be equalled or exceeded. Probability is calculated from historical streamflow. In the absence of historical data, computations based on precipitation records can be used, including transposition of rainfall records from nearby areas to the drainage area under study. (Probabilities of annual exceedence and recurrence intervals in years are reciprocals.) Reliability of the calculated probability increases with the amount of data. Longer records are needed for relatively improbably events than for likely events. A minimum of 20 years of data are desirable. The calculation of a recurrence interval more than twice the length of a historical record is likely to be inaccurate. If the observed record is too short, a longer record can be calculated using a parametric or statistical model. Also, a desirable observed record is homogeneous, that is, the entire record is unaffected by storage, diversions, or other human activities or at least affected to the same degree by these factors. If storage or diversion began during the period of record, that part is adjusted so the record is homogeneous.

Flood volume-frequency curves can be prepared from gaging station records using average flow for various consecutive days. The recurrence interval is computed using Equation 6-9 by arranging the flood volume in order of magnitude beginning with the largest. The data are plotted on extreme probability paper as illustrated in Figure 6-66.

Height-frequency curves can be prepared by using observed gage heights. If stage records are not available or the stage-discharge relationship has changed, a peak discharge-frequency curve can be prepared and converted to a height-frequency curve using the current-stage-discharge relationship. Indirect methods, as described in Section 6-15, can be used to prepare a stage-discharge relationship if one is not available.

Floods are a series of natural events, which as far as can be determined, do not fit any one specific known statistical distribution. However, to define flood probabilities a distribution must be assigned. The U. S. Water Resource Council[39] recognized the need for accurate and consistent estimates of magnitude-frequency data on major rivers for economical design of safe structures for flood control and other uses. Consequently, the Council issued guidelines for use of the log Pearson type III distribution for all federal planning involving water and recommended it to state and local governments when at least 10 years of records are available. The Gumbel distribution, using Equation 6-9 for calculating plotting positions, is still used for small streams.

Log Pearson Type III Distribution

The discharge-frequency curve is fitted to observed data by computing the discharge at selected exceedence probabilities by

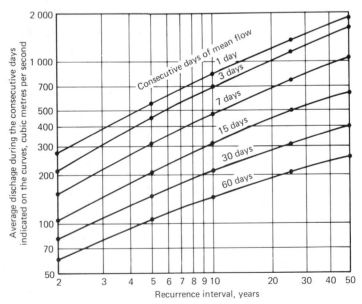

Figure 6-66 Flood-volume frequency curves from an annual series for the Elkhorn River at Waterloo, Nebraska.

$$\log Q_p = \overline{\log Q} + KS \qquad (6\text{-}63)$$

where $\log Q_p$ = logarithm of the annual peak discharge having a probability p
$\overline{\log Q}$ = average of the logs of the annual peak discharges of record from Equation 6-7
K = a factor that is a function of the skew coefficient G of logs of the observed Q and a selected exceedence probability, from Table 6-28
S = standard deviation of $\log Q$ from Equation 6-8

$$G = \frac{N^2 \Sigma(\log Q)^3 - 3N\Sigma\log Q\, [\Sigma(\log Q)^2] + 2(\Sigma\log Q)^3}{N(N-1)(N-2)S^3} \qquad (6\text{-}64)$$

where G = skew coefficient of logarithms of Q
N = number of observed floods
$\log Q$ = logarithm of annual peak discharge

The skew coefficient of a station record is insensitive to extreme events, and an accurate estimate is difficult to obtain from samples. Consequently, the generalized estimate of the regional skew from Figure 6-67 is recommended for short records. Computed skews are recommended for records of 100 years or more and a weighted skew used for records of 25 to 100 years.

$$\text{Weighted skew} = G\frac{(N-25)}{75} + \overline{G}\left[1 - \frac{(N-25)}{75}\right] \qquad (6\text{-}65)$$

where G = skew calculated from observed record
$\overline{G}$ = generalized regional skew
N = number of observed floods

Example 6-14

Annual flood peaks are available for Spring Creek near Cushing, Nebraska, from 1948 to 1976, Table 6.29. Compute the peak discharge having recurrence intervals from 2 to 50 years using log Pearson type III distribution.

Using the current station rating curve given below, plot a stage-frequency curve for Spring Creek.

Gage Height (m)	Discharge (m³/s)	Gage Height (m)	Discharge (m³/s)	Gage Height (m)	Discharge (m³/s)
4.5	22.6	7.0	127	8.6	249
5.0	36.8	7.5	153	8.8	297
5.5	53.8	8.0	181	9.0	374
6.0	76.5	8.2	198	9.2	487
6.5	99.1	8.4	221		

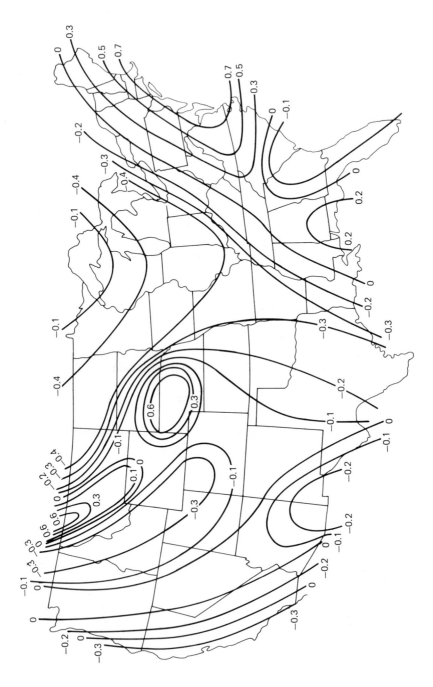

Figure 6-67 Generalized regional skew coefficients for use with Table 6-28 to obtain K for a log Pearson Type III flood analysis, Example 6-14.

Table 6-28 Coefficient K in Equation 6-63 for Various Skew Coefficients and Recurrence Intervals for Example 6-14

Skew Coefficient G	Recurrence Interval in Years						
	2	5	10	25	50	100	200
6.0	-0.32974	-0.06662	0.58933	1.96048	3.25128	4.68680	6.22616
5.5	-0.35456	-0.01028	0.69122	2.04739	3.28381	4.64022	6.08307
5.0	-0.37901	0.05798	0.79548	2.12432	3.3007	4.57304	5.88004
4.5	-0.39985	0.13737	0.89964	2.18874	3.29767	4.48303	5.72400
4.0	-0.41265	0.22617	1.00079	2.23786	3.27404	4.36777	5.50362
3.5	-0.41253	0.32171	1.09552	2.26862	3.22641	4.22473	5.25291
3.0	-0.39554	0.42040	1.18006	2.27780	3.15193	4.05138	4.96959
2.8	-0.38353	0.45980	1.21013	2.27470	3.11399	3.97301	4.84669
2.6	-0.36852	0.49872	1.23766	2.26743	3.07116	3.88930	4.71815
2.4	-0.35062	0.53683	1.26240	2.25581	3.02330	3.80013	4.58393
2.2	-0.32999	0.57383	1.28412	2.23967	2.97028	3.70543	4.44398
2.0	-0.30685	0.60944	1.30259	2.21888	2.91202	3.60517	4.29832
1.8	-0.28150	0.64335	1.31760	2.19332	2.84848	3.49935	4.14700
1.6	-0.25422	0.67532	1.32900	2.16293	2.77964	3.38804	3.99016
1.4	-0.22535	0.70512	1.33665	2.12768	2.70556	3.27134	3.82798
1.2	-0.19517	0.73257	1.34047	2.08758	2.62631	3.14944	3.66073
1.0	-0.16397	0.75752	1.34039	2.04269	2.54206	3.02256	3.48874
0.9	-0.14807	0.76902	1.33889	2.01848	2.49811	2.95735	3.40109
0.8	-0.13199	0.77986	1.33640	1.99311	2.45298	2.89101	3.31243
0.7	-0.11578	0.79002	1.33294	1.96660	2.40670	2.82359	3.22281
0.6	-0.09945	0.79950	1.32850	1.93896	2.35931	2.75514	3.13232

Table 6-28 Continued

Skew Coefficient	Recurrence Interval in Years						
G	2	5	10	25	50	100	200
0.5	−0.08302	0.80829	1.32309	1.91022	2.31084	2.68572	3.04102
0.4	−0.00651	0.81638	1.31671	1.88039	2.26133	2.61539	2.94900
0.3	−0.04993	0.82377	1.30936	1.84949	2.21081	2.54421	2.85636
0.2	−0.03325	0.83044	1.30105	1.81756	2.15935	2.47226	2.76321
0.1	−0.01662	0.83639	1.29178	1.78462	2.10697	2.39961	2.66965
0	0.00000	0.84162	1.28155	1.75069	2.05375	2.32635	2.57583
−0.1	0.01662	0.84611	1.27037	1.71580	1.99973	2.25258	2.48187
−0.2	0.03325	0.84986	1.25824	1.67999	1.94499	2.17840	2.38795
−0.3	0.04993	0.85285	1.24516	1.64329	1.88959	2.10394	2.29423
−0.4	0.06651	0.85508	1.23114	1.60574	1.83361	2.02933	2.20092
−0.5	0.08302	0.85653	1.21618	1.56740	1.77716	1.95472	2.10825
−0.6	0.09945	0.85718	1.20028	1.52830	1.72033	1.88029	2.01644
−0.7	0.11578	0.85703	1.18347	1.48852	1.66325	1.80621	1.92580
−0.8	0.13199	0.85607	1.16574	1.44813	1.60604	1.73271	1.83660

−0.9	0.14807	0.85426	1.14712	1.40720	1.54886	1.66001	1.74919
−1.0	0.16397	0.85161	1.12762	1.36584	1.49188	1.58838	1.66390
−1.2	0.19517	0.84369	1.08608	1.28225	1.37929	1.44942	1.50114
−1.4	0.22535	0.83223	1.04144	1.19842	1.26999	1.31815	1.35114
−1.6	0.25422	0.81720	0.99418	1.11566	1.16584	1.19680	1.21618
−1.8	0.28150	0.79868	0.94496	1.03543	1.06864	1.08711	1.09749
−2.0	0.30685	0.77686	0.89464	0.95918	0.97980	0.98995	0.99499
−2.2	0.32999	0.75211	0.84422	0.88814	0.90009	0.90521	0.90742
−2.4	0.35062	0.72495	0.79472	0.82315	0.82959	0.83196	0.83283
−2.6	0.36852	0.69602	0.74709	0.76456	0.76779	0.76878	0.76909
−2.8	0.38353	0.66603	0.70209	0.71227	0.71377	0.71415	0.71425
−3.0	0.39554	0.63569	0.66023	0.66585	0.66649	0.66663	0.66666
−3.5	0.41253	0.56242	0.57035	0.57136	0.57142	0.57143	0.57143
−4.0	0.41265	0.49784	0.49986	0.50000	0.50000	0.50000	0.50000
−4.5	0.39985	0.44402	0.44443	0.44444	0.44444	0.44444	0.44444
−5.0	0.37428	0.39993	0.40000	0.40000	0.40000	0.40000	0.40000
−5.5	0.35456	0.36363	0.36364	0.36364	0.36364	0.36364	0.36364
−6.0	0.32974	0.33333	0.33333	0.33333	0.33333	0.33333	0.33333

Table 6-29 **Annual Peak Discharge of Spring Creek near Cushing, Nebraska, From 1948 to 1976 for Example 6-14**

Year	(m³/s)	(log m³/s)	Year	(m³/s)	(log m³/s)
1948	35.1	1.545 3	1963	152	2.181.8
1949	78.2	1.893 2	1964	25.3	1.403 1
1950	17.8	1.250 4	1965	17.1	1.233 0
1951	12.7	1.103 8	1966	77.3	1.888 2
1952	24.4	1.387 4	1967	23.8	1.376 6
1953	71.6	1.854 9	1968	41.9	1.622 2
1954	72.5	1.860 3	1969	51.5	1.771 8
1955	81.3	1.910 1	1970	991.2	2.996 1
1956	1.42	0.152 3	1971	51.3	1.710 1
1957	33.1	1.519 8	1972	63.4	1.802 1
1958	34.6	1.539 1	1973	6.23	0.794 5
1959	6.37	0.804 1	1974	2.55	0.406 5
1960	7.43	0.871 0	1975	3.40	0.531 5
1961	41.9	1.622 2	1976	16.1	1.206 8
1962	19.8	1.296 7			

Solution

Transform the peak discharge to logarithmic units and compute the following statistics:

$$N = 29$$
$$\Sigma \log Q = 41.475\ 1$$
$$\overline{\log Q} = 1.430\ 1$$
$$\Sigma(\log Q)^2 = 68.604\ 9$$
$$\Sigma(\log Q)^3 = 124.900\ 8$$
$$\Sigma(\log Q)^4 = 247.877\ 8$$

From Equation 6-8

$$S^2 = \frac{68.604\ 9 - \dfrac{(41.475\ 1)^2}{29}}{28} = 0.311\ 9$$

$$S = 0.576\ 0$$

Using Equation 6-64 to compute the skew

$$N^2 \Sigma(\log Q)^3 = (29)^2 \times 124.900\ 8 = 105\ 041.57$$
$$3N\Sigma \log Q[\Sigma(\log Q)^2] = 3 \times 29 \times 41.475\ 1 \times 68.604\ 9 = 247\ 549.37$$
$$2(\Sigma \log Q)^3 = 2(41.475\ 1)^3 = 142\ 689.60$$
$$N(N-1)(N-2)(S)^3 = 29 \times 28 \times 27 \times 0.191\ 1 = 4\ 189.741\ 6$$

$$G = \frac{105\ 041.57\ -\ 247\ 549.37\ +\ 142\ 689.60}{4\ 189.741\ 6} = 0.043\ 4$$

The regional skew from Figure 6-67 is 0.20. From Equation 6-65 the weighted skew is

$$0.04\frac{(29\ -\ 25)}{75} + 0.20\left[1 - \frac{(29\ -\ 25)}{75}\right]$$

$$= 0.04 \times 0.053 + 0.20 \times 0.947 = 0.192$$

Using Equation 6-63 and interpolating K from Table 6-28, compute Q for each recurrence interval.

If the recurrence interval is 2 and skew is 0.1, $K = -0.166\ 2$
If skew is 0.2, $K = -0.033\ 25$

If skew is 0.192, $K = [-0.033\ 25\ -\ (-0.016\ 62)]\left(\frac{0.092}{0.10}\right) - 0.016\ 62 = -0.032\ 15$

$\log Q_2\ =\ 1.430\ 1\ +\ (-0.032\ 15) \times 0.576\ 0 = 1.4115, Q_2\ =\ 25.8\ m^3/s$

$\log Q_5\ =\ 1.430\ 1\ +\ 0.830\ 68 \times 0.576\ 0 = 1.908\ 6, Q_5\ =\ 81.0\ m^3/s$

$\log Q_{10}\ =\ 1.430\ 1\ +\ 1.300\ 7 \times 0.576\ 0 = 2.179\ 3, Q_{10}\ =\ 151\ m^3/s$

$\log Q_{25}\ =\ 1.430\ 1\ +\ 1.816\ 2 \times 0.576\ 0 = 2.476\ 2, Q_{25}\ =\ 299\ m^3/s$

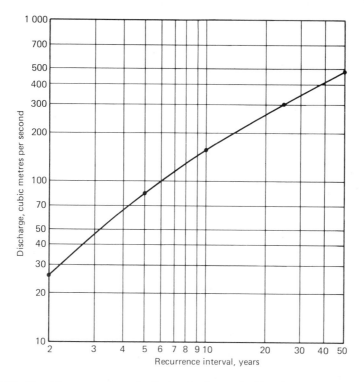

Figure 6-68 Flood-frequency curve for Spring Creek near Cushing, Nebraska, for Example 6-14.

$\log Q_{50} = 1.430\ 1 + 2.157\ 3 \times 0.576\ 0 = 2.672\ 7, Q_{50} = 471\ \mathrm{m^3/s}$

The curve is shown in Figure 6-68.

Using a straight-line interpolation between points on the rating curve, the gage heights corresponding to the above discharges are:

25.8 m³/s	4.6 m
81.0 m³/s	6.1 m
151 m³/s	7.5 m
299 m³/s	8.8 m
471 m³/s	9.1 m

Plot these data on Figure 6-69.

Design Flood

No matter how long the recurrence interval, the possibility always exists that a flood can be exceeded more than once during the interval. Usually expressed as a percentage, risk is the probability that a flood of a given magnitude will be exceeded during a specified time period. It is calculated from Equation 6-6, which was illustrated in Example 6-4.

$$P_{(N,r)} = \frac{N!}{r!(N-r)!} P^r (1-p)^{N-r}$$

$P_{(N,r)}$ is the probability of r events occurring in N possible events. The probability of a

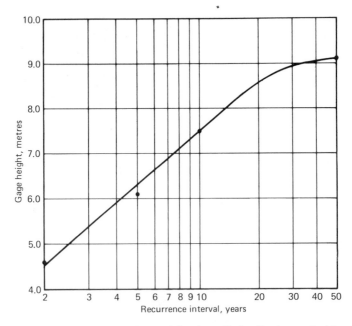

Figure 6-69 Stage-frequency curve of annual floods on Spring Creek near Cushing, Nebraska, for Example 6-14. The flattening above 8.8 metres is caused by the stream overflowing its banks.

single event is p. If $r = 0$, no floods will occur during the period N, the useful life of the structure. Equation 6-6 becomes

$$P_{(N,0)} = (1 - p)^N \tag{6-66}$$

which is the probability that a flood with an annual exceedence probability will not be exceeded in a period of N years. So the probability that the design flood will be exceeded one or more times is

$$P_{Ex} = 1 - (1 - p)^N \tag{6-67}$$

where P_{Ex} = probability of a flood of annual exceedence probability being exceeded one or more times during a period of N years

$$\text{Risk} = \text{percentage} = P_{Ex} \times 100 \tag{6-68}$$

Equation 6-68 was used to prepare Table 6-30 which shows, for instance, a 25-year flood as having a 34 percent chance of being exceeded within any 10-year period. Table 6-30 also shows a 100-year design flood having a 63 percent risk of being exceeded during a 100-year period, and a 25-year design flood with a 64 percent risk of being exceeded in a 25-year period. These calculated risks assume the recurrence interval of the annual floods is accurately known.

Table 6-30 Percent Risk of One or More Exceedances in a Specified Period

Flood Recurrence Interval (years)	Annual Probability of Flood Exceedence	Specified Time Period in Years							
		1	5	10	15	20	25	50	100
100	0.01	1	5	10	14	18	22	39	63
50	0.02	2	10	18	26	33	40	64	87
33.3	0.03	3	14	26	37	46	53	78	95
25	0.04	4	18	34	46	56	64	87	98.4
20	0.05	5	23	40	54	64	72	92	99.4
16.7	0.06	6	27	46	60	71	85	95	99.8
14.3	0.07	7	30	52	66	77	84	97.3	99.93
12.5	0.08	8	34	57	71	81	88	98.5	99.98
11.1	0.09	9	38	61	76	85	91	99.1	99.992
10	0.10	10	41	65	79	88	93	99.5	99.997

6-24 Flood Routing

Flood routing is the process of determining progressively the timing and shape of a flood wave at successive points along a stream. Generally, a flood control reservoir cannot be built immediately adjacent to the area to be protected; therefore, the released water must be routed to the protected area to determine the stage and evaluate the probable damage. Furthermore, flood routing is basic to flood forecasting.

As a flood wave passes along a natural channel, some of the water is stored temporily with the amount depending on the dimensions and variability of the channel and floodplain. Storage in the channel increases as long as inflow exceeds outflow, and reaches a maximum when inflow equals outflow; therefore, storage elongates the flood wave as it moves downstream.

All flood routing methods are based on the law of continuity; the volume of water discharged from a reach during an interval must equal the inflow minus the change in storage.

$$\bar{O} = \bar{I} - \frac{\Delta S}{\Delta t} \tag{6-69}$$

where $\bar{O}$ = mean outflow from a reach during a time interval Δt, cubic metres per second

$\bar{I}$ = mean inflow to a reach during a time interval Δt, cubic metres per second

$\Delta S = \bar{I} - \bar{O}$ = net change in storage during an interval, cubic metres

Δt = time period, days

Equation 6-69 can be rearranged as follows:

$$\Delta t \left(\frac{O_1 + O_2}{2} \right) = \Delta t \left(\frac{I_1 + I_2}{2} \right) - (S_2 - S_1) \tag{6-70}$$

where subscript 1 denotes the quantity at the beginning of an interval and subscript 2 denotes the quantity at the end of an interval. The assumption of the mean discharge equaling the average at the beginning and end of the interval is satisfactory if the interval is equal to or less than the time of travel through the reach, and no abrupt changes in flow occur during the period.

If the storage in a reach is plotted against inflow, an irregular loop rather than a single value graph develops where the storage is less than indicated on a rising stage and greater on a falling stage. If storage is plotted against outflow, the storage is greater than indicated on a rising stage and less than indicated on a falling stage. The loop is the effect of wedge storage as shown in Figure 6-70.

Most current methods of flood routing define storage in terms of inflow and outflow. The Muskingum method, one of several techniques, expresses storage as a function of weighted mean flow as follows:

$$S = K[xI + (1 - x)O] \tag{6-71}$$

where S = storage, cubic metres

K = slope of storage-weighted discharge relation, dimension of time

x = dimensionless constant which weights the inflow and outflow

I = inflow rate, cubic metres per second

O = outflow rate, cubic metres per second

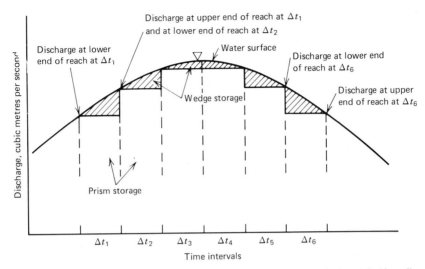

Figure 6-70 Successive positions of a flood wave as it passes through a single reach. If outflow is used as an index of storage, the wedge storage is ignored so the total storage is greater than indicated on a rising stage. As shown by interval Δt_6, the storage is less than indicated in a falling stage. Consequently, the outflow-storage relationship plots as a loop. If the inflow is used as the index, storage is less than indicated on a rising stage and greater on a falling stage.

This method applies to the condition of a uniform and unbroken water-surface profile in the reach where stage and discharge are uniquely defined, and K and x are constant throughout the range of flow routed.

The weighting factor x is chosen by trial and error so the indicated storage is the same on rising and falling stages. The equation for calculated weighted discharge is

$$\text{Weighted } O = Ix + (1 - x)O \tag{6-72}$$

Values of x range from 0 to 0.5

Equations 6-70 and 6-71 may be combined to form Equation 6-73.

$$O_2 = \frac{(0.5\Delta t - Kx)}{(K - Kx + 0.5\Delta t)} I_2 + \frac{(Kx + 0.5\Delta t)}{(K - Kx + 0.5\Delta t)} I_1 + \frac{(K - Kx - 0.5\Delta t)}{(K - Kx + 0.5\Delta t)} O_1 \tag{6-73}$$

which can be written as

$$O_2 = C_0 I_2 + C_1 I_1 + C_2 O_1 \tag{6-74}$$

$$\text{where } C_0 = \frac{0.5\Delta t - Kx}{K - Kx + 0.5\Delta t}$$

$$C_1 = \frac{Kx + 0.5\Delta t}{K - Kx + 0.5\Delta t}$$

$$C_2 = \frac{K - Kx - 0.5\Delta t}{K - Kx + 0.5\Delta t}$$

Discharge records are required to calculate K and x. The storage volume is calculated using Equation 6-69 and an inflow-outflow hydrograph or tabulation. Start at a time when the inflow and outflow are about equal. Local inflow can be estimated from precipitation or nearby streams and added to the gaged inflow to obtain total inflow to the reach. The total inflow is compared with the outflow to assure that they balance. The time interval Δt, between successive values of flow, is selected greater than $2Kx$ to avoid negative values of C_0. The storage in the reach is the difference between the cumulated inflow and cumulated outflow. A factor x is assumed and the weighted discharge calculated. Trial values of x are used until the weighted discharge

Table 6-31   Computation of Storage for Example 6-15

	Initial Flow		Cumulative Flow		
Date 1	Inflow (m^3/s) 2	Outflow (m^3/s) 3	Inflow (m^3/s) 4	Outflow (m^3/s) 5	Storage $(m^3 \cdot d/s)$ 6
1	121	118	121	118	3
2	217	142	338	260	78
3	314	206	652	466	186
4	473	272	1 125	738	387
5	612	481	1 737	1 219	518
6	595	518	2 332	1 737	595
7	753	549	3 085	2 286	799
8	1 303	719	4 388	3 005	1 383
9	1 699	966	6 087	3 971	2 116
10	1 634	1 263	7 721	5 234	2 487
11	1 357	1 450	9 078	6 684	2 394
12	977	1 470	10 055	8 154	1 901
13	615	1 181	10 670	9 335	1 335
14	983	1 014	11 653	10 349	1 304
15	1 280	1 022	12 933	11 371	1 562
16	1 391	994	14 324	12 365	1 959
17	1 170	1 090	15 494	13 455	2 039
18	957	1 263	16 451	14 718	1 733
19	581	1 138	17 032	15 856	1 176
20	416	850	17 448	16 706	742
21	323	583	17 771	17 289	482
22	263	388	18 034	17 677	357
23	222	292	18 256	17 969	287
24	176	242	18 432	18 211	221
25	172	218	18 604	18 429	175

plotted against storage approximates a single value curve; that is, one that does not form a loop. The slope of the curve equals K.

A flood wave is routed using Equation 6-74. Example 6-15 illustrates the Muskingum method of routing. In the example, a flood is given to determine the routing coefficients. Then, the method is used to route the same flood for the purpose of illustration. In practice, the best procedure is to route a different flood and compare the routed hydrograph with the observed graph.

Example 6-15

The instantaneous inflow and outflow of a stream reach is given in columns 2 and 3 of Table 6-31, and the 1200-h inflow and outflow are given in columns 2 and 3 of Table

Table 6-32 Computation of Weighting Factor x for Example 6-15

				Weighted Discharge	
	Inflow 1200 h	Outflow 1200 h	Storage 1200 h	$x = 0.25$	$x = 0.20$
Date	(m^3/s)	(m^3/s)	$(m^3 \cdot d/s)$	(m^3/s)	(m^3/s)
1	2	3	4	5	6
1	166	118	3	130	128
2	264	197	78	214	210
3	365	214	186	252	244
4	595	402	387	450	441
5	663	518	518	554	547
6	623	524	595	549	544
7	920	603	799	682	666
8	1 569	830	1 383	1 015	978
9	1 776	1 124	2 116	1 287	1 254
10	1 490	1 379	2 487	1 407	1 401
11	1 223	1 508	2 394	1 437	1 451
12	714	1 379	1 901	1 213	1 246
13	646	1 051	1 335	950	970
14	1 167	1 014	1 304	1 052	1 044
15	1 427	1 014	1 562	1 117	1 097
16	1 294	1 014	1 959	1 084	1 070
17	1 099	1 209	2 039	1 182	1 187
18	765	1 249	1 733	1 128	1 152
19	459	1 003	1 176	867	894
20	351	714	742	623	641
21	289	464	482	420	429
22	229	496	357	429	443
23	142	263	287	233	239
24	193	223	221	216	217

6-32. Calculate the values of K and x, and using those constants route the flow through the reach. The time interval is one day. Storage is expressed in cubic metre · days per second and discharge is in cubic metres per second.

Solution

Cumulate the inflow and outflow, and record in columns 4 and 5 of Table 6-31, respectively. Compute the storage by subtracting column 5 from column 4 and enter in column 6.

Enter the cumulative storage from Table 6-31 in column 4 of Table 6-32. Storage is a volume expressed in $m^3 \cdot d/s$. The discharge-storage relationship is the rate of discharge for a given storage, hence, the mean for the time period is used. The weighting factor x is computed by trial and error. Since it is 0.25 for most natural streams, the first trial assumes $x = 0.25$ to compute the weighted mean using Equation 6-72. Values are recorded in column 5, and plotted on Figure 6-71. The data for a rising stage plots to the left of that for the falling stage indicating that x is slightly too great. Estimate $x = 0.20$ and recompute the weighted discharge and plot the results on Figure 6-71. The rising and falling stage data coincide; therefore, $x = 0.20$.

The factor K is the slope of a straight line drawn through the curve $x = 0.20$.

$$K = \frac{(2\,500 - 0)m^3 \cdot d/s}{(1\,530 - 270)m^3/s} = 2.0$$

Compute the constants for Equation 6-74 and use them to calculate the routed outflow in Table 6-33. The inflow discharge is given in column 2.

$$C_0 = \frac{-2.0 \times 0.2 + 0.5 \times 1}{2.0 - 2.0 \times 0.2 + 0.5 \times 1} = \frac{0.1}{2.1} = 0.05$$

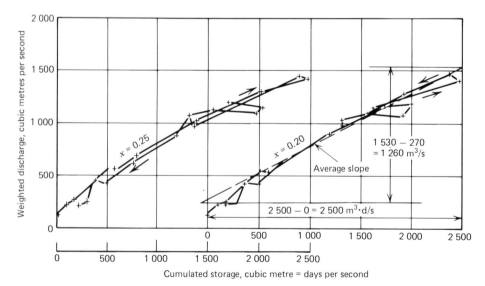

Figure 6-71 Determination of weighted factor x and storage coefficient K for Example 6-15.

$$C_1 = \frac{2.0 \times 0.2 + 0.5 \times 1}{2.1} = 0.43$$

$$C_2 = \frac{2.0 - 2.0 \times 0.2 - 0.5 \times 1}{2.1} = 0.52$$

$$Q_2 = 0.05I_2 + 0.43I_1 + 0.52O_1$$

Values of the computed mean daily outflow are given in Table 6-33. The outflow for

Table 6-33   Routed Flow Using Equation 6-74 for Example 6-15

Date 1	Mean Daily Inflow (m³/s) 2	Computed Mean Daily Outflow (m³/s) 3
1	121	118
2	217	124
3	314	173
4	473	249
5	612	363
6	595	482
7	753	544
8	1 303	672
9	1 699	995
10	1 643	1 330
11	1 357	1 466
12	977	1 395
13	615	1 176
14	983	925
15	1 280	968
16	1 391	1 123
17	1 170	1 241
18	957	1 196
19	581	1 062
20	416	822
21	323	622
22	263	475
23	222	397
24	176	311
25	172	246

the first day is given as 118 m^3/s. The outflow on the second is calculated as follows:

$$Q_2 = 0.05 \times 217 + 0.43 \times 121 + 0.52 \times 118 = 124 \text{ m}^3/\text{s}$$

6-25 Control and Mitigation of Floods

The term flood control tends to imply complete control of floods and has mislead the public into believing that control structures assure no risk. Actually, floods are a natural characteristic of a river that cannot be eliminated. Furthermore, the floodplain was created by the river to carry floods and will never be entirely vacated by the river. Therefore, flood control means a certain amount of protection depending on the price the public is willing to pay, not forgetting that some degree of risk always remains.

Flood control has come to mean physically restraining or routing the flood with structures, such as reservoirs, flood walls, levees, channel improvements, and bypass channels, or by land treatment. Each method has advantages and disadvantages, and each has definite adverse aftereffects.[40] Most flood control methods have been practiced worldwide for centuries. The flood control thrust in the United States began when Congress passed the Flood Control Act of June 22, 1936, recognizing the federal interest in reducing losses from rare and catastrophic floods.

Levees and flood walls are among the oldest, and most universally used, control structures for excluding flood water from part or all of the floodplain. These structures have two major disadvantages. They reduce the conveyance of the stream, which increases the flood height, and they prevent the stream from using the natural storage capacity of the floodplain; as a result, levees and flood walls may increase flood peaks downstream. When a levee is overtopped or breached, the flood waters enter the protected area without adequate warning. The occupants are unprepared to evacuate, and damage may be greater than if no dikes existed.

Flood control reservoirs hold water in excess of channel capacity for later release at a rate that can be safely carried. Some reservoirs have openings without gates so the outflow rate depends entirely on the quantity of water stored. Sometimes the water is released from these structures before the channel can carry the excess water without overflowing. Other flood control and multipurpose reservoirs have gates to regulate the release of water, permitting timed releases when the flow will not exceed channel capacity. The small reservoirs constructed by the Soil Conservation Service and those built by the Miami Conservancy District in Ohio are ungated, as are some structures built by the Corps of Engineers and others.

Reservoirs are effective in reducing flood peaks in the reach immediately downstream from the dam, but the effect diminishes rapidly with distance from the dam.[40] Consequently, the effect of small tributary reservoirs even though they may be numerous might be minimal on the main stream. Also, evaporation from small flood control reservoirs in semiarid regions reduces downstream supply.

Flood stages can be decreased to a limited extent by increasing the channel conveyance. Smoothing the banks, removing vegetation and other obstructions, and straightening reduces the roughness coefficient and increases the channel capacity. Straightening has adverse effects discussed in the next section.

Diversion or bypass channels are very effective in protecting heavily populated areas where topographic features are favorable. Diversion channels are generally confined by a pair of levees on the floodplain, thus reclaiming for use of the river part of the protected area. Several cities along the lower Mississippi River have been successfully protected by diversion channels.

Land treatment, such as contour farming, terracing, and associated structures like check dams and terrace outlet structures, reduce and delay runoff by creating surface storage and increasing infiltration. Infiltration rates decrease as a storm progresses. The storage capacity is occupied and the infiltration rate is greatly reduced in the early part of a great storm; consequently, the effect of land treatment is minimal on floods produced by great storms. If major storms occur when the ground is frozen, the effect of land treatment is negligible. As an asset, land management practices are a beneficial conservation measure by increasing infiltration to groundwater storage.

The purpose of flood control is to reduce damages caused by direct destruction of property or indirectly through the loss of services. Nonstructural methods, such as flood warning, can be used to reduce indirect damages, and floodplain zoning to reduce both indirect and direct damages. The flood warning system of the U. S. Weather Service is designed to warn occupants of flood-prone areas of the time and height of approaching floods so they can evacuate and protect property. The program has been very effective in reducing damage.

Floodplain zoning prohibits uses of the floodplain subject to water damage. Zoning is unpopular locally, because it does not enhance property values as do flood control structures. Zoning is becoming more acceptable because the flood insurance program, which is partly subsidized by the Federal Insurance Administration, requires restrictions on use of flood-prone areas. No construction is permitted in a designated floodway and all construction between the boundary of the 100-year flood and the floodway must be protected from damage. Use of floodplains for parks is being encouraged.

6-26 River Morphology

All except minor uses of streams change the flow, either total quantity, variability, or possibly both. Very often the stream channel is also changed, and the stream reacts in ways that can cause great damage. The purpose of this section is to describe some of the stream responses, and how with proper design the adverse responses can be avoided, or at least minimized.

The channels of most streams of concern to the hydraulic engineer and hydrologist are composed of noncohesive material subject to movement by flowing water. Streams in their natural state, unaffected by human activities or natural catastrophies, are in quasi-equilibrium. This condition is reached over a long period of time by the stream finely adjusting its channel to provide a velocity necessary to transport its sediment load with the discharge available. The term quasi-equilibrium is appropriate because the continually changing discharge causes the stream to constantly adjust; however, the adjustments are minor and for practical purposes the stream can be considered in equilibrium. The stream adjusts its channel to average dimensions of width, depth, slope, and meanders that depend on the sequence of flows and sediment load. According to Culbertson, Young, and Brice[41], alluvial channels are assumed to have attained some degree of equilibrium, and a pronounced change in any of the controlling variables leads to scour or fill.

Lane[42] presents the following qualitative relation affecting river morphology

$$Q_s d \sim Q_w S \qquad (6\text{-}75)$$

where Q_s = quantity of sediment
d = particle dimension of the sediment bed loads
$\sim$ = varies directly as
Q_w = water discharge
S = stream energy gradient

This equation is not an exact relationship, but serves as a guide to the response of a stream to imposed man-made changes. For a quantative response see Blench.[43]

Adjustment of the energy gradient can be made by changing the bed slope; however, more often the banks are less resistant to ·scour and the stream attacks the banks, widens the channel, and the stream becomes shallower. If the banks are resistant to erosion, the channel may scour and under some conditions head cutting develops. A head cut is a waterfall that moves upstream. Lowering the stream bed can have disastrous results by undermining bridge piers and abutments. If the channel is lowered at the mouth of a tributary, the tributary channels also lowers, thus, the effect spreads throughout the basin.

Reservoirs interrupt a stream's natural gradient. The sediment and water moving into the reservoir remains unchanged; therefore, the response of the stream is to deposit the bed load and decrease the gradient immediately above the reservoir, as illustrated in Figure 6-72. The effect moves upstream as sediment continues to be deposited and, if not interrupted by another man-made change, can eventually reach great distances above the reservoir. Figure 6-73a shows the change in the bed of the North Platte River at Lewellen, Nebraska, after Lake McConaughy was completed in 1941. Lewellen is 8 km above the head of the reservoir and the stream bed has risen 0.6 m.[44] It required 10 years for effect of the reservoir to reach Lewellen, but at present the rate of change is increasing. The rising stream bed causes the water table

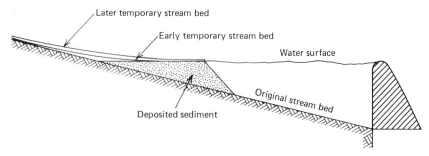

Figure 6-72 Longitudinal section of a reservoir showing the progressive change in the stream bed upstream from the dam.

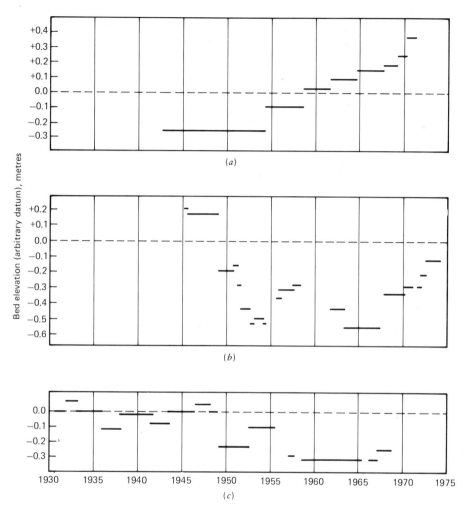

Figure 6-73 Changes in stream bed elevation during the past 45 years. (*a*) North Platte River at Lewellen (north channel). (*b*) North Platte River near Keystone. (*c*) Platte River near Overton (south channel). (From G. P. Williams, *The Case of the Shrinking Channels—the North Platte and Platte Rivers in Nebraska,* U. S. Geological Survey Circular 781, 1978.)

adjacent to the river to rise, water logging adjacent lands. Farms and towns at the head of other reservoirs have been abandoned due to waterlogging.

The effect of a reservoir on a channel downstream is more complex because the sediment load is reduced and the water discharge may be reduced by diversion directly from the reservoir. The variability of the discharge is also changed. Regardless of how the flow is affected, the stream is not in equilibrium. Figure 6-73*b* illustrates the response of the channel of the North Platte River near Keystone below Lake McConaughy to a reduction in sediment load and discharge. Between 1945 and 1955, the stream picked up sediment from the channel to replace the sediment deposited in the reservoir causing the bed to lower. By 1955 the reduction in flow had decreased the water-carrying capacity to the channel, which began to fill.

All reservoirs, except those exclusively for recreation, are designed to reduce high flows and store excess water for use or release at a later time. Thus, the stream is out of equilibrium below the dam because the channel is larger than needed to convey the regulated flow. The response is to reduce its capacity to carry water, while the channel becomes narrower and shallower. Vegetation grows in the abandoned channel further reducing the ability of the channel and floodplain to carry floods. Discharges formerly carried by the channel overflow the banks. Figure 6-74 illustrates the effect of re-

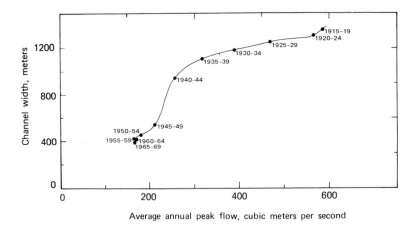

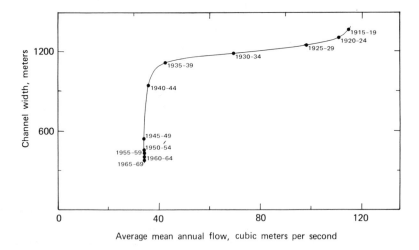

Figure 6-74 A reduction of either the mean or flood discharge results in a smaller channel width and capacity caused by encroaching vegetation and deposition of sediment. (Data from the Platte River near Overton.)

ducing the flow on the channel width of the Platte River near Overton. A series of reservoirs have been constructed in the Platte River system since shortly after the turn of the century. Each reservoir caused the channel width to decrease more. The greatest effect was after completion of the Seminoe Reservoir in Wyoming in 1939 and Lake McConaughy in 1942.

Diversions and return flows also influence stream morphology. When water is diverted from a sediment-laden stream, a desilting basin is commonly placed near the point of diversion. Sediment is removed and returned to the stream where the reduced flow is insufficient to transport the returned silt load. The response in the stream is to increase its gradient with the possible effect of waterlogging adjacent land.

Return flows from hydroelectric plants increase water discharge with no increase in sediment load. The reaction in the stream is to scour sediment from the bed thus decreasing the gradient. Extensive lowering of the stream bed may require adjusting water intakes and lowering of the water table may dry up wells and ponds in the vicinity. Williams[44] reported the bed of the Platte River at Overton, Nebraska, degraded about 0.3 metres since 1941 as illustrated in Figure 6-73c. The Central Platte Public Power and Irrigation District began returning relatively sediment-free water from their hydro plant to the river just above Overton at about that time.

Some projects are designed to divert water from one stream to another, or to release water at rates much greater than natural flow. This action increases velocity without affecting the other conditions. The stream reacts by increasing bank erosion making the bed wider and shallower, thus reducing the velocity. An example of this response occurred below Enders Reservoir on Frenchman Creek, which drained a sandy area and had a very uniform flow. A reservoir was constructed to supply irrigation water that was stored most of the year and released at high rates during the irrigation season resulting in troublesome bank erosions.

Channel straightening is sometimes performed by cutting off bends to improve drainage or avoid river crossings. Although this appears to be a simple solution, the results can be disastrous decades later. Straightening increases the energy gradient while other conditions remain unchanged. The first reaction is to degrade the channel immediately above the straightened section and aggrade immediately below. Then, the stream attacks either the banks or channel, whichever is least resistant. The channel of the Nemaha River in southeast Nebraska was straightened in the early 1900s. The banks of the Nemaha River are somewhat resistant to erosion; therefore, the river scoured its channel partly by head cutting. The stream channel has been lowered about 10 metres, which in turn caused a similar reaction on each tributary. Streambank erosion is still continuing. All county bridges in one county have been destroyed and bank erosion is the most serious problem facing landowners.

Disturbing a stream's equilibrium is not a local matter because given sufficient time the entire river system including tributaries can be affected. A stream provides the base level for its tributaries. If the stream is aggraded or degraded at the mouth of a tributary, the tributary is not in equilibrium and responds in such a way that it returns to equilibrium. Water resource projects are certain to disturb the equilibrium; however, if the designer understands the stream's response, adverse effects can be avoided and the design made more effective.

References

1. Koschmieder, H., "Methods and Results of Definite Rain Measurements," *Monthly Weather Review,* Vol. 62, 1934, pp. 5-7.

2. Weiss, L. L., "Relative Catch of Snow in Shielded and Unshielded Gages," *Monthly Weather Review,* Vol. 89, 1961, pp. 397-400.

3. Richards, P. A., and Larson, L. W., "Snow Fence Shielding of Precipitation Gages," *Journal Hydraulics Division American Society of Civil Engineers,* Vol. 97, 1971, pp. 1427-1440.

4. Soil Conservation Service, *National Engineering Handbook,* Section 4, Hydrology, 1972.

5. Gerdel, R. W., Hansen, B. L., and Cassidy, W. C., "The Use of Radioisotopes for Measuring the Water Equivalent of Snow Pack," *Transactions of the American Geophysical Union,* Vol. 31, No. 3, 1950, pp. 449-453.

6. Hiatt, W. E., "The Analysis of Precipitation Data," *The Physical and Economic Foundation of Natural Resources,* Interior and Insular Affairs Committee, House of Representatives, United States Congress, 1953.

7. U. S. Weather Bureau, *Rainfall Intensity-Duration-Frequency Curves,* Technical Paper, No. 25, 1955.

8. Hershfield, D. M., *Rainfall-Frequency Atlas of the United States for Durations from 30-Minutes to 24 Hours and Return Periods 1 to 100 Years,* U. S. Weather Bureau, Technical Paper, No. 40, 1961.

9. Frederick, R. H., Meyers, V. A., and Auciello, E. P., *Five to 60-Minute Precipitation Frequency for Eastern and Central United States,* National Oceanic and Atmospheric Administration, Technical Memorandum NWS Hydro-35, June 1977.

10. National Oceanic and Atmospheric Administration, *Precipitation-Frequency Atlas of the Western United States,* in eleven volumes, 1973.

11. Riedel, J. T., Appleby, J. F., and Schloemer, R. W., *Seasonal Variation of the Probable Maximum Possible Precipitation East of the 105th Meridian for Areas from 10 to 1000 Square Miles and Durations of 6, 12, 24, and 48 hours,* U. S. Weather Bureau, Hydrometeorological Report, No. 35, 1956.

12. U. S. Weather Bureau, *Probable Maximum Precipitation Estimates, United States East of the 105th Meridian,* Hydrometeorological Report, No. 51, 1978.

13. Langbein, W. B., "Annual Floods and Partial Duration Series," *Transactions of the American Geophysical Union,* Vol. 30, 1949, pp. 879-881.

14. Hydrology Committee, Water Resources Council, *Guidelines for Determining Flood Flow Frequency,* Revised Bulletin 17A, Washington, D.C., 1977.

15. Leonard, R. E., "Net Precipitation in a Northern Hardwood Forest," *Journal Geophysical Research,* Vol. 66, No. 8, 1961, pp. 2417-2421.

16. Helvey, J. D., "Interception by Eastern White Pine," *Water Resources Research,* Vol. 3, 1967, pp. 723-729.

17. Burgy, R. H., and Poneroy, C. R., "Interception Losses on Grassy Vegetation," *Transactions of the American Geophysical Union,* Vol. 39, 1958, pp. 1095-1100.

18. Scatterfield, D. R. and Haupt, H. F., "The Disposition of Snow Caught by Conifer Crowns," *Water Resources Research,* Vol. 6, No. 2, 1970, pp. 649-652.

19. Tholin, A. I., and Keifer, C. J., "The Hydrology of Urban Runoff," *Transactions of the American Society of Civil Engineers,* Vol. 125, 1960, pp. 1308-1355.

20. Green, W. H., and Ampt, G. A., "Studies of Soil Physics, Part 1—The Flow of Air and Water Through Soils," *Journal of Agricultural Science,* Vol. 4, 1911.

21. Bouwer, H., "Rapid Field Measurements of Air Entry Value and Hydraulic Conductivity of Soils as Significant Parameters in Flow System Analysis," *Water Resources Research,* Vol. 2, No. 4, 1966, pp. 729-738.

22. Aldabagh, A. S. Y., and Beer, C. E., "Field Measurement of Hydraulic Conductivity Above a Water Table With Air-Entry Permeameter," *Transactions of the American Society of Agricultural Engineers,* Vol. 14, 1971, pp. 29-32.

23. Hulsing, H., *Measurement of Peak Discharge at Dams by Indirect Methods,* Techniques of Water Resources Investigations of the United States Geological Survey, Book 3, Chapter A-5, 1968.

24. Bodhane, G. L., *Measurement of Peak Discharge at Culverts by Indirect Methods,* Techniques of Water Resources Investigations of the United States Geological Survey, Book 3, Chapter A3, 1969.

25. Simons, D. B., Richardson, E. V., and Albertson, M. L., *Flume Studies Using Medium Sand (0.45 mm),* United States Geological Survey Water Supply Paper, 1498-A, 1961.

26. Corbett, D. M., *Stream-Gaging Procedure, A Manual Describing Methods and Practices of the Geological Survey,* United States Geological Survey Water Supply Paper, 888, 1962.

27. U. S. Geological Survey, *Water Resources Data,* for each state, annually.

28. National Weather Service, *Daily River Stages,* annually.

29. U. S. Geological Survey, *National Water Data Exchange (NAWDEX),* Open-File Report, 1977, pp. 77-259.

30. Riggs, H. C., *Low-flow Investigations,* Techniques of Water-Resources Investigations of the United States Geological Survey, Book 4, Chapter B1, 1972.

31. Riggs, H. C., and Hardison, C. H., *Storage Analysis for Water Supply,* Techniques of Water-Resources Investigations of the United States Geological Survey, Book 4, Chapter B2, 1973.

32. Soil Conservation Service, *National Engineering Handbook,* Section 4, Hydrology, 1971.

33. Mitchell, W. D., *Model Hydrographs,* United States Geological Survey Water Supply Paper, 2005, 1972.

34. Snyder, F. F., "Synthetic Unit-Graphs," *Transaction American Geophysical Union,* Part I, 1938, pp. 447-454.

35. Corps of Engineers, *Flood-Hydrograph Analysis and Computations,* Manuals EM 1110-2-1405, August, 1959.

36. Hudlow, M. D., and Clark, R. A., "Hydrograph Synthesis by Digital Computer," *Journal Hydraulics American Society of Civil Engineers,* Vol. 95, HY3, May 1969.

37. Linsley, R. K., Jr., "Application of the Synthetic Unit Graph in the Western Mountain States," *Transaction American Geophysical Union,* Vol. 24, 1943.

38. Benson, M. A., *Factors Influencing the Occurrence of Floods in a Humid Region of Diverse Terrain,* United States Geological Survey Water Supply Paper, 1580 E, 1962.

39. United States Water Resources Council, *Guidelines for Determining Flood Flow Frequency,* 1977.

40. Leopold, L. B., and Maddock, T., Jr., *The Flood Control Controversy,* The Ronald Press Co., 1954.

41. Culbertson, D. M., Young L. E., and Brice, J. C., *Scour and Fill in Alluvial Channels With Particular Reference to Bridge Sites,* United States Geological Survey Open-File Report, 1967.

42. Lane, E. W., "The Importance of Fluvial Morphology in Hydraulic Engineering," *Proceedings of American Society of Civil Engineers,* Vol. 81, No. 746, 1955.

43. Blench, T., *Mobile-Bed Fluvialogy,* The University of Alberta Press, 1969.

44. Williams, G. P., *The Case of the Sinking Channels—The North Platte and Platte Rivers Nebraska,* United States Geological Survey Circular 781, 1978.

Problems

6-1 How are precipitation records used by a hydrologist?

6-2 Of what importance are statistics to a hydrologist?

6-3 Define precipitation.

6-4 What causes precipitation?

6-5 What is the only known mechanism for cooling air sufficiently to cause precipitation in quantity?

6-6 Name the three major mechanisms for lifting the air. Which one causes high intensity rainfall?

6-7 On which side of a topographic barrier is the precipitation greatest?

6-8 Name three types of recording precipitation gages. Which one is most suitable for measuring snowfall?

6-9   How is precipitation reported?

6-10   What effect does wind have on precipitation measurements?

6-11   What effect would a 16-m/s wind have on a rainfall catch?

6-12   What effect would a 35-km/h wind have on a snowfall catch in an unshielded gage?

6-13   How should precipitation gages be located with respect to surrounding objects?

6-14   What is an Alter shield and under what conditions is it used?

6-15   Describe how precipitation network measurements of unusual storms are supplemented.

6-16   What are some of the precautions that should be taken in making a "bucket survey"?

6-17   Why are snow surveys made?

6-18   Snow packs vary seasonally and annually so why can snow surveys be used to forecast runoff?

6-19   Why are north facing slopes preferred for snow surveys?

6-20   Describe briefly a snow sampler.

6-21   How is a snow pack measured?

6-22   Why is it necessary to test precipitation records for consistency?

6-23   Precipitation records have been collected at a station between 1955 and 1975; however, the station was moved a short distance in 1965. Precipitation records are available since 1940 at 12 nearby sites that have been tested and found consistent. Test the short site record for consistency and find the average precipitation at the present short record site for the period 1940 to 1975. (*Answer* 542 mm)

Mean Annual Precipitation at the 12 Control Stations

Year	mm	Year	mm	Year	mm
1940	654	1954	652	1968	550
1941	729	1955	311	1969	485
1942	774	1956	683	1970	644
1943	633	1957	737	1971	676
1944	741	1958	795	1972	546
1945	676	1959	601	1973	524
1946	644	1960	829	1974	760
1947	633	1961	653	1975	617
1948	614	1962	852		
1949	642	1963	829		
1950	460	1964	708		
1951	674	1965	552		
1952	546	1966	565		
1953	456	1967	846		

Annual Precipitation at the Short Record Site

Year	mm	Year	mm	Year	mm
1955	542	1962	529	1969	309
1956	429	1963	390	1970	529
1957	440	1964	293	1971	723
1958	528	1965	518	1972	428
1959	774	1966	384	1973	480
1960	443	1967	325	1974	505
1961	527	1968	462	1975	585

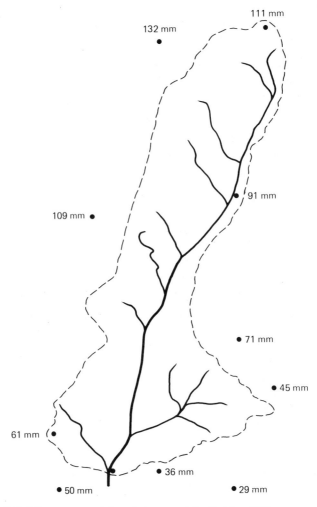

Figure 6-75 Rainfall measurements in a drainage area for Problem 6-24.

6-24   Compute the mean precipitation on the area shown in Figure 6-75 by the Thiessen method. (*Answer* 81 mm)

6-25   Compute the mean precipitation on the area shown in Figure 6-76 by the isoheytal method. (*Answer* 203 mm)

6-26   Why does a hydrologist need to know the frequency of occurrence of various size storms?

6-27   How much is the three-hour 10-year precipitation on a 200-km^2 area centrally located in the state of Michigan? On a 500 km^2 area? (*Answers* 48 mm, 44 mm)

6-28   (a) What is the probable maximum possible precipitation on a 500 km^2 area in 24 hours in the vicinity of Chicago, Illinois, which is located in Zone 2 at the south end of Lake Michigan? (b) What is the probable maximum possible precipitation on a 50-km^2 area in the same vicinity? (*Answers* (a) 560 mm (b) 666 mm)

6-29   Define probability.

6-30   If a box contains 20 black balls and 30 white balls, what is the probability of drawing a black ball? (*Answer* 0.4)

6-31   (a) If the ball in the preceding problem is returned to the box, what is the probability of drawing a black ball on another try? (b) A white ball? (c) If the ball is black and is returned to the box, what is the probability of the ball being black on the next try? That is, two black balls in succession. (d) If a black ball is withdrawn on the first try and is not returned to the box, what is

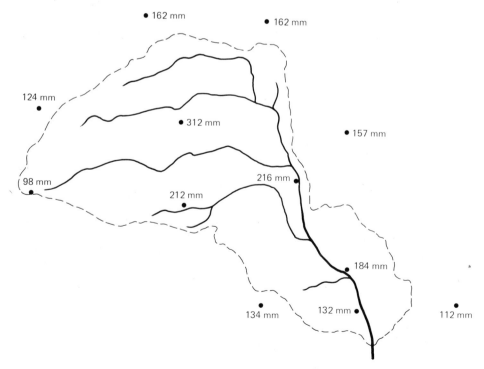

Figure 6-76   Rainfall measurements in a drainage area for Problem 6-25.

the probability of obtaining a black ball on the next try? (*Answers* (a) 0.4 (b) 0.6 (c) 0.16 (d) 0.388)

6-32   If the probability of an event occurring is 0.3, what is the probability of it not occurring? (*Answer* 0.7)

6-33   Give the equation for *N* factorial.

6-34   How many ways can *N* items be arranged?

6-35   How many arrangements (permutations) can be made of *N* objects if only *r* objects are used? Give the equation and demonstrate using three of four letters, *A*, *B*, *C* or *D*. (*Answer* 24)

6-36   How many combinations can be made of *N* objects if only *r* objects are used? Give equation.

6-37   Calculate the number of combinations of four letters if only three letters are used. Prove the answer by listing the combinations. (*Answer* 4)

6-38   Prepare a cumulative frequency curve of the following annual precipitation record. Are the data normally distributed? (Arithmetic probability paper is provided in the Appendix.)

Mean Annual Precipitation, Millimetres			
679	622	486	704
690	590	870	927
580	954	799	781
412	812	830	730
632	720	919	969
446	753	792	1 137
600	792	731	530
847	847	763	584
520	661	1 022	835
621	761	1 107	686
882	751		

6-39   Using the data given in Example 6-5, what is the probability of the precipitation at Lincoln not exceeding 400 mm? What is the probability of it exceeding 800 mm? (*Answers* 3.3 percent, 29 percent)

6-40   (a) Using the precipitation data in Problem 6-38 compute the mean and standard deviation. (b) What is the probability that the precipitation will be less than 500 mm in any year? (c) Greater than 850 mm? (*Answers* (a) mean = 747 mm, S = 166 mm, (b) 69 percent, (c) 26.6 percent)

6-41   What is a logarithmic transformation and why is it used?

6-42   When are data skewed? List two density distributions that correct for skew.

6-43   What is an *N*-year event and how is it related to probability?

6-44   Define (a) annual series and (b) partial-duration series. (c) When is it necessary to use a partial-duration series and why? (d) Why is the annual series used?

6-45   Maximum annual precipitation for 30-, 60-, and 120-minute intervals are given in Table 6-34. Prepare intensity frequency graphs using the Gumbel distribution. What are the (a) 10-year 30-minute, (b) 10-year 60-minute, and (c) 10-year 120-minute precipitations? (Linear Gumbel probability paper is provided in the Appendix.) (*Answers* (a) 45 mm, (b) 56 mm, (c) 63 mm.)

Table 6-34 **Data for Problem 6-45 and Problem 6-122**

Year	Precipitation in Millimetres		
	30 Minute	60 Minute	120 Minute
1954	30	135	138
1955	19	20	20
1956	20	30	33
1957	27	34	44
1958	29	36	50
1959	19	28	28
1960	19	25	27
1961	47	70	71
1962	30	34	35
1963	36	37	40
1964	28	31	32
1965	36	55	57
1966	22	24	27
1967	34	47	51
1968	65	73	75
1969	21	28	36
1970	38	53	54
1971	34	51	66
1972	17	18	22
1973	20	24	41
1974	21	25	30
1975	15	24	35
1976	21	22	26

6-46 Give the principle of least squares.
6-47 Describe a random sample.
6-48 Describe an independent sample.
6-49 What is a sampling error?
6-50 Describe (a) interception, (b) throughfall, and (c) stemflow.
6-51 What is the disposition of the rain that is intercepted, and what was the important finding of Burgy and Pomroy?
6-52 Describe depression storage. How much effect does it have on runoff?
6-53 Define infiltration.
6-54 List six factors affecting infiltration.
6-55 Define infiltration capacity.

6-56   Define infiltration index.

6-57   How does infiltration vary during a storm?

6-58   Name seven characteristics of a drainage basin. Which characteristic affects the volume of runoff and which affects the timing of runoff?

6-59   What are the two steps in obtaining a discharge record?

6-60   Describe stage or gage height.

6-61   What part of a gaging station determines the accuracy of the rating and the discharge record?

6-62   Describe a gaging station control and name its desirable features.

6-63   Discuss the desirability of the following station controls: (a) rock riffle, (b) riffle at the mouth of a tributary, (c) sandy streambed, and (d) a low weir.

6-64   What is the advantage of a stage recorder that drives the chart with a timer?

6-65   What is the advantage of a digital recorder?

6-66   Name four characteristics of a good measuring section.

6-67   Describe two types of current meters and give the advantages of each.

6-68   How is a current meter suspended in the water when measuring?

6-69   What are the positions of the current meter in the vertical when measuring?

6-70   What distance is measured for depth when making a discharge measurement through ice?

6-71   The width of a stream is divided into sections and a depth and velocity reading made in each section. How should the sections be spaced, and how many sections should be measured?

6-72   In making a discharge measurement, (a) why are horizontal angle corrections needed? (b) Vertical angle corrections?

6-73   Define indirect measurements and why are they needed?

6-74   Name four kinds of indirect measurements.

6-75   Compute the stream discharge using the following survey data. The two adjacent reaches are 9.45 m and 11.28 m in length, with water surface drops in reaches measured as 0.0686 m and 0.0653 m, respectively. The flow is confined to the main channel, therefore, subdivision of the cross sections is not required. (*Answer* 3.58 m^3/s)

Section	n	Area (m^2)	Wetted Perimeter (m)
1	0.38	3.17	5.94
2	0.35	2.76	6.19
3	0.38	2.92	6.40

6-76   Compute the discharge through the type-I channel contraction given in Figure 6-77. (*Answer* 134 m^3/s)

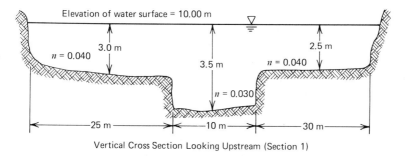

Vertical Cross Section Looking Upstream (Section 1)

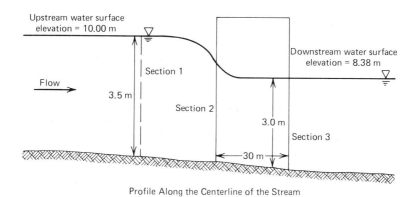

Plan view

Profile Along the Centerline of the Stream

Figure 6-77 Contracted section of a stream for Problem 6-76.

6-77 Water flowed over a dam under the following conditions (see Figure 6-42 for notation):

Dam length = 50 m
P = 5 m
h = 2 m
ht = 0
L = 3 m
Slope of the upstream face 1 to 1
The channel width above the dam is 50 m

What was the discharge? (*Answer* 243 m³/s)

6-78 Describe a discontinuous rating and its cause.

6-79 Why is it necessary to check streamflow records for consistency?

6-80 The energy gradient of some streams is not unique at some stages. How are flow calculations adjusted for this condition?

Table 6-35 Flow and Precipitation Data for Problem 6-81

Year	Flow (m³/s)	Precipitation (mm/a)
1959	6.12	834
1960	8.89	765
1961	4.08	714
1962	5.15	656
1963	3.82	605
1964	2.54	595
1965	8.01	952
1966	2.68	425
1967	3.28	623
1968	3.74	795
1969	8.69	886
1970	2.23	532
1971	4.50	599
1972	3.48	776
1973	7.67	975
1974	3.06	442
1975	3.77	656
1976	1.44	481

6-81   The calendar-year average flows of the West Fork of the Big Blue River near Dorchester, Nebraska, for the period 1958 to 1976 and the average annual precipitation at three sites in the basin that have been tested for consistency are given in Table 6-35. Test the streamflow against the precipitation record for consistency.

6-82   What is a flow-duration curve, and what is the significance of its slope?

6-83   Table 6-36 tabulates the discharge of the Big Blue River at Barnston during 1975. Prepare a flow duration curve. (a) What is the median flow? (b) What percentage of the time did the flow exceed 3.0 m^3/s? (Three-cycle log normal probability paper is provided in the Appendix.) (*Answers* (a) 6.8 m^3/s (b) 76 percent of the time)

6-84   Plot the low-flow frequency curves from the data given in Table 6-37 using the Gumbel distribution. (a) What is the seven-day 10-year low flow? (Three-cycle log extreme value paper is provided in the Appendix.) (*Answer* 0.51 m^3/s)

Table 6-37   Lowest Mean Discharges for 1-, 7-, and 30-Consecutive Days for Problem 6-84, Cubic Metres per Second

Year	One Day	Seven Days	Thirty Days	Year	One Day	Seven Days	Thirty Days
1951	0.71	0.88	1.33	1963	0.91	1.01	1.37
1952	0.59	1.09	1.49	1964	0.65	0.74	0.81
1953	0.71	0.97	1.03	1965	0.40	0.42	0.57
1954	0.74	0.78	0.81	1966	0.65	0.68	0.89
1955	0.57	0.61	0.67	1967	0.57	0.65	1.08
1956	0.40	0.44	0.49	1968	0.96	0.99	1.06
1957	0.51	0.52	0.67	1969	0.62	0.65	0.86
1958	0.71	0.76	1.10	1970	0.99	0.99	1.16
1959	0.82	0.85	1.02	1971	0.45	0.57	0.69
1960	0.40	0.61	0.68	1972	0.65	0.73	0.88
1961	0.59	0.64	0.77	1973	0.57	0.68	0.91
1962	0.51	0.58	0.78				

6-85   The maximum average one-day and seven-day flows for each year of record for the White River are tabulated in Table 6-38. Prepare one-day and seven-day high-flow frequency curves using the Gumbel distribution. What is the average seven-day high flow on the average of once in 10 years? (Three-cycle log extreme value paper is provided in the Appendix.) (*Answer* 4 m^3/s)

6-86   Compute the storage required on the White River to maintain a flow of 0.40 m^3/s with a 0.04 probability of failure. The flow data are listed in Table 6-39. (Three-cycle log extreme value probability paper is provided in the Appendix.) (*Answer* 1 252 800 m^3)

6-87   Define parametric hydrology.

6-88   Describe briefly statistical hydrology.

Table 6-36 Mean Daily Flow from October 1974 to September 1975 at Barnston, Nebraska, Cubic Metres per Second

Day	Oct.	Nov.	Dec.	Jan.	Feb.	Mar.	April	May	June	July	Aug.	Sept.
1	2.61	3.06	2.80	2.49	2.12	38.8	10.5	57.2	37.4	36.8	9.43	4.64
2	2.72	4.25	2.72	2.61	2.29	31.4	11.0	73.3	69.4	27.2	10.1	9.18
3	2.80	3.48	2.44	7.31	7.76	22.6	11.0	50.4	178	19.8	3.54	4.47
4	2.75	8.30	2.89	2.46	2.49	18.8	12.0	37.9	117	15.3	11.4	9.71
5	2.72	2.83	7.08	2.52	8.78	18.1	9.80	33.7	82.1	12.7	4.13	3.99
6	2.69	3.54	2.07	6.29	2.83	13.3	11.2	23.9	48.1	9.63	9.86	11.8
7	3.26	3.31	2.72	2.44	11.3	14.0	9.57	25.0	27.3	10.8	3.06	4.87
8	3.12	8.52	3.14	7.96	2.78	15.1	11.4	13.2	20.5	3.88	3.48	12.1
9	2.83	2.83	7.28	2.35	4.39	9.97	11.3	4.87	88.4	12.2	9.83	4.13
10	7.22	2.83	2.15	3.31	11.7	14.3	9.51	15.5	82.7	3.65	3.77	9.52
11	3.54	2.92	2.21	5.21	2.44	8.30	12.6	17.6	102	9.91	9.88	3.46
12	2.80	3.65	7.36	2.86	8.95	14.3	9.97	18.1	93.5	3.22	3.88	3.65
13	2.76	6.09	2.32	2.83	2.38	8.61	10.9	17.2	65.1	3.34	7.76	3.65
14	2.83	2.75	3.31	9.52	8.30	7.67	10.5	19.1	48.1	8.55	4.22	3.51
15	3.37	2.75	7.79	2.29	2.32	7.76	11.0	17.7	34.0	3.82	13.1	2.92
16	2.55	4.02	2.38	2.32	3.06	10.4	11.6	14.9	26.6	3.57	4.84	3.37
17	2.58	3.40	7.48	7.39	14.7	21.1	12.2	12.3	21.0	9.52	12.6	3.65
18	2.58	8.18	2.44	2.21	2.38	59.8	9.35	5.95	17.0	3.34	9.35	3.34

Table 6-36 Continued

19	2.27	2.92	2.69	2.66	10.4	64.3	10.8	15.7	15.9	3.46	5.24	2.97
20	2.27	2.92	7.99	8.24	2.32	59.2	11.4	5.18	84.1	4.05	11.0	2.92
21	2.27	2.97	2.52	6.32	2.49	64.9	4.36	14.8	65.1	10.6	8.84	2.83
22	2.27	3.54	3.12	2.32	9.57	59.5	12.3	5.47	90.6	49.8	3.74	2.89
23	2.75	3.68	9.63	2.95	2.44	49.8	11.1	12.2	142	68.8	3.94	2.75
24	3.29	7.36	2.61	9.01	3.34	36.5	12.7	5.66	127	48.7	4.13	2.75
25	3.14	2.80	2.63	2.12	9.49	26.8	15.0	7.14	125	39.1	7.84	2.75
26	2.72	2.83	7.25	2.41	2.44	19.9	13.2	16.8	122	31.2	3.94	2.75
27	2.78	3.31	2.52	7.73	10.4	28.0	19.2	11.8	116	24.6	3.99	2.69
28	3.91	2.92	2.66	2.55	14.3	34.6	18.7	20.3	110	21.8	4.05	2.63
29	3.85	3.09	7.42	6.66		19.6	18.7	43.6	93.5	20.3	4.07	2.95
30	3.96	6.54	2.55	2.55		20.3	31.2	91.8	62.3	18.7	4.19	2.69
31	6.63		7.84	8.16		15.9		76.7		12.5	4.30	

Table 6-38 Average High Discharges for One- and Seven-Consecutive Days of the White River for Problem 6-85, Cubic Metres per Second

Year	One Day	Seven Days	Year	One Day	Seven Days
1932	4.13	2.92	1956	2.72	1.06
1933	10.6	2.62	1957	1.30	0.98
1934	1.10	0.93	1958	15.4	2.80
1935	11.2	3.79	1959	4.33	1.16
1936	21.5	3.51	1960	9.03	3.26
1937	1.73	0.99	1961	1.05	0.73
1938	2.97	1.36	1962	2.35	1.07
1939	3.62	1.25	1963	1.61	1.03
1940	4.30	1.08	1964	1.22	0.89
1941	1.93	0.93	1965	2.52	1.27
1942	24.0	9.15	1966	2.46	1.16
1943	4.13	2.86	1967	3.27	1.95
1948	10.2	3.71	1968	5.75	2.63
1949	1.42	1.21	1969	5.04	3.99
1950	0.91	0.75	1970	2.69	1.14
1951	3.26	1.10	1971	7.31	3.65
1952	1.87	1.10	1972	3.68	2.12
1953	5.04	1.14	1973	1.44	0.97
1954	1.47	0.70			
1955	5.30	1.28			

Table 6-39 Annual Low Flows of the White River for Problem 6-86, Cubic Meters per Second

Consecutive Days	Recurrence Interval in Years						
	1.11	1.25	2	5	10	20	100
1	0.283	0.257	0.205	0.154	0.131	0.111	0.080
3	0.298	0.272	0.220	0.170	0.146	0.127	0.095
7	0.321	0.286	0.230	0.184	0.161	0.149	0.125
14	0.339	0.302	0.245	0.202	0.184	0.171	0.149
30	0.398	0.332	0.272	0.227	0.207	0.193	0.170
60	0.418	0.374	0.308	0.258	0.238	0.223	0.217
90	0.459	0.411	0.340	0.289	0.268	0.252	0.230
120	0.496	0.447	0.400	0.326	0.298	0.282	0.258
183	0.542	0.497	0.459	0.378	0.357	0.342	0.319
365	0.698	0.627	0.523	0.486	0.470	0.462	0.452

6-89 What is the basic assumption of the rational method?

6-90 Calculate the maximum rate of runoff with a recurrence interval of 10 years from a 2.50-km² average suburban area near the southern end of Lake Michigan. The time of concentration is one hour. Use the rational formula. (*Answer* 12.4 m³/s)

6-91 Calculate the maximum rate of runoff with a recurrence interval of 25 years from a 1.5-km² area with residential detached multiple family units at Springfield, Missouri. Use the rational method and a 30-minute time of concentration. (*Answer* 10.1 m³/s)

6-92 What kind of precipitation records can be used with the soil-cover complex method?

6-93 Give the rainfall-runoff relationship for the soil-cover complex method.

6-94 What does runoff from the soil-cover complex equation represent?

6-95 Calculate the 100-year runoff from a 24-hour rain on a 50-km² area in the vicinity of Springfield, Missouri. The soil is SCS Class C and the crops are one-third straight row, one-third small grain, and one-third pasture all in good condition but not terraced. Antecedent condition is type I. (*Answer* 80 mm)

6-96 Calculate the probable maximum possible runoff from a 50 km² area in the center of zone 5 in Figure 6-16. The soil in the area is Class C and the crops are about 50 percent small grain and 50 percent row crops. Assume the worst possible condition of crops on untreated land and type III antecedent conditions. (*Answer* 849 mm)

6-97 Define a hydrograph and describe the parts of a discharge hydrograph.

6-98 Define a unit hydrograph, and give the hypothesis on which a unit hydrograph is based.

6-99 Describe the ideal observed storm hydrograph for preparing a unit hydrograph.

6-100 What is bank storage and how does it affect the discharge hydrograph?

6-101 Why are several unit hydrographs averaged and how are they averaged?

6-102 A rain of 35 mm fell on the Bobtail Creek drainage basin during a one-hour period beginning at 0100 h. The drainage area is 78.2 km². The following table lists the measured discharge from the area with respect to time.
(a) Develop a one-hour unit hydrograph.

Hour	Discharge (m³/s)	Hour	Discharge (m³/s)
1	1.00	10	2.83
2	1.20	11	2.38
3	2.97	12	2.02
4	24.10	13	1.76
5	51.50	14	1.64
6	32.30	15	1.47
7	11.20	16	1.39
8	5.95	17	1.27
9	3.77		

(b) Compute and plot the hydrograph of surface runoff for a storm beginning at midnight using the Bobtail Creek unit hydrograph.

One-hour Period Ending at	Rain During Period (mm)	Infiltration Index (mm/h)
0200	100	25
0300	40	20
0400	123	15
0500	89	10

6-103 What is a synthetic unit hydrograph?

6-104 Why are synthetic hydrographs needed?

6-105 Define time of concentration.

6-106 The following information describing a stream in flood was obtained from maps and by a field survey. Calculate the time of concentration.

Reach	n	R (m)	S	Length (m)
1	0.030	3.00	0.000 300	2 000
2	0.035	2.25	0.000 415	2 000
3	0.040	0.95	0.001 125	1 500
4	0.045	0.70	0.001 125	1 000
5	Overland flow, 5 percent slope, short grass cover			1 000

(*Answer* 2.49 h)

6-107 Calculate the hydrograph of the storm in Problem 6-95, and the time of concentration from Problem 6-106. The drainage area is 40 km². Use the SCS dimensionless hydrograph.

6-108 What assumption is the basis for rainfall-runoff models?

6-109 Infiltration is an important variable parameter. What indicator is used in a model to continually monitor infiltration?

6-110 How does a statistical record differ from an observed record?

6-111 What information is needed to prepare (a) a rainfall runoff model? (b) a statistical model?

6-112 Describe sampling error.

6-113 Under what condition is the multiple regression technique used to compute streamflow records?

6-114 List five of the most important variables in a multiple regression for computing streamflow.

6-115 How are the constants in the regression equation evaluated?

6-116 (a) Are floods increasing in magnitude and frequency? (b) Why are flood damages increasing?

6-117 Why are flood records frequently broken?

6-118 How does the U. S. Weather Service define flood stage?

6-119 Name the three important dimensions of a flood.

6-120 What is the reliable limit for extension of a flood frequency curve?

6-121 How is a stage (gage height) frequency curve prepared?

6-122 Prepare a flood-frequency curve by the Log Pearson Type III method using the the data given in Table 6-40. (Three-cycle log extreme value probability paper is given in the Appendix.) (a) What are the 25-year and 18.5-year floods? (b) Compute the plotting position of the second highest flood by the Gumbel method and plot on the graph. (*Answers* (a) 660 m³/s, 610 m³/s, (b) 18.5 years)

Table 6-40 **Flood data for problem 6-122**

Year	Discharge (m³/s)	Year	Discharge (m³/s)	Year	Discharge (m³/s)
1940	629	1953	211	1966	235
1941	95.7	1954	233	1967	357
1942	64.3	1955	42.5	1968	58.6
1943	34.6	1956	223	1969	337
1944	388	1957	217	1970	20.6
1945	112	1958	193	1971	714
1946	42.5	1959	178	1972	237
1947	89.5	1960	266	1973	105
1948	170	1961	83.4	1974	23.4
1949	170	1962	549	1975	121
1950	236	1963	33.4		
1951	250	1964	248		
1952	206	1965	282		

6-123 Calculate the risk of exactly two 100-year floods occurring in 100 years. (*Answer* 0.185)

6-124 Calculate the risk of exactly three 25-year floods occurring in 15 years. (*Answer* 0.060)

6-125 What is (a) wedge storage? (b) Prism storage?

6-126 (a) Compute the routing constants (K and x) for the Muskingum method from the data tabulated in Table 6-41 using $\Delta t = 0.50$ day. The flood is from the headwater so the flow does not need to be adjusted for inflow. (*Answer* (a) $K = 1.0; x = 0.2$)

Table 6-41   Streamflow for Problem 6-126

Date and Time	Meadow Grove Discharge (m³/s)	Norfolk Discharge (m³/s)
9 Noon	15.5	14.3
Midnight	16.9	14.9
10 Noon	18.4	15.9
Midnight	20.4	17.0
11 Noon	24.1	18.6
Midnight	28.2	21.5
12 Noon	33.1	24.5
Midnight	45.3	28.5
13 Noon	56.6	36.0
Midnight	59.5	45.7
14 Noon	58.1	52.8
Midnight	56.1	55.2
15 Noon	49.8	55.3
Midnight	44.5	52.4
16 Noon	39.4	48.4
Midnight	36.8	43.7
17 Noon	33.4	39.7
Midnight	28.9	35.4
18 Noon	24.6	31.9
Midnight	21.8	27.8
19 Noon	18.7	26.8
Midnight	18.1	21.1
20 Noon	14.4	19.0
Midnight	12.2	16.2
21 Noon	12.0	13.4
Midnight	9.63	11.9

(b) Using the K and x calculated in part (a) route the following flood from Meadow Grove to Norfolk. The flow at Norfolk at noon on the thirteenth was 11.7 m³/s and at Meadow Grove as follows:

Date	(m³/s)	Date	(m³/s)	Date	(m³/s)
13 Noon	10.5	18 Noon	41.0	23 Noon	39.1
Midnight	11.5	Midnight	45.0	Midnight	33.5
14 Noon	13.5	19 Noon	44.3	24 Noon	28.0
Midnight	15.0	Midnight	44.0	Midnight	25.4
15 Noon	16.8	20 Noon	46.9	25 Noon	22.0
Midnight	19.4	Midnight	49.0	Midnight	18.8
16 Noon	23.9	21 Noon	48.3	26 Noon	15.1
Midnight	26.0	Midnight	50.0	Midnight	14.5
17 Noon	29.4	22 Noon	46.2	27 Noon	13.5
Midnight	33.5	Midnight	43.0	Midnight	12.8

6-127 What is the common meaning of the term flood control?

6-128 What is the most common, and probably the oldest, method of flood control?

6-129 What are the advantages and disadvantages of channel straightening as a flood control measure?

6-130 How effective are small headwater dams in controlling floods?

6-131 How does a bypass channel function?

6-132 What role do land use practices, such as contouring and terracing, play in flood control?

6-133 Name three nonstructural means of reducing flood damage.

6-134 What happens to a stream (a) above a newly constructed reservoir? (b) Below a new reservoir?

6-135 What happens to a noncohesive channel when a sizable part of the flow is diverted?

6-136 What happens to a tream channel in noncohesive material when the flow of the stream is increased?

Chapter 7

Water Quality
in Flowing
Waters

Rivers and streams are used as public and industrial water supplies, to support fish and wildlife, for recreation, and to provide natural purification of wastewater effluents. Dilution of treated wastes from municipalities and industries may conflict with beneficial uses of flowing waters if processing prior to discharge is inadequate. Therefore, control of quality is necessary to prevent exploitation of watercourses as waste receivers to the detriment of other uses. Standards now dictate in specific terms the limits of degradation beyond which a water may not be polluted for its defined purposes. Past preoccupation with the quantity of water, without regard to quality, has been a handicap in water resources planning.

The introductory sections of this chapter discuss the ecology of flowing waters and effects of pollution. After this preview, the subsequent topics on stream analyses have greater meaning. Mathematical modeling can become an abstract exercise unless water resources analysts are reminded that flowing waters are life-supporting ecosystems. Assessment of river basins must encompass all the physical, chemical, and biological aspects in order to be a viable component of the planning process.

7-1 Ecology of Flowing Waters

The perfect river runs swiftly down a mountain over rocks and boulders to the foothills, where the flow is still rapid enough to scour sand and small stones, thus retaining a gravel bed. When reaching the plains, the water velocity reduces to create silt deposits as the river meanders along a wide channel. Most rivers do not conform in detail to this scheme, even if they rise in the mountains and terminate in the plains. Geological irregularities cause swift and slow-flowing reaches to alternate, and shallow gravelly riffles can be found where there are meanders. Several classification systems have been proposed for describing various regions of a river. Zones may be defined by the fish species present, or on the basis of larger plants found along the shoreline, or by physical parameters, such as volume of flow, type of stream bed, temperature, and the like. Yet none of these appears to be satisfactory since rivers are strict individualists, each varying in its own way. Overriding all other considerations, local conditions within a river zone define the animals and plants present. The factors determining the kinds of animals present in any stretch of a river are current speed, nature of substratum, type of vegetation, temperature, dissolved oxygen, amount of silt, hardness of the water, and finally the geographical position of the river. The last point recognizes that all

280

creatures have a limited geographical range, so the same set of species cannot always be expected to exist in the same physical-chemical environment (habitat).

The dynamics of flowing water, exemplified by velocity and discharge, contribute to the formation of numerous habitats differing with respect to water movement, composition of substrate, and chemical characteristics. To survive in water flowing rapidly over a rocky bottom, algae and moss grow attached to the stream bed and animals are especially adapted to avoid being swept away by the current. Fish that migrate upstream to spawn, for example, trout, have powerful streamlined bodies for swimming against the current. In less turbulent regions of flow, if a favorable stream bed exists, rooted plants and flat-sided fish, like sunfish, find the environment suitable for their growth. The substrates of lower river courses are combinations of fine sand, silt, and clay. The animals adapted to the resulting turbid water are similar to those in lakes: worms, small clams, burrowing mayflies, and the like. Many of the fish present, such as carp and catfish, feed primarily on these benthic organisms.

Streams and rivers are also subject to dramatic seasonal variations creating unstable and ever-changing environments. After a heavy rain, flash floods can transform a small stream into a muddy torrent washing away much of the life and disrupting many of the habitats. Drought, on the other hand, can reduce flow to a trickle stranding stream animals on dry land or causing overcrowding in the remaining pools.

Natural habitats of rivers are often changed by construction of dams and channelization of flowing waters to generate power, control flooding, and improve navigation. In addition to quantity control, the quality of most surface waters are influenced by human activities. Pollution may merely change one type of natural water into another without causing serious changes. However, if excess contamination surpasses the boundaries of normal variation, the water loses its natural qualities through destruction of habitats. Three of the common problems are increase in turbidity caused by erosion from improper mining, lumbering, and agricultural practices; introduction of poisons discharged from industrial operations; and reduction in dissolved oxygen concentration below tolerance limits of aquatic animals by discharging municipal wastewaters that are only partially treated.

Aquatic Communities and Their Productivity

Maintenance of communities (the living components of an ecosystem) depends on food relationships and energy flow, which in turn are related to the physical and chemical environment. The fundamental operation in community metabolism rests upon the roles which organisms perform at different nutritional (trophic) levels in maintaining transfer of energy in food through a series of individuals.[1] These roles may be classified and defined as follows:

Producers are organisms capable of growth through synthesis of soluble nutrients using sunlight as a source of energy. This primary level of nutrition includes chlorophyll-bearing algae, larger green plants, and photosynthetic bacteria.

Consumers being incapable of photosynthesis depend directly, or indirectly, on producers as a food supply. First-order consumers, animals such as mayfly nymphs or snails, scrape algae off surfaces in the stream. These small herbivores, or plant eaters, are in turn devoured by second-order consumers, the carnivores, or flesh eaters such as dobsonfly larvae or sunfish. Third-order consumers are larger fish or animals like the otter, which eat the second-order consumers.

Decomposers are heterotrophic bacteria and fungi that break down organic matter of dead plants and animals to the elemental state, thereby returning inorganic nutrients to the system for reuse by producers.

The links in the food chain from producer to consumer, which represent levels of feeding and being fed upon, are termed trophic levels. A single food chain, for instance, algae to mayfly nymphs to sunfish to bass to mink, is only one pathway. Actually hundreds of interconnected food chains exist in any living community. Instead of being eaten by a mink, the bass might be caught by a fisherman who then becomes the fourth-order consumer. The mayfly nymph may escape hungry fish, only to emerge as an adult fly and be taken in midair by a swallow. Because all the simple food chains in a community are interrelated in this manner, the organization is more accurately described as a food web. Nevertheless, the basis of this complex system is always the green plants since they alone are able to unite inorganic nutrients into living tissue using sunlight energy.

The productivity of a stream, or river, is important in establishing both water quality standards and fishing regulations. One approach to measuring the amount of life in a stream is to sample the organisms that fish eat. A standard device used for this purpose, called a Surber sampler, consists of a square metal frame connected to a second frame that holds a net (Figure 7-1). The operator sets the open frame on the stream bottom; the net connected to the upright frame is swept downstream between his or her legs. The pebbles and other bottom materials enclosed by the open frame are washed in the flow so the current carries all the dislodged animals into the net. By counting and weighing the catch from a series of tests, a stream's productivity in terms of animal life per unit of bottom area can be estimated. In a rich stream the number of animals usually exceeds 2 000 per square metre, or 30 grams. A poor stream, on the other hand, yields fewer than 1000 animals, or less than 15 grams per square metre.[1] Based on a measure of the stream's richness in fish-food organisms, a rough estimate can be made of the number of fish a stream can support. Of course,

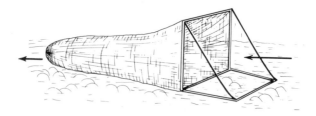

Figure 7-1 The Surber bottom sampler is used for measuring abundance of bottom organisms in shallow streams. Animals dislodged from the area being sampled (marked off by the open frame) are collected in the downstream net.

other factors, such as the availability of shelter and spawning areas, must be taken into consideration.

Sampling of a stream bottom measures only the "standing crop" present at that time. Actually, many aquatic insects go through two or more reproductive cycles in a single year, while others require more than a year to develop from egg to adult. Therefore, arriving at a figure for annual crop, which is a better measure of productivity, requires knowledge on the complete life cycle of every animal found. Another difficulty in the analysis of animal life in riffle areas results from the extreme variability in distribution and abundance of organisms. A large number of samples is needed to assure the sampling data are representative of actual conditions.

Productivities at various trophic levels were measured in a large artesian spring at Silver Springs in north-central Florida by Odum.[2] The majority of primary productivity resulted from the dense coating of algae covering rocks and stands of eelgrass growing in the stream bottom. Measurements of algal growths from sample areas revealed a dried weight of microscopic plants exceeding 500 g/m^2. The calculated annual growth rate, based on year-round testing, averaged 15 g dry weight of algae per square metre of rock and plant surface area per day.

The pyramid of biomass for Silver Springs, shown in Figure 7-2, illustrates the average standing crops existing on the first four trophic levels. The total biomass of primary producers, including both the freshwater eelgrass and its encrusting layers of algae, averaged 870 g/m^2. At the next level are first-order consumers—snails, turtles, mullet, and other plant-eating fish, and a variety of aquatic insects. This mass of herbivores averaged 40 g/m^2. Second-order consumers, such as sunfish, catfish, predatory beetles, and other small carnivores, came to 12 g/m^2. Composed of largemouth black bass and gar, the third-order consumers were only about 2 g/m^2.

The dramatic decline in weight or organisms present at each higher trophic level is because of inefficient energy transfer up the food chain. In converting food into the substance of their own bodies, animals lose a great deal of energy in the form of heat, as well as mobility and respiration. Thus the weight of organic matter, and the amount of energy stored in living bodies, is smaller at each step along a food chain. In addition, some animals die and decompose instead of supporting higher-level consumers. A biomass diagram converted to a pyramid of numbers graphically illustrates the natural limitation in fish production. Thousands of grazing insects that require millions of algae for food can support only a few fish.

Life in Swift Streams

Mountain streams are typically cold, well-oxygenated water flowing rapidly over a rocky bed. Habitats along the stream course are dictated by the following physical-chemical factors: speed of the current, type of rock substratum, temperature, level of oxygen saturation, and concentration of dissolved salts in the water. Slimy films of diatoms and masses of filamentous algae, anchored to the stream bed, incorporate thousands of different plant species. Any free-floating algae (phytoplankton) found in swift water have either broken loose from the attached communities, or entered from the outflows of lakes. Besides primary production in the stream, food is supplied by debris washed off the land and leaves falling from overhanging branches. Insects, such

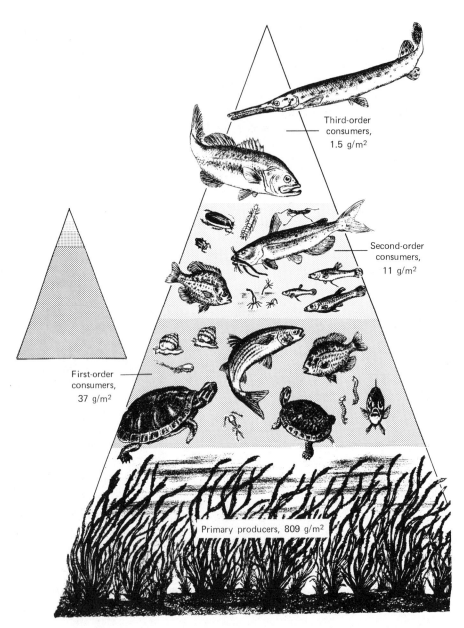

Figure 7-2 The pyramid of biomass for Florida's Silver Springs shows the rapid decline in weight of organisms at each successive level in the aquatic food chain of a stream. The smaller pyramid, inserted in the upper left, is drawn in more accurate proportions to illustrate the enormous base of plant producers necessary to support the animal community. (Adapted from H. T. Odum "Trophic Structure and Productivity of Silver Springs, Florida," *Ecological Monographs*, Vol. 27, 1957. Copyright 1957 by the Ecological Society of America.)

Third-order consumers, 1.5 g/m²

Second-order consumers, 11 g/m²

First-order consumers, 37 g/m²

Primary producers, 809 g/m²

as mayflies, falling to the water surface and drifting downstream contribute to the diet of fish. Stability of a stream bottom and the magnitude of current fluctuations control the number of rooted aquatic plants. While nonexistent in areas of scour, the silted bottoms of protected banks and ponds support a variety of macrophytes like water crowfoot, pond weeds, and lilies. River weeds reveal very few signs of damage even when full of insects or snails. A major function of rooted plants in the provision of food is their large surface area available for growth of attached algae, which are eaten by small animals.

The major factor controlling distribution of invertebrates is the nature of the stream substratum. Eroding bottoms are composed of rock and gravel, while the depositing beds are silt and clay. The intermediate condition, sand, being an unsuitable habitat for most animal life is usually barren. Inhabitants of an eroding substratum, created by turbulent cold water, are a rich assortment of immature insects, worms, beetles and their larvae, leeches, shrimps, and molluscs (Figure 7-3). The commonality of all these animals is their ability to withstand swift currents. Nymphs of mayflies and stoneflies are long-legged, flattened, or humpbacked, and avoid exposure by creeping down among the stones and gravel. These preadult forms of insects live and feed in water until they shed their shell-like external skeleton and become adult flies. Many caddis-flies construct heavy cases of coarse sand and pebbles to prevent being swept away. The insects' camouflaged cases also protect them from predatory fish. The caddisfly adult is delicate and mothlike. The larvae of black flies cling to exposed rocks with hooks and suckers at the hind ends of their bodies. With fan-shaped mouth brushes, the insects strain bits of food from passing water. The small black humpbacked adults are notorious pests that inflict painful bites.

A water penny (Figure 7-3) is the aquatic larva of a land-dwelling beetle enclosed in a thin copper-colored shell. It fastens securely to stones in fast-flowing water by means of grasping legs and a suction disc formed by the edge of the covering. Midge larvae are slender, fleshy, wormlike creatures that cling to rock surfaces with powerful suckers. Often confused with mosquitoes, the adults are delicate flies that do not bite.

The fish in rapid waters are either active swimmers, which can hold their places in turbulent water and shelter behind large stones or under the banks, or they have flattened bellies and live on the bottom among the stones away from the main force of the current. The first group includes trout and salmon that migrate upstream to spawn, often struggling through cascading rapids and riffles to reach their breeding areas. The second type of fish is exemplified by the bottom-dwelling sculpin common in cold upland streams. Being a weak swimmer, this fish maintains position by bracing its oversized pectoral fins against the upstream sides of stones. The sculpin has mottled skin to blend with the stream bed, and eyes near the top of its head to scan for insect prey. Darters are small fish resembling sculpin that hide among the stones in swift streams; they dart forward at high speeds when startled, and stop just as suddenly. Crayfish (crawdads) avoid the current by hiding beneath rocks and creep from one shelter to another. If forced into open water, a crayfish can flip its powerful tail forward in order to move rapidly backward. These scavengers eat practically anything—plant or animal, living or dead—and in turn are consumed by fish, turtles, birds, and mammals.

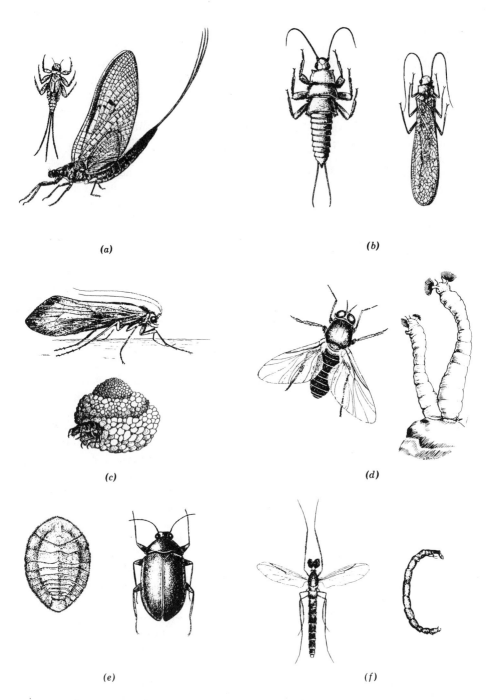

Figure 7-3 Insects found in eroding beds of mountain streams with cold, well-oxygenated, running water. (*a*) Mayfly nymph and adult fly. (*b*) Stonefly nymph and adult fly. (*c*) Caddisfly and adult fly. (*d*) Black-fly larva and adult fly. (*e*) Water penny (larva) and adult beetle. (*f*) Midge larva and adult fly.

Four main types of feeding habit are found in swift-water communities. Most may-fly nymphs and many caddis larvae scrape algae off the stones, which is the main foodstuff of the animals in eroding substrata. Still, debris and leaves from land vegetation are of considerable importance in the diet of many stonefly nymphs and some caddisflies. For larvae that cling to the gravel bed, the supply of food relies on the current carrying small particles of detritus and detached algae. A variety of nets and comblike structures, such as those of the black-fly larva, sift organics from the passing water. Carnivores, the fourth feeding habit, include fish, certain large stoneflies and caddisflies, many beetle larvae, and leeches. While herbivorous invertebrates number hundreds to thousands per square metre of stream bed, carnivores make up only a small portion of the animals, 1 to 6 percent, because of inefficiency in the passage of energy up through a food chain.

Life in Slow-Moving Rivers

In backwaters and regions of slower current, macrophytes root in the silted stream bottom: cattails, reeds, water lilies, and other pond weeds shelter increased invertebrate and fish populations. Attached mosses and algae yield abundant food for animals including nymphs of mayflies and stoneflies, and larvae of beetles and other insects. Since the weeds provide nursery areas for young fish, sunfish and bass are plentiful. Their flattened bodies are adapted to swimming through dense stands of vegetation.

Muddy rivers with sluggish flow are likely to be warm and deficient in oxygen during summer because of poor reaeration. Contrary to mountain streams, this habitat supports a less diverse and relatively uninteresting community of plants and animals. Apart from a few carnivores, mostly fish, the inhabitants are scavengers feeding on decaying organic matter in the bottom muds. The depositing bed is an unsuitable substrate for algae, although growths may be found on debris and shoreline weeds if the water is clear enough to allow sunlight penetration.

Common bottom dwellers that feed on detritus are worms and molluscs. Segmented worms (Figure 7-4), like earthworms, burrow in the mud; their blood contains hemoglobin, an efficient collector of oxygen. By sticking their tails up into the water above the mud, the worms are able to take in an adequate amount of dissolved oxygen. Larvae of several species of midges also have red blood, hence their popular name blood worms. Most midge larvae make tubes in the mud and feed on the organic matter that they drag into their burrows using strings of saliva they have spread out on the mud's surface. Some species of molluscs, living just below the mud surface, project tubes for withdrawing and discharging water from which they extract the nutrients. Other molluscs (snails) move along the river bottom feeding on decaying organics. On solid objects like sticks and stones, life includes moss, sponges, flatworms, leeches, and snails. However, few of the normal stone-dwelling insects find the warm temperature, oxygen deficiency, and turbidity tolerable.

Carp, giants of the minnow family, find muddy rivers and ponds an ideal habitat. They root in the bottom eating worms, plants, small animals, and fish eggs. Bullheads also search for food by scouring the bottom consuming most plants and animals, living or dead. Where the physical and chemical environment is less severe largemouth

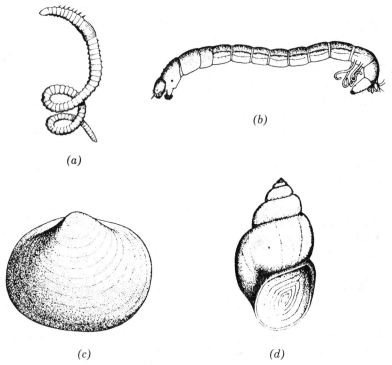

Figure 7-4 Worms and molluscs are common scavengers found in the muddy bottom of sluggish rivers. (a) Segmented worm (*Tubifex*). (b) Blood worm (larva of midge). (c) Bivalve mollusc (clam). (d) Univalve mollusc (snail).

bass, crappies, buffalo fish, gar, eels, and a number of others thrive in rivers and streams.

7-2 Effects of Pollution

The three classifications of surface-water contamination are point sources, where wastewaters discharge from outfall sewers or drainage channels; diffuse sources (pollutants dispersed on the land by human activities) conveyed overland by rain water or snowmelt; and background pollution derived from natural origins. The latter varies with geology and topography of the site, type of vegetative cover, and climatic conditions. Most frequently, runoff from uninhabited areas transports decaying organic matter, sediment, and dissolved minerals to tributary streams.

Principal point sources are municipal effluents, industrial wastes, cooling waters from power plants, and intermittent discharges, such as over-flows from stabilization ponds and bypassing treatment facilities (Figure 7-5). The characteristics of municipal effluents, being dictated by governmental regulations, are easily defined and the quantity of flow predictable from the sewered population. According to criteria established

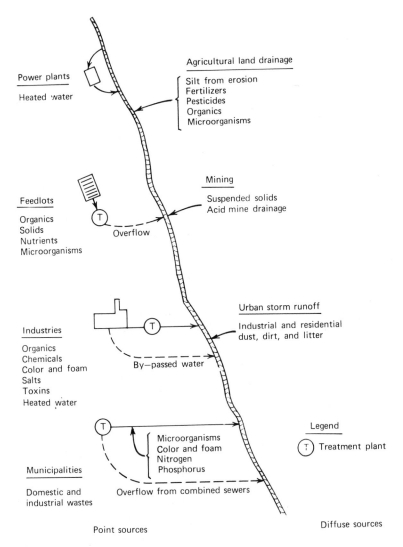

Figure 7-5 Principal sources of water pollution. (From M. J. Hammer, *Water and Waste-Water Technology, SI Version,* John Wiley & Sons, Inc., 1977.)

for secondary treatment, the average allowable BOD and suspended solids are a maximum of 30 mg/1; in selected locations, tertiary standards limit the phosphate content to less than 1 mg/1 of phosphorus and require partial oxidation of the ammonia nitrogen. The nature of industrial pollution varies and is much more difficult to forecast. Effluent limitations are based on the best control technology available for that particular industry. Processing of existing wastewaters is based on such mitigating factors as age of the industrial plant, cost of treatment, and environmental impact (other than on water quality) of applying the controls. New manufacturing facilities are required to meet more stringent performance standards, including a ban on discharging selected pollutants.

The important diffuse sources are agricultural land drainage from cultivated fields, livestock feedlots, and areas used for spreading manure; seepage and erosion from surface mining; and urban storm drainage from industrial and residential areas. Silt is the key pollutant, with erosion of cultivated farmland being the greatest contributor followed by strip mining, construction sites, and city streets. Along with the sediment, land runoff carries over 90 percent of the nitrogen and phosphorus conveyed to surface waters. Tailwater, which is the portion of irrigation water that runs off the ends of fields, can also contribute nutrient salts to canals that eventually drain to a river. Land management to control soil erosion, collection of feedlot effluent, modern irrigation practices, and conservative methods of fertilizer application can materially improve the quality of flowoff water. Despite implementation of these measures, intensive crop and livestock production along with rainfall-runoff patterns of thunderstorm weather makes absolute control impractical.

Contamination in urban runoff is mostly the dust and dirt associated with city streets including fallout of air pollutants, spillage from vehicles, and litter discarded by people. On the average, storm drainage contains 10 to 30 mg/l of BOD, high coliform counts, several hundred milligrams per litre of suspended solids, and measurable amounts of nitrogen and phosphorus. Industrial areas contribute greater amounts than residential areas and may also add heavy metals, oil, and other impurities from manufacturing. Actual measurements from a given area fluctuate widely with season of the year and duration of rainfall. After a long dry period, the first flush concentrations are higher than the mean values. These data, related to short periods of precipitation, often distort the seriousness of storm-water discharge on a receiving river. The pollutional load of surface drainage over longer time periods normally accounts for only a very small fraction of the total waterborne waste generated by a residential area or industrial tract. Confusion also arises where combined sewers are included in urban drainage. Obviously, even small overflows of domestic and industrial wastes can cause significant contamination of runoff from precipitation. Combined storm and sanitary flows, bypassed directly to a receiving watercourse during storms, do frequently constitute significant pollution and a potential health hazard.

Species Diversity

A normal healthy stream has a balance of plant and animal life represented by a great variety of individuals. Pollution disrupts this balance resulting in a reduction in the number of species and dominance of the surviving organisms. Complete absence of species normally associated with a particular habitat reveals extreme degradation. Of course, biological diversity and population counts are meaningful only if existing communities in a polluted environment are compared to those normally present in that particular habitat. For instance, while a mountain stream devoid of mayfly and stonefly nymphs would be a strong indication of pollution, their absence in a slow-moving, muddy river is natural.

Fish are good indicators of water quality, and no river should be considered in satisfactory condition unless a variety of fish can live and thrive in it. Being an end product of the aquatic food chain, fish reflect not only satisfactory water quality for themselves but also a suitable habitat for food supply, shelter, and breeding sites. Many lower animals are more sensitive to poisons than are fish, however, few data on toxicity are available owing to the difficulty of working with invertebrates in the laboratory. For field investigations, the immobility of invertebrates is important. While fish may avoid temporary pollution and recolonize an area after a poison is flushed away, the absence of animals reflects the occurrence of transient pollution, for instance, an industrial spill.

Poisons

Even though depletion of dissolved oxygen is more commonly blamed, poisons appear to cause the most damage to plant and animal life in streams. The list of toxic agents is long: heavy metals including zinc, copper, cadmium, chromium, mercury, and lead; organic compounds like cyanide, phenols, detergents, and chlorinated hydrocarbons; oxidants, for example, a chlorine residual; and, poisonous gases—ammonia and hydrogen sulfide. The effects of toxic pollution are illustrated in Figure 7-6a. After a poison enters a river, its concentration slowly declines either because of dilution or chemical reaction. Animal populations are reduced and then slowly reappear in small numbers increasing in diversity with recovery. Algal species, like animals, are affected differently by different poisons and some reappear sooner than others. Heavy regrowths of algae may precede the return of invertebrates because of the absence of grazing animals, and then slowly decline in mass to a normal balanced population.

The effects of toxins are frequently magnified by environmental conditions, for example, temperature has a direct influence on morbidity. At a given concentration of toxicant, a rise of 10°C generally halves the survival time of fish; poisons therefore become more lethal in rivers during the summer. Many substances such as cyanides, cresols, detergents, and ammonia, become more lethal with decreasing dissolved oxygen content. Also, the rate of oxygen consumption of fish is altered by the presence of toxins, and their resistance to low oxygen levels may be impaired. The pH of a water alone has damaging effects on most animals when the value is below about 5 or above 9; while within this range, hydrogen ion concentration can influence some poisons. For instance, ammonia is more toxic in alkaline than acid water because its un-ionized form is more poisonous than the ammonium ion. Conversely, cyanide is less poisonous in alkaline water than acid solution. Dissolved salt content can also influence toxicity; particularly the presence of calcium, which reduces the adverse effect of some heavy metals. Other heavy metals, however, exhibit increased toxicities when they occur together.

Poisonous effects on fish life also relate to the character of the stream, species of fish, and season of the year. During the winter, fish are much more resistant because of the cold water. The rapid rise of temperature in spring and hot periods in summer are both critical times when fish are susceptible to unfavorable conditions and likely to die. During spawning, even slight pollution can cause damage to salmon and trout.

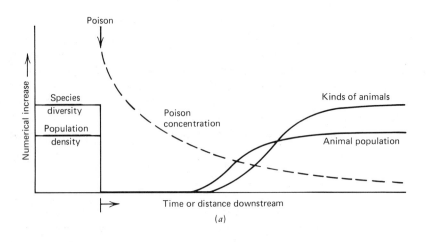

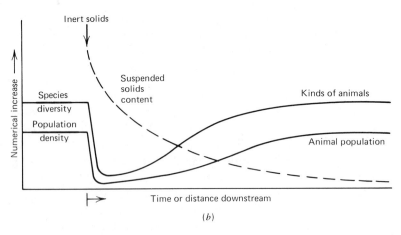

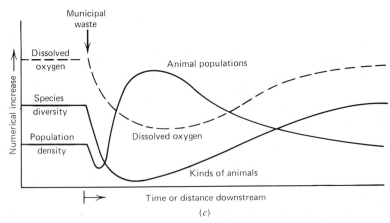

Figure 7-6 Pollutional effects on aquatic animals (invertebrates). (*a*) Toxic chemicals. (*b*) Nonbiodegradable suspended solids (silt). (*c*) Municipal waste (organic matter).

Inert Solids

The common sources of inorganic suspensions are soil erosion from agricultural land and construction sites, washing of sand and gravel, quarrying operations, and mine slurries. By the combined effects of increased turbidity and deposition on the stream bed, inert solids reduce both the population densities and kinds of animals present (Figure 7-6b). Very fine suspensions appear to eliminate the animals indirectly by shading out plant life, thus preventing food production. Although migratory fish may pass through a polluted river reach, resident species find feeding difficult since most fish feed by sight.

Settleable inert solids destroy, or in mild cases alter, the vegetation that produces corresponding changes in the animal community. The direct result of silting a gravel stream bed is a shift from the typical invertebrates found in an eroding substrate to the burrowing creatures that thrive in a soft river bottom. Deposition of suspended solids can seriously damage spawning sites where salmon and trout bury their eggs in gravel. Since moving water carries oxygen to the eggs, they are asphyxiated if the interstices in the bed are blocked by silt.

Organic Matter

Biological decomposition of carbonaceous waste exerts a demand that gradually depletes the dissolved oxygen level in a river. If reaeration is not adequate, the animals and fish are stifled by this deficiency. Pollution with organic matter also involves the addition of suspended solids and poisons, which magnifies the problem of deoxygenation. While the classic example of raw municipal wastewater is no longer appropriate (untreated discharge not being permitted), this combination of biodegradable organics, settleable solids, and toxins exist at reduced concentrations in treated effluents. Conventional wastewater handling, which removes substantial portions of the BOD and suspended solids, leaves about one half of the nitrogen in the form of ammonia. Consequently, one of the key concerns in disposal of treated municipal waste by dilution in flowing water is ammonia toxicity. Nitrogen can be converted, at considerable cost, to nontoxic nitrate by tertiary biological oxidation.

Industrial contaminants often present in municipal wastes include phenol, cadmium, chromium, and lead; these are usually reduced to very low levels through pretreatment at the industrial site followed by processing with the city's domestic wastewater. Water use also increases the concentration of inorganic salts that are not removed in treatment. Of greatest concern are phosphates, which in combination with inorganic nitrogen, can induce excessive growths of algae and aquatic weeds.

The general response of stream biota to partially stabilized municipal wastewater is illustrated in Figure 7-6c. Decomposition of the organic matter and resulting uptake of dissolved oxygen by bacteria and protozoans continues after discharge even if chlorination of the effluent temporarily depletes these microbial populations. If the dilutional flow is inadequate, massive colonies of fungi, filamentous bacteria, and stalked protozoans create ragged white- and brown-colored growths on solid objects in the stream, and may even form a carpet over the mud bottom. As the dissolved oxygen concentration sags, the variety of animals decreases and the numbers of those surviving rise sharply. Clean-water invertebrates disappear if overcome by poisons and lack of oxygen. Their replacements are pollution fauna consisting largely of sludge and blood worms that thrive in the blanket of settled solids. Referring to these as pollution organisms is, of course, not entirely proper since they are normal inhabitants of river muds; however, they are favored by organic pollution. Fish are repelled by the adverse environment, and may be killed if they cannot escape or tolerate these conditions. In either case, an assortment of fish species does not reappear until a suitable habitat for reproduction and feeding is reestablished downstream.

Immediately below the outfall of partially stabilized wastewater, the populations of algae decrease; but then, as nutrient salts are assimilated, they greatly increase in numbers. While blue-greens are more resistant, the mixture of algae usually encompasses numerous species that shift with the physical-chemical environment, often dictated by season of the year. Further downstream, in the zone of cleaner water, the increased density of grazing invertebrates generally keeps the algal populations under control, except during summertime blooms. These rapidly developing population explosions occur in slow-moving rivers during hot summer weather, when the temperature is near optimum for blue-green species and reduced turbidity allows adequate sunlight penetration. Under normal conditions, algae benefit stream life by supplying oxygen during photosynthesis. In contrast, dense blooms turn the water "pea soup" green and emit offensive odors, and at night decomposing algae can exert significant oxygen demand.

Rooted plants react to settled solids, high turbidity, and poisons much the same as algae. Increased fertility of the water and bottom muds downstream encourages plant growth. The capability of aquatic weeds to respond obviously depends on the habitat, particularly the stability of the substratum.

Heat

Temperatures of flowing waters in the United States range from freezing to over $40°C$ as a function of location, season, time of day, hydrology, and other variables. Naturally occurring animals adapt to the thermal regime in association with such factors as length of day and other species in the community. Shifting the environment by heating the water can have far-reaching effects. A fly nymph in an artificially warmed stream, for example, may emerge for its mating flight too early in the spring and be immobilized by the air temperature. Similarly, fish may hatch too soon to find an adequate amount of food organisms, because the food chain depends ultimately on plants whose abundance in turn is a function of day length and temperature. During any month of the year, waste heat added to flowing water should not increase the temperature more than $5°$ above the natural level to reduce the possibility of these adverse effects. Above about $40°C$, most normal river creatures are eliminated.

The rate of artificial temperature change must also be controlled to less than a few degrees per hour. Even though animals can endure the extremes at appropriate seasons, gradual autumnal cooling acclimates them to winter while slow warming in the spring is preparation for the summer heat. Spawning areas of trout and salmon must be maintained in a completely natural state; therefore, discharge of heated effluents are generally banned in these waters.

Heated outfalls entering polluted waters magnify other environmental problems. A rise in temperature increases the rate of biological activity accelerating the use of oxygen; it also reduces the saturation level of dissolved oxygen. This combination of factors causes a sharper drop in the oxygen sag curve. Heat magnifies the toxicity of most poisons. Finally, higher temperatures favor less desirable microscopic plants, such as unesthetic growths of bacteria and fungi, or blue-green algae in place of green species.

7-3 Instream Flow Requirements

A river used for wastewater dilution relies on natural self-purification to assimilate wastes and to restore its quality. In the mixing zone, the degree of pollution is determined by the effluent quality and residual contamination in the natural flow. Downstream recovery is a function of the river-basin characteristics: reaeration capacity and additional dilution flow from tributaries, subsequent waste contributions, and season of the year. Deep meandering flows with natural pools have poor reaeration and slow times of passage; whereas shallow channels with rapid water have high reaeration rates. The most critical condition for waste assimilation usually results at low flow and high temperature during the fall of the year, although, in some cases, the worst may occur in winter under ice cover.

Quality standards, specified for the best intended use of surface waters, establish maximum allowable pollutant concentrations based on the 1-in-10-year seven-consecutive-day low flow. These criteria set guidelines for establishing effluent standards for wastewaters disposed of in a stream with limited dilutional flow. Although a major river can easily accept a city's treated wastewater without deleterious effects, a stream at low flow can be grossly polluted by the same discharge. Considerable dilution by natural water is considered necessary to permit downstream withdrawal for a public water supply. The major health concerns of such indirect reuse relate to the unpredictability of long-range physiological effects from trace contaminants, possible presence of undetectable viruses, and uncertainties as to the effectiveness in processing of polluted waters. Many organic and inorganic chemicals are difficult to remove by conventional water and wastewater treatment. Major refractory compounds are inorganic salts, ammonia, and phosphates; trace refractories encompass heavy metal ions and nonbiodegradable organics. While foam, color, taste, and odor compounds are unesthetic, heavy metals and ammonia are major poisons to aquatic life. Phosphates promote eutrophication.

If a river basin has multiple-purpose reservoirs, drought flows can be augmented by releasing impounded waters to provide greater dilution. The propriety of flow regulation for pollution control depends on the priorities for water use, timing of discharges, and the quality of released water. Maintaining the pool level for recreation, or power production, may preclude release for low-flow augmentation. In general, the direction of present water quality management is toward improving the treatment of point sources before using flow regulation to aid waste disposal. Situations do exist, however, where even after the best possible treatment, stream quality objectives cannot be met because of a high residual load. In other cases, time sequencing of flow releases may be combined for the benefit of other uses of the river.

Where treated effluents are disposed of in major rivers, the principal factor in waste-assimilation ability is dilution. A tenfold dilution during periods of drought flow is often satisfactory, particularly since average annual flow (being many times greater than the 1-in-10-year seven-consecutive-day low flow) materially increases absorption capacity most of the time. Discharge of a typical secondary effluent on a 1-to-10 ratio to streamflow increases the BOD only 3 mg/l and the ammonia nitrogen about 2 mg/l. With only a fivefold dilution, however, the ammonia nitrogen adds 3 to 4 mg/l, which is slightly greater than the maximum allowable concentration of 3.5 mg/l normally prescribed for warm-water streams. Furthermore, if the flow is sluggish or the channel contains pools and backwaters, reaeration probably cannot satisfy the biological demand at a five-to-one dilution without dropping the dissolved oxygen below the minimum level to protect fish and aquatic animals.

Many municipalities must discharge treated wastewaters into drainage channels subject to extremely low natural flows and, in some cases, dry stream beds. Other means of disposal, such as land irrigation or pumping to the ocean, are often infeasible alternatives. Then, the question, "To what degree should the wastewater be reclaimed?" becomes a critical issue involving a pyramid of environmental, technical, economical, and political issues. Even though each case must be evaluated separately, a few comments on general situations are appropriate. If a substantial discharge enters a mountain stream in a recreational area, for example, from a ski resort complex, the environmental concerns are paramount. The sensitive aquatic communities are easily destroyed by poisons, like the chlorine residual in an effluent after disinfection; esthetic characteristics of the natural water must be maintained; and, the sanitary quality is essential, since hikers and campers are likely to drink untreated stream water. Flowing waters in the plains, although less environmentally sensitive, may still require a high degree of purity to accommodate indirect reuse. In groundwater-limited regions, the highest beneficial use is for public water supply. Perhaps the second most important consideration is water-based recreation in riverside parks or at reservoir sites. Even the lowest common denominator of esthetics is clearly strained by inadequate dilution: anyone who has inspected a stream composed of one-half secondary effluent can attest to the odor that lingers in the channel many miles downstream from the outfall sewer. In sparsely populated agricultural regions, a drainage channel may become an extension of the treatment process provided natural reaeration is adequate to maintain a reasonable dissolved oxygen level. The economics of more intensive purification than secondary treatment, other than perhaps disinfection of the effluent with chlorine, may be neither environmentally justified nor politically feasible. The increased turbidity, musty odor, and traces of foam caused by disposal after conventional treatment are often more tolerable than the costs to reclaim the wastewater effluent (without the benefit of substantial dilution) to natural stream-water quality. Moreover, the character of the aquatic habitat is more likely to be dictated by hydrology and pollution from diffuse sources. Organics from animal manure and silt from cultivated fields are washed into streams forming the muddy channel bottom, and flash floods periodically disturb the biological environment; these repercussions may be more significant than conventionally treated point sources.

7-4 Sampling and Testing

Apart from public health, our primary interest in pollution is its adverse effects on aquatic biology (esthetics, fishing, and water-based recreation). Despite the essentially biological character of pollution, appraisal of water quality incorporates physical, chemical, and bacteriological, as well as biological investigations. A study of aquatic plant and animal communities provides a record of prevailing conditions; even intermittent discharges of a poisonous substance, otherwise difficult to observe, are often revealed by biological investigations. However, biotic studies can only disclose the general type of contamination; they do not, except in rare cases, reveal the substances involved. Distinguishing between organic and poisonous pollution requires chemical measurements, such as, dissolved oxygen, ammonia, temperature, and pH. Chemical parameters can be expressed quantitatively, and even though environmentally permissible concentrations may not be precisely known, numerical data are extremely useful in establishing regulatory limits for control of pollution. Table 7-1 is a general listing of considerations in the assessment of water quality in streams and rivers.

Biological Assessment

Appropriate biological indicators of pollution must be selected for each investigation, since no rigid system is universally acceptable. Fish are perhaps the least satisfactory because they are mobile, difficulty to enumerate, and less abundant than other stream life. Bacteria, algae, rooted plants, and invertebrates being less mobile, more abundant, and easier to collect offer greater possibilities. Microorganisms suffer the following technical disadvantages: (1) they are not easy to sample quantitatively unless they can be induced to grow on plates, such as algae; (2) most microorganisms must be examined alive, which means laboratory facilities must be readily available; and (3) extensive microbial examinations often do not reveal a great deal more than such readily identifiable features of pollution as filamentous growths of fungi obvious to an investigator observing the stream bed.

Benthic animals are normally the best choice of indicators in shallow flowing waters. They can be collected, identified, and counted with reasonable ease, and biologists know enough about their environmental needs and life cycles to make associations between the condition of a water and the presence, or absence, of many animal species. Furthermore, larger invertebrates (fly nymphs, larvae, and worms) are suited to investigating cases of mild pollution, not identified by fish kills or unsightly microbial growths.

The following biological study[5] exemplifies an investigation of invertebrate populations in a heavily polluted river during low flow in late summer. The clean-water stream bed, composed of rock and coarse gravel, supported 20 species of benthos that were mostly immature insects (Figure 7-7). Because of predation and competition for available food among these invertebrates, the total population was less than 500 per square metre. A few kilometres downstream from this station, a discharge of untreated textile-mill waste was so toxic that the entire animal community was eliminated. Sterile black sludge covered the river bottom. The first signs of life, 10 km below the

Table 7-1 Parameters for Assessing Quality of Flowing Waters

Biology	Species and density of algae
	Coliform bacteria
	Extent of attached filamentous growths
	Types and numbers of bottom animals
	Species of fish
Deoxygenation	Dissolved oxygen
	Biochemical oxygen demand
	Temperature
	Ammonia and nitrate nitrogen
	Chemical oxygen demand
	Benthos oxygen uptake
Poisons	Ammonia nitrogen
	Heavy metals (Ag, Ar, Cd, Cr, Cu, Hg, Ni, Pb, Zn)
	Organics (pesticides, industrial compounds)
	Chlorine residual (chloramines)
Nutrients	Orthophosphate
	Organic phosphate
	Ammonia nitrogen
	Nitrate nitrogen
	Organic nitrogen
Salts	Total dissolved solids (filtrable residue)
	Chlorides
Esthetics	Floating substances
	Suspended matter (nonfiltrable residue)
	Turbidity
	Color
	Odor

outflow, were a few green and filamentous blue-green algae growing attached to rocks. Further downstream, the population of sludge worms, thriving on the decaying organic deposits, rose to a peak of 7 000 per square metre. Gradually, the total number of organisms decreased accompanied by a return of species variety. Appearance of fly nymphs heralded the beginning of stream recovery and the next two stations, located at 8 km intervals, had more kinds of animals present. At the final sampling site 35 km below the major source of pollution, population diversity was again present; however, the total population was higher than the clear-water upstream zone because of organic enrichment from the wastewater discharges. The population trends discussed are easily visualized by the three-dimensional presentation in Figure 7-7.

Fecal coliforms are a special group of bacteria used extensively to indicate pollution of natural waters. These nonpathogenic microorganisms reside in the intestinal tract of warm-blooded animals and are egested in large numbers in human feces, which averages about 50 million coliforms per gram. Domestic wastewaters generally contain

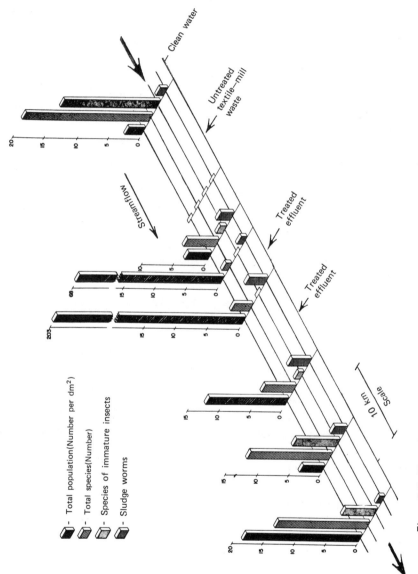

Figure 7-7 Three-dimensional presentation of benthic animal populations from the biological investigation of a highly polluted stream. (From K. M. Mackenthun, *The Practice of Water Pollution Biology*, U. S. Dept. of the Interior, Federal Water Pollution Control Administration, 1969.)

299

more than a million coliforms per 100 ml. Pathogenic bacteria and viruses, causing enteric diseases in humans, originate from the fecal discharges of diseased persons. Consequently water contaminated by fecal pollution is identified as being potentially dangerous by the presence of coliform bacteria. This correlation between coliforms and human pathogens is not, however, absolute since these bacteria can originate from warm-blooded animals and soil in addition to the feces of man. Therefore, presence of coliforms in surface waters may result from any one or a combination of three sources: wastes of humans, farm animals, or soil erosion. Although special tests can be conducted to separate fecal coliforms from soil types, human bacteria cannot be distinguished from those of animals. The significance of fecal coliform testing in pollution surveys then depends on a knowledge of the river basin and the probable source of the observed coliforms.

Biochemical Oxygen Demand (BOD)

BOD is the quantity of oxygen used in aerobic stabilization of wastes and polluted waters. Laboratory measurement specifies the incubation temperature as $20°C$ and the standard value as the demand exerted in five days. The depletion of dissolved oxygen relates to the rate of organic matter degradation (Equation 7-1) and nitrification of ammonia, if it occurs (Equation 7-2).

$$\text{Dissolved oxygen} + \text{organic matter} \xrightarrow{\text{bacteria and protozoa}} \text{carbon dioxide} + \text{biological growths} \qquad (7\text{-}1)$$

$$\text{Dissolved oxygen} + \text{ammonia nitrogen} \xrightarrow{\text{nitrifying bacteria}} \text{nitrate nitrogen} + \text{bacterial growth} \qquad (7\text{-}2)$$

The biochemical oxygen demand exerted by a diluted wastewater progresses with time in the general form as shown in Figure 7-8. After an initial adjustment of the biological populations (lag period), which may be so short as to pass unnoticed, the bacteria metabolize waste organics and the protozoa consume the new bacterial growth in a predator-prey reaction; both processes take up dissolved oxygen and release carbon dioxide. Since the rate of biological activity decreases as available food supply diminishes, the carbonaceous oxygen demand progresses at a decreasing rate with time. The model of this reaction can be expressed mathematically in the following form:

$$BOD_t = L(1 - 10^{-kt}) \qquad (7\text{-}3)$$

where BOD_t = biochemical oxygen demand at time t, milligrams per litre
     L = ultimate BOD, milligrams per litre
     k = deoxygenation rate constant, per day
     t = time, days

Nitrifying bacteria, if present in sufficient numbers, can also exert an oxygen demand in the BOD test; however, nitrification often lags several days behind carbonaceous metabolism. Unexpected nitrogen oxygen demand can disrupt laboratory tests where only the carbonaceous BOD is desired. While no standard method is rec-

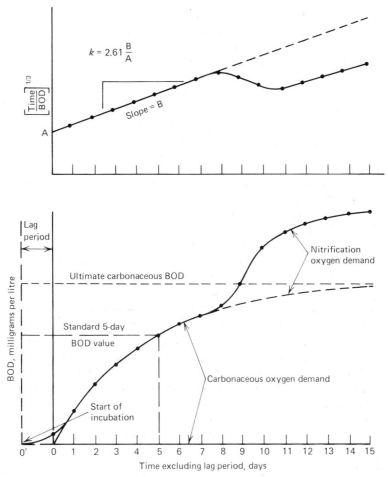

Figure 7-8 A schematic biochemical-oxygen-demand curve showing a time lag, the carbonaceous demand, and nitrification reaction and the graphical method for determining the first-order-kinetics k-rate for the carbonaceous phase.

ommended for preventing nitrification, the inhibiting chemicals of allylthiourea or 2-chloro-6-trichloromethyl pyridine can be used to stop nitrate formation in test bottles.[8]

Strengths of raw municipal wastewaters are usually between 150 and 350 mg/l, with 200 mg/l common for predominantly domestic waste. Biologically treated effluents range from 20 to 50 mg/l; the effluent standard for secondary treatment specifies a maximum allowable average of 30 mg/l.

The rate constant k for the carbonaceous demand (Equation 7-3) can be determined from laboratory BOD-time data as illustrated in Figure 7-8. If a time lag exists, the approximate origin of a first-order-kinetics curve should be established by sketching a projection through the plotted points to intersect the horizontal axis. Then, values of the cube root of time in days over BOD in milligrams per litre, calculated from the laboratory data, are plotted as ordinates against the corresponding times. The best-fit line drawn through these points, excluding those affected by nitrification, is used to calculate the k-rate by the following relationship:

$$k = 2.61\frac{B}{A} \qquad (7\text{-}4)$$

where k = deoxygenation rate constant, per day
A = intercept of the line on the ordinate axis
B = slope of the line

Values for k-rates are often in the range of 0.2 to 0.1 for raw municipal wastewaters and 0.1 to 0.05 for biologically treated effluents.

BOD analyses associated with water pollution surveys are conducted on both wastewater discharges and polluted surface waters. If the sample is a domestic waste, or an unchlorinated effluent from a biological treatment system, each test is prepared by placing a measured amount of wastewater into a 300-ml BOD bottle and then filling it with dilution water (Figure 7-9). The latter is prepared by adding prescribed dosages of phosphate buffer (pH 7.2), magnesium sulfate, calcium chloride, and ferric chloride to distilled water that has been stabilized at 20°C in an incubator, and then aerated to provide an oxygen content near saturation.[7] The wastewater supplies the biodegradable organic matter and microbial populations; the dilution water furnishes the oxygen and biological nutrients. Dissolved oxygen depletion, during incubation at 20°C, may be monitored by periodically inserting a laboratory DO probe into the neck of the BOD bottle. If oxygen content is measured by destructive chemical testing, several bottles must be incubated since each sample can provide only one reading. The number of bottles prepared for analysis of a wastewater should be at least three for measuring initial DO, three at each of two or more dilutions for testing after five days incubation, and additional bottles as necessary for intermediate times to supply data for k-rate determination.

If an effluent has been chlorinated, the chemical residual must be destroyed before testing. The standard procedure is to either allow the sample to stand for about two hours to dissipate the residual chlorine, or reduce it by adding a small amount of sodium sulfite solution.[7] Microbial populations in chlorinated-dechlorinated specimans, or wastes requiring neutralization, are generally too weak to perform the BOD reactions. Active microorganisms for seeding can be added to either the dilution water or the individual test bottles. A suitable culture of bacteria and protozoa for seeding is untreated, settled, domestic wastewater that has been aged at room temperature for 24 to 36 hours.

Polluted surface waters, because of their lower oxygen demands, require special sample preparation to compensate for the large volumes of sample placed in the test bottles. In fact, most moderately-contaminated streams have BOD values less than 8 mg/l so that addition of laboratory dilution water is not required (Figure 7-9). Natural samples are brought to a temperature of 20°C and then aerated to increase the dissolved oxygen to near saturation. Oxygenation is accomplished prior to siphon-

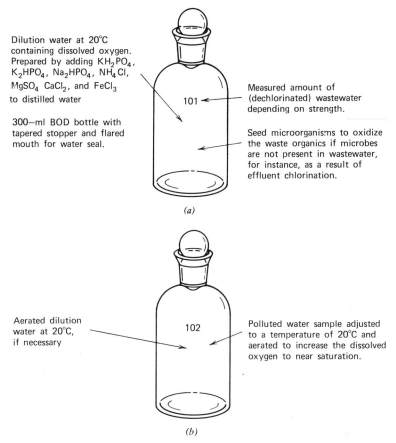

Dilution water at 20°C containing dissolved oxygen. Prepared by adding KH_2PO_4, K_2HPO_4, Na_2HPO_4, NH_4Cl, $MgSO_4$ $CaCl_2$, and $FeCl_3$ to distilled water

300—ml BOD bottle with tapered stopper and flared mouth for water seal.

Measured amount of (dechlorinated) wastewater depending on strength.

Seed microorganisms to oxidize the waste organics if microbes are not present in wastewater, for instance, as a result of effluent chlorination.

(a)

Aerated dilution water at 20°C, if necessary

Polluted water sample adjusted to a temperature of 20°C and aerated to increase the dissolved oxygen to near saturation.

(b)

Figure 7-9 Preparation of biochemical oxygen demand (BOD) tests on (a) wastewater sample: measured portion of wastewater after dechlorination, if necessary; seed microorganisms, if not present in the sample; and, buffered dilution water at 20°C containing dissolved oxygen, and (b) polluted surface water: stream sample after adjusting to 20°C and aerating, and dilution water, if needed.

ing the water into individual test bottles by bubbling air through a diffuser tube immersed in the sample container. Surface water samples are not seeded. When separation of the carbonaceous and nitrogen oxygen demands is desired, some tests can be conducted using chemicals to suppress the nitrification reaction. If dilution water is used in test preparation, both BOD and NOD results can be influenced by the added reagents. Of particular concern is the ammonium chloride included in the phosphate buffer, since this supply of ammonia nitrogen can contribute to bacterial NOD. *Standard Methods* states: "The (BOD) test is of limited value in measuring the actual oxygen demand of surface waters. The extrapolation of test results to actual stream oxygen demands is highly questionable because the laboratory environment does not reproduce stream conditions, such as, temperature, sunlight, biological population, water movement, and oxygen concentration."[7] Despite this, the BOD test is the best method available for evaluating the oxygen demand of polluted waters, and no replacement is apparent. Neither chemical oxygen demand (COD) nor total organic carbon (TOC) has proved successful. An extensive comparison of TOC and BOD tests on river waters showed poor statistical correlation, concluding that these tests measure different aspects of organic pollution in natural waters.[8]

The biochemical oxygen demand of a seeded wastewater test is calculated by:

$$\text{BOD} = \frac{(D_1 - D_2) - (B_1 - B_2)f}{P} \qquad (7\text{-}5)$$

where BOD = biochemical oxygen demand, milligrams per litre

D_1 = initial dissolved oxygen (DO) in test bottle containing the diluted, seeded, wastewater sample, milligrams per litre

D_2 = DO of wastewater sample after incubation, milligrams per litre

B_1 = initial DO in test bottle containing diluted seed sample, milligrams per litre

B_2 = DO of seed sample after incubation, milligrams per litre

f = ratio of seed volume in seeded wastewater test to seed volume in BOD test on seed

   = $\dfrac{\text{percentage or millilitres of seed in } D_1}{\text{percentage or millilitres of seed in } B_1}$

P = decimal fraction of wastewater sample used

   = $\dfrac{\text{volume of wastewater added per bottle}}{\text{volume of BOD bottle}}$

The D_1-D_2 term is the dissolved-oxygen uptake by the mixture of wastewater and dilution water that has occurred during the incubation period. The effect of oxygen demand by seed in the test bottle is compensated for by subtracting the quantity $(B_1 - B_2)f$. The B_1 and B_2 are initial and final dissolved oxygen values from a separate BOD test on the seed material, and f is the ratio of seed volume in the wastewater test to the amount used in the test on the seed. The denominator P is the volume of wastewater to quantity of wastewater plus dilution water. Dividing the DO depletion of the bottle contents by this fraction, expresses the oxygen demand relative to the amount of wastewater added in the test, hence, the BOD of the wastewater. If the wastewater has adequate microbial populations and no seeding is required, the BOD can be calculated using the relationship

$$\text{BOD} = \frac{D_1 - D_2}{P} \qquad (7\text{-}6)$$

Finally, the formula can be simplified as follows for polluted water samples that require no dilution.

$$\text{BOD} = D_1 - D_2 \qquad (7\text{-}7)$$

The portion of wastewater, or polluted water sample, for preparing BOD bottles can be selected from Table 7-2 or computed from Equation 7-6. For example, for a waste-

Table 7-2 Polluted Water and Wastewater Portions and Dilutions for Preparing BOD tests

By Direct Measurement of Wastewater into a 300-ml BOD bottle		By Mixing Wastewater into Dilution Water $\left(\dfrac{\text{Wastewater volume}}{\text{Total volume of mixture}}\right)$	
Wastewater (ml)	Range of BOD (mg/l)	Percentage of Mixture	Range of BOD (mg/l)
300	0 to 6	100	0 to 7
100	6 to 21	50.0	4 to 14
50.0	12 to 42	20.0	10 to 35
20.0	30 to 105	10.0	20 to 70
10.0	60 to 210	5.0	40 to 140
5.0	120 to 420	2.0	100 to 350
2.0	300 to 1050	1.0	200 to 700
1.0	600 to 2100	0.5	400 to 1400

water with an estimated BOD of 30 mg/l, the appropriate amount for a 300-ml bottle is 50 ml, or a 20 percent mixture. Similarly, applying Equation 7-6 for a desired oxygen decrease of 5 mg/l, the calculated waste portion is 50 ml per 300 ml bottle. A valid BOD test uses at least 2 mg/l of dissolved oxygen; however, the final DO should not be less than 1 mg/l. Since the initial oxygen content in dilution water is about 9 mg/l, an average amount of 5 mg/l is available for biological uptake between the minimum desired 2 mg/l and the maximum of 8 mg/l. (Example 7-1 and 7-2 illustrate BOD calculations and test results.)

Chemical Assessment

Dissolved oxygen is the most common chemical measurement in stream surveys since it is the primary water quality standard established for protection of fish and other aquatic life. The general esthetics of a stream are also closely allied to adequate oxygen content. Readings are made continuously with a recording meter, or periodically around the clock, in order to measure minimum, maximum, and average concentrations at each station. The minimum allowable oxygen content for warm-water fish is commonly established at an average of 4.0 mg/l; the lowest concentration permitted during the diurnal cycle is often 3.0 mg/l. Requiring more stringent limitations, minimums for cold-water fish are fixed at 6 or 7 mg/l, particularly during spawning times. Figure 7-10 is a typical method for illustrating dissolved oxygen data.

Dissolved oxygen saturation values, based on a normal atmosphere of 21 percent oxygen gas, for various temperatures and chloride concentrations are tabulated in the

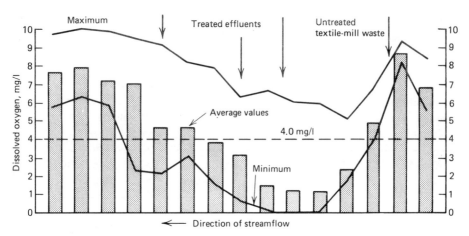

Figure 7-10 Dissolved oxygen profiles showing diurnal maximum, minimum, and average values for the polluted stream characterized biologically in Figure 7-7.

appendix. The table footnote explains how to correct oxygen solubility values for barometric pressure. The change of barometric pressure with altitude depends on the rate of decrease in density of the air. For most engineering computations, sufficient accuracy is achieved by assuming a pressure decrease of 8 mm of mercury per 100 m of increased elevation near the earth's surface.

The most popular method of measuring dissolved oxygen is by using a submersible probe that can be lowered into a stream or lake (Figure 7-11*a*). The tip consists of two solid metal electrodes in contact with a salt solution, which is contained by a thin plastic membrane, and a sensor for measuring temperature. Membrane electrodes are relatively inexpensive, easy to calibrate, and reliable.

A common chemical technique for determining dissolved oxygen is the azide modification of the iodometric method. The standard test uses a 300-ml BOD bottle for containing the water specimen. A special sampler is required to collect unaerated water for chemical testing (Figure 7-11*b*). Upon removing the stopper from the submerged

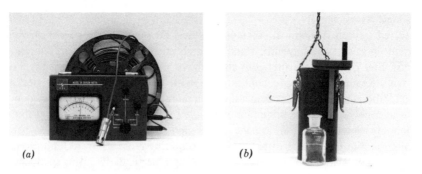

(*a*)   (*b*)

Figure 7-11 Apparatus for measuring dissolved oxygen in stream and lake surveys. (*a*) Dissolved oxygen meter and field probe with the extension wire wound on a reel. (*b*) Sampler to collect unaerated water in a bottle for chemical testing.

sampler, water enters through a tube extending to the bottom of the enclosed bottle; air is ejected out of the top. The bottle fills and overflows into the chamber of the container, thus wasting the initial inflow that contacted the air.

Beside dissolved gases, determinations for temperature, pH, and chlorine residual are made immediately upon water collection. Nitrogen and phosphorus samples should be chemically preserved, stored under refrigeration, and analyzed as soon as possible, either separately or after compositing. Satisfactory preservation for other chemical constituents listed in Table 7-1 may require only storage at low temperature (4°C) and testing the next day. The accepted methods for handling samples for specific analyses are presented in *Standard Methods*.[7]

Heavy metals are of concern in water pollution surveys because of their adverse physiological effects on both humans and aquatic animals, widespread use in manufacturing processes, and occurrence in biologically treated municipal effluents. Calcium, chromium, copper, mercury, nickel, lead, and zinc in trace concentrations are often found in a wastewater discharge from industrial cities. In addition to effluent testing in river reconnaissance, examination of bottom sediments is helpful in delineating areas of high concentration and possible sources. Heavy metals bond with soil particles, and accumulate in stream beds during periods of low flow. Mud specimens, collected with a small sampling dredge, are usually sieved and the finest fraction (less than 20 μm) scanned for presence of trace metals. Laboratory analyses employ atomic-absorption spectroscopy, emission spectroscopy, and polarography, which require sophisticated laboratory equipment.

Sampling

A grab, or catch, sample represents only the conditions at the time and location of collection. In surveying a river, the individual grabs from several locations across the channel are combined to form an integrated sample describing the water at that particular site. A composite sample is a mixture of individual grabs, or integrated volumes, collected over a period of time, often 24 hours, and proportioned according to flow.

For small streams, a single sample taken from the middle of the main flow at six-tenths depth represents the average water quality. Wide, deep rivers require the selection of several collection points traversing the channel. If the depth is greater than 3 metres, specimens from two-tenths and eight-tenths depths are blended at each vertical section, and individual grabs are integrated to account for variations in velocities of flow at the collection points across the channel. Moderately sized rivers are usually tested at three points, as illustrated in Figure 7-12, with the samples integrated in equal portions. Some sampling locations in a cross section may be eliminated if the initial test results show no significant difference from one point to another.

A popular type of water sampler, shown in Figure 7-13, consists of a cylindrical tube with a stopper on each end controlled by a closing device. The tube is lowered into position with the rubber plugs held open. To release the stoppers and trap water in the tube, a weight (called a messenger) is dropped down the supporting cord to trip the closing mechanism. The type of collector illustrated in Figure 7-11b can also be used in stream sampling.

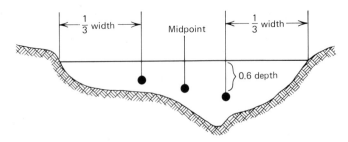

Figure 7-12 Suggested sampling points for a river with nonuniform depth.

Municipal and industrial discharges are composited according to their wastewater flow patterns. Individual grabs taken at regular time intervals, for example, every hour, are collected and stored in a refrigerator or ice chest; coincident flow rates are read from the flow meter installed at the treatment plant, or determined from a temporary flow-recording device. The composite is formed by mixing individual volumes together in direct proportion to the flow rates at the times of sampling.

Example 7-1

A BOD analysis was conducted on the unchlorinated effluent from a municipal treatment plant. Several identical tests, with 30 ml of wastewater added to each 300 ml bottle, were prepared and chemically tested for dissolved oxygen after various intervals of time. By titrating three samples immediately, the initial dissolved oxygen was determined as 8.7 mg/l. The time-residual DO data for the incubated bottles are listed in columns 1 and 2 of Table 7-3. Plot a BOD-time curve, determine the carbonaceous k-rate, five-day BOD, and calculated ultimate BOD value.

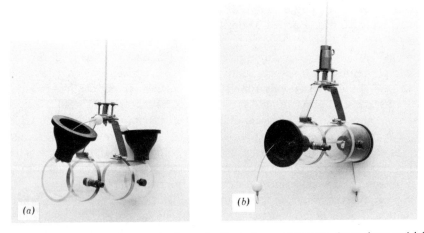

Figure 7-13 Van Dorn water sampler for collecting submerged samples from rivers and lakes. (a) Open sampler set for lowering to desired underwater depth. (b) Capped cylinder, containing the water sample, closed by tripping the release mechanism with a weight slid down the supporting cord.

Table 7-3 BOD-time Data for Example 7-1

(1) Time of Incubation (days)	(2) D_2 (mg/l)	(3) D_1-D_2 (mg/l)	(4) BOD (mg/l)	(5) Lag Period (days)	(6) t (days)	(7) $\left(\dfrac{t}{BOD}\right)^{1/3}$
0	8.7		0	1.2		
0.5	8.5	0.2	2	1.2		
1.3	8.2	0.5	5	1.2	0.1	0.27
2.4	7.6	1.1	11	1.2	1.2	0.48
3.3	6.7	2.0	20	1.2	2.1	0.47
4.8	5.9	2.8	28	1.2	3.6	0.50
7.0	4.9	3.8	38	1.2	5.8	0.53
9.0	4.3	4.4	44	1.2	7.8	0.56
11.0	3.9	4.8	48	1.2	9.8	0.59
13.0	2.8	5.9	59	1.2	11.8	0.58
15.0	2.5	6.2	62	1.2	13.8	0.61
19.0	0.7	8.0	85	1.2	17.8	0.59

Solution

The time of incubation, residual dissolved oxygen, and DO uptake are listed in the first three columns of Table 7-3. The BOD for each measurement, calculated by Equation 7-6 using a P of 0.10, is given in column 4.

After plotting the BOD-time data, as shown in Figure 7-14, a curve was sketched through the initial points establishing a new origin to eliminate the time lag. The lag period of 1.2 d was then subtracted from the times of incubation to calculate t and $(t/BOD)^{1/3}$ values as given in columns 6 and 7.

The computation for k-rate using Equation 7-4 is shown on Figure 7-14, and the five-day BOD value was determined graphically with reference to the new origin. The ultimate carbonaceous BOD is calculated from Equation 7-3 as follows:

$$L = \frac{BOD_5}{(1-10^{-5k})} = \frac{35}{(1-10^{-5 \times 0.08})} = 58 \text{ mg/l}$$

Example 7-2

Stream samples were collected above and below the outfall sewer from a municipal treatment plant. The upstream water, being relatively unpolluted, was aerated and siphoned directly into BOD bottles without dilution. Dissolved oxygen readings on two incubated bottles were taken using an oxygen meter and probe.

Flow below the wastewater discharge consisted of approximately one-third effluent and two-thirds stream water; consequently, the BOD was estimated to be in the range of 15 to 20 mg/l. To prevent premature loss of dissolved oxygen in the test bottles, the polluted downstream samples were diluted with upstream water by placing 50 ml and 250 ml, respectively, in the 300-ml BOD bottles.

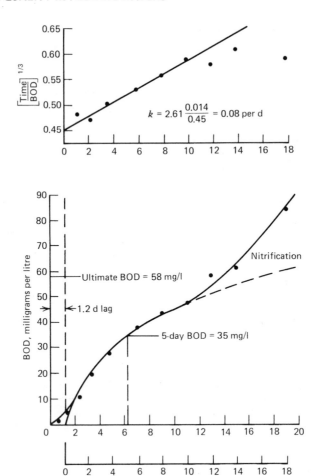

Figure 7-14 BOD-time curve and graphical determination of k-rate for the wastewater data given in Example 7-1.

The solution below explains the analytical methods used to determine the ultimate BOD and k-rate values.

Solution

For the stream water collected above the outfall, BOD values were calculated from the laboratory DO data by Equation 7-7 and the BOD-time graph sketched as shown by the dashed line in Figure 7-15. The graphically determined k-rate was 0.083 per d; however, the best-fit line drawn through the t versus $(t/BOD)^{1/3}$ values ignored the rapid oxygen uptake that occurred during the first two days of incubation.

The individual BOD measurements for the polluted water analyses were calculated by Equation 7-5. The upstream water used for dilution exerted an oxygen demand in the test bottle equal to $(B_1 - B_2)f$, where $(B_1 - B_2)$ is the oxygen uptake in the dilution water and f is the ratio of dilution volume to polluted stream sample in the BOD

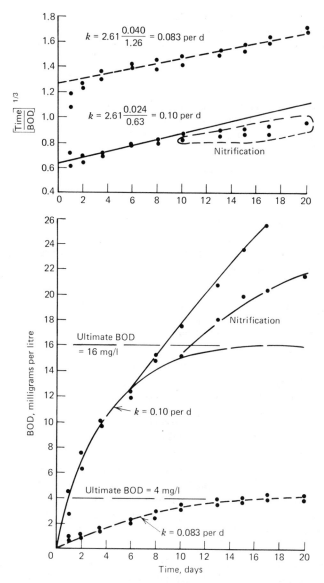

Figure 7-15 BOD-time curves and graphical determination of k- rates for polluted stream waters described in Example 7-2.

bottle. P is the decimal fraction of polluted water, and $(D_1 - D_2)$ the DO drop in the test bottle containing the mixture of polluted and dilution waters. As an illustration, consider data from one test measurement. After stabilization at $20°C$ and aeration, 50 ml of downstream polluted sample and 250 ml of upstream dilution water were added to the bottle (P = 50/300). The initial DO was 7.9 mg/l (D_1), which dropped to 3.9 mg/l (D_2) after six days incubation. The value for (B_1 - B_2) is the DO drop, or

BOD exerted, in the test bottles of undiluted upstream water, which averaged 2.3 mg/l taken from the sixth day of the BOD-time curve in Figure 7-15. The f is 250/300. Substituting these into Equation 7-5, the BOD on the sixth day is computed as:

$$BOD_6 = \frac{(D_1 - D_2) - (B_1 - B_2)f}{P} = \frac{(7.9 - 3.9) - (2.3)(250/300)}{(50/300)} = 12.5 \text{ mg/l}$$

The plotted BOD-time data for the two test bottles of polluted stream water resulted in an ultimate BOD of 16 mg/l and k-rate of 0.10 per d (Figure 7-15). Nitification started in one of the tests on the eighth day, and in the other shortly after the tenth day.

7-5 Dispersion of Wastewaters

Analyses of surface flows require calculating pollutant concentrations after a wastewater is discharged to a stream, or when a tributary joins a main watercourse. Equation 7-8 can be used for balancing such factors as chemical concentrations, dissolved oxygen, BOD, and temperature.

$$C = \frac{C_1 \times Q_1 + C_2 \times Q_2}{Q_1 + Q_2} \tag{7-8}$$

where C = concentration in combined flows
           Q_1 = quantity of flow
           C_1 = concentration of constituent in Q_1
           Q_2 = quantity of flow
           C_2 = concentration of constituent in Q_2

Some pollutants in natural waters, like the chloride ion, are nonreactive and diminish in concentration only with increased dilution; these are often referred to as conservative substances. Their concentrations in a stream are computed by applying Equation 7-8 after wastewater discharges and mixing of freshwater tributaries. Nonconservative pollutants decrease with time through physical, chemical, or biological reactions occurring in the stream water, or at the interface with the channel bottom. These are organic, inorganic, radiological, thermal, or biological constituents; the most common being BOD, fecal microorganisms, ammonia, nitrates, phosphates, silt, pesticides, and temperature.

Where field data are available, the reaction kinetics of nonconservative substances can be described by mathematical rate constants. If the quantity of a substance decreases at a constant rate with time, the reaction is expressed as

$$-\frac{dC}{dt} = K \tag{7-9}$$

which when integrated and rearranged becomes

$$C_t = C_0 - Kt \tag{7-10}$$

where C_t = concentration after a time period of t, milligrams per litre

C_0 = initial concentration, milligrams per litre
K = rate constant (zero-order kinetics), milligrams per litre·day
t = time, days

This type of reaction is called zero-order kinetics, and plots as a straight line on arithmetic graph paper.

Many reactive pollutants, rather than decaying uniformly with time, start at a high depletion rate that gradually decreases as the reaction proceeds. The most common is first-order kinetics where the rate of reaction is proportional to the remaining concentration of unreacted material. This is expressed mathematically as

$$-\frac{dC}{dt} = kC \tag{7-11}$$

which integrates to yield

$$\log_e \frac{C_t}{C_0} = -kt \tag{7-12}$$

or

$$C_t = C_0 e^{-kt} \tag{7-13}$$

where C_t = concentration after a time period of t, milligrams per litre
C_0 = initial concentration, milligrams per litre
k = rate constant (first-order kinetics), per day
t = time, days
e = base of Napierian logarithms, 2.718

Equation 7-13 plots as a transcendental curve on arithmetic paper and a straight line on a semilogarithmic graph.

Reaction rates of chemical and bacteriological constituents are temperature dependent and can be adjusted by the following relationship which increases, or decreases, the rate of decay with a rise, or fall, in temperature.

$$k_{T_1} = k_{T_2} \theta^{(T_1 - T_2)} \tag{7-14}$$

where k_T = rate constant at temperature T
θ = temperature coefficient
T = temperature

The value of the temperature coefficient in the formula defines the magnitude of the rate change with temperature. A θ equal to 1.047 doubles or halves the k-rate for a 15°C temperature change (a 4.7 percent change for each degree), while 1.072 doubles the coefficient for a 10°C rise.

Example 7-3

A shallow stream receives a treated wastewater effluent of 1100 m³/d containing an ammonia-nitrogen concentration of 25 mg/l; the natural flow above the outfall is

$0.033 \ m^3/s$ with no residual ammonia. At the time of analysis, slime growths attached to the channel bottom included substantial populations of nitrifying bacteria. Using dye injections to measure travel time, water samples were collected at selected intervals for a downstream distance of about 3 km and tested for ammonia-nitrogen content. The average results from several measurements were 6.6 mg/l at 0.0313 d, 4.7 at 0.075, 3.2 at 0.125, 2.6 at 0.188, and, 1.9 mg/l at 0.229 d. Plot these data on arithmetic and semilogarithmic graph papers, and calculate the rate constants.

Solution
Calculating the initial ammonia-nitrogen concentration by Equation 7-8

$$\frac{1100 \times 25 + (0.033 \times 86\ 400) \times 0}{1100 + 0.033 \times 86\ 400} = 6.9 \ mg/l$$

Figure 7-16 is a plot of the data on arithmetic paper. Although the overall graph is a curve, the initial straight-line portion can be represented by zero-order kinetics with a rate constant computed by Equation 7-10.

$$K = \frac{C_0 - C_t}{t} = \frac{7.1 - 2.6}{0.15} = 30 \ mg/l \cdot d$$

As shown in Figure 7-17, the values for the entire stream segment have a better straight-line correlation on semilog paper (first-order kinetics). The k-rate of the solid line on the graph can be calculated from Equation 7-13:

$$1.7 = 7.1e^{-k \times 0.25}$$

$$k = 5.7 \ per \ d$$

Or, by calculating the slope of the line and converting to the Napierian base ($\log_e N = 2.30 \log N$)

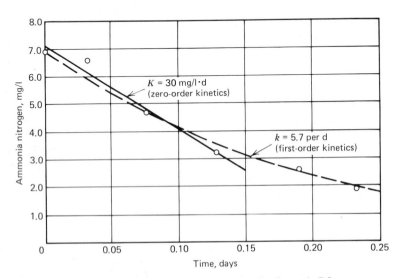

Figure 7-16 Arithmetic plot of ammonia nitrogen-time data for Example 7-3.

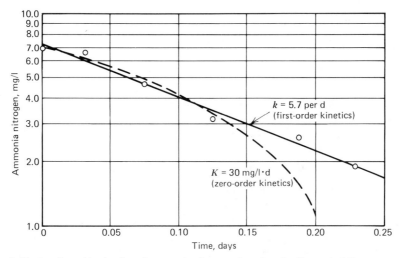

Figure 7-17 Semilogarithmic plot of ammonia nitrogen-time data for Example 7-3.

$$\text{Slope} = k = \frac{2.30\,(\log 7.1 - \log 1.7)}{0.25 - 0} = 5.7 \text{ per d}$$

Substituting these computed rate constants into Equations 7-10 and 7-13, respectively, the zero-order and first-order formulas are:

$$C_t = 7.1 - 30t \qquad\qquad (7\text{-}15)$$

and

$$C_t = 7.1e^{-5.7t} \qquad\qquad (7\text{-}16)$$

Equation 7-15 is plotted on Figure 7-17 as a dashed line, and Equation 7-16 on Figure 7-16. These graphs demonstrate that the decay of ammonia-nitrogen content for this stream evaluation is best described by first-order kinetics.

7-6 Deoxygenation of Polluted Waters

Depletion of oxygen in flowing waters is caused by biochemical oxygen demand (BOD) resulting from decomposition of organic matter and nitrogen oxygen demand (NOD) because of nitrification. These reactions can occur in both water suspension and at the interface of the stream bed. The classic formula states that the rate of biological oxidation of organic matter is proportional to the remaining concentration of unoxidized matter, which is expressed in the first-order-kinetics formula:

$$-\frac{dL}{dt} = k_1 L \qquad\qquad (7\text{-}17)$$

which integrates to yield

$$\log_e \frac{L_t}{L_o} = -k_1 t \qquad (7\text{-}18)$$

or

$$L_t = L_o e^{-k_1 t} \qquad (7\text{-}19)$$

where L_t = ultimate BOD after a time period of t, milligrams per litre
L_o = initial ultimate BOD concentration, milligrams per litre
k_1 = deoxygenation rate constant, per day
t = time, days
e = base of Napierian logarithms, 2.718

This expression has been successful in representing deoxygenation in large rivers unaffected by benthal oxygen demand or nitrification. Values for L and k_1 are commonly determined from long-term laboratory BOD tests on the polluted river waters and wastewater discharges. Extrapolating laboratory data to field application, however, ignores the inherent differences between the natural environment and that of an incubated bottle. Two primary concerns are settling of organic matter on the river bottom and decrease in biodegradability of suspended wastes with time, both of which influence the rate and extent of deoxygenation caused by organic matter. In spite of these irregularities, deoxygenation data from actual river surveys satisfied Equation 7-19 reasonably well, mainly because the coefficient of sedimentation removal and shift in natural degradability did not prevent the overall reaction from fitting first-order kinetics.

Shallow streams can react quite differently than large rivers owing to benthal oxygen demand. In channels below waste outfalls, active biological growths can cover the stream bed as a result of deposition and absorption of suspended organics. These dense microbial populations usually extract BOD at a rate much greater than predicted by the k-rate from laboratory testing. Furthermore, if the slime growths support nitrifying bacteria, heavy oxygen demands can be exerted by *Nitrosomonas* converting ammonia to nitrite and *Nitrobacter* that continue the oxidation to the nitrate ion. Viable populations of nitrifiers are more frequently associated with shallow surface-active stream reaches than deep, slow-moving waters. Other environmental conditions correlating with high NOD observations are: high ammonia-nitrogen content relative to the carbonaceous BOD concentration, either from industrial or poorly diluted domestic wastes; warm temperatures resulting from hot-water discharges or natural summer weather; and, aerobic conditions at a slightly alkaline pH.

Ruane and Krenkel[10,11] suggest that the rate of nitrification may fit either zero-order or first-order kinetics (Equations 7-10 or 7-13) depending on the particular stream conditions. Some of their conclusions based on actual field studies are as follows. (1) The nitrification rate is best determined using nitrogen data from field studies, as opposed to laboratory NOD tests. The lag period associated with incubated water samples does not occur in surface-active streams where nitrification starts near the point of waste discharge. (2) Nitrification balance in streams is very complex. Ammonia concentration varies as a result of nitrification, deamination of organic nitrogen compounds, rooted aquatic plant uptake, and conversion in organic nitrogen by algal synthesis. Nitrate content is affected by nitrification, denitrification, respiratory reduction, and plant synthesis. (3) While determination of the NOD rate constant is possible from field data based on either decrease in ammonia or increase in nitrate, validity of the results depends on defining the other factors affecting these nitrogen compounds. At present, no method is available for quantitatively relating these variables, and few attempts have been made to account for them in stream analyses.

7-7 Reaeration of Flowing Waters

Polluted water exposed to air absorbs oxygen to replace that taken up in the stabilization of organic wastes. The rate of reaeration, or reoxygenation, is directly proportional to the dissolved oxygen deficit, which is the difference between the saturation concentration at a given temperature and the actual content. Introducing the rate constant k_2, this relationship is expressed mathematically as

$$-\frac{dC}{dt} = k_2(C_s - C) = k_2 D \tag{7-20}$$

where C = concentration of dissolved oxygen, milligrams per litre
   t = time, days
   k_2 = reaeration rate constant, per day
   C_s = concentration of dissolved oxygen at saturation for desired temperature, milligrams per litre
   D = dissolved oxygen deficit, milligrams per litre

Although atmospheric reaeration is the primary source, oxygen can also be added to a river by unpolluted tributaries or rainfall-runoff water. Algae and rooted aquatics can provide significant oxygen by photosynthesis; however, this contribution cannot be expressed reliably in mathematical terms.

Even though oxygen deficit regulates the rate of absorption, the reaeration capacity of a stream relates directly to: the physical and hydrological characteristics of the watercourse, turbulence, water depth, surface area, temperature, and other factors. Equation 7-21 is a popular formula correlating the reaeration rate constant to the hydraulic properties of velocity and depth of flow. The specific values for c, n, and m must be determined under different flow conditions for each individual river reach. The values in Equation 7-22 are based on survey data from three major rivers.[12] Based on this survey, the reaeration coefficients in major rivers decrease in the downstream direction, even though discharge increases, since lesser slopes result in lower reaeration capacities relative to their quantities of flow.

$$k_2 = c \frac{V^n}{H^m} \tag{7-21}$$

where k_2 = reaeration rate constant, per day
   V = mean velocity of flow, metres per second

H = mean depth of flow, metres

c, n, m = constants for a particular river reach

$$k_2 = 2.2 \frac{V}{H^{1.33}} \qquad (7\text{-}22)$$

Several other relationships for quantifying k_2 are summarized by Covar.[13] Besides velocity and depth of flow, some formulations include slope of the channel and molecular diffusivity. Nevertheless, their preciseness has been severely restricted because, until recently, the only available means of testing a formula has been to estimate the real reaeration capacity by indirect oxygen balance computations. This method leads to an unknown and unavoidable degree of error; hence, the mathematical predictive equations could not be tested, verified, or improved. Recent experience indicates that none is sufficiently general or accurate for widespread application, and only direct field measurement of the reaeration coefficient can provide positive assurance of accurate results.[14]

The field application of the tracer technique involves simultaneous release of three tracers: a fluorescent dye, tritiated water as a dispersion indicator, and dissolved krypton-85 (a radioactive form of the chemically-inert, noble gas krypton) as a gaseous tracer.[15,16] A mixture of these three substances is released at the head of each stream reach being analyzed. The dye measures time of flow, reveals longitudinal dispersion, and indicates when to sample for the other two tracers. Since tritium has negligible adsorption losses, it provides an accurate measure of total dispersion. The krypton-85, present in the dissolved state, undergoes the same dispersion as the tritiated water and, in addition, is lost to the atmosphere as a result of turbulent streamflow. The change in concentration of this dissolved tracer gas between two sampling points, relative to the change in concentration of tritium, permits calculation of the dissolved krypton-85 gas loss. This measurement of gas transfer to the atmosphere is used to calculate the reoxygenation rate constant as follows:

$$k_2 = \frac{\log_e (R_1/R_2)}{0.83t} \qquad (7\text{-}23)$$

where k_2 = reaeration (reoxygenation) rate constant, per day

R_1 = measured ratio of krypton-85 activity to tritium activity at start of stream reach

R_2 = measured ratio of krypton-85 to tritium activity at downstream end of reach

t = time of passage of dye peak through the stream reach, days

The tracer method is based on the following premises: the concentration of tritiated water in streamflow changes only as the result of dispersion; the krypton-85 concentration decreases additionally only because of loss to the atmosphere; and, the ratio of exchange coefficient values for krypton-85 and oxygen is a constant value of 0.83, which is not significantly affected by temperature, turbulence, or usual concentration of water pollutants.[15] During tracer evaluations, mean water temperature is determined by measurements upstream and downstream corresponding with passage of the dye peak. Field values of the reaeration rate constant can be adjusted for other temperatures, within the range of 0°C to 30°C, by the relationship

$$k_{2,T_1} = k_{2,T_2} (1.022)^{(T_1 - T_2)}$$

(7-24)

where k_{2,T_1}, k_{2,T_2} = reaeration rate constants at T_1 and T_2, per day
T_1, T_2 = temperature, degrees Celsius

Being a direct function of turbulence, reoxygenation is related through an energy dissipation model to the hydraulic properties of change in elevation head and time of flow.[14] Therefore, the rate constant in a free-flowing stream is directly proportional to the rate of energy expenditure, or stated mathematically

$$k_2 = C \frac{\Delta h}{t}$$

(7-25)

where k_2 = reaeration rate constant, per day
Δh = change in water surface elevation between two stream locations, metres
t = time of passage through the stream reach of Δh, days
C = gas escape coefficient

The coefficient C, which associates gas transfer and stream mixing, is affected by a variety of physical conditions and hydraulic features of a channel, thus, its value is unique for each stream. Low magnitudes of C are usual for relatively large, deep, unobstructed rivers with uniform slope while high values occur for small, turbulent streams characterized by abrupt changes of slope and direction. Based on several hundred observations in different rivers, Tsivoglou and Neal[14] suggest a value for C of 0.18 per metre at 20°C for moderately polluted and reasonably well-mixed rivers with flows greater than 0.7 m³/s; 80 percent of the results fell within the range of 0.10 to 0.26 per metre. Small tributaries with discharges less than 0.3 m³/s had a mean value of 0.36 per metre. The reaeration rate constants applied in evaluating a particular stream should, of course, be based on tracer studies, rather than assumed values. By performing field analyses under varying flow conditions, an escape coefficient can be determined by plotting k_2 measurements versus calculated $\Delta h/t$ values; C is the slope of a straight line drawn through the data. Prior to graphing field data, k_2 is corrected to 20°C and, therefore, the C value is keyed to this temperature. The escape coefficient can be corrected for water temperature by the numerical relationship given in Equation 7-24.

Surface flows often have low-level, instream dams that behave as waterfalls providing significant reaeration. Foree[16] evaluated small dams and falls by comparing field reoxygenation measurements as a function of the difference between upstream and downstream water elevations (dam height). By plotting the deficit ratio of dissolved oxygen (Equation 7-26) versus elevation difference, the expression in Equation 7-27 was developed to correlate r and H for dams across small streams in Kentucky.

$$r = \frac{C_s - C_u}{C_s - C_d} \tag{7-26}$$

where r = dissolved oxygen deficit ratio at dam or waterfall
C_s = dissolved oxygen (DO) at saturation, milligrams per litre
C_u = DO immediately upstream, milligrams per litre
C_d = DO immediately downstream, milligrams per litre

$$r = e^{0.47H} \tag{7-27}$$

where r = dissolved oxygen deficit ratio at 20°C
H = difference in water surface elevation immediately above and below the dam or waterfall, metres

The radioactive tracer technique can be performed for a range of deficit ratios independent of actual dissolved oxygen concentrations by calculating r from Equation 7-28. This allows measurements even though significant dissolved oxygen deficits do not exist at the time of field observations. Corrections of r for water temperature can be made by the relationship in Equation 7-29.

$$r = (R_u/R_d)^{1.20} \tag{7-28}$$

where R_u, R_d = measured activity ratios of krypton-85 to tritium above and below the dam or waterfall

$$\log_e r_{T_1} = \log_e r_{T_2} (1.022)^{(T_1 - T_2)} \tag{7-29}$$

where $\log_e r_{T_1}, \log_e r_{T_2}$ = Napierian logarithms of the dissolved oxygen deficit ratios at T_1 and T_2
T_1, T_2 = temperatures, degrees Celsius

After field studies and analyses to determine the relationship between deficit ratios and elevation drop, predicted values of dissolved oxygen below dams and falls are computed by rearranging Equation 7-26 to the form

$$C_d = C_s - \frac{(C_s - C_u)}{r} \tag{7-30}$$

Example 7-4
The radioactive tracer technique was used to determine the reaeration rate constant for a 3.2-km stream reach with a flow of 0.45 m³/s at a water temperature of 22°C. The elapsed time between passage of the dye peak at the upstream and downstream ends was 0.21 d and corresponding ratios of krypton-85 activity to tritium activity were 0.15 and 0.093, respectively. The water elevation change through the reach was 0.90 m. Calculate reaeration rate constants for 20°C based on the field data and assuming an escape coefficient of 0.36 per m.

Solution

Measured reaeration rate constant by Equation 7-23

$$k_2 = \frac{\log_e (0.15/0.093)}{0.83 \times 0.21 \text{ d}} = 2.7 \text{ per d}$$

Correcting for temperature using Equation 7-24

$$k_{2,20°C} = 2.7 (1.022)^{(20-22)} = 2.6 \text{ per d}$$

Calculated k_2 from Equation 7-25

$$k_2 = 0.36 \frac{0.90}{0.21} = 1.5 \text{ per d}$$

Example 7-5

A low-level dam with a drop in water surface elevation of 1.9 m traverses the stream cited in Example 7-4. Predict the downstream dissolved oxygen concentration for the following conditions: upstream DO of 5.9 mg/l, water temperature of 22°C, and a land elevation of 500 m above sea level.

Solution

Using Equation 7-27,

$$r = e^{0.47 \times 1.9} = 2.44 \text{ at } 20°C$$

Changing to a temperature of 22°C by Equation 7-29

$$\log_e r_{22°C} = (\log_e 2.44)(1.022)^{(22-20)} = 0.93$$

$$r_{22°C} = e^{0.93} = 2.5$$

From the Appendix, $C_s = 8.3$ mg/l at 22°C after correcting to an elevation of 500 m (barometric pressure of 720 mm).

Downstream dissolved oxygen from Equation 7-30

$$C_d = 8.3 - \frac{8.3 - 5.9}{2.5} = 7.3 \text{ mg/l}$$

7-8 Oxygen Sag Equations for Carbonaceous Demand

The classical model for oxygen balance in free-flowing surface waters, proposed by Streeter and Phelps, was published in 1944.[17] Expressed in Equation 7-31, the mathematical formulation states that the rate of change of dissolved oxygen deficit equals the difference between deoxygenation of the water, due to bacterial decomposition of carbonaceous organic matter, and reaeration from the atmosphere caused by the dissolved oxygen deficit and turbulence. Substituting in the relationship from Equation 7-19 and integrating, the form of the oxygen-balance model becomes the sag curve equation given by Equation 7-32, which is shown graphically in Figure 7-18.

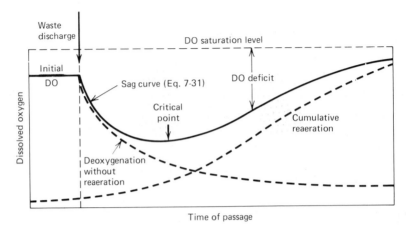

Figure 7-18 Dissolved oxygen sag resulting from a single source of organic waste discharged to a free-flowing stream. The cumulative deoxygenation and reaeration curves combine to form a composite graph of dissolved oxygen deficit (Equations 7-31 and 7-32).

$$\frac{dD}{dt} = k_1 L - k_2 D \tag{7-31}$$

$$D = \frac{k_1 L_0}{k_2 - k_1} (e^{-k_1 t} - e^{-k_2 t}) + D_0 (e^{-k_2 t}) \tag{7-32}$$

where D = dissolved oxygen deficit, milligrams per litre
k_1 = deoxygenation rate constant, per day
k_2 = reaeration rate constant, per day
L_0 = initial ultimate carbonaceous BOD, milligrams per litre
D_0 = initial dissolved oxygen deficit, milligrams per litre
t = time, days
e = base of Napierian logarithms, 2.718

Of particular interest is the critical point defined by the lowest DO concentration and the time of passage required to reach this level of maximum oxygen depletion. At this point, the rates of deoxygenation and reaeration exactly balance, thus, the deficit is not changing and the critical value D_c becomes

$$\frac{dD}{dt} = k_1 L - k_2 D = 0 \qquad D_c = \frac{k_1 L}{k_2} \tag{7-33}$$

where D_c = critical dissolved oxygen deficit, milligrams per litre

Substituting in Equation 7-19 and simplifying, the calculation for critical time is

$$t_c = \frac{1}{k_2 - k_1} \log_e \left[\frac{k_2}{k_1} \left(1 - D_0 \frac{k_2 - k_1}{k_1 L_0} \right) \right] \tag{7-34}$$

where t_c = critical time, the time of passage to the minimum dissolved oxygen level, days

The rate constants in the oxygen sag equations can be adjusted for temperature as follows:

$$k_{1,T} = k_{1,20} \, (1.047)^{(T-20)} \tag{7-35}$$

$$k_{2,T} = k_{2,20} \, (1.022)^{(T-20)} \tag{7-36}$$

where T = temperature, degrees Celsius

The temperature coefficient of 1.047 for deoxygenation is common among most authors.[13,17] Although the coefficient for reaeration has varied historically, the most reliable value appears to be 1.022.[15]

Application of the oxygen sag equation requires BOD data, dissolved oxygen measurements, water temperatures, reaeration rates, and velocities of flow. Originally, the rate of deoxygenation was assumed to equal the carbonaceous demand exerted by BOD tests. However, the biological oxygen uptake in actual field studies is frequently found to be influenced by deposition of suspended organic matter, benthic extraction where masses of microbial growth are attached to the river bottom, and other natural processes not taking place in an incubated glass bottle.

Actual dissolved oxygen concentrations, including diurnal fluctuations, are necessary at frequent intervals along the river. The resulting profiles must be keyed to other parameters, such as temperature, hydrological conditions, and waste loads. Presence of dense growths of algae or rooted aquatic plants, and their potential effects through photosynthesis and respiration, should be noted even though these abnormalities cannot be quantitatively defined.

Reaeration rates and times of passage are best determined by field application of the tracer technique. (The alternative method, which is less desirable, accounts for oxygen inputs and withdrawals over relatively short river segments, and then calculates reaeration rates by comparing net oxygen deficits to actual oxygen measurements.) Intensive surveys usually record channel conditions, such as mean depth of flow, average velocity, slope of the river bed, and flow contributions of tributaries, in an attempt to correlate measured k_2 rates to quantities of flow. This is necessary so calculations can be performed for flows other than those occurring during field observations.

Natural pools and impoundments behind instream dams are difficult to evaluate since the sag equation is applicable only to steady-state, one-dimensional free flow. They may act as deep, slow-moving rivers causing longitudinal and latitudinal dispersion or like long, narrow lakes that stratify allowing flow to short-circuit across the surface.

The ideal river survey entails a comprehensive sampling program under conditions of known waste loads and stable river hydrology. To minimize variations, intensive monitoring should be performed over a short time span of uniform conditions; late summer and fall seasons are often selected owing to the combination of low flows, high temperatures, and uniform weather. A BOD-DO model is written by inserting the measured k-rates into the oxygen sag equation. Next, this model is verified by computing dissolved oxygen profiles and comparing these with actual field observations. After the assimilative capacity of a river has been defined by verified, self-purification factors, expected stream conditions can be forecast for anticipated waste loadings under various hydraulic conditions. While applying these procedures to the Streeter-Phelps equation has been reasonably successful for large rivers, the self-purification process in small streams frequently deviates from this model. One of the main causes appears to be nitrogen oxygen demand not incorporated into Equation 7-32.

Example 7-6

A relatively unpolluted river, with a summer low flow of 28.0 m^3/s at a water temperature of 27°C, has a dissolved oxygen level of 7.4 mg/l and ultimate BOD residual of 4.0 mg/l upstream from two wastewater discharges. The first is a major industrial effluent of 2.2 m^3/s at a temperature of 18°C containing an ultimate BOD of 160 mg/l and DO concentration of 4.0 mg/l. Thirty-five kilometres below this outfall a municipal effluent contributes an additional 6000 kg/d of ultimate BOD, and 23 km further downstream the river enters a reservoir. Field measurements, during the month of August when the quantity of flow was approximately 30 m^3/s, resulted in an average velocity of 0.32 m/s, mean depth of 1.1 m, and the dissolved oxygen data shown in Figure 7-19. Laboratory BOD analyses on the polluted river water yielded carbonaceous k-rates that averaged 0.10 per d (to the base 10 at 20°C). From this preliminary information, calculate an oxygen sag curve and compare it to the measured DO values shown in Figure 7-19.

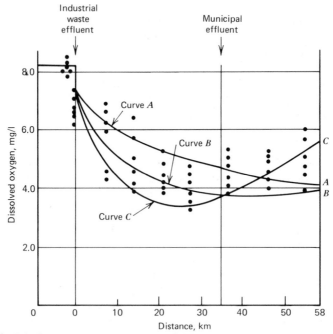

Figure 7-19 Calculated oxygen sag curves and field dissolved oxygen measurements for the river in Example 7-6.

Solution

The combined flow downstream from the industrial discharge is

$$Q_1 + Q_2 = 28.0 + 2.2 = 30.2 \text{ m}^3/\text{s}$$

Using Equation 7-8 the initial ultimate BOD, dissolved oxygen, and temperature are calculated as follows:

$$L_o = \frac{4 \times 28.0 + 160 \times 2.2}{28.0 + 2.2} = 15.4 \text{ mg/l}$$

$$C_o = \frac{7.4 \times 28.0 + 4.0 \times 2.2}{30.2} = 7.2 \text{ mg/l}$$

$$T = \frac{27 \times 28.0 + 18 \times 2.2}{30.2} = 26°C$$

The deoxygenation rate constant is converted from base 10 to base e by multiplying by 2.30, and then corrected for temperature using Equation 7-5.

$$k_{1,20°C} = 2.30 \times k = 2.30 \times 0.10 = 0.23 \text{ per d}$$

$$k_{1,26°C} = 0.23 \, (1.047)^{(26-20)} = 0.30 \text{ per d}$$

Based on Equations 7-22 and 7-36

$$k_{2,20°C} = 2.2 \frac{0.32}{(1.1)^{1.33}} = 0.62 \text{ per d}$$

$$k_{2,26°C} = 0.62 \, (1.022)^{(26-20)} = 0.71 \text{ per d}$$

Initial dissolved oxygen deficit at $26°C$ is

$$D_o = C_s - C_o = 8.2 - 7.2 = 1.0 \text{ mg/l}$$

The time of passage to minimum DO of the sag curve is determined using Equation 7-4

$$t_c = \frac{1}{0.71 - 0.30} \log_e \frac{0.71}{0.30} \left(1 - 1.0 \frac{0.71 - 0.30}{0.30 \times 15.4}\right) = 1.9 \text{ d}$$

$$\text{Critical distance} = \frac{1.9 \text{ d} \times 0.32 \text{ m/s} \times 86\,400 \text{ s/d}}{1000 \text{ m/km}} = 52 \text{ km}$$

However, this critical point is not reached since the municipal outfall occurs 35 km downstream, which is equal to a time of passage of

$$t = \frac{35 \text{ km} \times 1000 \text{ m/km}}{0.32 \text{ m/s} \times 86\,400 \text{ s/d}} = 1.27 \text{ d}$$

The DO deficit at this time is computed using Equation 7-32,

$$D = \frac{0.30 \times 15.4}{0.71 - 0.30} \, (e^{-0.30 \times 1.27} - e^{-0.71 \times 1.27}) + 1.0 \, (e^{-0.71 \times 1.27})$$

$$= 3.1 + 0.4 = 3.5 \text{ mg/l}$$

Therefore, at 35 km downstream

$$DO = 8.2 - 3.5 = 4.7 \text{ mg/l}$$

Equation 7-19 is used to compute the remaining BOD in the river after an elapsed time of 1.27 days.

$$L_t = 15.4e^{-0.30 \times 1.27} = 10.5 \text{ mg/l}$$

The additional BOD concentration contributed by the municipal effluent

$$L = \frac{6\ 000\ 000}{30.2 \times 86\ 400} = 2.3 \text{ mg/l}$$

Hence, $L_0 = 10.5 + 2.3 = 12.8$ mg/l

and, from the calculation above, $D_0 = 3.5$ mg/l

The time of passage to minimum DO below the municipal outfall is

$$t_c = \frac{1}{0.71 - 0.30} \log_e \frac{0.71}{0.30} \left(1 - 3.5 \frac{0.71 - 0.30}{0.30 \times 12.8}\right) = 1.0 \text{ d}$$

Critical distance $= \dfrac{1.0 \times 0.32 \times 86\ 400}{1000} = 27 \text{ km}$

But the distance to reservoir is only 23 km, so the time of passage is only 0.83 d and the corresponding deficit is

$$D = \frac{0.30 \times 12.8}{0.71 - 0.30} (e^{-0.30 \times 0.83} - e^{-0.71 \times 0.83}) + 3.5 (e^{-0.71 \times 0.83})$$

$$= 4.1 \text{ mg/l}$$

DO $= 8.2 - 4.1 = 4.1$ mg/l

The calculated oxygen sag, drawn as curve A on Figure 7-19, shows a poor fit with the actual DO measurements indicating that more extensive field studies are required to realistically model this river. Nevertheless, assuming the BOD data and times of passage are correct, values of the rate constants can be arbitrarily adjusted in an attempt to fit the oxygen data better. For example, curve B was calculated by doubling the deoxygenation rate constant from 0.23 to 0.46 per d. Curve C is based on a doubled reaeration rate of 1.42 per d and deoxygenation rates of 0.46 per d from 0 to 35 km and 0.23 between 35 and 58 km.

Example 7-7

A municipal treatment plant, with an effluent of 110 000 m^3/d, discharges into a creek channel with a 1-in-10-year seven-consecutive-day low flow of 0.31 m^3/s. Based on field observations, flow upstream from the outfall during the summer had an average residual ultimate BOD of 5 mg/l, minimum DO level of 5 mg/l, and maximum temperature of 28°C. The reaeration rate constant downstream, measured by the radioactive tracer technique, averaged 5.6 per d. From oxygen-balance data, collected at same time, the deoxygenation rate constant was calculated as 0.35 per d. (This rather high deoxygenation rate appeared to be caused by biological growths attached to the stream bed. Significant nitrogen oxygen demand was not observed, perhaps because nitrifier populations were depleted by effluent chlorination.) The regulatory effluent limitations of the wastewater discharge are an average five-day BOD of 30 mg/l and minimum dissolved oxygen of 5.0 mg/l. The mean summer wastewater temperature is 23°C.

The stream quality standard for dissolved oxygen is a minimum allowable mean of 5.0 mg/l. Is this criterion likely to be achieved? A second waste discharge enters the stream after a time of passage equal to 1.6 d. What is the estimated DO in the stream at this second outfall if the DO is the minimum of 5.0 mg/l at the upstream municipality?

Solution

Since both the upstream flow and wastewater are a DO of 5 mg/l and the stream cannot be allowed to drop below this DO level, the minimum allowable DO level occurs in the mixing zone at the outfall and the critical time is zero. By rearranging Equation 7-33,

$$L_o = \frac{k_2}{k_1} D_o \tag{7-37}$$

The dissolved oxygen deficit for this problem is determined as follows:

$$T = \frac{23(110\,000/86\,400) + 28 \times 0.31}{(110\,000/86\,400) + 0.31} = \frac{23 \times 1.27 + 28 \times 0.31}{1.58} = 24°C$$

$$D_o = C_s - C_o = 8.5 - 5.0 = 3.5 \text{ mg/l}$$

The maximum allowable ultimate BOD in the stream by Equation 7-37 i

$$L_o = \frac{5.6}{0.35} \, 3.5 = 56 \text{ mg/l}$$

Based on this, the BOD contribution in the wastewater effluent can be calculated using Equation 7-8

$$56 = \frac{C_1 \times 1.27 + 5 \times 0.31}{1.58}$$

C_1 (ultimate BOD in wastewater) = 68 mg/l

If a k-rate to base 10 of 0.05 per d is assumed, the calculated five-day BOD value using Equation 7-3 is

$$BOD_5 = L (1 - 10^{-kt}) = 68 (1 - 10^{-0.05 \times 5}) = 30 \text{ mg/l}$$

For a k of 0.10 per d, the calculated BOD_5 is 46 mg/l.

This solution indicates that the stream water-quality criterion of 5 mg/l dissolved oxygen can be maintained.

The DO after 1.6 d is calculated as follows:

$$D = \frac{0.35 \times 56}{5.6 - 0.35} (e^{-0.35 \times 1.6} - e^{-5.6 \times 1.6}) + 3.5 (e^{-5.6 \times 1.6}) = 2.1 \text{ mg/l}$$

$$DO = 8.5 - 2.1 = 6.4 \text{ mg/l}$$

7-9 Oxygen Sag Equations Incorporating Nitrification

Nitrification is the biological oxidation of ammonia nitrogen to the nitrate form; the oxygen uptake in this process is referred to as nitrogen oxygen demand (NOD). Nitrifiers are specific species of autotrophic bacteria that perform this reaction to yield energy for growth and reproduction. The oxygen uptake can be expressed by the reaction

$$2NH_4HCO_3 + 4O_2 + Ca(HCO_3)_2 = Ca(NO_3)_2 + 4CO_2 + 6H_2O \qquad (7\text{-}38)$$

Stoichiometrically from this equation, 4.57 mg of oxygen are required to convert 1.0 mg of ammonia nitrogen (expressed as N) to the nitrate ion. Conversions using actual bacterial cultures have consumed slightly less oxygen than this amount.

The potential seriousness of NOD on a stream is related to the amount of reduced nitrogen in waste discharges. Although selected industrial wastes contain high concentrations of nitrogen, a far more prevalent source is treated municipal wastewater, which has a high potential NOD relative to BOD. A typical municipal wastewater after conventional biological processing to reduce the ultimate BOD to 60 mg/l, or less, still contains about 20 mg/l of ammonia nitrogen with a calculated NOD of 90 mg/l. However, while a carbonaceous oxygen demand is certain to be exerted on the receiving water, the nitrification reaction depends more on a suitable environment in the watercourse, and may not cause a measurable oxygen demand.

Ammonia nitrogen contributed by wastewaters obviously must be oxidized to realize the potential NOD. If present, algae and aquatic weeds are strong competitors with the nitrifying bacteria for the uptake of ammonia; thus during the summer, photosynthesis can be a dominant reaction. During cool seasons of the year, nitrification may be much less significant since it is suppressed by low water temperatures with the rate dropping rapidly below $10°C$. Autotrophic bacteria also require aerobic conditions, neutral to slightly alkaline pH, and an adequate supply of carbon dioxide; these are common in surface waters and are not normally limiting. Finally, and most importantly, nitrifying bacteria are more effective where they appear as attached benthic growths rather than in water suspension. Being specific in their metabolic requirements, these bacteria are sensitive to their surroundings. Apparently, in the fluctuating environmental conditions of surface waters, strong populations can develop only when abundant ammonia nitrogen is supplied by water flowing over an attached culture. A culture suspended in streamflow has only those nutrients available in the surrounding water which are not replenished with time, unless additional waste is discharged to the watercourse. Several field studies[10,18,19] have demonstrated the occurrence of nitrification in shallow surface-active streams, and contrastingly its absence in deep slow-moving rivers leading to the hypothesis that nitrification results from attached rather than suspended bacterial populations.

The first-order-kinetics equation for depletion of NOD with time is expressed in Equation 7-39, which states mathematically that the rate of nitrification is proportional to the remaining unoxidized ammonia nitrogen.

$$N_t = N_0 e^{-k_n t} \qquad (7\text{-}39)$$

where N_t = NOD remaining after a time period of t, milligrams per litre
N_0 = initial NOD concentration, milligrams per litre
k_n = deoxygenation (nitrification) rate constant, per day
t = time, days
e = base of Napierian logarithms, 2.718

The model for oxygen balancing incorporating both carbonaceous BOD and first-order NOD in free-flowing streams is expressed in Equation 7-40. Substituting in the relationships from Equations 7-19 and 7-39, the integrated sag curve equation becomes Equation 7-41. This formula has an arrangement similar to Equation 7-32 except it includes nitrification.

$$\frac{dD}{dt} = k_1 L + k_n N - k_2 D \tag{7-40}$$

$$D = \frac{k_1 L_0}{k_2 - k_1} (e^{-k_1 t} - e^{-k_2 t}) + \frac{k_n N_0}{k_2 - k_n} (e^{-k_n t} - e^{-k_2 t}) + D_0 (e^{-k_2 t}) \tag{7-41}$$

where D = dissolved oxygen deficit, milligrams per litre
k_1 = deoxygenation rate constant for BOD (carbonaceous), per day
k_2 = reaeration rate constant, per day
k_n = deoxygenation rate constant for NOD, per day
L_0 = initial ultimate carbonaceous BOD, milligrams per litre
N_0 = initial ultimate NOD, milligrams per litre
D_0 = initial dissolved oxygen deficit, milligrams per litre
t = time, days

Application of these formulas requires determining values for initial nitrogen oxygen demand N_0 and the deoxygenation rate constant k_n. Actual stream analyses are the only reliable source for these parameters. Laboratory oxygen-demand tests, conducted in a manner similar to carbonaceous BOD measurements, are very questionable. Oxidation of ammonia nitrogen in a water sample enclosed in a glass bottle has little relationship to nitrification in a free-flowing, surface-active stream. A lack of perception, relative to the complexities of nitrogen transformations in a natural environment, has led some analysts to assume that all of the ammonia contributed to a stream is converted to nitrate, and therefore the NOD exerted in a stream equals 4.57 times the ammonia-nitrogen discharged. A nitrification rate constant must then be arbitrarily assumed to complete the data needed for NOD oxygen-sag calculations.

The schematic in Figure 7-20 illustrates common pathways of nitrogen in surface waters. Conventional wastewater treatment designed to remove organic matter, leaves most effluent nitrogen in the form of ammonia. If organic matter is washed into the water, or aquatic plants decay, additional ammonia is contributed; this is probably a minor amount during the critical summer season of low streamflow. Nitrate is the end product of *Nitrosomonas* converting ammonia to nitrite followed by *Nitrobacter* oxidation to nitrate. Since the later step is more rapid, only rarely are measurable concentrations of nitrite found in natural waters. Unless a stream is free of vegetation, not all ammonia is oxidized since photosynthesis can take up a significant amount. Agricul-

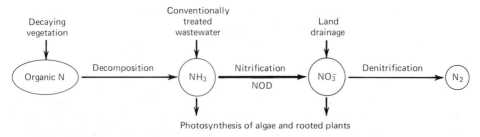

Figure 7-20 Possible transformations of nitrogen most common in surface waters.

tural land drainage often contributes nitrate to surface waters, thus, unrealistically increasing the quantity of nitrogen oxidized in the stream. Perhaps more common is the disappearance of ammonia without an equivalent quantity of nitrate being formed. In some cases, this has been attributed to both inorganic forms being taken up by aquatic plants. An alternative more difficult to prove, and yet a real possibility, is the loss of nitrate in gaseous form by denitrification. This is an anaerobic bacterial reaction performed by heterotrophs extracting the oxygen from nitrate during metabolism. Studies[18] have indicated that nitrification-denitrification can take place within slime growths attached to stream beds even though the flowing water contains dissolved oxygen.

Field determinations of NOD and k_n require comprehensive sampling for ammonia and nitrate nitrogen under known conditions of flow including mean depths, quantities, and times of passage. Numerical parameters are determined from field measurements by plotting on graph paper as illustrated in Example 7-3. Whether to base nitrification data on ammonia depletion, or nitrate production, must be decided separately for each case. Variations in individual stream surveys do not permit outlining specific analytical procedures. In some cases, nearly all of the upstream ammonia nitrogen appeared downstream as nitrate, while in others the ammonia declined in concentration without significant nitrate buildup. Observed nitrification rate constants, from field studies on different rivers, also show great variability ranging from less than 1.0 per day to over 5 per day.

The rate of surface-active nitrification for a given stream reach is proportional to the quantity of water passing over the slime growth and turbulence of flow. If the volume of water is small, the effect of attached masses is large and, conversely, if the volume is large the benthic effect is minimal. Hence, shallow streams are affected by slimes while major rivers overwhelm the influence of bottom growths. Shallow streams also frequently have rocky bottoms, or rooted weeds, that provide more bacterial growth surfaces than do uniform channels. Based on the volumetric concept, k_n for quantities of flow differing from those occurring during field observations may be computed based on the change in mean depth of flow as follows:

$$k_{n_1} = k_{n_2} \left(\frac{d_1}{d_2}\right) \qquad (7\text{-}42)$$

where k_{n_1}, k_{n_2} = deoxygenation rate constants for benthic NOD at d_1 and d_2, per day

d_1, d_2 = average depths of streamflow, metres

Nitrification may also be represented by zero-order kinetics, which can be combined with the first-order BOD reaction as follows:

$$\frac{dD}{dt} = k_1 L + K_n - k_2 D \qquad (7\text{-}43)$$

$$D = \frac{k_1 L_0}{k_2 - k_1}(e^{-k_1 t} - e^{-k_2 t}) + \frac{K_n}{k_2}(1 - e^{-k_2 t}) + D_0(e^{-k_2 t}) \qquad (7\text{-}44)$$

where K_n = deoxygenation rate constant for NOD based on zero-order kinetics, milligrams per litre per day

The zero-order rate constant can be determined from field measurements of either ammonium ion decrease, nitrate concentration increase, or the average of these two values. The best choice is made based on knowledge of the particular stream; however, the rate of increase in nitrate is usually more reliable because the ammonia content is more likely to be affected by other factors. The change in nitrogen concentration is multiplied by a factor of 4.57 to convert to the NOD rate constant (Equation 7-38).

The complexities of evaluating nitrification are exemplified by the studies performed on the Holston River, Tennessee.[10,20] An upstream tributary (South Fork Holston River) and a 23-km length of the main river were polluted by wastewater discharges containing large amounts of ammonia nitrogen from chemical manufacturing and organic matter from domestic sources. The velocity of flow during the study period was 0.2 to 0.3 m/s with a mean depth of 0.6 to 1.9 m. The rate of ammonia depletion was nearly twice the measured rate of nitrate-nitrite formation. Since this discrepancy could not be quantified, an average rate was used to calculate NOD. The upper portion of Figure 7-21 is a graph of the BOD-NOD data determined from field sampling compared to mean calculated values. Their good agreement demonstrates the significant contribution of nitrification to the oxygen demand in this stream. Despite this, the lower portion of Figure 7-21 shows a computed dissolved oxygen profile lower than the measured values. The analysts attributed this abnormality to the influence of aquatic weeds on the dissolved oxygen concentration. Wide fluctuations were apparently the result of photosynthesis and respiration by the abundant growth of aquatic plants.

Example 7-8
The nitrogen data listed in Table 7-4 are from a comprehensive field survey of a small river heavily polluted with nitrogenous wastes from municipal and industrial discharges. Plot these measurements on semilogarithmic and arithmetic graph papers, and calculate the rate constants and NOD value.

The other average conditions in this reach of the river are: an initial dissolved oxygen level of 7.2 mg/l, C_s of 9.2 mg/l ($20°C$), initial ultimate BOD of 26 mg/l with a k_1 to

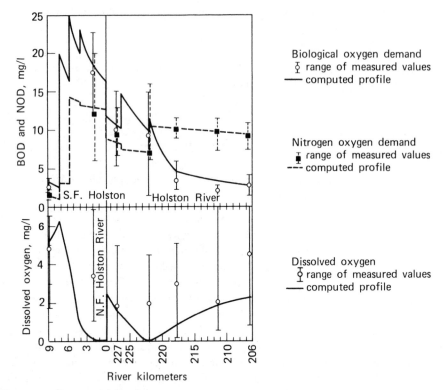

Biological oxygen demand
  ⚲ range of measured values
  —— computed profile

Nitrogen oxygen demand
  ▪ range of measured values
  --- computed profile

Dissolved oxygen
  ⚲ range of measured values
  —— computed profile

Figure 7-21 Oxygen demand and dissolved oxygen profiles illustrating the effects of both carbonaceous BOD and nitrification on a polluted stream. (From V. Novotny and P. A. Krenkel, "A Waste Assimilative Capacity Model for a Shallow, Turbulent Stream," *Water Research*, 1975, p. 238.)

Table 7-4 Nitrogen Data for Example 7-8

(1) Time of Passage (days)	(2) Measured Organic Nitrogen (mg/l)	(3) Measured Ammonia Nitrogen (mg/l)	(4) Measured Nitrite-Nitrate Nitrogen (mg/l)	(5) Calculated Total Nitrogen (2)+(3)+(4) (mg/l)	(6) Calculated Ammonia Reduction by Nitrification (mg/l)
0	2.6	10.2	4.6	17.4	10.2
0.43	2.1	9.1	5.0	16.2	9.8
0.64	2.1	8.1	5.2	15.4	9.6
0.94	1.7	7.6	5.5	14.8	9.3
1.53	2.1	5.0	6.0	13.1	8.8
1.80	2.0	4.0	6.7	12.7	8.1

base e of 0.17 per d, and a mean reaeration rate constant of 1.20 per day. Based on these data and the calculated nitrification parameters, diagram the oxygen sag curves represented by Equations 7-32, 7-41, and 7-44.

Diurnal dissolved oxygen levels ranged from lows of 0.5 mg/l, just before daybreak for several kilometres below the waste discharges, to highs in excess of 8.0 mg/l on sunny afternoons resulting from photosynthetic production of oxygen. The majority of the DO measurements were between 2 and 5 mg/l.

Solution

Figure 7-22 is a semilogarithmic diagram of the data in Table 7-4. The organic nitrogen concentration remained relatively unchanged; however, the nature of the organic compounds varied—most of the upstream solids were related to waste discharges, while the downstream organic nitrogen was bound in both detritus and algae. Ammonia nitrogen steadily decreased with time as the nitrite-nitrate content increased, but at a slower rate. The total nitrogen decrease was attributed to plant synthesis, both algae and rooted aquatics, and possibly to some biological denitrification in benthic slime growths.

The k_n values based on decrease of ammonia are:

$$k_n \ (0 \text{ to } 0.94 \text{ d}) = \frac{\log_e 10.2 - \log_e 7.6}{0.94 - 0} = 0.31 \text{ per d}$$

$$k_n \ (0.94 \text{ to } 1.80 \text{ d}) = \frac{\log_e 7.6 - \log_e 4.0}{1.80 - 0.94} = 0.75 \text{ per d}$$

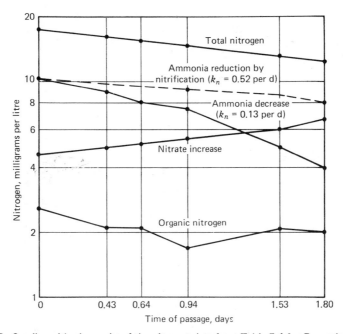

Figure 7-22 Semilogarithmic graphs of the nitrogen data from Table 7-4 for Example 7-8.

Using these numbers as deoxygenation rate constants assumes that nitrification accounts for all of the ammonia depletion. However, this is probably not realistic since a portion of the ammonia was undoubtedly taken up by photosynthesis (Figure 7-20).

The nitrite-nitrate nitrogen buildup of 2.1 mg/l, from 4.6 mg/l to 6.7 mg/l, is not sufficient to account for the ammonia nitrogen drop of 6.2 mg/l (10.2 mg/l to 4.0 mg/l). Therefore, either the nitrate was lost by denitrification and plant uptake, or competing reactions like photosynthesis extracted the ammonia before it could be oxidized. If the latter is true, the overall reaction can be viewed as first-order with respect to the ammonia nitrogen concentration, such that, the effective rate constant is the sum of the rate constants for the individual first-order reactions.

$$\frac{d[NH_3-N]}{dt} = k_n[NH_3-N] + k_s[NH_3-N] = (k_n + k_s)[NH_3-N] \qquad (7\text{-}45)$$

To determine the nitrification k_n, the incremental increases of nitrite-nitrate concentrations are subtracted from the initial ammonia nitrogen and the resulting data used to calculate the rate change. For example, the nitrite-nitrate increases in column 4 of Table 7-4 (0.4, 0.2. . . .) were deducted from 10.2 mg/l to yield the values in column 6. The resulting ammonia reduction by nitrification is drawn as a dashed line in Figure 7-22. The rate constant is

$$k_n = \frac{\log_e 10.2 - \log_e 8.1}{1.8 - 0} = 0.13 \text{ per d}$$

Applying this value as a deoxygenation rate constant assumes only a portion of ammonia is nitrified, with the remainder being extracted by other reactions. Based on Equation 7-45, the k_s for photosynthesis is calculated as 0.39 per d by subtracting 0.13 per d (k_n of nitrification) from 0.52 (k_n of ammonia reduction).

Figure 7-23 shows arithmetic graphs of the ammonia and nitrite-nitrate data from Table 7-4. The K_n based on ammonia nitrogen decrease between 0 and 0.94 is

$$K_n = 4.57 \left(\frac{10.2 - 7.6}{0.94 - 0}\right) = 11.9 \text{ mg/l·d}$$

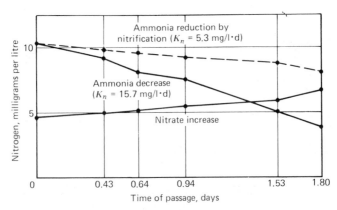

Figure 7-23 Arithmetic graphs of the ammonia and nitrite-nitrate data from Table 7-4 for Example 7-8.

The multiplication factor of 4.57 converts milligrams of nitrogen to milligrams of NOD based on the relationship expressed in Equation 7-38. The K_n for nitrite-nitrate increase is

$$K_n = 4.57 \left(\frac{10.2 - 8.1}{1.80 - 0}\right) = 5.3 \text{ mg/l·d}$$

The initial nitrogen oxygen demand N_o is computed by multiplying the beginning ammonia nitrogen concentration by the 4.57 conversion factor for nitrogen to NOD.

$$N_o = 4.57 \times 10.2 = 47 \text{ mg/l}$$

The oxygen sag equation for carbonaceous BOD is derived by substituting the following into Equation 7-32: $k_1 = 0.17$ per d, $L_o = 26$ mg/l, $k_2 = 1.2$ per d, $C_s = 9.2$ mg/l, and $C_o = 7.2$ mg/l

$$D = \frac{0.17 \times 26}{1.20 - 0.17}(e^{-0.17t} - e^{-1.20t}) + (9.2 - 7.2)(e^{-1.20t})$$

$$D = 4.29(e^{-0.17t} - e^{-1.20t}) + 2.0(e^{-1.20t})$$

This curve is plotted in Figure 7-24.

The oxygen sag formula incorporating both carbonaceous BOD and first-order NOD, with a $k_n = 0.31$ per d and $N_o = 47$ mg/l, is written by substituting into Equation 7-41.

$$D = 4.29(e^{-0.17t} - e^{-1.20t}) + \frac{0.31 \times 47}{1.20 - 0.31}(e^{-0.31t} - e^{-1.20t}) + 2.0(e^{-1.20t})$$

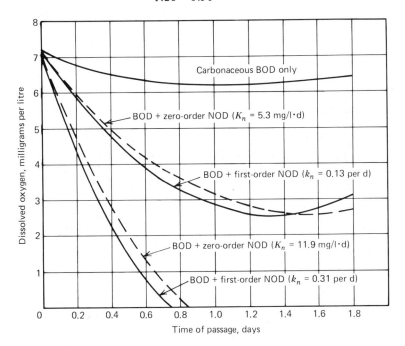

Figure 7-24   Calculated oxygen sag curves for Example 7-8.

$$D = 4.29(e^{-0.17t} - e^{-1.20t}) + 16.4(e^{-0.31t} - e^{-1.20t}) + 2.0(e^{-1.20t})$$

Inserting a k_n of 0.13 per d for 0.31 per d, the formula becomes

$$D = 4.29(e^{-0.17t} - e^{-1.20t}) + 5.71(e^{-0.13t} - e^{-1.20t}) + 2.0(e^{-1.20t})$$

These two formulas are drawn as solid lines on Figure 7-24.

The model for oxygen sag including carbonaceous BOD and zero-order nitrification kinetics (Equation 7-44) for a K_n of 11.9 mg/l·d is

$$D = 4.29(e^{-0.17t} - e^{-1.20t}) + 9.9(1 - e^{-1.20t}) + 2.0(e^{-1.20t})$$

For a K_n of 5.3 mg/l·d, the coefficient of 9.9 in the second term becomes 4.4. These sag curves are represented by the dashed lines on Figure 7-24.

A comparison of the oxygen sag curves, sketched in Figure 7-24, with the range of mean DO observations indicates that nitrification exerts considerable oxygen demand and the rate constants relate more to observed nitrification than ammonia nitrogen reduction.

7-10 Mathematical Models

A water-quality model is a set of mathematical statements representing conditions in a river or stream. They range from simple equations, easily solved by hand calculations, to complex interacting formulas programmed for digital-computer analysis. If the model is deterministic, the output has an explicit solution. A less common form is the stochastic approach that includes probability functions and expresses answers in terms of the frequency, or likelihood, of a particular occurrence. After a mathematical formulation has been written to represent a surface-water system, the model can be used to predict water quality under varying circumstances. The management of surface waters involves an understanding of how proposed actions, like effluent reductions or low-flow augmentation, might affect water quality.

The most common model simulates steady-state, one-dimensional flow: the quantities of flow are assigned, and water passage is ideal plug-flow with neither longitudinal dispersion nor lateral diffusion. The usual model application is to evaluate alternative engineering plans for water-quality control, such as ascertaining the degrees of waste treatment required, the necessity of low-flow augmentation, or optimum locations of proposed treatment facilities. The discharges selected for evaluating capacity of a river to assimilate wastes are often the seven-consecutive-day 1-in-10-year low flows adopted by regulatory agencies for determining allowable pollutant concentrations. Pollutional loads from point and diffuse sources include both conservative and reactive contaminants. The most critical model inputs relate to the capacity of a watercourse to absorb wastes, for example, in a dissolved oxygen model, rate constants for reaeration and NOD are particularly difficult to define. Ultimately, the availability of reliable field data for calibration and verification of these parameters dictates the value of a model. After calibration of the mathematical formulas based on observed conditions, they must be verified by an entirely different set of field measurements to prove the equations are representative. Only after successful verification can a model be considered reliable in forecasting the response of a stream to anticipated future conditions.

Consider DO-BOD modeling of the simple stream illustrated in Figure 7-25. First, the physical system must be defined by dividing the stream into reaches with similar channel characteristics and locating waste discharges, junctions, and dams. The hydrology is described by quantitative data, inputs and withdrawals, and flow characteristics like mean depth and velocity. Velocity can be estimated for a particular reach by the relationship

$$V = aQ^b \tag{7-46}$$

where the coefficients a and b have been defined by hydraulic measurements made on that section of the stream. For a given discharge, the depth of flow is often predicted mathematically by employing the Manning formula for open channel flow assuming a rectangular stream cross section. These data are essential for computing times of passage (length of reach divided by average velocity) and rate constants. The reaeration k_2 for a specific quantity of flow can be calculated from equations founded on field

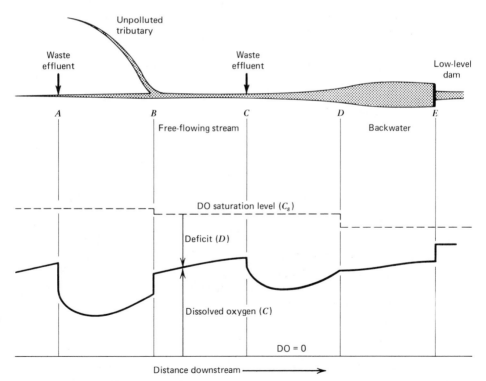

Figure 7-25 Schematic dissolved oxygen profile for a simple stream consisting of four reaches with differing characteristics.

data (Equations 7-21 and 7-25). Similarly, deoxygenation coefficients that relate to benthic oxygen uptake, particularly k_n, require correlation to quantity of flow by actual observations.

Water temperature must be incorporated into a model to adjust rate constants (Equation 7-14) and saturation values of dissolved oxygen. The later can be expressed mathematically taking into account temperature, barometric pressure, and vapor pressure.[7] Thus, solubility of oxygen, as tabulated in the appendix, can be adapted to computer programming.

After describing the physical system in Figure 7-25, mathematical expressions can be formulated to model dissolved oxygen under varying effluent loads and fixed hydraulic conditions. An oxygen sag equation (Equation 7-32 or 7-41) can be written for each reach by substituting in given values for k_1, k_2, and k_n. Mixing equations (Equation 7-8) are arranged for BOD, NOD, DO, and temperature at the beginning of each reach. At the starting point A, estimated upstream residuals of BOD and DO deficit and waste effluent data are used to calculate L_0, N_0, and D_0 for the first section (A to B). Where a tributary joins the stream at B, mixing equations are again employed to compute a new set of additional values for the sag equation of reach from B to C. Residuals of BOD and NOD in the streamflow just above point B are figured by the oxygen demand depletion equations (Equations 7-19 and 7-39). The next discontinuity in the dissolved oxygen curve occurs at C, where the second waste effluent enters the river. At D, the dramatic break in slope reflects a change in reaeration rate, and finally at E the sudden increase in dissolved oxygen is a result of aeration from overflowing a dam (Equation 7-26 or 7-30). For this stream with only four reaches, hand computations can be performed quickly and easily. However, if the system had a significantly larger number of reaches, programming the model for analysis on a digital computer would be advantageous.

Several different steady-state digital computer models have been developed for use by water resources agencies.[22] One of the simplest, *Simulation of Water Quality in Streams and Canals (Qual-I)*,[23] can route the parameters of temperature, BOD, dissolved oxygen, and three conservative minerals, either separately or simultaneously, in a branching stream system with multiple waste inputs and withdrawals (Figure 7-26). Dilution for flow augmentation can also be computed to meet any specified dissolved oxygen level. Input data are limited to the following maxima: 25 reaches, 25 waste inputs, 5 headwaters, 5 junctions, and 500 computational elements. The program (written in FORTRAN IV) begins by routing computations from the headwaters of the river system. Incremental flows and waste inputs enter into the calculations as they are encountered while moving downstream. Upon reaching the end, the number of simultaneous equations is equal to the number of computational elements. When these are solved, the solution advances forward in time one hour. This process is repeated until steady-state conditions are reached, which occurs at the time of passage from the uppermost point of the system.

In applying the Qual-I model, the first step is to select segments of the stream, or canal, system to be simulated and layout a schematic diagram as shown in Figure 7-26. Next, individual reaches exhibiting relatively uniform characteristics are designated based on available water quality data, changes in stream geometry, and location of

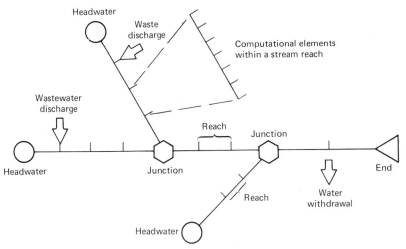

Figure 7-26 Schematic diagram of a Qual-I model for simulating water quality in hypothetical stream.[23]

waste inputs and junctions. The final step is choosing the desired degree of resolution by selecting the number of computational elements for every reach. For each element specified, numerical values of the water quality parameters in the program are printed on the program output. A program documentation and users manual describes the proper format for input data.[23]

The limitation of Qual I to simulate only carbonaceous BOD and dissolved oxygen as dependent constituents prompted evolution of a Qual-II model to include the interactions of plant nutrients, algal production, and benthic oxygen demand. The concept of this second generation water-quality model is illustrated in Figure 7-27. The arrows show the normal flow of oxygen in a moderately polluted water; however, directions may be reversed in some circumstances. For example, while atmospheric oxygen is usually absorbed into solution, supersaturation caused by algal photosynthesis can drive oxygen out of the water. Oxygen produced from photosynthesis, as modified by temperature and light intensity, is mathematically founded on the algal growth rate. The latter represented by production of chlorophyll (a measurable parameter) is coupled to availability of nutrients and sunlight. The nitrogen cycle incorporates oxidation of ammonia to nitrite and nitrate, release of ammonia from decaying vegetation, and synthesis of nitrate. Being less complex, the phosphorus cycle allows phosphates to interact only between algae and a sink (deposition outside the system). Carbonaceous BOD is the classical first-order reaction, and benthic oxygen uptake is expressed as a fixed demand per unit of stream cross-sectional area. The differential equation describing the rate of change of oxygen in this model is written as:

$$\frac{dO}{dt} = K_2(O_s - O) + (\alpha_3\mu - \alpha_4\rho)A - K_1L_1 - K_4/A_x - \alpha_5\beta_1N_1 - \alpha_6\beta_2N_2 \qquad (7\text{-}47)$$

where O = concentration of dissolved oxygen

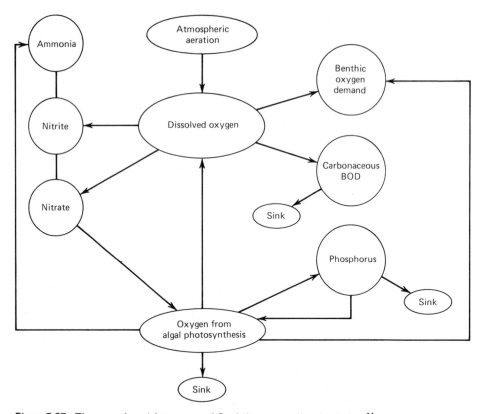

Figure 7-27 The general model structure of Qual-II water-quality simulation.[24]

K_2 = reaeration rate constant based on diffusion analogy
O_S = dissolved oxygen saturation level
α_3 = photosynthetic oxygen production per unit of algal biomass
μ = growth rate of algae as defined by availability of nutrients and intensity of sunlight
α_4 = oxygen uptake per unit of algal biomass
ρ = respiration rate of algae
A = algal biomass concentration
K_1 = rate of decay of carbonaceous BOD
L_1 = concentration of carbonaceous BOD
K_4 = constant benthic oxygen demand
A_x = average stream cross-sectional area
α_5 = rate of oxygen uptake per unit of ammonia oxidized
β_1 = rate constant for biological oxidation of ammonia nitrogen
N_1 = concentration of ammonia nitrogen
α_6 = rate of oxygen uptake per unit of nitrite oxidized
β_2 = rate constant for biological oxidation of nitrite nitrogen
N_2 = concentration of nitrite nitrogen

The complex set of 10 chemical and biological equations simulated by Qual II contain a total of 23 input parameters, including both constants and temperature-dependent variables.[24] Obviously, comprehensive field surveys must be conducted prior to implementing this model. Useful data on photosynthesis are very limited, and only in rare cases have nitrification and benthic oxygen demands been quantitatively evaluated in the field. In fact, even with carefully conducted stream surveys, models including nitrification in actual streams have become a descriptive rather than predictive endeavor. In a sense, proficiency in computer modeling has outpaced the ability to quantify the natural environment of a stream or river. Unfortunately, modelers faced with poor data for calibration tend to rely heavily on mathematical optimization techniques to quantify model parameters. In simple terms optimization involves two steps. First, a numerical range is assigned to each model variable. Second, numerous computer runs are conducted, and values for each parameter are simultaneously varied within the ranges previously established. The assigned numbers resulting in the "best fit" are considered to be the optimum values. Often these are not checked independently for accuracy within the river system being modeled. When conducted in this manner, calibration in effect becomes little more than computerized "curve-fitting" instead of a process governed by scientific understanding.[25] Numerical ranges for most parameters can and should be established by independent field and laboratory study. Predictive capability of a river-quality model necessitates collection and analysis of independent sets of statistically reliable data for both calibration and verification.[25]

7-11 Assessment of Water Quality

The objective of river-basin planning is to ensure an adequate supply of water to meet beneficial uses. Planning components outlined on the right side of Figure 7-28 are goals and policies for development of a river basin, including population projections, economic development, land use, and environmental quality; resource needs for water supply, recreation, and others; existing and anticipated problems relative to water pollution; information on hydrology and water quality; alternative developmental plans; and management decisions. Unfortunately, a particular planning alternative is often selected without knowing its full impact on water quality, since existing water-resources data are rarely adequate to project future conditions. The function of water-quality assessment is to compliment river-basin planning by forecasting the effects of alternative actions.

The first step in water-quality assessment requires an evaluation of data on pollution problems, for example, dissolved oxygen deficiency relative to wastewater discharges, or turbidity from land erosion. Analyses of river hydrology include flow characteristics—magnitude, probability, and duration of droughts and floods—and channel morphology: bed slope, cross-sectional geometry, and the nature of bed materials. Data collection normally requires intensive sampling and testing over a two- or three-year period for in-depth assessment. Chemical and biological information must be keyed to hydrologic measurements, waste discharges, and season of the year. Existing data from regulatory agencies are generally useless since surveillance sampling involves

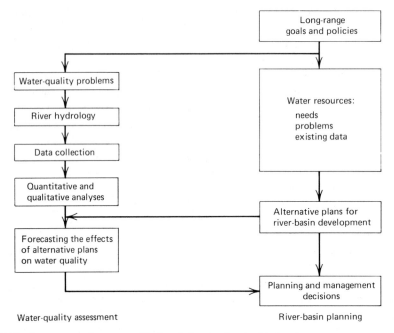

Figure 7-28 Assessment of water quality in relation to river-basin planning.

collecting grabs at widely dispersed sites under varying conditions. For a reconnaissance-level study, complete sets of physical-chemical-biological data are needed to establish and verify mathematical models used in predicting water quality under differing conditions. In addition to these quantitative methods, analyses can be qualitatively presented by employing charts, tables, figures, and maps.

Assessment results must be technically valid, practical, and available at the time planning decisions are made. Often these objectives are foiled by planning agencies trying to shorten study periods to accommodate decision-makers who want to act quickly. As a result, a water-quality forecast for some future condition may be in considerable error, thus, either preventing a worthwhile project from being considered, or allowing a development that will result in environmental degradation.

References

1. Reid, G. K., and Wood, R. D., *Ecology of Inland Waters and Estuaries*, 2nd Edition, D. Van Nostrand Co., New York, 1976.

2. Odum, H. T., "Trophic Structure and Productivity of Silver Springs, Florida," *Ecological Monographs*, Vol. 27, 1957, pp. 55-112.

3. Usinger, R. L., *The Life of Rivers and Streams*, McGraw-Hill Book Co., New York, 1967.

4. Hynes, H. B. N., *The Biology of Polluted Waters*, Liverpool University Press, Liverpool, England, 1960.

5. Mackenthun, K. M., *The Practice of Water Pollution Biology*, U. S. Dept. of the Interior, Federal Water Pollution Control Administration, Washington, D.C., 1969.

6. Hammer, M. J., *Water and Waste-Water Technology, SI Version*, John Wiley & Sons, Inc., New York, 1977.

7. *Standard Methods for the Examination of Water and Wastewater*, 14th Edition, American Public Health Association, American Water Works Association, and Water Pollution Control Federation, 1975.

8. Young, J. C., "Chemical Methods for Nitrification Control," *Journal Water Pollution Control Federation*, Vol. 45, 1973, pp. 637-646.

9. Maier, W. J., and McConnell, H. L., "Carbon Measurements in Water Quality Monitoring," *Journal Water Pollution Control Federation*, Vol. 46, 1974, pp. 623-633. '

10. Ruane, R. J., and Krenkel, P. A., "Nitrification and Other Factors Affecting Nitrogen in the Holston River," *Proceeding of the IAWPR Conference on Nitrogen as a Water Pollutant*, Copenhagen, 1975.

11. Lopez-Bernal, F. F., Krenkel, P. A., and Ruane, R. J., "Nitrification in Free-Flowing Streams," *Proceeding of the IAWPR Conference*, Sydney, Australia, 1976.

12. Langbein, W. B., and Durum, W. H., "The Aeration Capacity of Streams," *Geological Survey Circular 542*, U. S. Geological Survey, Washington, D.C., 1967.

13. Covar, A. P., "Selecting the Proper Reaeration Coefficient for Use in Water Quality Models," *Environmental Modeling and Simulation*, U. S. Environmental Protection Agency, Washington, D. C., 1976.

14. Tsivoglou, E. C., and Neal, L. A., "Tracer Measurement of Reaeration: III, Predicting the Reaeration Capacity of Inland Streams," *Journal Water Pollution Control Federation*, Vol. 48, 1976, pp. 2669-2689.

15. Tsivoglou, E. C., Cohen, J. B., Shearer, S. D., and Godsil, P. J., "Tracer Measurement of Stream Reaeration: II. Field Studies," *Journal Water Pollution Control Federation*, Vol. 40, 1968, pp. 285-305.

16. Foree, E. G., "Reaeration and Velocity Prediction for Small Streams," *Journal Environmental Engineering Division, Proceedings Am. Society of Civil Eng.*, Vol. 102, No. EE5, 1976, pp. 937-952.

17. Phelps, E. B., *Stream Sanitation*, John Wiley & Sons, Inc., New York, 1944.

18. Tuffey, T. J., Hunter, J. V., and Matulewich, V. A., "Zones of Nitrification," *Water Resources Bulletin*, American Water Resources Assoc., Vol. 10, No. 3, June, 1974.

19. Rickert, D. A., Hines, W. G., and McKenzie, S. W., "Methodology for River-

Quality Assessment with Application to the Willamette River Basin, Oregon," Geological Survey Circular 715-M, *U. S. Geological Survey*, Washington, D. C., 1976.

20. Novotny, V., and Krenkel, P. A., "A Waste Assimilative Capacity Model for a Shallow, Turbulent Stream," *Water Research*, Vol. 9, Pergamon Press, 1975, pp. 233-241.

21. *Simplified Mathematical Modeling of Water Quality*, U. S. Environmental Protection Agency, Washington, D.C., March, 1971, and *Addendum to Simplified Mathematical Modeling of Water Quality*, May, 1972.

22. *Evaluation of Water Quality Models: A Management Guide for Planners*, EPA-600/5-76-004, U. S. Environmental Protection Agency, Washington, D.C., July, 1976.

23. *Qual-I, Simulation of Water Quality in Streams and Canals*, Program Documentation and Users Manual, Texas Water Development Board, Austin, Texas, 1970.

24. *Computer Program Documentation for the Stream Quality Model Qual-II*, U. S. Environmental Protection Agency, Washington, D.C., 1973.

25. Hines, W. G., Rickert, D. A., McKenzie, S. W., and Bennett, J. P., "Formulation and Use of Practical Models for River-Quality Assessment," *Geological Survey Circular 715-B*, U. S. Geological Survey, Washington, D.C., 1975.

Problems

7-1   List three of the common pollution problems in flowing waters.

7-2   Define the term "food web."

7-3   Describe the operation of a Surber sampler.

7-4   Why does the biomass on each higher trophic level in Figure 7-2 decrease in quantity?

7-5   Describe the role of macrophytes in the aquatic food chain.

7-6   What is a common characteristic of the insects shown in Figure 7-3?

7-7   List the four types of feeding habits found in swift-water communities, and name an organism found in each type.

7-8   Why are worms common bottom dwellers in slow-moving rivers but not in swift streams?

7-9   What are the common pollutants originating from diffuse sources in rural areas?

7-10 State why fish are good indicators of water quality.

7-11 Describe how other conditions in a river can magnify the toxicity of a poison.

7-12 How does pollution by inert solids influence aquatic life?

7-13 List the pollutants found in typical municipal wastewater. Which ones are only partly removed by conventional (secondary) treatment?

7-14 How can artificial heating adversely affect life in flowing waters?

7-15 Name the major health concerns related to use of a polluted river as the source for a public water supply.

7-16 What is the minimum desired dilution in a river of effluent from a municipal wastewater treatment plant? Why?

7-17 A large wastewater effluent is discharged into a stream with low natural flow. How do the environmental repercussions of pollution in the receiving watercourse differ between a mountain stream in a resort area compared to a stream in an agricultural region in the plains?

7-18 What organisms are the best biological indicators of pollution in stream surveys? Why?

7-19 Does the presence of fecal coliforms in water conclusively prove pollution by human wastes? Explain.

7-20 Define biochemical oxygen demand (BOD) and the deoxygenation rate constant k.

7-21 List the chemicals added to the dilution water in a standard BOD test.

7-22 For BOD tests on treated wastewater, how does the preparation differ between an unchlorinated and a chlorinated effluent?

7-23 Describe the procedure for preparing a BOD test on a polluted river sample that does not require the addition of dilution water. What equation is used to calculate the BOD from the test results?

7-24 What volume of domestic wastewater with an estimated BOD of 250 mg/l should be added to conduct a five-day test in a standard 300 ml bottle? (*Answer* 5.0 ml)

7-25 Why is the dissolved oxygen concentration in a stream likely to have a diurnal variation? What are the minimum allowable concentrations for warm-water fish?

7-26 What are the best sampling sources for heavy metals?

7-27 Describe the procedures for preparing a composite sample of a wastewater effluent.

7-28 A BOD analysis was conducted on the unchlorinated effluent from a municipal treatment plant. Several test bottles were prepared using a 10.0 percent mixture of wastewater in dilution water. The initial dissolved oxygen concentration of the mixture was measured as 7.7 mg/l by titrating several bottles shortly after preparation. The time-residual DO data for the incubated bottles were as follows: 7.2 mg/l after 0.5 days; 6.7 mg/l, 0.9 d; 6.0 mg/l, 1.9 d; 5.4 mg/l, 3.0 d; 4.9 mg/l, 4.0 d; 4.6 mg/l, 5.0 d; 4.3 mg/l, 6.0 d; 3.9 mg/l, 7.0 d; 3.3 mg/l, 8.0 d; 2.0 mg/l, 9.0 d; and 1.8 mg/l at 10.0 days. Plot a BOD-time curve, determine the carbonaceous k-rate, 5-day BOD, and calculated ultimate BOD value. (*Answers* $k = 0.11$ per day, BOD = 31 mg/l, ultimate BOD = 43 mg/l)

7-29 A seeded BOD analysis was conducted on a chlorinated-dechlorinated wastewater effluent. The seed was aged, settled, domestic wastewater. BOD tests on the seed were set up by adding 10.0 ml per 300-ml bottle. The seeded wastewater samples were prepared by adding 30.0 ml of effluent and 1.0 ml of seed per test bottle. The results of the laboratory tests are listed below. Plot a BOD-time curve, determine the carbonaceous k-rate, and calculate the ultimate carbonaceous BOD. (*Answers* lag period = 1.3-1.5 d, k = 0.08-0.12 per day, 55-65 mg/l)

Time of Incubation (days)	Seed Test B_1 (mg/l)	Seed Test B_2 (mg/l)	Sample Test D_1 (mg/l)	Sample Test D_2 (mg/l)
0	8.3	—	8.3	—
1.0	8.3	6.3	8.3	7.8
2.0	8.3	6.1	8.3	6.7
3.0	8.3	5.3	8.3	4.8
4.0	8.3	4.3	8.3	4.5
5.0	8.3	4.1	8.3	4.1
6.0	8.3	3.9	8.3	3.7
7.0	8.3	3.8	8.3	3.2
8.0	8.3	3.7	8.3	3.0
9.0	8.3	3.6	8.3	2.5
10.0	8.3	3.7	8.3	2.5
11.0	8.3	3.5	8.3	2.0
12.0	8.3	3.2	8.3	1.2
13.0	8.3	3.3	8.3	0.2

7-30 A water sample from a stream was aerated and siphoned into a BOD bottle without dilution. Repeated dissolved oxygen measurements were taken on the same bottle using a DO meter with a laboratory probe as incubation proceeded. The time-residual DO data were as follows: initial DO = 8.0 mg/l; 7.5 mg/l after 0.8 days; 6.2 mg/l, 1.9 d; 5.7 mg/l, 2.8 d; 4.5 mg/l, 4.0 d; 4.0 mg/l, 5.0 d; 3.3 mg/l, 5.9 d; 2.7 mg/l, 7.0 d; 1.5 mg/l, 8.8 d; 0.8 mg/l, 9.8 d; and 0.2 mg/l at 11.7 d. Estimate the carbonaceous k-rate, 5-day BOD, and ultimate BOD.

7-31 What determines the decrease in concentration of a conservative pollutant, like salt from a brine waste, in the streamflow below the outfall sewer?

7-32 A reactive chemical disposed of by dilution in a river dissipates at a rate proportional to first-order kinetics with a rate constant equal to 0.50 per day. The waste discharge is 400 l/s containing 30 mg/l. The river above the sewer outfall has a flow of 5.0 m³/s with a residual chemical concentration of 2.0 mg/l. If the mean velocity in the river is 0.15 m/s, calculate the flow distance required for the chemical concentration to decrease to its upstream level of 2.0 mg/l. (*Answer* 18.4 km)

7-33 Laboratory experiments were conducted to determine the first-order kinetics decay of a reactive chemical and the rate coefficient for Equation 7-14. If the k-rate was measured as 0.10 per day at 20°C and 0.18 per day at 30°C, what is the value of θ and the calculated k-rate at 25°C?

7-34 The deoxygenation rate constant applied in a stream analysis is commonly based on laboratory BOD testing. What deoxygenation factors in a stream are not accounted for in the standard laboratory BOD test?

7-35 In your own words, state the meaning of Equation 7-20.

7-36 List the factors that influence the reaeration capacity of a stream.

7-37 The characteristics of a uniform 10-km stream reach are: $Q = 1.5$ m^3/s, average $V = 0.34$ m/s, mean depth of flow = 0.33 m, and an elevation drop of 4.6 m for 10 km. Estimate the reaeration constant by Equations 7-22 and 7-25. (*Answers* 3.3 per day, 2.4 per day.)

7-38 Outline the step-by-step procedure for determining the rate of reoxygenation of a stream reach by the tracer method.

7-39 What is the advantage of determining the reaeration of an instream dam by the tracer technique rather than simply measuring the existing dissolved oxygen levels upstream and downstream?

7-40 A wastewater effluent of 500 l/s with a BOD = 45 mg/l, DO = 0.4 mg/l, and temperature of 17.5°C enters a stream where the flow is 4.5 m^3/s with a BOD = 6.0 mg/l, DO = 8.4 mg/l, and temperature of 22.5°C. From laboratory BOD testing, the k_1 of the wastewater diluted with stream water is 0.10 per day at 20°C (base 10). The k_2 in the stream below the sewer outfall is 0.53 per day at 20°C (base e) based on tracer studies. (a) Calculate the minimum dissolved oxygen level using the oxygen sag equation. (b) How much would the critical oxygen level increase if the wastewater was aerated to a DO of 8.4 mg/l prior to discharge? (*Answers* (a) 2.27 d, 5.1 mg/l, (b) 0.2 mg/l)

7-41 A streamflow of 0.090 m^3/s, recovering from a wastewater discharge several kilometres upstream, merges with a tributary drainage of 0.030 m^3/s. The combined flow of 0.12 m^3/s travels for another 2.6 km where it enters into a major river. At the point where the stream and the tributary join, the ultimate BOD and dissolved oxygen in the stream are 8.0 mg/l and 6.0 mg/l, respectively; and the values in the tributary drainage are an ultimate BOD of 2.0 mg/l and DO equal to 8.0 mg/l. The combined flow in the channel to the river is uniform at 0.06 m/s and 20°C with a measured reaeration constant of 0.60 per day (base e) and deoxygenation rate of 0.23 per day (base e). What is the lowest calculated dissolved oxygen concentration in the stream reach between the entrance of the tributary and the confluence with the river? (*Answer* 6.5 mg/l)

7-42 A wastewater discharge enters a stream 32 km above a backwater pond. The waste characteristics are $Q = 15\ 000$ m^3/d, five-day BOD = 50 mg/l, $k_1 = 0.23$ per day (base e), DO = 2.0 mg/l, and $T = 20$°C. The stream above the outfall has $Q = 1.4$ m^3/s, five-day BOD = 4.0 mg/l, $k_1 = 0.23$ per day (base e), DO = 8.0 mg/l, and $T = 20$°C. The 32-km river reach has an average velocity of 0.15 m/s and $k_2 = 0.87$ per day (base e). The backwater is one-half kilometre long with an estimated $k_2 = 0.12$ per day (base e) and time of passage (retention time) = 12 h. Outflow from the backwater falls over a dam with a height of 3.0 m. Compute the dissolved oxygen concentrations at the upstream and downstream ends of the backwater, and after the waterfall. (*Answers* 6.8 mg/l, 6.2 mg/l, 8.5 mg/l)

7-43 Under what conditions is streamflow most likely to exert nitrogen oxygen demand (NOD)?

7-44 In a stream where nitrification is known to occur, why is the disappearance of ammonia-nitrogen likely to exceed the appearance of nitrate nitrogen?

7-45 Solve part (a) Problem 7-40 again using Equation 7-41 including nitrification. The ammonia-nitrogen content in the wastewater is 20 mg/l, with none in the stream above the sewer outfall. Use a k_n equal to 0.15 per day (base e) in the temperature range of 18 to 22°C. (*Answers* 2 d, 3.7 mg/l)

7-46 A wastewater effluent discharged into a stream channel during the summer constitutes approximately three-quarters of the streamflow. Just below the outflow sewer the average conditions of the mixed wastewater and natural flow are an ultimate BOD of 55 mg/l, dissolved oxygen of 7.7 mg/l, and temperature of 23°C. Based on field studies: the k_1 is 0.46 mg/l at 20°C (base e), which is greater than the laboratory k-rate due to benthic oxygen demand; the reaeration coefficient k_2 at 20°C equals 3.2 (base e), since the stream is shallow with a relatively high average velocity of 0.34 m/s; and the deoxygenation rate constant K_n for NOD is estimated at 4.0 mg/l·d at 23°C based on the rate of nitrate formation. The stream flows in a relatively uniform channel without any significant tributaries or additional wastewater discharges for 50 km where it enters a major river. The lowest dissolved oxygen measurements in the streamflow ranged from a mean of 2 mg/l at night to a high daytime average 6 mg/l. Using Equation 7-44, calculate the approximate critical DO to check the agreement between the parameters used in the sag equation and DO measurements in the stream.

7-47 What procedure is followed to verify the mathematical model developed for a surface-water system?

7-48 How is time of flow introduced into the DO-BOD model of a stream so that it can provide solutions at different quantities of streamflow?

7-49 Which oxygen sag equation does the Qual-I model use?

7-50 What are the practical problems in applying complex models such as Qual II diagramed in Figure 7-27 and defined mathematically in Equation 7-47?

7-51 List some of the common problems in the assessment of water quality for river-basin planning.

Chapter 8
Hydrology of Impounded Waters

Natural lakes have long been recognized as a catalyst for the growth of cities. They provide water for domestic and industrial uses, recreation, fisheries, esthetics, and transportation that was particularly important prior to modern commerce. Where natural impoundments were absent, man-made lakes have been constructed for the same purposes plus water storage essential for irrigated agriculture, flood control of the fertile plains so they could be safely inhabited, and hydroelectric power to support industry. Thus, natural lakes and man-made reservoirs throughout the world are extensively used for social benefits. The hydrology of impoundments is essential for understanding their development and application. Water quality is closely linked to mixing, stratification, and detention time; hence, the physical shape of basins, thermal stratification, and water movements are discussed in considerable detail. The traditional areas of hydrology included are flood routing, reservoir yield, evaporation, and the water budget. Hopefully, these discussions portray the tremendous importance of lakes and reservoirs in the development of water resources.

8-1 Formation of Lakes

Most lakes were formed by glacial, volcanic, or tectonic processes. Tectonic basins are depressions caused by deep movements that resulted in faulting or upwarping of the earth's crust. The basin of Lake Tahoe in the High Sierra Mountains is a trough created from displacement of fault blocks forming steep walls. The impounded water has a surface area of 500 km^2 and a maximum depth of 500 m. Lake Okeechobee in southern Florida is a relic marine basin uplifted to become land while retaining its form. While very large in area (1 880 km^2), the mean depth is only about 4 m. Deformation of the earth's crust also created Great Salt Lake in Utah when uptilting formed a closed basin.

Volcanic activity has created small crater lakes in the cinder cones of old peaks, and has also formed basins when extruded lava flows solidified forming dams across preexisting river valleys. Crater Lake, Oregon, with an area of 64 km^2 and a depth of 608 m (seventh-deepest lake in the world), was formed by the collapse of a volcanic cone.

Glacial activity, during the most recent period of major ice advance and retreat, resulted in an abundance of lakes in North America and Europe. In mountainous regions, the ice scoured out shallow rock basins to form impoundments, while continental ice sheets in nonmountainous areas carved both large and small depressions. The Laurentian Great Lakes, which collectively form the largest continuous volume of fresh water in the world, were formed by ice scour, water erosion, and subsidence under massive ice sheets. The Finger Lakes of New York were gouged by sheet ice. As the glaciers retreated, rock and soil deposits dammed up valleys and depressions creating numerous lakes. The Madison, Wisconsin, lakes are examples of basins formed by morainal damming of preglacial valleys. Kettle lakes were created when large blocks of buried ice melted leaving irregular depressions in the glacial till.

Natural impoundments of more recent origin include solution lakes and depressions formed by river and wind activity. Solution basins, created by percolating water slowly dissolving soluble rock strata, such as limestone, are usually circular and conically shaped sinks with fluctuating water levels. Flood plains of rivers contain lakes developed by the processes of erosion and deposition. The most characteristic form is the shallow, crescent-shaped lake, called an oxbow, created when a looping bend of a stream channel is cut off and blocked by deposited sediments. The most common wind-formed basins are shallow depressions that extend below the water table in sand-dune regions.

8-2 Construction of Reservoirs

The large number of dams constructed throughout the United States has elevated man-made lakes into a prominent position in freshwater resources. For flood control, excess flows are captured and released as soon as practicable. On the other hand, conservation regulation stores the amount in excess of current needs and releases it later for downstream irrigation, water supplies, recreation, fishery, navigation, or dilution of wastewaters. Of prime importance in reservoir site selection is topography of the river valley: water storage capacity must be adequate to achieve the desired purposes in flow regulation; the mean depth should be great relative to surface area to minimize the area of land flooded and reduce evaporation; and foundation conditions are important to dam safety. River flow data, both historical and projected, are necessary to ensure proper design. Perhaps the most difficult aspect of multipurpose design is resolving the competition among the various purposes for use of the available storage. In addition to the conflict between early release of reservoir water to restore flood control capacity and holding supplies for future use, peak demands for power production may not coincide with the seasonal needs of irrigation and navigation. Also, irrigation may require diversions for upstream consumption while navigation and other downstream uses are maintained by releasing stored water. All of these are at odds with recreation and fishery management in the reservoir, that prefer a constant lake level and very limited variation in the volume of stored water.

Fundamental concepts of dam design and operation are essential to understanding the differences between natural lakes and reservoirs. Single-purpose impoundments are relatively simple compared to large multipurpose structures. The essential feature of a simple reservoir for recreation is a nearly constant pool level. As illustrated in Figure

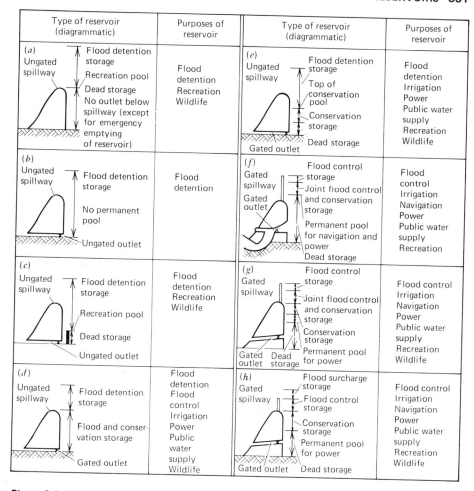

Figure 8-1 Different types of reservoirs for single or multiple purposes based on the dam and spillway design. (Adapted from V. T. Chow, editor-in-chief, *Handbook of Applied Hydrology*, McGraw-Hill Book Co., New York, 1964.)

8-1*a*, fluctuations of pool level only occur during floods, or if evaporation exceeds inflow. The rate of discharge predetermined during design is controlled by the size of the ungated spillway. Flood detention ponds (Figure 8-1*b*) are held empty, except during floods, by a low-level ungated outlet that is sized for a specified outflow. This unattended operation reduces peak flows from runoff and snowmelt. Figure 8-1*c*, a combination of the first two types, provides both flood control capacity and dead storage below an established permanent pool elevation, with both an ungated outlet and spillway installed for passage of flows. Single-purpose reservoirs for a conservation use, such as a municipal water supply or irrigation, require a gated outlet for release of water from selected levels in the lake to supply the demand during periods of deficient streamflow (Figure 8-1*d*).

Several purposes can be served by one reservoir if they are within the physical limitations of the site and availability of water. The combination may include distinctly different and competitive uses, or involve the joint application of water or storage space. Releases may be relatively constant year-round, for instance to maintain a minimum river flow, or seasonal for irrigation. Storage beyond flood detention for conservation uses (Figure 8-1e) requires a semipermanent pool and regulated outflow. Multipurpose reservoirs with a permanent pool for navigation or hydropower, plus storage for flood control and water conservation, are complex in design and operation. The last three diagrams (Figure 8-1f, g, and h) illustrate some examples of the proportioning of impounded water among various uses. Outflows are normally controlled by gated outlets or a gated service spillway. An emergency spillway is necessary to pass extreme floods.

8-3 Morphology of Impoundments

The form of a lake influences physical, chemical, and biological characteristics of the aquatic environment. Steep-sided, V-shaped basins are usually deep and biologically unproductive whereas shallow depressions with greater contact between water and sediments exhibit greater productivity. A majority of both natural and man-made lakes are relatively small and shallow being less than 20 m in mean depth.

The morphology of an impoundment is best described by a map showing the shoreline and depth contours (bathymetric chart). The outline is usually obtained by aerial photography and the shape of the bottom by sonic soundings. To numerically define a lake, the common morphometric parameters are maximum open-water length, surface area, storage volume, maximum depth, mean depth calculated by dividing the volume by the surface area, length of shoreline, and shoreline development. The latter is the ratio of shoreline length to the circumference of a circle whose area is equal to the lake's surface area; hence, a circular body would have a value of unity.

$$D_L = \frac{L}{2(\pi A)^{0.5}}$$

(8-1)

where D_L = shoreline development, dimensionless
L = length of shoreline, km
A = surface area, km^2

Many natural lakes are subcircular and elliptical in form with D_L between 2 and 3, while elongated reservoirs in river valleys have values of about 5. Table 8-1 is morphometric data for the Great Lakes. For reservoirs with operating pools, the morphometric parameters vary with water level elevation.

Hydrographic data of a lake are often presented as elevation-area and elevation-volume curves as shown in Figure 8-2. These are useful in limnological studies of natural lakes and for design and operation of reservoirs. Change in storage volumes for flood retention, power generation, irrigation supply, and so forth can be translated into water-level variations for studies of the operation of a reservoir to regulate flows for various purposes.

Table 8-1 Morphometric Data for the Great Lakes

	Area (km^2)	Maximum Depth (m)	Mean Depth (m)	Volume (km^3)	Shoreline Length (km)	Shoreline Development
Superior	83 300	307	145	12 000	3 000	2.9
Huron	59 510	223	76	4 600	2 700	3.1
Michigan	57 850	265	99	5 760	2 210	2.6
Erie	25 820	60	21	540	1 200	2.1
Ontario	18 760	225	91	1 720	1 380	2.8

Source. G. E. Hutchinson, *A Treatise on Limnology*, Vol. I, John Wiley & Sons, Inc., New York, 1957.

The water renewal time of an impoundment is equal to the water volume divided by the rate of outflow, normally expressed in time units of months or years. If the quantity of inflow is used in the calculation, the time is less due to evaporation and seepage losses. Although renewal times vary from days to hundreds of years, natural lakes generally have long retention periods relative to man-made lakes. Times for river reservoirs are generally in the range of one month to 1 year, while values for lakes are usually between 2 and 10 years. Large, deep lakes can have retention times exceeding 20 years.

8-4 Thermal Stratification

The greatest source of heat to impounded water is solar radiation. Heat can also be exchanged by evaporation, influent and effluent flows, seepage, and precipitation as

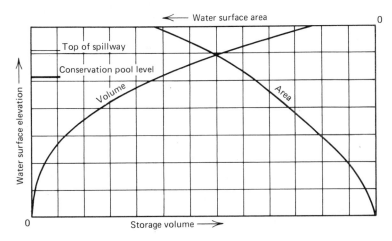

Figure 8-2 Typical depth-area and depth-volume curves developed for design and regulation of a multiple-purpose reservoir.

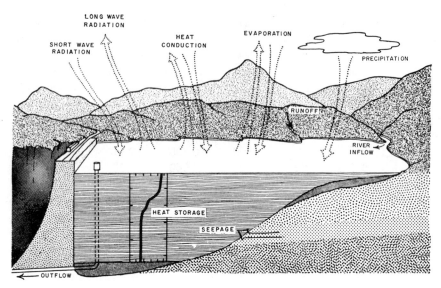

Figure 8-3 Major processes of heat transfer in a lake. A temperature profile is shown as an insert. (From J. F. T. Saur and E. R. Anderson, "The Heat Budget of a Body of Water of Varying Volume," *Limnology and Oceanography*, Vol. 1, 1956.)

diagrammed in Figure 8-3. The amount of solar energy reaching a lake depends primarily on latitude and season of the year. In the temperate zone, lakes lose heat to their surroundings during winter and increase in heat content during the summer when solar radiation is greatest. While a small portion is lost by reflection and scattering, most incident light is absorbed by the water to varying degrees depending on wavelength. Long wavelength light, the red portion of the spectrum, dissipates within one meter of pure water, while shorter wavelengths (blue) penetrate much deeper. Since much of solar energy is of long wavelength in the infrared portion of the spectrum, the upper two meters of lake water absorb over one-half on the sun's radiation, which results in heating of the water.

Absorption and dissipation of solar energy within the first few meters of water depth leads to thermal stratification during summer months. Although the depth of heat distribution is increased by wind-driven mixing, the warmer surface water with its lower density remains on top of the cooler bottom stratum. (The maximum density of water occurs at a temperature of 4°C.) Figure 8-4 illustrates typical profiles of the penetration of solar radiation and temperature during thermal stratification. The epilimnion (surface stratum) is warmed by sunlight and continuously circulated by wind and to a limited extent by convection currents. Intensity of wind circulation, depth of light penetration, magnitude of solar heating, and other climatic factors influence the thickness of the epilimnion. While larger open bodies of water usually mix to a depth of 10 m or more, lakes protected from the wind often stratify within 5 m of the surface. The hypolimnion (cooler bottom stratum) is undisturbed by water

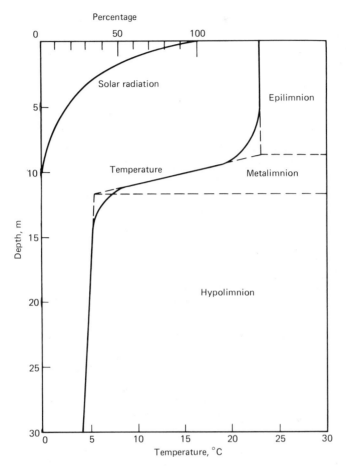

Figure 8-4 Thermal stratification of impounded water into epilimnetic, metalimnetic, and hypolimnetic strata. The penetration of solar radiation and temperature profiles are typical of a moderate-sized lake in late summer.

circulation and dark; therefore, it is photosynthetically unproductive. The intermediate zone that exhibits marked thermal discontinuity is called the metalimnion. The term thermocline, often used interchangeably with the word metalimnion, is the layer of maximum rate of decrease in temperature.

The stability of thermal-density stratification is strongly influenced by the size and morphology of the lake. Deep bodies of water enter summer stratification in late spring and do not mix again until the epilimnion is cooled by the onset of winter. Shallow impoundments open to continuous wind-induced circulation may be continuously mixed leading to a nearly uniform temperature profile. In other small lakes and reservoirs, windless hot summer periods can produce transient stratification that is easily destabilized by cooler, windy weather. Thermal stratification can also be modified by inflow or outflow when the discharges are large relative to the volume of the impoundment. For example, cool river water entering a reservoir flows under the warmer epilimnion and causes turbulence reducing the thermal gradient. A similar phenomenom occurs frequently in alpine or northern lakes that receive large flows of cold water from melting snow during late summer.

Dimictic Lakes and Reservoirs

Dimictic impoundments overturn and circulate freely twice a year in spring and fall; they are thermally stratified in summer and under ice cover in winter. This seasonal cycle of stratification and circulation is observed in cool, temperate climatic regions and at high elevations in subtropical latitudes. A typical depth-time diagram of isotherms for a lake in northern United States is shown in Figure 8-5 along with temperature profiles for the four seasons of the year.

In winter the densest water sinks to the bottom and ice covers the surface, preventing wind-induced circulation. Warm spring rains and rising air temperature melt the ice cover exposing the water surface to solar radiation and brisk spring winds. By these combined actions, winter stagnation is disrupted and the lake undergoes complete recirculation referred to as the spring overturn. Deep lakes and reservoirs, protected from the wind by surrounding topography, mix briefly raising the water temperature to only the maximum density value of 4°C prior to the onset of stratification. In shallower lakes, the water temperature can increase to above 10°C before circulation ceases. With increased heat input and subsidence of spring winds, an epilimnion forms trapping the cool dense water below a thermocline. Stable thermal stratification is maintained until autumn when shorter, cooler days cause the lake to lose heat faster than it is absorbed. When the surface water is cooled to a higher density than the hypolimnion, vertical currents lead to autumnal circulation. These density currents aided by wind action continue until finally the densest water stays at the bottom and the surface freezes.

Warm Monomictic Impoundments

Water temperature in monomictic lakes and reservoirs never falls below 4°C at any depth; therefore, they circulate freely in the winter and are stratified during the summer. Warm monomixis occurs in many reservoirs in warm regions of the temperate zone and is prevalent in coastal lakes of North America and northern Europe. Circulation is often continuous from October to April, and stratification from May through September.

Lakes of Other Thermal Classification

Amictic lakes, insulated and protected from outside influences by a perennial ice cover, are largely limited to the Antarctic and high altitudes. Cold monomictic lakes, found in polar regions, contain waters that never exceed a temperature of 4°C. Winter stagnation occurs under ice cover, and circulation takes place at a temperature not greater than 4°C in summer. Cold polymictic lakes, with frequent or continuous circulation at a temperature slightly above 4°C, are found at high altitudes in equatorial

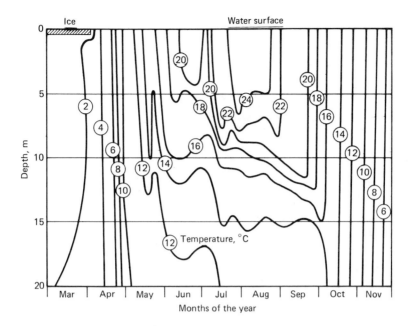

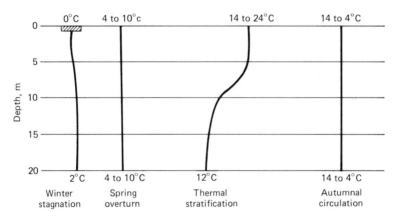

Figure 8-5 A depth-time diagram of isotherms and temperature profiles of a dimictic lake illustrating the seasonal cycle of stratification and circulation.

regions. Warm polymictic lakes in the tropics exhibit frequent periods of circulation at high temperatures. Stratification does not occur in these lakes since the annual temperature variations in these regions are small. Oligomictic are warm tropical lakes that have rare periods of circulation at irregular intervals.

Most lakes are said to be holomictic (wholly mixing) since circulation is complete, extending the entire depth of the impoundment. If turnover does not include a

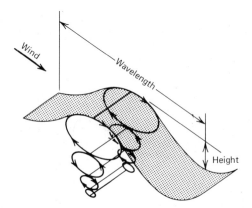

Figure 8-6 Diagram of a surface wave showing wavelength, wave height, and attenuation of vertical displacement with depth.

bottom stratum that is perennially stagnant, the lake is called meromictic (partly circulating). This phenomenon exists if the density of deep water is sufficient to prevent blending with the upper layers. For example, estuarine lakes often exhibit meromixis due to a denser saline water underlying the fresh water.

8-5 Surface Water Movements

Surface waves, produced by wind blowing over open water, are a train of alternate crests and troughs that appear to progress across the lake's surface. Actually, the individual water particles move in vertical orbits and make only minor net forward progress (Figure 8-6). The vertical motion decreases rapidly, disappearing at a depth of approximately one-half wavelength. The ratio of wave height to wavelength varies from 1:100 to 1:10, with the latter being the largest waves in a given wave train. Based on observation under strong winds, wave heights are proportional to the square root of the fetch (over-water distance of wind action) and to the first power of the wind velocity over the fetch. The resultant wave train at the end of a fetch contains a mixture of waves with heights that are approximately normally distributed. The average height of the highest waves can be determined for inland reservoirs and lakes by detailed analyses presented by others.[2]

As surface waves approach a shore, they come in contact with the bottom of the lake. Disturbance of the deep-water orbital movements starts at a water depth equal to approximately one-half the wavelength and terminates with waves breaking in the shallow water. About 90 percent of the wave energy is delivered in the breaking process with only a 10 percent loss resulting from bottom friction while approaching the shore. An understanding of dissipating wave energy is essential to shore-erosion studies, treatment of impoundment slopes to prevent deterioration, determination of dam height above the still water level, and wave pressures against sea walls and breakwaters. Data for these designs, which are beyond the scope of this book, can be found

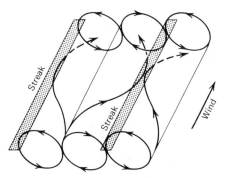

Figure 8-7 Diagram of Langmuir circulation showing parallel, helical currents oriented in the direction of the wind. Streaks of floating materials form where the surface flows converge and plunge downward.

in advanced texts and handbooks on hydraulics.

Surface mixing in the form of parallel helical currents, oriented in the direction of the wind, is called Langmuir circulation (Figure 8-7). Direction of the helices alternates clockwise and counterclockwise creating streaks where surface flows converge and plunge downward leaving accumulations of algae, zooplankton, foam, and other floating materials. Langmuir circulation is most likely to occur when wind speed exceeds 2 to 3 m/s.

Currents of surface water across and large swirls around in lakes result from a combination of wind action, the earth's rotational forces, horizontal density gradients, and river inflow. Although dependent on shape of the basin, the pattern of surface currents varies seasonally with changing climatic conditions. The speed of wind-driven currents is often about 2 percent of the wind velocity.

8-6   Internal Water Movements

Sustained winds blowing across a body of water drive surface currents toward the downwind end of a basin. Resulting turbulence of the surface layer is not transmitted into the hypolimnion during thermal stratification due to the stable metalimnetic barrier. However, when the temperature difference between surface and bottom waters is reduced by a change in seasons, progressive erosion of the density stratification ultimately results in overturn and complete circulation of the impounded water. Then the combined action of surface waves, Langmuir circulation, and currents confined to the epilimnion during the summer produce massive internal water movements.

Currents created by river influents can cause significant internal disturbance of stratified lakes and reservoirs where the inflow is large relative to the volume of the impoundment. Depending on the density difference between river and lake water, three basic types of inflow movements can result, as illustrated in Figure 8-8. Overflow occurs when the density of the entering water is less than the impounded water, whereas underflow is caused when these conditions are reversed. Interflow results

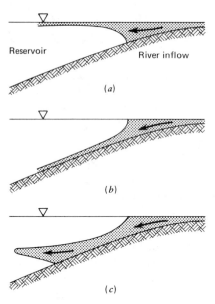

Figure 8-8 The three types of river flows entering reservoirs are (a) overflow where influent water density is less than reservoir water density, (b) underflow when the inflow is heavier than the impounded water, and (c) interflow with the water entering between the epilimnion and hypolimnion.

when the influent density is greater than the epilimnion, but less than the hypolimnion. The degree of subsequent intermixing is a function of the density difference, quantity of inflow, flushing rate, other water movements within the impoundment, shape of the basin, method of water withdrawal, and others.

Discharge structures at dams withdraw reservoir water from the surface, near the bottom, or from an intermediate depth. The type of outlet employed relates to the purpose of the reservoir and its operation. For example, flood flows are often released over a surface spillway while discharge for power generation is usually drawn from an intermediate depth. A great variety of flow patterns can be produced internally in an impoundment with different combinations of density currents entering and depths of withdrawal. If overflow is combined with a high discharge, or underflow with low discharge, flow through the reservoir is direct with a relatively short retention time. In contrast, combining opposing inflow and outflow minimizes short circuiting; the entering river water slows down and is stored while the effluent is taken from above or below this zone. Even though inflow-outflow patterns are most often associated with the quantitative aspects of reservoir hydrology, they play a very important role in water quality management.

8-7 Flood Routing Through Reservoirs

Flood plains, formed above the banks of a river, are favored sites for towns and farms

because of the flat topography and rich soils. While attracting settlements, these areas
are also periodically inundated when flows exceed the capacity of the river channel.
Control measures to reduce this conflict between the natural river environment and
occupancy can be implemented by modifying the hydrology of the basin. In the upstream areas of a watershed, runoff can be retarded by agricultural conservation
practices of contour cultivation and constructing small collection ponds. Downstream
measures consist of channel improvements to increase the discharge capacity of the
watercourse; levees to raise the height of the river bank and prevent overflowing; and
reservoirs to provide detention storage.

Storage of streamflow decreases the peak of a flood without reducing the quantity
of water, since evaporation and seepage are generally insignificant—high inflows
increase the volume of impounded water while outflow is released at a lower rate. Consider a simple detention reservoir with an ungated outlet (Figure 8-1a, b, or c). Inflow
and outflow hydrographs for a single flood event would appear similar to those shown
in Figure 8-9a with the sharp peak of a major storm reduced to a steady flow spread
over several days. This is an example of a rigid operating schedule built into the structure by virtue of ungated outlets, eliminating the need for operating personnel. In

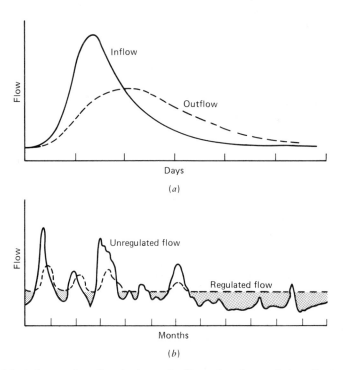

Figure 8-9 Inflow and outflow hydrographs illustrating the regulating affect on floods routed
through reservoirs. (a) An ungated reservoir collecting and releasing storm runoff. (b) A large multipurpose dam designed to regulate a river for both flood control and to release water during periods
of low flow.

case of an extreme flood, or succession of large storms, an emergency spillway allows high discharges to prevent failure of the dam.

Large multipurpose reservoirs (Figure 8-1f, g, and h) are operated by controlling gated outlets to meet the needs for hydropower, navigation, and conservation releases, as well as flood control. The reservoir release schedule for day-to-day control is based on current forecasts of streamflow and anticipated precipitation. The judgment of operating personnel relies on past experience. Figure 8-9b sketches hydrographs illustrating flood storage and release of impounded water during periods of low river stage. Long-range-planning schedules apply principally to reservoir systems where storage is large compared to annual river discharge. Specified procedures are always applied for seasonal flood control and conservation releases to ensure the most effective operation of the system. Stored water is held for dry years to supplement downstream deficiencies. Several major rivers in the United States, for example, the Tennessee River (Figure 9-24), contain a series of reservoirs along the main stem. Operations of the various segments require careful coordination and none can be considered independent of the others.

Determining the hydrograph for reservoir discharge depends on the type of outflow structure and operation of control gates in the dam. If the water surface in the reservoir is level (as is the case except in very shallow reservoirs) and the position of the outlet gates is fixed, the outflow and storage volume are functions of the lake level only. Thus, flood routing calculations follow the simple procedure outlined below. However, the routing process becomes more complex if outflow is varied by operating gates during the period of flood flow.

The continuity equation for routing of flow is as follows. The difference between inflow and outflow during a given period of time equals the change in storage during the same interval. In mathematical terms,

$$\left(\frac{I_1 + I_2}{2} - \frac{O_1 + O_2}{2}\right)(t_2 - t_1) = S_2 - S_1 \qquad (8\text{-}2)$$

where I = rate of inflow, cubic metres per second
O = rate of outflow, cubic metres per second
t = time, seconds
S = volume of water in storage, cubic metres

The subscripts 1 and 2 refer to the beginning and end of the time interval.

For flood routing calculations, Equation 8-2 can be restated by substituting Δt for the time interval $t_2 - t_1$ and rearranging so that the terms relating to the time t_2 at the end of the time interval are on the right side.

$$(I_1 + I_2) + \left(\frac{2S_1}{\Delta t} - O_1\right) = \left(\frac{2S_2}{\Delta t} + O_2\right) \qquad (8\text{-}3)$$

where Δt = time interval $t_2 - t_1$, seconds

Flood routing computations are performed by repetitive solutions of Equation 8-2 for successive time periods Δt. The quantities initially known are (1) an inflow hydrograph giving values of I at specific times t; (2) a reservoir storage curve that graphs pool elevation versus volume of water in storage; (3) an outflow rating curve, which is a plot of pool elevation versus rate of outflow; (4) a selected time interval Δt to be used throughout the routing as the interval for successive solutions of Equation 8-3; (5) a starting pool elevation; (6) an initial time for the computations to begin. In each solution of Equation 8-3, all terms on the left side are known: I_1 and I_2 from the inflow hydrograph, S_1 and O_1 from the results of calculations of the previous time interval, and Δt as a preselected constant. Both terms on the right side of the formula are functions of pool elevation at the end of the time interval. Although Equation 8-3 can be solved by trial (by assuming various pool elevations to find the S_2 and O_2 values that satisfy Equation 8-3), direct solution is generally preferred. To facilitate computations, Equation 8-3 is rewritten as follows:

$$(I_1 + I_2) + \left(\frac{2S_1}{\Delta t} + O_1\right) - (2O_1) = \left(\frac{2S_2}{\Delta t} + O_2\right) \tag{8-4}$$

Values of S and O for the same pool elevation are available, respectively, from a reservoir storage curve and an outflow rating curve. From these data, a routing curve is prepared by plotting pool elevation versus the corresponding value of $(2S/\Delta t + O)$. Therefore, with the rate of inflow known and all the other terms on the left side of Equation 8-4 based on the given pool elevation, the magnitude for $(2S_2/\Delta t + O_2)$ is calculated. Entering the routing curve with this value yields the pool elevation at the end of the time interval. From this new elevation, outflow O_2 is available from the outflow rating curve. Time is now advanced by Δt, and the solution initiated for the next time period. I_2, O_2, and $(2S_2/\Delta t + O_2)$, which were just determined, become I_1, O_1, and $(2S_1/\Delta t + O_1)$, and I_2 is obtained from the inflow hydrograph. Thus, all the terms are known to calculate the next $(2S_2/\Delta t + O_2)$. After successive solutions have routed the flood through the reservoir, the discharge hydrograph can be plotted as O_2 versus t. Example 8-1 illustrates flood routing through a reservoir.

In the design of a reservoir project, an important application of flood routing is to determine the height of the dam and discharge capacity of the emergency spillway. Routing calculations are performed for different spillway capacities to yield peak pool elevations. From these analyses, the most economical combination of dam elevation and spillway design can be selected. The flood used to test the safety of a design is called the spillway design flood. Where dam failure by overtopping would result in loss of human life or costly property damage, the probable maximum flood is used in reservoir routing. This probable maximum flood is estimated to result from the probable maximum precipitation in the upstream drainage area. The probable maximum precipitation is obtained by applying the principles of atmospheric physics to determine the maximum depth of rain and snow possible over a given geographic region. For dams in remote locations where failure does not threaten human life, a flood less than the probable maximum may be selected as the spillway design flood.

The terrain of a dam site may not allow sufficient reservoir volume for all beneficial conservation purposes and complete flood control. Therefore, supplementary flood protection, such as channel improvements and levees, may be constructed downstream

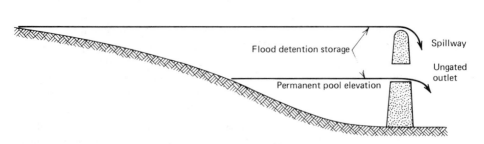

Figure 8-10 A sketch of the flood detention reservoir for Example 8-1.

Table 8-2 Values of Water Elevation, Storage, Outflow, and $2S/\Delta t + O$ Based on $\Delta t = 4$ hours, Example 8-1

(1) Elevation	(2) Storage	(3) Outflow	(4) $\dfrac{2S}{\Delta t} + O$
(m)	(m^3)	(m^3/s)	(m^3/s)
262.0	60 000	0	8.3
262.5	69 000	0.17	9.8
263.0	80 000	0.38	11.5
263.5	92 000	0.64	13.4
264.0	104 000	0.93	15.4
264.5	117 000	1.28	17.5
265.0	130 000	1.66	19.7
265.5	143 000	2.07	21.9
266.0	157 000	2.55	24.4
266.5	172 000	2.93	26.8
267.0	188 000	3.30	29.4
267.5	206 000	3.63	32.2
268.0	222 000	3.94	34.8
268.5	239 000	4.23	37.4
269.0	259 000	4.51	40.5
269.5	279 000	4.76	43.5
270.0	300 000	4.98	46.6
270.5	321 000	5.22	49.8
271.0	342 000	5.40	52.9
271.5	364 000	5.60	56.2
272.0	386 000	5.78	59.4
272.5	409 000	5.98	62.8
273.0	432 000	6.14	66.1

for a balanced program that economically reduces the risk of flood damage. Flood-plain zoning can be an effective legislative method supplementing a river basin plan by controlling occupancy of high risk flood-plain areas.

Example 8-1

This sample solution illustrates a common method for flood routing through a reservoir. The schematic in Figure 8-10 shows the flood control impoundment that has a conservation pool for recreation and wildlife. Peak flows pass through the ungated outlet with a spillway provided for extreme floods only.

The first step is to tabulate the volume of water in storage S and rate of outflow O for increasing water levels starting at the crest of the ungated outlet. Normally, these

Table 8-3 Computations for Flood Routing Through a Reservoir, Example 8-1

(1) Date	(2) Time	(3) I	(4) $I_1 + I_2$	(5) $\frac{2S_1}{\Delta t} + O_1$	(6) $-2O_1$	(7) $\frac{2S_2}{\Delta t} + O_2$	(8) Elevation	(9) O_2
	(h)	(m³/s)	(m³/s)	(m³/s)	(m³/s)	(m³/s)	(m)	(m³/s)
Apr 26	1200	0.1				10.1	262.6	0.2
	1400	0.5	0.6	10.1	− 0.4	10.3	262.6	0.2
	1600	1.6	2.1	10.3	− 0.4	12.0	263.1	0.4
	1800	4.0	5.6	12.0	− 0.8	16.8	264.3	1.2
	2000	8.0	12.0	16.8	− 2.4	26.4	266.4	2.9
	2200	9.6	17.6	26.4	− 5.8	38.2	268.6	4.3
	2400	9.2	18.8	38.2	− 8.6	48.4	270.3	5.1
Apr 27	200	8.1	17.3	48.4	−10.2	55.5	271.3	5.5
	400	7.0	15.1	55.5	−11.0	59.6	272.0	5.8
	600	6.0	13.0	59.6	−11.6	61.0	272.2	5.9
	800	5.1	11.1	61.0	−11.8	60.3	272.1	5.8
	1000	4.2	9.3	60.3	−11.6	57.7	271.7	5.7
	1200	3.4	7.6	57.7	−11.4	53.9	271.1	5.5
	1400	2.6	6.0	53.9	−11.0	48.9	270.4	5.2
	1600	2.0	4.6	48.9	−10.4	43.1	269.4	4.7
	1800	1.6	3.6	43.1	− 9.4	37.3	268.5	4.2
	2000	1.2	2.8	37.3	− 8.4	31.7	267.4	3.6
	2200	0.9	2.1	31.7	− 7.2	26.6	266.5	2.9
	2400	0.7	1.6	26.6	− 5.4	22.8	265.7	2.2
Apr 28	200	0.5	1.2	22.8	− 4.4	19.6	265.0	1.7
	400	0.4	0.9	19.6	− 3.4	17.1	264.4	1.2

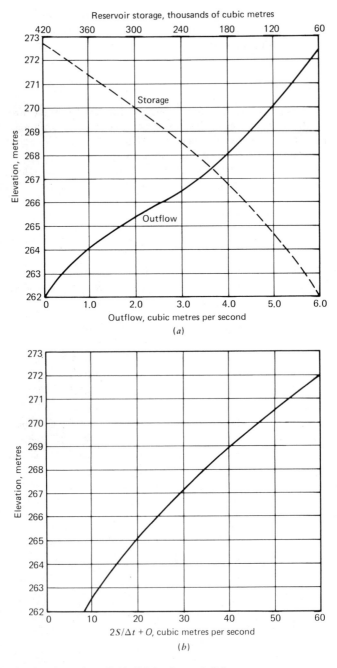

Figure 8-11 Graphs of data from Table 8-2 for Example 8-1.

data are part of the dam design and readily available. After listing as shown in Table 8-2, corresponding values of $2S/\Delta t + O$ are computed to facilitate the use of Equation 8-4. Figure 8-11a shows curves of volume of water in storage at various pool elevations and rate of outflow versus water level elevation. The lower diagram in Figure 8-11b is $2S/\Delta t + O$ (Table 8-2, column 4) plotted against elevation.

Routing computations are repetitive solutions of Equation 8-4 with the data organized as shown in Table 8-3. (1) List times and corresponding flows of the input hydrograph in columns 1, 2, and 3. (2) Add adjacent inflows and tabulate under the heading $I_1 + I_2$ in column 4. (For example, the value at 2000 h is $4.0 + 8.0 = 12.0$ m³/s.) (3) Next write the starting values for outflow and elevation. From the elevation, determine the initial magnitudes of $2S_2/\Delta t + O_2$ and O_2 from Figure 8-11. (4) The value of $2S_2/\Delta t + O_2$ at 1200 h is also $2S_1/\Delta t + O_1$ for 1400 h, and $2O_1$ is twice the value of the O_2. (5) The $2S_2/\Delta t + O_2$ for 1400 h is then calculated by Equation 8-4, which is column 4 plus column 5 minus column 6 ($0.6 + 10.1 - 0.4 = 10.3$ m³/s). (6) From this value of $2S_2/\Delta t + O_2$, the water level elevation is determined using Figure 8-11 or interpolated from the data listed in Table 8-2. The O_2 at this elevation is taken from Figure 8-11a. (7) The $2S_2/\Delta t + O_2$ and O_2 at 1400 h are now moved to $2S_1/\Delta t + O_1$ and $2O_1$ at 1600 h and the calculation for $2S_2/\Delta t + O_2$ repeated.

After completing the computations in Table 8-3, inflow and outflow hydrographs can be plotted from the data in columns 3 and 9 as shown in Figure 8-12. Since the area under a hydrograph represents the quantity of flow, the area displaced from under the peak of the inflow must equal the amount added under the outflow curve.

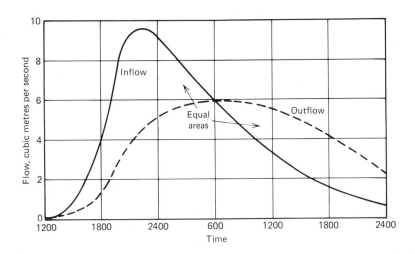

Figure 8-12 Inflow and outflow hydrographs from the data in Table 8-3, Example 8-1. The inflow is column 3 plotted against time in column 2, and the outflow is column 9 versus time.

8-8 Reservoir Yield

The primary method of water conservation is to impound excess flows during wet weather and release stored water as needed during dry periods. Reservoir yield depends on the amount of storage available, and on the amount and variation of natural streamflow, with allowances for losses through evaporation and seepage. Demand for the impounded water varies with downstream requirements for irrigation, water supplies, power generation, water quality, and navigation that vary with time of the year. In a simple case, the amount of storage needed to supply constant demand can be determined from a hydrograph of streamflow or a mass curve. For the hydrograph on the top of Figure 8-13, the storage needed to maintain a constant outflow of 7.5 m^3/s is represented by the area between the horizontal line at that flow and the top of the hydrograph bars.

A mass curve, as shown in the bottom Figure 8-13, is the cumulative summation of streamflow plotted against time. The ordinate at any time represents the total volume of flow that entered the reservoir since the starting time of the curve. The ordinate of the mass curve is also the area under the above hydrograph from the starting time to any given time. The slope of a line joining any two points of a mass curve equals the uniform rate of flow that would yield the same total incremental volume in the same time period. For example, the slope of the line connecting the origin in Figure 8-13 to the last point on a mass curve is the average flow for the five-year period equaling 9.6 m^3/s. Sloping lines for the assumed constant demand of 7.5 m^3/s are also drawn on Figure 8-13. This slope is fitted tangent to the mass curve at its various peaks until a point of tangency is found where the maximum deficit exists between the tangent line and the mass curve. The maximum difference in ordinates between the tangent line and the mass curve is the supplementary reservoir storage needed to meet the demand represented by the slope of the tangent line. In Figure 8-13, the maximum storage required to meet a demand of 7.5 m^3/s is during 1976 when the vertical distance between the demand line and mass curve is greatest. This corresponds to a vertically scaled amount of 75×10^6 m^3, which is the same as the quantity represented by the shaded area under the hydrograph from September 1975 through May 1976. The storage need based on these data only apply to the low-flow period during the five years analyzed. This record is too short for a realistic design and was presented for illustrative purposes only.

Determining the safe yield of a large reservoir that protects life and valuable property justifies a more accurate analysis. Stochastic hydrology can be used to generate a synthetic record of flows having a variety of sequences, in addition to the same statistical characteristics as the observed historical record. This synthetic record extends the observed data to a much longer period resulting in a more reliable basis for hydrologic design.

Computing reservoir yield should consider losses by evaporation and seepage, and possible reduction of storage volume by accumulation of sediment. Erosion, transportation, and deposition of sediment are natural processes influenced by the characteristics of the watershed and climate. Since silt carried by flowing water drops

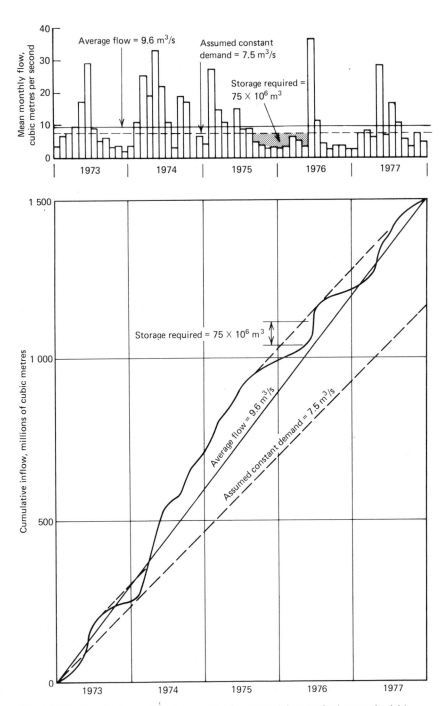

Figure 8-13 Flow hydrograph and mass curve for determining required reservoir yield.

out of suspension when the velocity is reduced, all reservoirs gradually fill starting at the inlet and progressing toward the dam. Loss of storage capacity is adverse to both flood control and water conservation. The present approach in dam design is to provide additional space for accumulation of sediment and to reduce the amount entering by instituting upstream erosion control.

8-9 Evaporation

The change of liquid water to the vapor state occurs when some molecules in the water mass attain enough kinetic energy to eject from the surface. The motion of escaping molecules produces a partial pressure of aqueous vapor called vapor pressure. As a stabilizing effect, some of the molecules colliding with those in the air drop back into the water mass. At saturation, the continuous processes of evaporation and condensation are in equilibrium. The net loss depends on the difference between vapor pressures of the liquid and overlying air. As stated by Dalton's law, the rate of evaporation is proportional to the deficit in vapor pressure.

$$E = C(e_s - e_a) \tag{8-5}$$

where E = evaporation, millimetres per unit of time
C = coefficient depending on various factors, such as wind speed
e_s = saturation vapor pressure at the temperature of the surface water
e_a = actual vapor pressure in the air

Evaporation is controlled by several factors that change the vapor pressure of a body of water or the air above: temperatures of water and air, wind, atmospheric pressure, salt content of the water, and nature of the evaporating surface. Temperature is the primary factor correlating directly with rate of evaporation. By providing energy, solar radiation increases the temperature and vapor pressure of the water; conversion from liquid to the vapor state requires approximately 2 500 joules for each gram of water. Wind has the second most important effect by displacing overlying moist air with drier air. It may also heat or cool the impounded water, thus raising or lowering the evaporation rate.

The four generally accepted methods of computing lake evaporation are water budget, energy budget, mass transfer, and lake-to-pan relations. For a water-budget determination, inflow, outflow, precipitation, and seepage data are balanced to yield the unmeasured evaporation loss. Application of these calculations rarely produce reliable results, since small errors in volume of inflow and outflow can result in large deviations of computed evaporation. The energy-budget technique, which involves measuring solar radiation and other heat transfers, requires elaborate instrumentation only feasible for special investigations. Mass-transfer procedures are based on observations of surface water temperatures, dew point, and wind movements that are available for only a few reservoirs. Also, these three methods are applicable for existing lakes and usually applied in research rather than reservoir design. Estimating evaporation by pan measurements is relatively inexpensive and gives reasonable results.

The standard Weather Bureau Class A Land Pan is the most frequently used evaporation pan in the United States. The circular vessel is constructed of unpainted galvanized iron, 1.22 m in diameter and 254 mm deep, and rests on a wooden frame raised 150 mm above the ground to allow air circulation underneath. After filling to a depth of about 200 mm, changes in the water surface are measured daily with a hook gage in a stilling well, and water is added before the level drops to 180 mm. Evaporation is computed as the difference between observed levels, adjusted for any precipitation recorded by a nearby rain gage. A Class A station also has an anemometer for measuring wind speed and a shelter to house the recording instruments.

Pan evaporation measurements are always greater than actual losses from lakes and reservoirs, primarily because of the much smaller water surface exposure. Observed pan coefficients range from 0.60 to 0.80 with 0.70 the commonly accepted value; for example, an annual Class A pan loss measured as 2 000 mm signifies a lake evaporation of 1 400 mm applying a coefficient of 0.70. The Weather Bureau has complied evaporation data and published maps of the conterminous United States showing average annual Class A pan evaporation, pan coefficients, average annual lake evaporation, and the percentage of annual loss occurring from May through October. Figure 8-14 shows the average annual lake evaporation. As illustrated in Figure 8-15, the period of May through October accounts for most of the loss, ranging from 62 to 82 percent of the average annual evaporation.

8-10 Water Budget

The water balance of an impoundment is represented by a general formula equating total inputs to total outputs plus change in storage.

$$\begin{array}{c}\text{Surface} \\ \text{inflow}\end{array} + \begin{array}{c}\text{seepage} \\ \text{inflow}\end{array} + \begin{array}{c}\text{precipitation} \\ \text{on lake}\end{array} = \begin{array}{c}\text{outflow}\end{array} + \begin{array}{c}\text{seepage} \\ \text{loss}\end{array} + \begin{array}{c}\text{evaporation}\end{array} + \begin{array}{c}\text{change in} \\ \text{storage}\end{array} \qquad (8\text{-}8)$$

Surface inflow includes streamflows plus surface drainage from the immediate watershed of the lake. Records of streamflows are available from gaging stations operated by governmental agencies, usually the U. S. Geological Survey. Adjacent land runoff can be estimated from precipitation data and watershed runoff formulas. Precipitation directly on the water surface can be estimated from precipitation records. The quantity of subsurface seepage is difficult to establish; estimates are usually based on flow-net computations using assumed soil permeabilities and data on adjacent water tables.

On the deficit side of the water budget, outflows through dam orifices or over spillways are determined from known hydraulics of the structures. Seepage losses are based on infiltration and groundwater flow. Evaporation loss is either taken from Weather Bureau measurements, or local evaporation pan data corrected for a large impoundment. Aquatic plants do not materially influence water loss, hence total evaporation normally incorporates losses from surfaces of water plants as well as exposed water. Furthermore, transpiration of aquatic plants alone cannot be readily measured.

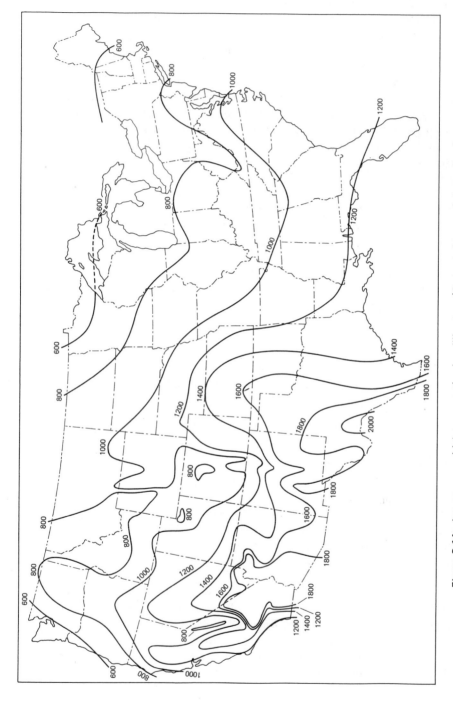

Figure 8-14 Average annual lake evaporation in millimetres. (Converted to metric by author from M. A. Kohler, T. J. Nordenson, and D. R. Baker, *Evaporation Maps for the United States*, U. S. Weather Bureau, 1959.)

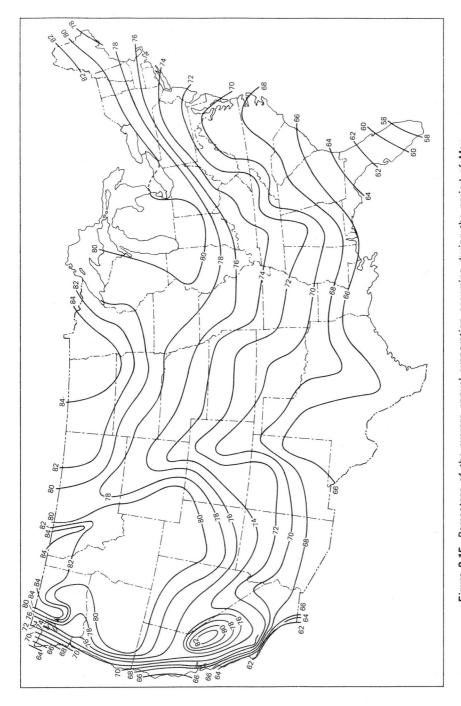

Figure 8-15 Percentage of the average annual evaporation occurring during the period of May through October. (From M. A. Kohler, T. J. Nordenson, and D. R. Baker, *Evaporation Maps for the United States*, U. S. Weather Bureau, 1959.)

373

Accurate water balance information for proposed reservoirs in dry climates is particularly important. The gain in regulation by adding more reservoir storage may be offset by the corresponding increase in evaporation. This condition appears to exist on the Colorado River that already has seven major reservoirs on the main stem. Hoover Dam constructed in 1935 was built primarily to regulate flow for downstream use. Glen Canyon Dam was later placed upstream for hydropower, to regulate flow for irrigation withdrawals, and to reduce the sediment load on Lake Mead behind Hoover Dam. Downstream reservoirs are the Davis, Parker, Palo Verde, Imperial, and Laguna dams.

Figure 8-16 summarizes the effect of various amounts of storage capacity on flow regulation for the Colorado River basin. The ordinate represents the degree of regula-

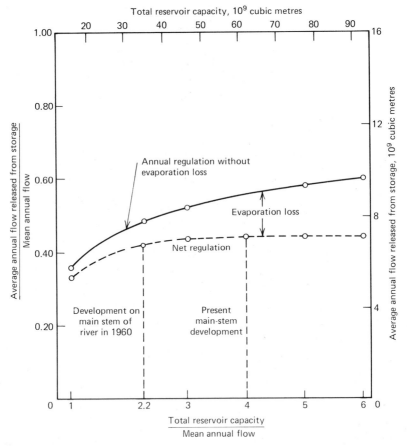

Figure 8-16 The effect of various amounts of storage capacity on flow regulation in the Colorado River basin. (For computation, the mean river flow at Lee's Ferry was taken as 16 × 10⁹ m³/a, and the evaporation loss assumed at 27 000 m³/a per million cubic metres of reservoir capacity.) (Adapted from L. B. Leopold, *Probability Analysis Applied to a Water-Supply Problem*, U. S. Geological Survey Circular 410, 1961.)

tion expressed as the ratio of the average annual flow released from storage to the mean annual flow. The abscissa is the degree of development expressed as total reservoir capacity divided by mean annual flow; the present development has a numerical value of about 4 based on main-stem reservoirs. The annual regulation without evaporation loss indicates greater benefit with increasing reservoir storage; however, including evaporation losses results in significantly diminished net regulation. Based on the calculations used to sketch Figure 8-16, reservoir capacity in excess of about three times the mean annual flow provides little additional water control when evaporation is subtracted from annual flow released from storage. In other words, evaporation losses offset the hydraulic benefit of the additional regulation. Plans to construct two more dams, Bridge Canyon Dam above Lake Mead and Marble Canyon Dam near the upstream boundary of the Grand Canyon National Park below Glen Canyon Dam, have been canceled, at least temporarily.

Evapotranspiration losses from irrigation, in combination with reservoir evaporation, result in rising salinity in river water. Total dissolved solids in the Lower Colorado are projected to exceed 1 000 mg/l in the 1980s and continue to increase unless costly salinity control projects are undertaken.

References

1. Chow, V. T., editor-in-chief, *Handbook of Applied Hydrology, A Compendium of Water-Resources Technology*, McGraw-Hill Book Co., New York, 1964.

2. Saville, T., Jr., McClendon, E. W., and Cochran, A. L., "Freeboard Allowances for Waves in Inland Reservoirs," *Transactions, American Society of Civil Engineers*, Vol. 128, 1963, Part IV, pp. 195-226.

3. Reid, G. K., and Wood, R. D., *Ecology of Inland Waters and Estuaries,* 2nd Edition, D. Van Nostrand Co., New York, 1976.

4. Wetzel, R. G., *Limnology*, W. B. Saunders Co., Philadelphia, PA, 1975.

5. Kohler, M. A., Nordenson, T. J., and Baker, D. R., *Evaporation Maps for the United States*, Technical Paper No. 37, U.S. Weather Bureau, Washington, D.C., 1959.

Problems

8-1   What types of glacial activities created lake basins?

8-2   How is an oxbow lake formed?

8-3   Name three major criteria applied in selection of a reservoir site.

8-4   List the common purposes served by a reservoir. Which of these are most likely to be conflicting uses?

8-5   Calculate the shoreline development for Lake Michigan, which has a shoreline length of 2 210 km and surface area of 57 850 km^2. (*Answer* 2.6)

8-6   Morphometric data for Lake Ontario are given in Table 8-1. Compute the water renewal time for this lake based on an annual mean discharge of 6 900 m^3/s. (*Answer* 7.9 a)

8-7 What is the major source of heat input to a lake? How does absorption of this heat influence density stratification during summer months?

8-8 What is a dimictic impoundment? Describe the diagrams given in Figure 8-5.

8-9 Define warm monomixis.

8-10 Why do surface waves break as they approach the shore?

8-11 Describe the water movements in Langmuir circulation relative to the wind.

8-12 The three types of river flows entering reservoirs are depicted in Figure 8-8. How is each of these likely to affect residence time of the inflow and mixing of impounded water if the outlet is near the bottom of the dam?

8-13 Solve Example 8-1 using the following inflow data:

Date	Time (h)	Inflow (m^3/s)	Date	Time (h)	Inflow (m^3/s)
July 14	1000	0.5	July 15	200	4.4
	1200	0.9		400	3.3
	1400	1.8		600	2.4
	1600	4.4		800	1.8
	1800	7.0		1000	1.3
	2000	8.2		1200	0.9
	2200	7.8		1400	0.6
	2400	6.3		1600	0.4

The initial outflow and elevation at 1000 h are 0.4 m^3/s and 263.0 m. Figure 8-11a is too small for accurate computations; therefore, an outflow-elevation curve should be drawn from the data listed in Table 8-2 on graph paper with minimum scales of 1.0 cm per metre of elevation and 1.0 cm per 0.5 m^3/s. The easiest method to determine elevation from a given value of $2S/\Delta t + O$ is by interpolation using the listed data in Table 8-2. The alternative is to plot $2S/\Delta t + O$ versus elevation on graph paper as shown in Figure 8-11b.

Plot the inflow and outflow hydrographs.

8-14 The water level elevation and storage volume data for a flood control reservoir are as follows:

Elevation (m)	Storage ($10^6 m^3$)	Elevation (m)	Storage ($10^6 m^3$)
260.0	5.0	274.0	43.8
262.0	7.3	276.0	53.1
264.0	11.0	278.0	63.6
266.0	16.0	280.0	78.3
268.0	21.5	282.0	95.0
270.0	28.0	284.0	111.9
272.0	35.3	284.5	123.6

Elevation 123.6 m is the crest of the emergency spillway.

The elevation and discharge data for the outlet tunnel through the dam with the gates wide open are:

Elevation (m)	Discharge (m³/s)	Elevation (m)	Discharge (m³/s)
250.5	0	268.0	204
252.0	9	270.0	216
254.0	41	272.0	227
256.0	82	274.0	238
258.0	120	276.0	250
260.0	142	278.0	259
262.0	160	280.0	269
264.0	177	282.0	278
266.0	190	284.5	286

Elevation 250.5 is the crest of the gated outlet tunnel.

Tabulate the storage and discharge data for elevations 260.0 m through 284.5 m and calculate $2S/\Delta t + O$ for a time interval of six hours. (Refer to Table 8-2.) Elevations for values of $2S/\Delta t + O$ can be determined by interpolation of the data in this table. If graphical solution is desired, an elevation versus $2S/\Delta t + O$ diagram can be drawn. (Refer to Figure 8-11b.)

Plot an elevation versus outflow curve using the above discharge data given for the gated tunnel outlet. (Refer to Figure 8-11a.)

Data for the inflow hydrograph of a flood are as follows:

Time (h)	Inflow (m³/s)	Time (h)	Inflow (m³/s)	Time (h)	Inflow (m³/s)
0	14	64	878	132	85
12	57	72	850	144	57
24	142	84	708	156	28
36	340	96	453	168	28
48	595	108	283	180	28
60	850	120	170	192	28

Plot the inflow hydrograph as cubic metres per second versus hours starting with time zero.

Assume the reservoir is at elevation 260.0 m when the flood begins, and the gates to the outlet tunnel are opened such that the pool elevation remains at 260.0 m until the inflow and outflow reach 142 m³/s. At this time, the gates are wide open and water begins to accumulate in the reservoir since inflow exceeds the capacity of the discharge tunnel. Plot the outflow hydrograph on the same paper as the inflow hydrograph. At what time and elevation does the water level in the pool peak? (*Answers* Outflow increases to 142 m³/s at 24 h and reaches a maximum of 280 m³/s at 108 h. The pool level starts to rise at 24 h and peaks at 283 m in 108 h.)

8-15 The following are mean monthly discharges for a stream in cubic metres per second.

Year	Jan	Feb	Mar	Apr	May	Jun	Jul	Aug	Sep	Oct	Nov	Dec
1973	15	180	64	27	82	13	15	7	3	9	109	37
1974	63	92	62	84	15	117	31	50	133	80	97	50
1975	149	162	235	101	95	56	10	9	5	34	81	126
1976	35	86	94	153	66	125	91	33	9	5	38	44
1977	57	64	160	188	130	21	33	6	4	65	97	109

Plot these data as a hydrograph and a mass curve as illustrated in Figure 8-13. What is the average monthly flow for this five-year period? What is the maximum regulated flow rate that could be maintained during this five-year period if a reservoir storage volume of 250×10^6 m³ was available? Assume the reservoir is filled to overflow elevation in February 1973.

8-16 What are the two most significant factors influencing rate of evaporation?

8-17 What weather monitoring instruments are included in a Class A evaporation station?

8-18 List the ranges of average annual lake evaporation in the following states: Pennsylvania, Nebraska, and Arizona.

8-19 Using Figure 8-15, what is the mean percentage of the average annual evaporation occurring during the period of May through October for Pennsylvania, Nebraska, and Arizona.

8-20 How is each item in the water balance (Equation 8-8) usually determined?

8-21 What is the water quantity consideration and water quality problem that is limiting the development of additional dam construction on the Colorado River?

Chapter 9

Water Quality in Impounded Waters

Natural lakes are important for municipal and industrial water supplies, recreational activities, sport and commercial fishing, and transportation. Where natural basins were not created by geological processes, man-made lakes have been constructed for these purposes plus additional benefits. Many dams form long narrow reservoirs used for flood control, hydroelectric power, navigation, and low-flow augmentation. Thousands of impoundments on small drainage channels provide flow control, irrigation water, and waterbased recreation.

Historically, the development of water resources has emphasized the control of water quantity, primarily by building dams. Today, most of the projects that are feasible have been completed. As a result, the major considerations in water resources management are now maintenance of the structures, optimizing operations, and control of water quality. The beneficial use of impounded water and dilution of wastes (from agricultural land drainage and urban wastewaters) are often in serious conflict. Clean water is in great demand while quality control in impoundments is very difficult, and in some cases appears to be impossible to achieve.

The introductory sections of this chapter discuss water quality relative to public use, chemistry, and ecology of impounded waters. Following this background information, the phenomenon of eutrophication is presented in sections devoted to the analysis of lakes, causes of overfertilization, and allowable nutrient loadings. The final section consists of case histories of specific lakes and ecological studies of different types of impoundments.

9-1 Influence of Water Quality on Public Use

In addition to the world-famous Great Lakes (Table 8-1), the United States has 25 natural lakes with water surfaces greater than 250 km², about 150 with areas exceeding 25 km², and thousands of smaller ones. They are primarily located in glaciated areas of the northern states (Minnesota, Michigan, Wisconsin, Maine, New York, Montana, and Idaho) and coastal regions (Louisiana and Florida). Natural lakes, because of their constant water levels and long retention times (2 to 10 years), are ideally suited to the common public uses of water supply and recreation. In contrast, they cannot readily assimilate plant nutrients, notably nitrogen and phosphorus, found in wastewaters and farmland drainage. Therefore, eutrophication is the greatest threat

379

to lakes since it results in characteristics particularly detrimental to quality for municipal supply and water sports.

The United States has approximately 110 man-made lakes with water surface areas greater than 100 km^2, and thousands of smaller lakes and ponds. In the management of water resources, these impoundments usually provide more than one of the following beneficial uses: hydroelectric power, flood control, navigation, irrigation, source for industrial processing and cooling waters, municipal supply, and production of fish. Dams are normally constructed for one or two primary reasons with the hope of gaining additional secondary benefits; however, new problems can also be created by impounding flowing water. In contrast to natural lakes, reservoirs have controlled discharges that result in fluctuating water levels. Thus, both the downstream needs and impoundment uses are difficult to satisfy; for example, recreation is most adequately served by holding a constant pool elevation while releases for irrigation can exceed inflows during the prime holiday season. Commonly recognized hazards in damming a river are blocking the migration of fish, deposition of sediment at the river inlet, erosion of the downstream channel, and health problems that are most prevalent in tropical climates. Creation of a storage reservoir is not a remedy for development of water resources in every river basin, nevertheless, with proper planning and operation the benefits gained can often offset the perpetual care required to maintain a man-made lake.

Water supplies from rivers normally require extensive treatment because of the daily and seasonal fluctuations in quality, caused by climatic conditions, and pollution from agricultural and industrial activities in the watershed. Impounding an unstable surface flow enhances the quality characteristics for water supply by settling of suspended silt, the disinfecting action of sunlight, and natural biological activity. The quality of stored water relates to physical, chemical, and biological features of the basin. If eutrophic, the most disagreeable tastes and odors can occur during thermal stratification resulting from algal blooms in the epilimnion and anaerobiosis of the hypolimnion. The poorest quality present in other lakes is often during spring and fall circulations. Just the same, both natural and man-made impoundments are generally better water sources than rivers, but not as good as groundwater.

Water-related infections identified with creation of man-made lakes are waterborne, insect-borne, and snail-borne diseases.[1] The major intestinal illnesses of cholera, typhoid, and dysentery transmitted by fecal discharges are best controlled by sanitary collection and disposal of domestic wastes. Transmission can also occur during direct contact of infected individuals and by contaminated food products.

Schistosomiasis (bilharziasis) is a snail-borne, parasitic disease caused by a worm that infests human intestinal organs. Eggs excreted in fecal and urinary discharges hatch into miracidia that enter snails and leave as cercariae capable of infecting other humans by boring through the skin to enter blood vessels. The extension of freshwater snail populations by construction of reservoirs and associated irrigation systems in the tropics and subtropics cause the spread of this debilitating malady. Unfortunately, no generally accepted solution exists for either preventing the transmission or immunization against this infection. Health education combined with effective sanitation measures, including disposal of human wastes, safe water supplies, and adequate bathing facilities, are preventative measures that should be built into each water resources project. (Schistosomiasis does not occur in the continental United States since the intermediate snail host must be one of several specific species not found in this country.) Current control measures rely extensively on addition of toxic chemicals (molluscicides) to eradicate the intermediate snail vectors thus breaking the cycle of transmission.

Malaria is the most common mosquito-borne infection; others are yellow fever, dengue, encephalitis, and filariasis. The most effective controls are shoreline sanitation and insecticide applications to reduce insect populations. Since many different species throughout the world act as disease vectors, each with different ecology, the most effective methods for mosquito eradication depend on local considerations. Onchocerciasis is transmitted by a small blackfly vector that spends its preadult life in the flowing waters of streams. Also known as river blindness, this disease is found in west and central Africa, Mexico, and parts of Central and South America. Control measures are chiefly directed against the aquatic stages of the fly. Since spillways provide ideal breeding sites, submerged discharge pipes are preferred in the hydraulic design of dams. Trypanosomiasis (African sleeping sickness) is carried by the tsetse fly, which in west Africa makes its habitat in lakeside and riverside vegetation. Localized control is practiced by use of insecticides and selective vegetation clearance.

Commercial and recreational fisheries of lakes depend on a relatively unpolluted aquatic environment. Sport fishing in the United States has a recreational benefit far greater than the cash value of the fish caught. Along with other activities like picnicking, hiking, and camping, water-based recreation is healthy for the participants and provides an economic base for communities near lakes that rely on tourism. Both the satisfaction of the vacationer and the income of the resort proprietor are closely related to water quality in the lake.

In many nations, subsistence and commercial fisheries are important assets derived from natural and man-made lakes. Their multiple use requires establishing and enforcing pollution control, or risking loss in aquatic production. Siltation destroys habitat by covering food supplies and spawning grounds. Since industrial sites and intensive agriculture are likely to develop near surface-water sources, toxic chemicals and pesticides are potential contaminants. Domestic wastes, farmland drainage, and many industrial discharges contain organic matter, which can contribute directly to oxygen depletion, and nutrients that promote eutrophication. Upon mass die-off, excessive blooms of algae can stress the aquatic environment leading to fish kills. Abundant supplies of nitrogen and phosphorus can also stimulate the growth of higher aquatic plants.

The proliferation of aquatic weeds is a serious problem in many tropical reservoirs.[2] Heavy plant infestations in shallow areas and floating mats in open water contribute to loss of stored water by transpiration. Although weeds provide shelter and forage grounds for fish, dense plant beds interfere with fishing and may cause stunted growth because of overcrowding. Human health can be influenced since the quiet water and weed beds often make an ideal habitat for malaria mosquitoes and bilharzia snails.

Low salinity is an important quality parameter for irrigation water, especially in hot arid regions. Cycles of salination and land abandonment span thousands of years in irrigation history. The majority of water applied to cultivated fields is lost though evapotranspiration leaving behind salts that were dissolved in the irrigation water. Accumulated salts, particularly sodium and boron, in the root zone restrict the ability of plants to absorb water. Forcing salts deeper into the soil, practiced to flush the root zone, results in greater water use and contamination of the groundwater. If buried drains are employed, the underflow returned to surface channels increases the salt content in the water flowing downstream. Buildup of salinity is a major water-quality problem along the lower Colorado River. Great quantities of water evaporating from several storage reservoirs increases the salt concentration. This, along with the return of excess irrigation water, slowly increases the salt content of the remaining river water to a level too saline for land application.

Lakes may be categorized in many ways: according to their origin (Section 8-1), mixing regimes (Section 8-3), water chemistry, or biology. The most important classification related to both chemical and biological characteristics is based on fertility of the impounded water. Oligotrophic lakes are nutrient poor and biologically unproductive. Typical examples are deep, cold-water, and spring-fed lakes exhibiting transparent water, limited plant growth, and low fish production. A small increase in nutrient level results in a mesotrophic lake with some aquatic plant growth, greenish water, and moderate populations of sport fish. Eutrophic lakes are nutrient rich with lush growths of aquatic weeds, blooms of algae, and large population of tolerant fish. The latter often exhibit water quality undesirable for water supplies, human health, fisheries, and recreation.

9-2   Chemistry of Impounded Waters

Salinity (ionic composition) of inland waters is dominated by the four major cations, which in their normal order of abundance are calcium, magnesium, sodium, and potassium; the major anions are bicarbonate, sulfate, and chloride. The ionic characteristics of a particular lake are governed by the type of bedrock in the drainage area, atmospheric precipitation, and the balance between evaporation and precipitation. In limestone regions, hard-water lakes with plentiful calcium carbonate are common, while soft waters in coastal regions contain substantial sodium chloride resulting from the influence of sea water. Total salinity of impounded waters is generally within the range of 80 to 180 mg/l, except for some waters in arid and semiarid regions where salinities can be much higher.

Of the major ions, calcium and magnesium are required for plant growth. Additional essential elements include sulphur, silica, and the metallic micronutrients of iron, manganese, zinc, copper, boron, cobalt, molybdenum, and vanadium. Only rarely are the concentrations of these elements sufficiently low to inhibit biological growth in impounded waters. Carbon, nitrogen, and phosphorus are the common macronutrients for aquatic life with the latter being the most common growth-limiting factor in natural waters. Following the presentation on oxygen, these three key biological nutrients are discussed relative to their distribution in impounded waters.

Oxygen Content

The principal sources of dissolved oxygen (DO), fundamental to the biology of a lake, are from the atmosphere and algal photosynthesis. Solubility is affected by temperature, barometric pressure, and salinity of the water (as tabulated in the appendix). The diffusion of oxygen into a lake is a slow process because of the small surface area relative to the impounded volume. To establish equilibrium between the DO content and atmospheric oxygen, the water must circulate, as most lakes do during the spring and fall of the seasonal cycle. During wind mixing, oxygen equilibrium at the prevailing water temperature is established quickly in moderate-sized lakes. Normally, the spring overturn produces near saturation DO before thermal stratification is established. In deep, cold lakes the water does not warm much beyond 4°C allowing an initial hypolimnetic DO of 13 mg/l. Additional warming prior to stratification decreases this value, for example, the temperature profile of the lake illustrated in Figure 8-5 shows an initial temperature of 12°C and resulting DO of about 11 mg/l.

The vertical distribution of oxygen observed in an oligotrophic lake during summer stratification is essentially a function of temperature; the warmer epilimnion has a lower DO than the hypolimnion. Due to low biological productivity, the oxygen content is not greatly influenced by either photosynthesis or decay of organic matter. In an eutrophic lake, the DO levels established in the spring based on temperature are greatly modified by biological activities. During thermal stratification, oxygen in the hypolimnion is depleted by bacterial decomposition of organics as the summer progresses, while the epilimnion can become supersaturated by algal photosynthesis on sunny days. An eutrophic dimictic lake also exhibits a DO reduction during winter stratification, which can become severe during prolonged periods of ice and snow cover. Figure 9-1 summarizes the four seasonal phases in oligotrophic and eutrophic dimictic lakes.

Horizontal variations in oxygen content are caused by basin morphology, dense growths of aquatic plants along the shore, blooms of algae, wind mixing, and interaction with the bottom sediments. Currents from rivers entering natural lakes, and internal water movements in reservoirs caused by inflow-outflow patterns can create marked differences in both horizontal and vertical distributions of dissolved oxygen.

Inorganic Carbon

Much of the carbon in lake water occurs in inorganic forms (CO_2, HCO_3^-, and $CO_3^=$) with the remainder bound in organic matter, either detritus or living biota. Carbon dioxide, which is 0.032 percent of the atmosphere by volume, dissolves in water to a concentration of approximately 0.5 mg/l at 20°C. After reacting with H_2O, the carbonic acid ionizes to form bicarbonate and carbonate radicals. Below pH 4.5 dissolved carbon dioxide is in equilibrium with carbonic acid in solution, Equation 9-1. Increasing the pH creates bicarbonate ion, which is the dominant form at pH 8.3, Equation 9-2. Above 8.3, a portion of the bicarbonate converts to carbonate ion.

$$CO_2(air) \rightleftarrows CO_2 \text{ (dissolved)} + H_2O \rightleftarrows H_2CO_3 \qquad (9\text{-}1)$$

$$\underset{\text{pH 4.5}}{H_2CO_3} \rightleftarrows H^+ + \underset{\text{pH 8.3}}{HCO_3^-} \rightleftarrows H^+ + CO_3^= \qquad (9\text{-}2)$$

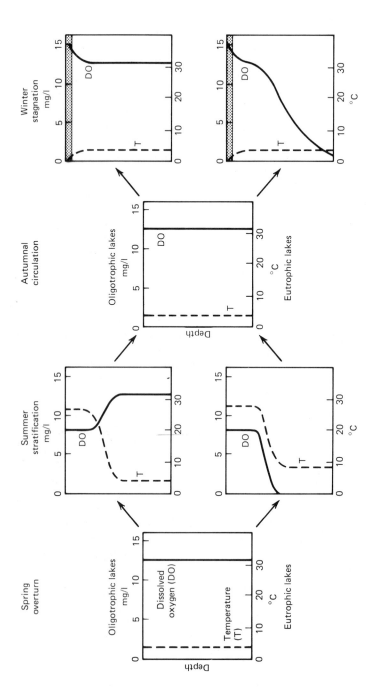

Figure 9-1 Idealized vertical distribution of dissolved oxygen (DO) and temperature (T) during the seasonal cycle of oligotrophic and eutrophic lakes. (Modified from R. G. Wetzel, *Limnology*, W. B. Saunders Co., Philadelphia, 1975.)

In addition to diffusion from the atmosphere, inorganic carbon is derived from bacterial decomposition of organic matter, respiration of aquatic animals, groundwater seepage, and surface drainage. Water enriched with CO_2, from the atmosphere or biological activity, dissolves limestone ($CaCO_3$) to form soluble calcium bicarbonate ($Ca(HCO_3)_2$). Thus, water entering impoundments after contact with natural calcium deposits contributes an abundant supply of carbon. In contrast, an increase in pH of a lake with hard water rich in bicarbonate can result in precipitation of relatively insoluble calcium carbonate.

$$Ca^{++} + HCO_3^- + OH^- \rightleftarrows CaCO_3\downarrow + H_2O \qquad (9\text{-}3)$$

The most important biological use of CO_2 is as a carbon source for photosynthesis. Algae and submerged macrophytes, which are about 50 percent carbon by dry weight, require an abundant supply. Many aquatic plants are capable of assimilating bicarbonate ions when free CO_2 is in very low supply. However, since natural lakes are rarely outside the pH range of 6 to 9, carbon dioxide is available from the carbonic acid equilibrium illustrated by Equations 9-1 and 9-2. The chemical function of the bicarbonate-carbonate balance is to stabilize the pH of water against abrupt changes. If organic acids are formed in water, the excess hydrogen ions react with carbonate ions to form bicarbonates rather than shifting the pH. Conversely, with a loss of carbon dioxide, the pH change is buffered by release of hydrogen ions from bicarbonates.

The Nitrogen Cycle

The common forms of nitrogen are gaseous (N_2), ammonia (NH_3 or NH_4^+), nitrite (NO_2^-), nitrate (NO_3^-), and nitrogen bound in organic compounds. The biochemical processes involving nitrogen are fixation of N_2, assimilation of inorganic N, deamination (release of NH_3), nitrification, and denitrification. For practical purposes, the nitrogen cycle (Figure 9-2) in lakes is microbial in nature: bacterial oxidation and reduction of compounds are coupled with photosynthetic utilization by algae and higher aquatic plants.

Natural lakes in regions remote from the influence of human activities are commonly deficient in nitrogen. The major source is from the atmosphere through precipitation and fixation, which rarely provides more than an ultraoligotrophic nutrient supply. The input from atmospheric fallout is usually less than 1 $g/m^2 \cdot a$, and N_2 fixation may be even less significant owing to the low populations of blue-green algae. Drainage entering the lake is often from unproductive forestland. Organic nitrogen is bound and cycled in photosynthetic and microbial organisms. Upon death, decomposition liberates ammonia, which if not resynthesized immediately, can be oxidized to nitrate. Unassimilated nitrate can, under reducing conditions, be returned to the atmosphere by denitrification.

The nitrogen budget in an eutrophic lake is much greater because the entering surface waters are rich in nutrients. Drainage from cultivated farmland and cattle feedlots contain nitrogen from inorganic fertilizers and manure. Being mostly in the nitrate ion form, it is unreactive (mobile) and not likely to be removed from solution, even if filtered through soil to enter a lake in groundwater. Another significant input

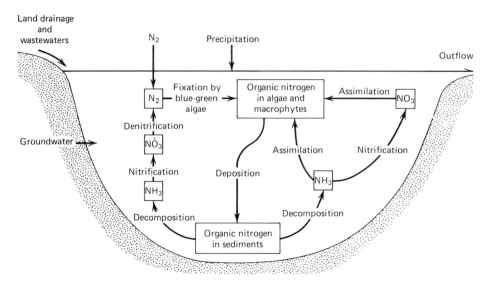

Figure 9-2 General transformations of nitrogen in lakes.

can be from municipal wastewaters, since processing for removal of organic matter reduces the nitrogen content less than 50 percent. Abundant during the growing season, blue-green algae may fix an appreciable amount of atmospheric nitrogen, although the inorganic ionic forms are preferred if available in sufficient supply. The majority of nitrogen in a fertile lake passes through the following cycle. Inorganic nitrogen is supplied by surface waters containing municipal wastewaters and rural drainage. By synthesis into planktonic organisms, both algae and bacteria, it is converted into organic nitrogen; this is particularly evident in the epilimnion during the summer. Death and decomposition releases ammonia that may be oxidized to nitrate. Both of these inorganic forms can be resynthesized into new cell growth, or the nitrate converted to N_2 by denitrification in the hypolimnion. Nitrogen losses from an eutrophic lake include sedimentation in the bottom muds, discharge in the outflow, denitrification, and fish catch.

The Phosphorus Cycle

Phosphorus in natural waters occurs as various types of phosphate in three classifications: orthophosphate ($PO_4^{\equiv}$), polyphosphates (polymers of phosphoric acid), and organically bound phosphates. These may exist in filterable (dissolved) or nonfilterable (particulate) forms, and subdivided into chemical types shown in Figure 9-3 by standardized tests. Because of the importance as a plant nutrient, analyses for phosphates are emphasized in water-quality studies of impounded waters. A key problem in the interpretation of test results is the somewhat confusing relationship between the various forms of phosphate and their biological synthesis, which is further complicated by the complexity of biotic cycling of phosphorus. Although no precise definition exists, the biologically available phosphate in natural waters is often

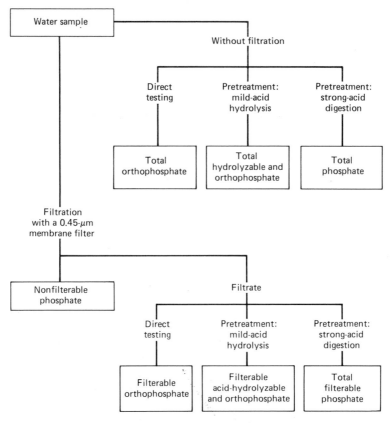

Figure 9-3 Flow chart for classification of phosphate fractions in natural waters as defined by *Standard Methods*[3] testing procedures.

assumed to be dissolved (filterable) ortho and acid-hydrolyzable phosphate. Sometimes the nonfilterable, acid-hydrolyzable phosphate adsorbed onto particulate matter is included, because it may be solubilized in lake water.

Phosphate is a growth-limiting plant nutrient in oligotrophic lakes. Since soils derived from weathered rock contain very limited amounts of phosphorus, contributions from surface waters in undeveloped and sparsely populated regions result primarily from decomposition of natural organic matter. The orthophosphate anion, being chemically reactive, is not readily transported in groundwater. Additions from precipitation and atmospheric fallout are highly variable depending on wind erosion and air pollution. The biologically available phosphates entering an oligotrophic lake during the growing season are rapidly synthesized by plants. Usually 90 percent or more of the total phosphorus in impounded waters is organically bound. The key cycle (Figure 9-4) is orthophosphate synthesized into plant growth, followed by death and decay releasing the phosphate back to solution for resynthesis. Particulate phosphates, whether entering in this form or being complexed in the lake water, may be eliminated

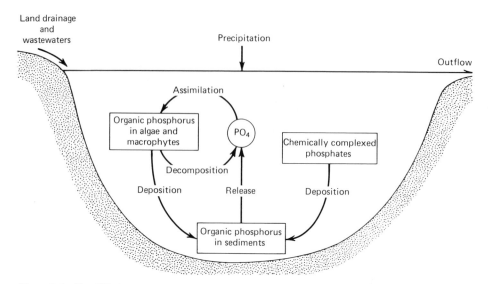

Figure 9-4 Simplified phosphorus cycle in lake water showing the most common pathways.

from the cycle by settling to the bottom. Sediments can serve as a sink retaining phosphate adsorbed onto clay and chemically combined with metal cations like iron.

Runoff from agricultural land and municipal waste discharges are rich in phosphates and lead to accelerated productivity, which is the most conspicuous aspect of eutrophication. As a result of technological advancements, huge amounts of phosphate rock are mined and processed into agricultural fertilizers, animal feeds, chemical builders for detergents, and other commercial products. Most of this phosphorus is ultimately discharged to surface waters, either directly after use (as with household detergents) or indirectly, for example, as manure from cattle feed fodder grown with commercial fertilizer. In the phosphorus cycle of a fertile lake, the influent flow provides excess nutrients to support flourishing biological growths. The phosphate accumulated in the sediments can be resuspended during lake overturns for resynthesis. Large lakes retain the majority of applied phosphorus, while a substantial portion of soluble phosphate is flushed through the storage reservoirs of river impoundments. Thus, loss in the outflow is inversely proportional to the water retention time.

9-3 Ecology of Lakes and Reservoirs

Phytoplankton and Macrophytes

Green plants are the primary producers in aquatic ecosystems using the energy of light for photosynthesis (Equation 9-4). Their carbon source is

$$CO_2 + PO_4 + NH_3 \xrightarrow[\text{growth}]{\substack{\text{energy from} \\ \text{sunlight}}} \text{new cell} + O_2 \tag{9-4}$$

carbon dioxide, or bicarbonates; major inorganic nutrients are phosphate and nitrogen as ammonia or nitrate; and, required trace elements include calcium, magnesium, boron, cobalt, and others. Selected plant species are able to fix gaseous nitrogen if nutrient salts are not available. The products of photosynthesis are new plant growth and oxygen. Chlorophyll is the common green pigment that biochemically converts sunlight to useful energy; other pigments are yellow, brown, and red. In the absence of sunlight, plants use some of the previously formed photosynthate, which when combined with oxygen, provides the necessary energy for continued survival.

Planktonic algae are commonly more significant in large lakes than attached forms. (The term plankton refers to unattached organisms dispersed individually, or in colonies, in water. Phytoplankton is the drifting plant life, while zooplankton encompasses planktonic animals.) Diatoms, an important group of algae in many lakes, have outer skeletons composed of silica (Figure 9-5). In temperate lakes, these algae develop maximum populations in clear, cool water during the spring when nutrients are released by wind mixing and added by land drainage. The most common blue-green algae grow either as filaments with cells arranged linearly within a sheath (*Anabaena*) or in large colonies (*Anacystis*). These microorganisms are associated with eutrophic lakes, and produce unpleasant tastes and odors difficult to remove in water treatment. Green algae exhibit wide diversity occurring as desmids, composed of two halves joined by a narrow bridge (*Closterium*), or as a colony of green cells (*Pediastrum*). A few algae are motile. *Euglena*, possessing features of both plant and animal, is a photosynthetic protozoan with a large flagellum that propels the organism by a whiplike action. Only a few members of the phytoplankton have powers of locomotion to maintain their position in water. Most algae slowly settle out of suspension in quiescent water. The exceptions are the blue-greens with gelatinous sheaths, or gas vacuoles, which improve buoyancy and reduce sinking rates. Consequently, a bloom of blue-green phytoplankton often creates unsightly floating masses that wash onto the shore.

For a given lake during a particular season of the year, the amount of phytoplankton is determined by a number of factors including water temperature, lighting conditions, mixing, species competition, predation, and nutrient availability. The critical temperature for photosynthesis by diatoms is lower than for blue-green algae that are much more tolerant of warm waters. Hence, blue-greens prevail in temperate lakes in the autumn, but are much less competitive during the spring in cold water. Green algal species encompass a broad temperature-tolerance range. Both temperature and sunlight intensity influence the rate of photosynthesis. In addition to helping keep cells in suspension, water movements carry the phytoplankton into and out of the photic zone, and transport nutrients from lower depths and littoral regions to the open waters. Planktonic communities usually include a spectrum of algae with one or two dominant species. Because of competition and changing environmental conditions, existing populations are rarely stable. A shift in dominance can occur either slowly or rapidly as in the case of a blue-green bloom. Growth dynamics are also affected by selective grazing of predatory organisms.

Algal productivity during the growing season is normally controlled by the avail-

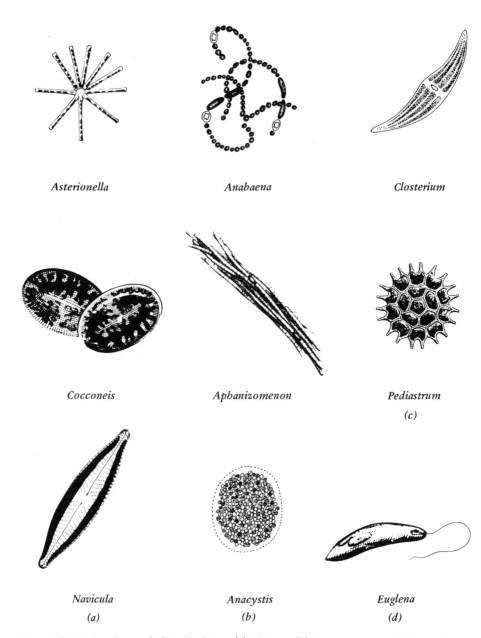

Asterionella	*Anabaena*	*Closterium*
Cocconeis	*Aphanizomenon*	*Pediastrum*
		(c)
Navicula	*Anacystis*	*Euglena*
(a)	*(b)*	*(d)*

Figure 9-5 Various forms of phytoplanktons. (*a*) Diatoms. (*b*) Blue-green algae. (*c*) Green algae. (*d*) A motile alga.

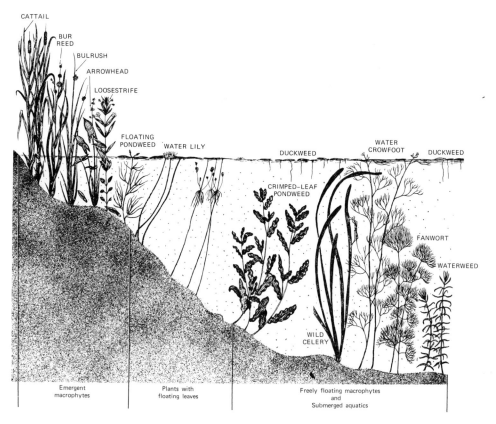

Figure 9-6 Aquatic macrophytes found in the littoral (shore) region of lakes.

ability of nutrients, particularly phosphorus. Photosynthesis produces plant growth, which continues until a key nutrient is depleted, assuming some other environmental factor does not stifle reproduction first. Oligotrophic lakes support few algae, mostly diatoms and green species, while eutrophic impoundments exhibit heavy phytoplanktonic growth. Unfortunately, the plant life in most enriched lakes is dominated by blue-green algae. The combination of abundant nutrients, selective predation, reduced light penetration, and other features of polluted water appear to promote this least desirable phytoplankton.

The littoral region of a lake is the transition zone between land and open water that supports a variety of rooted aquatic macrophytes. This shore area, relative to the amount of open water, depends on the basin geomorphology. In moderate-sized impoundments, littoral flora constitute a major source of synthesis of organic matter contributing to productivity. Aquatic plants are broadly classified on the basis of their attachment (Figure 9-6). Emergent plants growing in wet soil and shallow water include reed grass, cattails, bur reed, and bulrushes. Water and nutrients available from

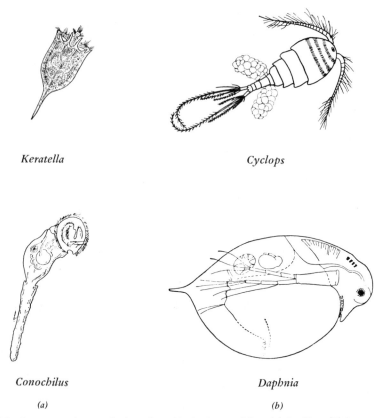

Keratella

Cyclops

Conochilus

Daphnia

(a)

(b)

Figure 9-7 Representative zooplankton found in freshwater lakes. (a) Rotifers. (b) Crustaceans.

the sediments combined with carbon dioxide from the atmosphere promote dense growths. In water depths from about 0.5 to 3 m, the habitat is best suited for rooted plants with floating leaves as typified by the water lily. Submerged aquatics like pondweeds, filamentous algae, and ferns, draw carbon dioxide and inorganic nutrients from the surrounding water. Although water pressures to about 10 m are tolerable, reduced light penetration due to turbidity usually restricts growth of submerged aquatics to shallower depths. Free-floating macrophytes range from large plants with rosettes of aerial or floating leaves with submerged roots (water hyacinth) to small-leaved plants with few roots (duckweed).

Zooplankton and Fish
The composition of freshwater zooplankton is dominated by rotifers and two sub-classes of crustaceans, the Cladocera and Copepoda. Rotifers are microscopic (usually 200 to 500 μm) soft-bodied invertebrates having conspicuous organ-systems (Figure 9-7). An anterior corona of cilia surrounding the mouth aids in feeding and swimming. Most possess toelike appendages that can be used for attachment on a

surface and in a creeping locomotion. Rotifer diets, which vary with species and size, include organic detritus, algae, and other microscopic zooplankton.

Copepods and Cladocerans belong to the same taxonomic class as crabs, lobsters, shrimp, and crayfish. Although most are quite small, many are visible to the naked eye. These zooplankton have branched swimming feet or a shell-like covering with a variety of appendages (Figure 9-7). *Daphnia*, a water flea of the order Cladocera, has a bivalve carapace, a compound eye on the head, and antennae for locomotion. Cladocera feed by filtering particles, mostly algae, from a stream of water flowing through the valves. Typical of one group of copepods, *Cyclops* has an elongated body composed of a head region bearing antennae and a thorax with swimming legs that propel the body in short jerky movements. Eggs are characteristically carried in two sacs attached laterally. Mouth parts on the head are employed to seize and ingest plant or animal food particles.

Fish are cold-blooded animals with backbones, gills, fins, and usually scales. Their internal structure, similar to other animals, includes a gullet, stomach, intestine, liver, spleen, and kidney. They have a brain protected by the skull, and most have an air bladder below the backbone to maintain buoyancy. Fish gills act as lungs. Fine red filaments attached to the gill contain blood cells that absorb dissolved oxygen from water, which is then distributed through other parts of the body by blood circulation. All carnivorous fish pass through an early growth stage in which zooplankton is the major source of food. Upon reaching larger size, they feed on smaller fish. Some fish, like the alewife, continue to consume plankton throughout their life. Most predator species, often considered by fishermen as the best game fish, hunt by sight and are seriously impaired by turbid water.

Like all animals, fish are susceptible to a variety of diseases. Illnesses include disorders of the internal organs, while parasites are common external agents. Water pollution can affect both the environment of adults directly and reduce the reproductive success of fish. For example, siltation can cover fish eggs, or certain heavy metals and organic chemicals reduce hatch. Unfortunately, the most susceptible to adverse environmental changes are the choice food fish, like grayling, whitefish, and brook and rainbow trout. These intolerant species require cold water, high dissolved oxygen concentrations, and low turbidity. Tolerant fish, exemplified by carp, black bullhead, and bowfin, can withstand wide fluctuations in surroundings, warm water, low dissolved oxygen, and high turbidity. Many moderately tolerant fish, such as walleye and northern pike, are both good angling and eating. Their location in warm-water lakes near densely populated areas has promoted them as prize game fish by sportsmen. However, pollution from surrounding agriculture, urbanization, and industrial expansion have in many cases polluted these warm-water lakes and reservoirs causing a shift in fish populations to more tolerant species like bluegill and yellow perch.

Aquatic Communities

The conspicuous regions of a lake, as shown in Figure 9-8, are: the lake surface, limnetic zone including trophogenic and tropholytic strata, littoral zone, and profundal region.[4] Each is inhabited by typical plant and animal populations. The lake surface, as the interface between air and water, supports a diverse community of

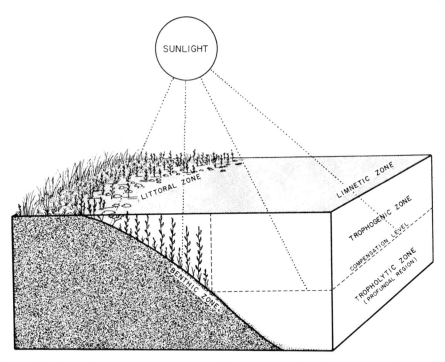

Figure 9-8   The major horizontal and vertical life zones of a lake. (From G. K. Reid and R. D. Wood, *Ecology of Inland Waters and Estuaries*, 2nd Edition, D. Van Nostrand Company, New York, 1976. By permission.)

organisms. On the top, are freely floating plants and swimming insects such as whirligig beetles. Some snails, flatworms and, seasonally, the larvae and pupae of dipterous insects, reside submerged on the undersurface of the water.

The limnetic zone is the open water area bounded by rooted vegetation. During the plant growing season, shallow impoundments may have a very limited open region. The limnetic zone extends vertically from the surface to the bottom through two distinct regimes that have different physical and chemical conditions resulting in separate biological communities. The environment of the upper lighted, or trophogenic, zone is suitable for planktonic plant and animal communities. Algal photosynthesis provides the food production to support herbivore populations. In the lower (tropholytic) region, decomposition predominates. Many animal species in this dark hypolimnion, which are adapted to conditions of reduced oxygen, obtain food from organic particles precipitating from the trophogenic zone above. In shallow lakes and ponds with relatively clear waters, the tropholytic region may be poorly defined or missing. Between the two limnetic strata is the compensation level where algal photosynthesis equals algal respiration over a 24-hour period. In highly turbid or strongly colored lakes, this plane can lie within a meter of the surface, while in clear lakes the depth to compensation can be 10 m or more. Being restricted by light requirements, the compensation level marks the lower limit of photoplankton production. Some zooplankton species have a diurnal migration pattern moving to the tropholytic zone during the day and returning to the surface region for grazing during the night.

Algae occupy the primary trophic level in the aquatic food chain of the limnetic zone. During the growing season, their productivity is normally limited by the supply of inorganic nutrients. Sunlight, temperature, or some other environmental factor can stifle reproduction at other times. Small animals like copepods, being unable to manufacture cells by photosynthesis, obtain energy and nutrients secondhand by eating plants. This second trophic level serves, in turn, as the food supply for fish that comprise the third- and fourth-order consumers. A plot of biomass measurements at various trophic levels is commonly depicted in a pyramid shape as illustrated in Figure 9-9. The total mass of living substance decreases from one level to the next higher and, since production is directly related to energy, the pyramid also indicates the amount of available energy at each trophic step. Metabolism and resynthesis results in losses of both energy and mass with each transfer through the food chain. (Figure 7-2 illustrates a pyramid of biomass showing actual field measurements.)

A littoral zone extends from the shoreline to the boundary of rooted plants. The extent of growth occupying this area is influenced by many factors: suitability of bottom soil, nutrient availability, light transmission, wave action, and water-level fluctuations. Although dominated by macrophytes, the littoral region is an ideal habitat for many species of microscopic plants and animals. Submerged stems and leaves provide surface areas for colonies of algae and zooplankton, including many forms not occurring in the limnetic zone. Planktivorous fish feed on the abundant animal populations, while being sheltered from larger predatory fish. Larger animals such as snakes, turtles, and frogs are conspicuous carnivores of the shoreline community.

The profundal region is the lower portion of the hypolimnion in contact with the lake bottom (Figure 9-8). In fertile lakes, it is characterized by absence of light, low dissolved oxygen, and high carbon dioxide content. The sediments are soft, flocculent, oozelike materials rich in organic matter. Fungi, bacteria, and certain protozoans are abundant on the mud surface. Worms and molluscs are common bottom dwellers that feed on the decaying organics. Miscellaneous animals include nematodes, leeches, and insects.

9-4 Sampling and Testing

Planning a limnological investigation requires data on the morphology and hydrography of the lake. (For discussions of these topics refer to Sections 8-3 through 8-5). Proper interpretations of chemical analyses and biological measurements are founded on such factors as: size and shape of the basin, mean depth, hydraulic retention time (water renewal time), thermal stratification, and internal water movements.

The location and number of sampling sites for a survey depends on the problem under investigation and conditions to be studied. Influent streams and discharge flows are sampled and tested, as described in Section 7-4, to determine the amounts of substances entering and leaving an impoundment. The overflow discharge from a lake

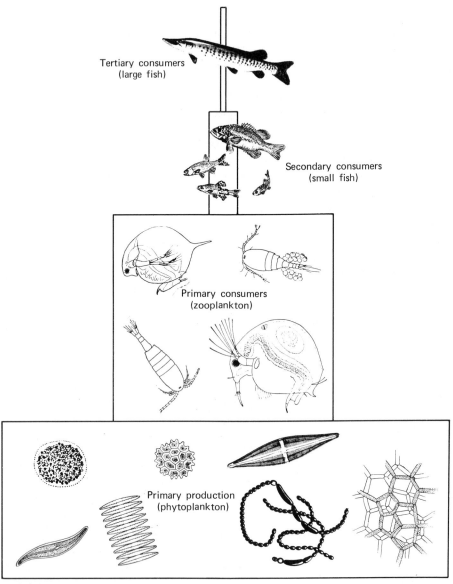

Figure 9-9 A pyramid of the trophic levels illustrating the typical aquatic community in the limnetic zone of lakes. The horizontal bars represent both relative biomass and energy at various levels in the aquatic food chain.

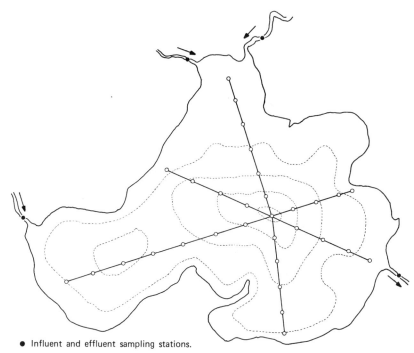

● Influent and effluent sampling stations.

○ Transectional sampling sites for periodic or seasonal collections.

Figure 9-10 Diagram of a natural lake basin showing suggested sampling sites. (From K. M. Mackenthun, *The Practice of Water Pollution Biology*, U. S. Department of the Interior, Washington, D. C., 1969.)

often represents the composite character of the epilimnetic water. In contrast, discharge from a reservoir penstock located below the thermocline reflects water quality in the hypolimnion. Within a lake or reservoir, the number and location of sampling stations selected should represent actual conditions. Sampling along transection lines, as illustrated in Figure 9-10, has the advantage of incorporating all the major life zones of a lake—littoral and profundal benthos, shoreline macrophytes, and limnetic algae, zooplankton, and fish.

Temperature and dissolved oxygen profiles are often used to characterize the seasonal cycle in lakes (Figure 9-1). The easiest method of measuring temperature and dissolved oxygen is with a portable meter and submersible probe (Figure 7-11). The extension wire, attached to the probe, can be calibrated to measure depth below the surface.

Clarity of water may be expressed in terms of turbidity, vertical illumination, or visibility. Turbidity is the interference of light passage through water caused by soil particles, organics, plankton, and other suspended materials. Very pure water (drinking

Figure 9-11 The Secchi disk is a 200-mm circular plate lowered into a lake to measure water transparency. It has opposite quarters painted gloss white and black and is suspended by a calibrated line attached at the center. Secchi disk visibility is the mean depth at which the disk can be seen when raised and lowered in the water on the shady side of a boat.

quality) has less than one unit of turbidity, a typical "clear" lake water is about 25 units, and muddy water exceeds 100 units. For field measurements, a portable photoelectric colorimeter is commonly used. Vertical illumination is measured with a submarine photometer that senses the transmitted light. Extinction curves (light intensity versus depth) are of interest in studies related to photosynthesis. The most frequently reported visibility is the maximum depth at which a circular disk is visible to the naked eye. The Secchi disk (Figure 9-11) is a weighted circular plate, 200 mm in diameter, with the surface painted black and white in opposing quarters. When attached at the center to a calibrated line, it hangs in a horizontal plane. Secchi disk transparency is the average depth at which the plate disappears, when viewed from the shaded side of a boat, and reappears after being lowered and raised slowly into view. Observations range from less than one-half metre caused by soil turbidity, or plankton during the growing season, to greater than 10 m in extremely clear lakes.

Subsurface water for chemical testing is collected in special containers like the Van Dorn sampler (Figure 7-13). After lowering the open sampler to the desired depth, a weight is dropped down the supporting cord to release rubber closures that seal water in the tubular chamber. A bottle sampler (Figure 7-11) can also be used by lowering a sealed empty bottle, and pulling the stopper to allow filling at the desired depth. Common chemical analyses are pH, conductivity, calcium, magnesium, silica, alkalinity, sulfate, filterable solids, total solids, carbon dioxide, phosphorus, and nitrogen. Various forms of the latter nutrients are discussed in Section 9-2.

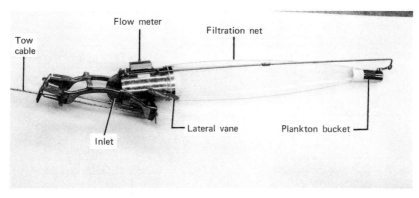

Figure 9-12 The Clarke-Bumpus plankton sampler is equipped with a flow meter in the front to measure the quantity of water filtered. When towed behind a boat, the lateral vanes cause the net to ride in a position at a right angle to the metal suspending frame.

Plankton can be grouped into two size ranges during sampling with the division based on passage through a net with clear openings of 64 μm (number 25 mesh). The organisms retained by the net are considered net plankton, while those passing through are nannoplankton. A net towed behind a boat for some distance provides the greatest quantity of plankton with minimum effort. The most advanced sampler of this type is the Clarke-Bumpus net, which has a metering device in front to determine the quantity of water that passes through it during a tow (Figure 9-12). While the unit is being pulled through the water, lateral vanes mounted on the sides of the intake cause the net to trail in a position approximately at a right angle to the metal suspending frame. The usual procedure for gathering nannoplankton is to volumetrically collect water using a subsurface sampler and filter it through a plankton net stretched over an open container. The microorganisms are then separated from the filtrate by centrifugation, or membrane filtration, in a laboratory.

Dredges of the type pictured in Figure 9-13 are designed to grab bottom material for collection of benthic organisms. While resting on the lake bottom, the spring-loaded jaws are closed by dropping a messenger down the supporting rope. Sampling is most successful in soft, muddy substrates. Compacted or gravel bottoms are more difficult to seize, and special heavy dredges are necessary. After emptying grab samples into a tub, water is added and the large particles crushed by hand. This slurry is poured through a sieve with clear openings of approximately 0.5 mm, and the retained materials washed with water. The benthic organisms are then picked off the screen and preserved in a formalin solution for laboratory examination.

Productivity of a community relates to both standing crop and rate of production. Standing crop, which is the biomass of phytoplankton present at the time of observation, is a poor measure of productivity because the time factor for development of the biomass is not included. A high-standing crop does not necessarily mean a high rate of production. For example, an abundant momentary algal mass may have taken a long

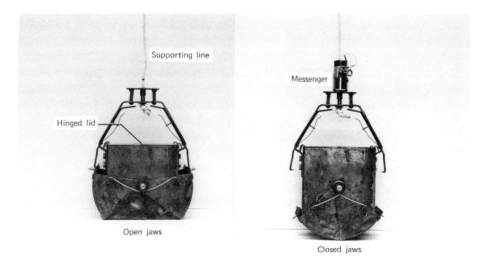

Figure 9-13 An Ekman dredge, with a 15 cm by 15 cm box, for sampling benthos shown with jaws in the open and closed positions. With the dredge resting on the lake bottom, a brass messenger is dropped down the supporting line to trip the spring-loaded jaws closed. The hinged top plates open for easier descent and close during lifting to minimize sample disturbance.

time to develop, indicating a low rate in turnover of nutrients. What is important is the rate at which populations of a community are created, which is quantitatively related to primary production.

Primary production is the quantity of new phytoplankton synthesized over a given period of time. It is measured in situ by the rate of photosynthesis expressed as the inorganic carbon assimilated per unit of time. The following is the field procedure for the carbon-14 technique.[5]

1. Collect water samples from several depths below the surface at the chosen testing site.
2. Place portions of the water from each depth in a light (clear) bottle and a dark bottle, add a measured amount of $Na_2C^{14}O_3$ solution to each bottle, and re-stopper.
3. Resuspend the bottles at the depths from which the samples were drawn and incubate for a specified time, usually a two- to four-hour midday period.
4. Retrieve the bottles and store at refrigeration temperature in transit to the laboratory.
5. Prepare each sample by membrane filtration and special washing of the filtered algae.
6. Determine the amount of C^{14} assimilated in the phytoplankton of the water sample by scintillation counting. From these results, the total carbon uptake is then calculated and expressed as milligrams per litre of carbon synthesized per unit of time.
7. Finally, primary production for the sampling site is calculated per unit of lake

surface area by multiplying the carbon uptake rate at each depth by the corresponding volume of water represented by the sample tested. Common units are milligrams of carbon per square metre per day, or grams of carbon per square metre per year.

9-5 Cultural Eutrophication

The phenomenon of eutrophication has been used by limnologists for over 50 years to describe the normal processes that occur in lakes and lead to their eventual extinction. In most natural environments, the aging of lakes was a very slow process taking decades to cause a perceptible change. Cultural eutrophication is the accelerated fertilization of impoundments, streams, and estuaries arising from pollution associated with population growth, industrial development, and intensified agriculture. The response of aquatic ecosystems to increased input of nutrients is greater productivity to the detriment of water quality—excessive growth of phytoplankton reducing transparency, increased organic content depleting dissolved oxygen, decaying blue-green algae releasing foul tastes and odors, loss of less tolerant fish species, and littoral zones choked with aquatic weeds. In many documented cases of cultural eutrophication, these responses have arrived in a surprisingly short period of a few years after introduction of excess nutrients.

Chemical Factors

The major plant nutrients are orthophosphate, inorganic nitrogen (nitrate and ammonia), and carbon dioxide. Micronutrients include iron, silica, and organic compounds such as vitamins. The majority of natural waters contain an adequate supply of these trace elements and sufficient dissolved carbon dioxide is available from natural sources to support massive growths of algae. In the majority of lakes, either phosphorus or nitrogen is the limiting nutrient controlling aquatic plant production. Although not universally accepted, most authorities feel that phosphorus is the key element since soluble phosphate is more likely to be depleted in lake waters during the growing season than nitrate and ammonia. Furthermore, several species of blue-green algae can fix gaseous nitrogen if inorganic forms are in short supply.

Nitrogen and phosphorus are contributed to surface waters from several sources—the most abundant being agricultural land drainage and municipal wastewaters. In many farming areas, high additions of chemical phosphates and nitrogenous fertilizers are applied to increase crop yields. Inorganic nitrogen is highly soluble in water and leaches readily from the soil; phosphates, even though relatively immobile in soil, are conveyed by rainfall runoff in both dissolved form and adsorbed on soil particles. Manure from cattle-feeding operations and dairy farming spread on land in the winter contribute nutrients to spring runoff. Nutrient discharges from land can be managed by timing the application of fertilizers and manure, controlling the amounts applied, and cropping and soil conservation practices. Despite these efforts, local weather and topography can seriously restrict their effectiveness, for example, in regions where frequent high-intensity rainfalls lead to heavy runoff and unavoidable erosion.

Raw sanitary wastewaters average 5.8 kg of nitrogen and 1.5 kg of phosphorus per person per year; about 60 percent of the latter is from phosphate builders in household detergents. Principal sources of nitrogen are feces, urine, and food wastes. Ordinary physical-biological treatment, which eliminated 90 percent of the biodegradable organic matter, removes a maximum of 40 percent of the nitrogen and 30 percent of the phosphorus from municipal wastewaters; nutrient removals may be significantly less than these values for some treatment plants. If chemical precipitation is incorporated in processing, the level of phosphorus in the effluent can be reduced to 1.0 mg/l, which is a removal of about 90 percent. Where treated wastewaters are discharged to natural lakes and estuaries, either directly or via rivers, effluent standards have been adopted by state regulatory agencies to limit phosphorus pollution. Nitrogen is much more difficult and costly to remove from wastewaters. Therefore, while emphasis is being placed on phosphorus extraction, nitrogen discharges are not normally limited for the purpose of retarding fertilization of surface waters. Control of phosphorus rather than nitrogen is also justified on the implicit assumption that phosphorus is the limiting nutrient in controlling eutrophication. The conversion of ammonia to nitrate (nitrification) can be practiced by biological treatment to reduce toxicity of the effluent. Partial denitrification, by bacterial conversion of nitrate to gaseous nitrogen, is occasionally performed to reduce the nitrate content in protecting a public water source. (The limit for nitrate concentration in drinking water is 10 mg/l of nitrogen.)

Natural lakes, estuaries, reservoirs sited in river valleys, and small impoundments for soil and water conservation are all subject to nutrient enrichment. If the primary source of inflow is agricultural land drainage, adequate nutrient control is rarely practical. Awkward eutrophication problems often arise when reservoirs constructed for flood control and protection of agricultural land are also expected to provide water-contact recreation. Impounding nutrient-rich runoff naturally causes a productive ecosystem that interferes with such activities as swimming, water skiing, and fishing. The most practical method for controlling fertilization from municipal wastewaters is to remove the majority of phosphate by chemical precipitation or dispose of the wastewater by some means other than dilution, for example, irrigation of cropland. But, these processes are only being applied where nutrient discharges threaten lakes or slow-moving rivers, such as the Great Lakes, Lake Tahoe, the Potomac River and estuary, and San Francisco Bay. Rapidly flowing waters are less susceptible to adverse effects because mixing increases light-limiting turbidity and prevents oxygen stratification. Therefore, nutrient controls are not being imposed on major river systems even though they incorporate main-stem reservoirs for flow control. The lakes most likely to be preserved in their oligotrophic state are mountain lakes with undeveloped watersheds. Moderately fertile lakes in populated areas can be protected from point source pollution by stringent controls; however, if diffuse sources are prevalent, overenrichment is likely. The latter is also true of man-made impoundments in lightly populated agricultural regions. Finally, many river reservoirs are destined to be eutrophic in locations where management of nutrients from rural and urban sources is not feasible.

Oligotrophic waters support small numbers of organisms of many different species. The pyramid of biomass is stable. With inorganic nutrients in short supply, primary production of green plants is limited, which in turn restricts the populations of zooplankton and fish. This unproductive ecosystem is typified by cold-water mountain lakes and sand-bottomed, spring-fed impoundments with transparent water.

Although slightly more fertile, mesotrophic lakes still have a balanced ecosystem. The water has a greenish hue from phytoplankton during the growing season, and moderate blooms of algae occur in the late summer and fall. Fish populations are larger and include favored game species. If used as a public water supply, algal turbidity in a mesotrophic lake is likely to create filtration and odor-control problems resulting in greater chemical usage in summer and fall.

Excess nutrient enrichment in eutrophic lakes leads to high rates of photosynthesis in both rooted aquatics and phytoplankton. Weed growth in the littoral zone is limited by such factors as overcrowding and shading. Phytoplankton increases turbidity, and during blooms creates a "pea soup" appearance. Algae settle out of suspension increasing the biodegradable organic content of the hypolimnion leading to reduced oxygen content. Periodic blooms of predominately blue-green algae occur from summer through late fall. These species impart intense foul tastes and odors to the water and float on the surface in decaying mats that are windblown to the shore. While some increase in plant productivity favors greater populations of desirable fish, surplus algae in a pulsing growth pattern create an intolerable environment for preferred food fish. They simply cannot survive and compete in turbid and low-dissolved-oxygen waters. Tolerant species become dominant—trout and cisco give way to perch and bass, which can yield to bullheads and carp if the surroundings continue to deteriorate. Nutrient enrichment disrupts a balanced ecosystem, and diminishes water quality for public supply and recreation. Cultural eutrophication is the aging of naturally infertile lakes by artifically increasing the nutrient input resulting from the activities of our industrial society.

Physical Factors

The two major physical factors influencing photosynthesis are temperature and light. Although objectionable species of algae, like the blue-greens, are generally considered warm-water microorganisms, their presence is not restricted by cold temperatures. For example, blue-green algae are often found in eutrophic lake waters during winter; apparently they are tolerant of adverse temperatures if other environmental conditions are suitable. Inadequate sunlight penetration restricts phytoplankton in highly colored, or muddy, waters. Shallow lakes and reservoirs are often light-limited resulting from soil turbidity held in suspension by wind mixing, thus, restricting plant growth even though adequate nutrients are available. Blooms of algae in enriched impoundments, such as a wastewater stabilization pond, can be self-shading and reduce their own rate of photosynthesis.

The form of a lake and the hydrological characteristics of a basin directly affect biological processes, mainly through residence time of the water and thermal stratification. A very short retention time in a watercourse, or impoundment, reduces the effects of eutrophication. For this reason and because of soil turbidity, many major rivers are not excessively productive even though their nitrogen and phosphorus levels exceed the minimum desirable in a lake. On the other hand, slow-moving rivers that act like long, narrow impoundments during periods of low flow and estuaries are susceptible to overfertilization. The water renewal times of natural lakes and most reservoirs, ranging from several months to years, are sufficiently long to produce a highly productive ecosystem if nutrients are available.

Thermal stratification and seasonal mixing strongly influence biological reactions in a lake. During summer stratification, plankton flourish in the mixing trophogenic zone while the hypolimnion is dark and stagnant. In this lower region, dissolved oxygen diminishes and anaerobiosis of the bottom releases hydrogen sulfide and odorous organic compounds. This is a critical time for intolerant fish since the upper water layer can be excessively warm while the lower stratum is too low in dissolved oxygen. Some of the nutrients stored at the bottom during stagnation are returned to the photosynthetic zone during deep mixing; the spring circulation is particularly important since nutrient recycling coincides with the beginning of the growing season.

Trophic Levels

The chemical parameters of greatest interest in assessing the trophic level of a lake are dissolved oxygen content and nutrient concentrations. Hypolimnetic oxygen depletion during thermal stratification is a common index separating oligotrophic from eutrophic lakes (Figure 9-1). Major problems with this measure are that the rate of oxygen loss depends not only on the decomposition of organic matter, but also to a significant extent on the lake's morphology (a physical characteristic). Because the dynamics of oxygen utlization are complex, the difference in amount of oxygen present at the beginning and end of stratification provides only an indirect estimate of lake productivity. In terms of concentration levels, a minimum dissolved oxygen of 6 mg/l is critical for cold-water fish found in oligotrophic lakes; whereas, in eutrophic lakes a minimum of 3 mg/l is considered the lower tolerance limit of warm-water fish. Highly eutrophic waters become anaerobic near the bottom with noticeable production of hydrogen sulfide.

Nutrient availability in the trophogenic zone has been related to the trophic level of moderate-sized lakes in northern United States. The generally accepted upper concentration limits—at the time of spring overturn—for lakes free of algal nuisances are 0.3 mg/l of inorganic nitrogen and 0.01 mg/l of orthophosphate phosphorus. A study of plant growth relative to annual average nutrient concentrations in Wisconsin lakes[6] revealed annual mean total nitrogen and phosphorus concentrations greater than 0.8 mg/l and 0.1 mg/l, respectively, resulted in algal blooms and nuisance weed growths during most of the growing season. Lakes were essentially free of nuisances if the annual average for total organic nitrogen was less than 0.2 mg/l and the total average phosphorus concentration was less than 0.03 mg/l.

Primary productivity is the best biological measure of fertility level. Transparency of the water, amount of phytoplankton, quantity of chlorophyll, and frequency and number of algal blooms are indirect measurements associated with productivity. In general, oligotrophic lakes have an annual primary production less than 100 grams of carbon per square metre of water surface, while eutrophic lakes exceed 300 g/m²·a of carbon.[7] An algal bloom is usually defined as 10 to 50 million cells per litre (depending on the species present), chlorophyll density greater than 40 mg/m³, and a Secchi disk depth of less than one metre. Any one of these measurements performed regularly from spring through fall will reveal cycles in the density of phytoplankton. Eutrophic lakes exhibit several peaks during this period, while oligotrophic waters lack any conspicuous blooms. Based on measurements throughout the growing season, eutrophic lakes generally have chlorophyll exceeding 10 mg/m³ and mean transparency is less than 2 m caused by plankton. Also, the types and diversity of algal species present indicate overenrichment. Fertile ecosystems support large populations of common blue-greens, like *Anabaena, Anacystis,* and *Aphanizomenon*, with corresponding low numbers of green algae and diatoms. Figure 9-14 illustrates how overfertilization afflicts a large lake.

Numerous small lakes and reservoirs also exhibit the effects of eutrophication, but the responses may be considerably different because of smaller surface area and shallower depth. The source of extra nutrients is frequently farmland runoff but also can originate from conventionally treated wastewaters, or seepage from septic tank drainfields. In clear-water lakes (Figure 9-15a), fertilization promotes photosynthesis with macrophytes and phytoplankton competing for the dissolved nutrients. Transitory stratification leads quickly to anaerobiosis of the bottom stratum. Large populations of tolerant fish succeed game species that find the environment unsuitable. Swimming and water skiing are inhibited by weed beds. Even onshore activities, like picnicking, can be discouraged by foul odors emanating from heavy blooms of blue-

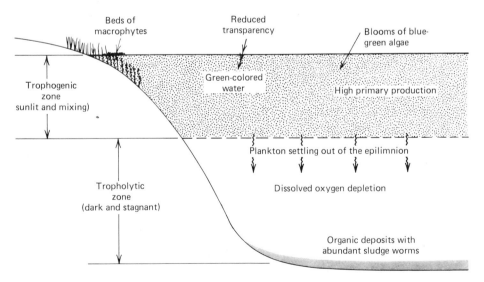

Figure 9-14 Characteristics of an eutrophic lake in the autumn after months of thermal stratification.

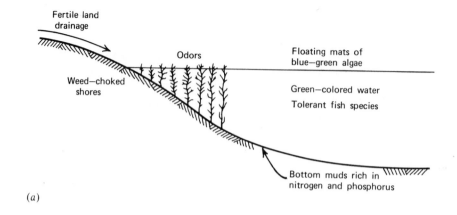

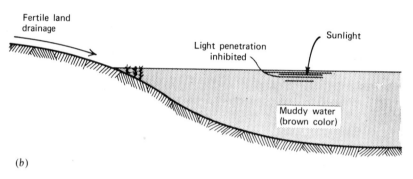

Figure 9-15 The nature of small, eutrophic lakes and reservoirs is often defined by clarity of the water. (a) Fertile, clear-water lakes with low soil turbidity exhibit high productivity. (b) Turbid, light-inhibiting waters prevent excessive plant growth by limiting photosynthesis. (From M. J. Hammer, *Water and Waste-Water Technology, SI Version*, John Wiley & Sons, Inc., New York, 1977.)

green algae. Small impoundments, continuously mixed by wind action, are often light-limited by soil turbidity and support neither dense weed beds nor algal blooms (Figure 9-15b). Photosynthesis is retarded by the lack of sunlight, rather than a shortage of plant nutrients. Although limiting productivity may have some esthetic advantages, the high turbidity is detrimental to reproduction of game fish.

Methods of Retarding Eutrophication

Cultural eutrophication of a lake can be controlled, or its effects minimized, by reducing the inflow of nutrients. Reduction of nutrient loading is the only sure, proven method. However, before initiating corrective measures, a quantitative survey of nitrogen and phosphorus sources and a limnological study of the lake are essential. These data can reveal the trophic level and determine whether the majority of nutrients are from wastewaters or land drainage. If the latter dominates, no ready solution is available for reduction of input other than land management to control soil erosion and loss of fertilizers. Conservation practices are difficult to institute and monitor, and often only partially successful. In contrast, point sources of municipal and industrial wastes can be controlled by disposal on land, diversion around the lake, or removal of nutrients prior to dilution in surface waters.

Irrigation of biologically treated wastewater is practiced by many towns and small cities in semiarid regions. In a few cases, reclaimed wastewater is impounded for recreational reservoirs, spread in basins for groundwater recharge, injected into coastal aquifers as a barrier against seawater intrusion, or reused as an industrial water supply. Diversion of discharges around lakes has been used to avoid costly advanced treatment. While reducing eutrophication in the endangered lake, diversion may be transferring the problem to the alternate receiving watercourse. The degree of recovery, after instituting land disposal or diversion of wastes, depends on the flushing action of nutrient-poor water entering the lake. If the water retention time is short, the rate of fertilization can be rapidly reversed.

Where the only feasible method of treated-wastewater disposal is by dilution in surface waters subject to eutrophication, treatment processes must include reduction of plant nutrients. At present, emphasis is being placed on phosphorus removal since phosphate is believed to be the controlling factor in the enrichment of most lakes. Furthermore, efficient and relatively inexpensive methods are available for up to 90 percent removal of phosphorus, whereas comparable elimination of nitrogen is not feasible. The effluent standard of not more than 1.0 mg/l of phosphorus has been established by several states for wastewater discharges that flow into lakes and estuaries.

Although reduction of nutrients is the only sure way of retarding eutrophication, several temporary measures can be used to reduce nuisances in small eutrophic lakes and reservoirs. The most popular are chemical control of plant growths, harvesting of aquatic weeds, destratification by mechnical mixing, and aeration of the hypolimnion. Algicides are used extensively for control of the phytoplankton in water-supply reservoirs. Filamentous green algae form scums that clog water plant filters and, in addition, algal blooms impart foul tastes and odors to water. Copper sulfate, the most popular algicide, is generally applied at regular intervals throughout the growing season to control algal populations.

Herbicides, like 2,4-D and sodium arsenite, are effective in reducing weed growth in the littoral zone. Use of chemicals is often limited to boat docks, swimming areas, and fishing points of recreational lakes and reservoirs since their application is both expensive and requires close supervision. Rooted aquatic plants can also be harvested with boat-mounted underwater weed cutters, with optional barge-loading conveyors for larger units. Cutting weeds below the waterline improves esthetics and allows clearance for motor boat propellers. Harvesting of plants is not considered a feasible means of removing nutrients from a lake, since one tonne of wet weeds contains only about one-quarter kilogram of phosphorus and two and one-half kilograms of nitrogen.

Mechanical destratification, by pumping cold water from the bottom and discharging it at the surface, has been effective in improving quality in deep water-supply reservoirs. This mixing lowers the temperature of the surface water, and can add dissolved oxygen to the hypolimnion. The reduction in epilimnetic temperature appears to shift algal populations from troublesome blue-greens to more tolerable green species. In small lakes and reservoirs, where the loss of dissolved oxygen in the hypolimnion is a serious problem, surface waters may be pumped to the bottom or the deep water oxygenated by diffused aeration. The latter, although usually more costly, may be preferred since oxygenation can be performed without destratification. Deep mixing circulates nutrients stored in the hypolimnion into the photic zone stimulating additional algal synthesis.

9-6 Allowable Nutrient Loadings

Data on the indicator parameters of nutrient concentrations, phytoplankton productivity, transparency, and hypolimnetic oxygen depletion cannot be applied directly in

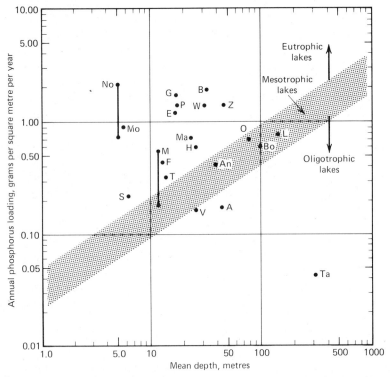

Figure 9-16 A graph of annual phosphorus loading versus mean depth for selected oligotrophic and eutrophic lakes. The lower bar line is the limit of permissible loading, and the upper is excessive loading. The lakes are : Ta Tahoe, A Aegerisee, V Vanern, L Leman, O Ontario, Bo Constance, An Annecy, Ma Malaren, T Turlersee, F Fureső, S Sebasticook, H Hallwillersee, M Mendota, Mo Moses, No Norrviken, E Erie, P Pfaffikersee, G Greifensee, B Baldeggersee, W Washington, and Z Zurichsee. (From R. A. Vollenweider, *Scientific Fundamentals of the Eutrophication of Lakes and Flowing Waters with Particular Reference to Nitrogen and Phosphorus as Factors in Eutrophication*, Organization for Economic Co-operation and Development, Paris, France, 1970.)

engineering analyses. However, by relating trophic level to nutrient loading, from both external sources and cycling within a lake, eutrophication can be described by mathematical models. This concept was expressed by Vollenweider[7] when he correlated data on annual phosphorus loadings, mean lake depth, and degree of enrichment for selected lakes throughout the world. Figure 9-16 shows the position of each lake on the basis of annual phosphorus loading and mean water depth. The oligotrophic lakes are separated from the eutrophic ones by a shaded mestrophic transition zone. Table 9-1 lists the nutrient loading levels based on the plotted data. Permissible loading is the

Table 9-1 Allowable Nitrogen and Phosphorus Loading Levels in Lakes from Figure 9-16

Mean Depth (m)	Permissible Loading $(g/m^2 \cdot a)$		Excessive Loading $(g/m^2 \cdot a)$	
	N	P	N	P
5	1.0	0.07	2.0	0.13
10	1.5	0.10	3.0	0.20
50	4.0	0.25	8.0	0.50
100	6.0	0.40	12.0	0.80
150	7.5	0.50	15.0	1.00
200	9.0	0.60	18.0	1.20

Source: R. A. Vollenweider, *Scientific Fundamentals of the Eutrophication of Lakes and Flowing Waters With Particular Reference to Nitrogen and Phosphorus as Factors in Eutrophication*, Organization for Economic Co-operation and Development, Paris, France, 1970.

maximum allowable for a lake to remain oligotrophic indefinitely; the permissible phosphorus values are points along the line separating oligotrophic and mesotrophic lakes in Figure 9-16. Excessive loadings cause a lake to become eutrophic, and the tabulated values are from the line between eutrophic and mesotrophic levels. The nitrogen loadings given in Table 9-1 are based on a tolerable nitrogen to phosphorus loading ratio of 15:1 by weight. (Typical plant tissue of phytoplankton and macrophytes contains phosphorus, nitrogen, and carbon in the approximate ratio of 1P : 7N : 40C per 100 dry weight.) The phosphorus loadings include all biologically available forms of which the majority are dissolved orthophosphate and acid-hydrolyzable phosphate. The principal inorganic nitrogen forms taken up by plants are nitrate and ammonia.

The loading versus depth relationship is only approximate and other factors, notably water renewal time (theoretical water filling time), influence degree of eutrophication. The effect of doubling the phosphorus loading with unaltered inflow is quite different from doubling the rate of water flow into a lake to increase the nutrient loading. One of the first reported cases, where lakes did not fit the trophic level-phosphorus loading scheme as shown in Figure 9-16, was described by Dillon.[8] In a study of the total phosphorus budgets of 19 lakes in southern Ontario, Canada, Dillon found several had very high loadings with corresponding low chlorophyll a concentrations, high transparency, and small oxygen deficits during the summer. According to Vollenweider's categorization, these lakes should have been eutrophic. This discrepancy was attributed to the high rates of water flowing through these lakes as a result of large watershed areas relative to lake volumes.

In order to account for water renewal time the phosphorus loading-mean depth relationship was modified, as illustrated in Figure 9-17, to include mean residence time of the water. The depth parameter (on the horizontal scale in Figure 9-16) is replaced with areal water loading computed by dividing water renewal time into depth. The resulting units are metres of water height applied to the lake in one year, or cubic metres per square metre of surface area per year. Lake Tahoe (Ta) is a specific case of the predicted status being affected by this alteration. Because the loading is low (40 mg/m²·a of P) and mean depth extremely large (300 m), the original plot (Figure

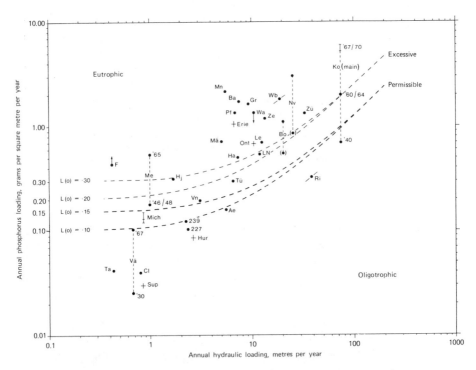

Figure 9-17 Phosphorus loading versus hydraulic loading ($q = z/t$) for lakes at different trophic levels. Those above the excessive line are classified as eutrophic, while those below the permissible line are oligotrophic. (From R. A. Vollenweider, "Input-Output Models with Special Reference to the Phosphorus Loading Concept in Limnology," *Schweizerische Zeitschrift für Hydrologie*, Birkhäuser Verlag Basel, Vol. 37, 1975.)

9-16) predicted Lake Tahoe would remain ultraoligotrophic. But, with a water displacement time of about 700 years, a moderate phosphorus loading would be expected to affect this lake more severely than others. In the new formulation (Figure 9-17), Lake Tahoe remains in the oligotrophic region but is much closer to the limit of permissible loading.

Both of these phosphorus loading models assume a direct relationship between nutrient supply and degree of eutrophication. In reality, although these two are closely associated, nutrient concentration rather than supply controls the standing crop of phytoplankton in a lake. This can be expressed by the following scheme:

$$\text{Nutrient loading} \longrightarrow \text{concentration} \rightleftarrows \text{biological transformation}$$
$$\searrow \text{elimination} \nearrow \qquad (9\text{-}4)$$

While the right-hand part incorporates the related reactions of photosynthesis, nutrient release, and resynthesis, the connection between loading and concentration is unidirectional. Although detailed input-output equations, which describe the mass balance of nutrients in a lake system, can be derived mathematically, existing experimental data are too scarce to verify such models. On the other hand, loading and concentration can be empirically correlated. From an assessment of eutrophication data on numerous lakes of the temperate zone, Vollenweider[9] developed the following equation:

$$P = \frac{L/q}{1 + (z/q)^{0.5}} = \frac{Lt/z}{1 + (t)^{0.5}} \qquad (9\text{-}5)$$

where P = phosphorus concentration in lake water, g/m^3
L = annual phosphorus loading, $g/m^2 \cdot a$
q = annual hydraulic loading, m/a $(m^3/m^2 \cdot a)$
    = mean depth/retention time (z/t), m/a
z = mean depth, m
t = water renewal time (theoretical water-filling time), a
    = mean depth/hydraulic loading (z/q), a

Both the concentration term (P) and the nutrient loading divided by hydraulic loading (L/q) have the same dimensions, expressed in grams per cubic metre. The denominator is an empirical term that compensates for undefined factors, such as those involving nutrient recycling and elimination.

The commonly accepted, critical phosphorus concentration is 10 mg/m^3 $(0.010 \ g/m^3)$ in spring at the end of winter mixing of mono- and dimictic lakes. Below this value lakes are found to be oligotrophic, while greater phosphorus concentrations are likely to result in noxious blooms of algae in the epilimnion during the summer and hypolimnetic oxygen depletion detrimental to cold-water fish. Observed phosphorus levels greater than 20 $mg/m^3 (0.020 \ g/m^3)$ at spring overturn produce an abundant standing crop of phytoplankton (and macrophytes) creating eutrophic conditions. To calculate phosphorus loadings from these concentration values, Equation 9-5 is rearranged into the following expression:

$$L_c = P_c q \left[1 + \left(\frac{z}{q} \right)^{0.5} \right] = \frac{P_c z}{t} \left[1 + (t)^{0.5} \right] \qquad (9\text{-}6)$$

where L_c = critical annual phosphorus loading, g/m^2·a
$\quad\quad P_c$ = critical phosphorus concentration at spring overturn, g/m^3
$\quad\quad q$ = annual hydraulic loading, m/a
$\quad\quad z$ = mean depth, m
$\quad\quad t$ = water renewal time, a

If 0.010 g/m^3 is inserted for P_c, the L_c quantity is the phosphorus loading that separates oligotrophic and mesotrophic lakes (permissible loading). A P_c of 0.020 g/m^3 yields the loading on the boundary between mesotrophic and eutrophic levels (excessive loading).

Loading criteria are difficult to verify directly; however, Equations 9-5 and 9-6 can be evaluated for consistency with available data on actual phosphorus loadings and corresponding levels of phytoplankton production attained in lakes. Figure 9-18,

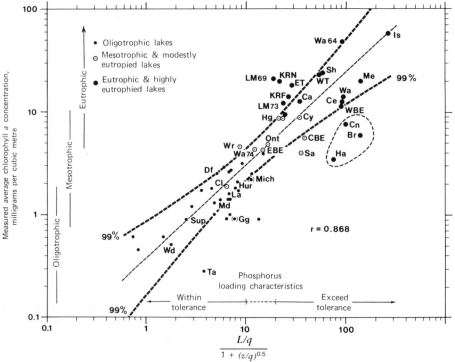

Figure 9-18 Statistical relationship between average epilimnetic chlorophyll concentration and phosphorus loading characteristics according to Equation 9-5. (From R. A. Vollenweider, "Advances in Defining Critical Loading Levels for Phosphorus in Lake Eutrophication," *Memorie dell'Instituto Italiano di Idrobiologia*, Vol. 33, 1976.)

a test of this hypothesis, is a plot of average epilimnetic chlorophyll concentration in 60 lakes (mostly summer averages) plotted against the phosphorus content calculated by Equation 9-5. Although a few values are uncertain, the relationship gives a correlation coefficient of 0.868. Also, the exponent derived from the least square fit deviates only slightly from unity. Each lake plotted has been characterized as oligo-, meso-, or eutrophic. The commonly recognized critical phosphorus loadings (concentrations) are marked off on the abscissa, and the accepted values of summer chlorophyll concentration that define trophic levels of lakes are shown on the vertical scale. As a whole, Figure 9-18 supports the realism of phosphorus loading criteria as calculated by Equation 9-6 with the selected P_c boundaries of 0.010 g/m^3 as the upper limit of oligotrophic and 0.020 g/m^3 as the lower limit of eutrophic waters. "The spectrum of lakes covered includes shallow to deep, and little to highly flushed basin, and hence, represents a valid sample of lakes of the temperate zone."[9]

"It is self evident that the relationship in Figure 9-18 can be used to predict biomass, in terms of chlorophyll, in relation to the specific phosphorus loading characteristics. In absolute terms, the prediction is probably quite good for low and medium productive lakes, yet less certain for highly productive lakes. According to the experience gained thus far in applying the prediction to lakes not included in the correlation analysis, one can expect that at least the peak values of chlorophyll measured will fall within the 99 percent confidence limits given in Figure 9-18. For lakes receiving a very high phosphorus load, one has reason to believe that their production level is not solely controlled by phosphorus, and hence, one would expect the relationship to break down" (Vollenweider, 1976).[9]

The following examples apply the concepts of allowable nutrient loadings in illustrative calculations. Caution is advised in applying these formulas in actual eutrophication problems without complete evaluation of the particular circumstances because of the great variety of individual lake situations that may differ from a standard behavior. "In spite of the progress made in quantifying the loading-trophic response relationship, many open questions remain, so that each individual case must be judged in its own right. This is particularly true for lakes of modest mean depth in which the sediment-water interaction may become an important modifying factor, and so forth" (Vollenweider, 1978).

Example 9-1

The mean depth of Lake Ontario is 84 m, and the water renewal time 7.9 years. Prior to initiation of the phosphorus reduction program, which is now in progress by joint agreement between the United States and Canada, the estimated phosphorus loading was 680 mg/m$^2 \cdot$a[9]. The corresponding average epilimnetic chlorophyll content was 4.8 mg/m^3. Plot the position of Lake Ontario on Figures 9-16, 9-17, and 9-18.

Solution

In Figure 9-16, the coordinates of 0.68 g/m$^2 \cdot$a phosphorus loading and 84 m mean depth coincide with point "O," which represents Lake Ontario.

To enter Figure 9-17, the annual hydraulic loading is

$$q = \frac{z}{t} = \frac{84 \text{ m}}{7.9 \text{ a}} = 10.6 \text{ m/a}$$

and the phosphorus loading is 0.68 g/m^2·a.
The plotting point is labeled "Ont."
   For Figure 9-18, the phosphorus concentration (loading) is calculated by Equation 9-5.

$$P = \frac{(0.68 \text{ g/m}^2 \cdot \text{a})/(10.6 \text{ m/a})}{1 + (7.9 \text{ a})^{0.5}} = 0.0168 \text{ g/m}^3 = 16.8 \text{ mg/m}^3$$

The coordinates of 4.8 mg/m^3 chlorophyll and 16.8 mg/m^3 phosphorus concentration plot at the circled dot labeled "Ont."

Example 9-2

Limnological investigations of a man-made lake resulted in the following data: Physical parameters of 140 km^2 surface area, 17 m mean depth, 43 m maximum depth, and 1.0 $\times$ 10^9 m^3 average annual inflow; chemical measurements of 0.08 mg/l average phosphate phosphorus in the inflow, 0.03 to 0.05 soluble phosphorus at the time of spring overturn, and an average of 3 mg/l dissolved oxygen at a water temperature of 16°C in the hypolimnion after prolonged thermal stratification; and, biological observations including a mean chlorophyll a concentration of 25 mg/m^3 and corresponding Secchi disk readings of 1.0 to 1.5 m in the epilimnion (upper 10 to 15 m) during late summer and fall. What is the trophic state of the reservoir, and recommended values for permissible and excessive phosphorus loadings?

Solution

The annual phosphorus loading equals

$$\frac{\text{Inflow} \times P \text{ concentration}}{\text{Surface area}} = \frac{1.0 \times 10^9 \text{ m}^3/\text{a} \times 0.08 \text{ g/m}^3}{140 \times 10^6 \text{ m}^2} = 0.57 \text{ g/m}^2 \cdot \text{a}$$

Graphing 0.57 g/m^2·a and 17 m (mean depth) on Figure 9-16 indicates the lake is eutrophic. The permissible and excessive phosphorus loadings for a mean depth of 17 m are 0.14 g/m^2·a and 0.28 g/m^2·a, respectively (Figure 9-16 or Table 9-1).
   The annual hydraulic loading equals

$$\frac{\text{Inflow}}{\text{Surface area}} = \frac{1.0 \times 10^9 \text{ m}^3/\text{a}}{140 \times 10^6 \text{ m}^2} = 7.1 \text{ m/a}$$

The intersection of 7.1 m/a with 0.57 g/m^2·a phosphorus loading in Figure 9-17 is in the eutrophic region just above the excessive boundary. For a hydraulic loading of 7.1 m/a, the permissible phosphorus loading ($L = 0.10$) is 0.18 g/m^2·a and the excessive ($L = 0.30$) is 0.44 g/m^2·a. These values are higher than those based on mean depth alone because of the relatively short renewal time of water in the reservoir, which is

$$t = \frac{z}{q} = \frac{17 \text{ m}}{7.1 \text{ m/a}} = 2.4 \text{ a}$$

The phosphorus concentration (loading) is calculated using Equation 9-5.

$$P = \frac{(0.57 \text{ g/m}^2 \cdot \text{a})/(7.1 \text{ m/a})}{1 + (2.4 \text{ a})^{0.5}} = 0.032 \text{ g/m}^3$$

This phosphorus value with the mean of chlorophyll measurements (25 mg/m³) plots in Figure 9-18 on the dashed line representing the upper 99 percent confidence limit, which is located among points of eutrophic lakes.

The critical annual phosphorus loadings are computed using Equation 9-6 as follows:

Permissible $P = (0.010 \text{ g/m}^3)(7.1 \text{ m/a})[1 + (2.4 \text{ a})^{0.5}] = 0.18 \text{ g/m}^2 \cdot \text{a}$

Excessive $P = (0.020 \text{ g/m}^3)(7.1 \text{ m/a})[1 + (2.4 \text{ a})^{0.5}] = 0.36 \text{ g/m}^2 \cdot \text{a}$

The trophic state of this lake is best described as eutrophic based on its plotting position on all three diagrams. In addition, the field measurements of soluble phosphorus at spring overturn, hypolimnetic dissolved oxygen deficit of 7 mg/l below saturation (10 mg/l at 16°C), summer chlorophyll, and reduced transparency in the epilimnion all indicate eutrophic waters.

The permissible annual phosphorus loading is 0.18 g/m²·a and the excessive loading is 0.36 g/m²·a, whereas the present phosphorus addition is 0.57 g/m²·a. Therefore, in order to retard further eutrophication, a phosphorus reduction of about one third is required, while recovery toward an oligotrophic state needs at least a two-thirds reduction in the present phosphorus input.

Example 9-3

A natural lake, which serves as a source for municipal water and the focal point for regional recreation, shows early indications of increasing fertility. The mean depth equals 12 m, and the surface area is 168 km². The principal inflow into the lake is a river with an average discharge of 7.1 m³/s. A phosphorus survey of the drainage basin revealed three major sources: seepage from septic-tank drainfields and rainfall runoff entering the lake from shore areas contribute approximately 10 000 kg of phosphorus per year; a town located 5 km upstream from the lake discharges 4 000 m³/d of biologically treated wastewater containing an average of 10 mg/l of phosphorus into the river; and, the river above the town's outfall sewer has a mean concentration of 0.020 mg/l from land drainage.

The town is expanding rapidly toward a population of 20 000, which will increase the wastewater flow to 8 000 m³/d. If the expanded treatment plant incorporates phosphorus reduction to 1.0 mg/l in the effluent, will the lake be protected from further eutrophication?

Solution

Water retention time in the lake is calculated by:

$$t = \frac{\text{Volume}}{\text{Inflow}} = \frac{168 \times 10^6 \text{ m}^2 \times 12 \text{ m}}{7.1 \text{ m}^3/\text{s} \times 31.5 \times 10^6 \text{ s/a}} = 9.0 \text{ a}$$

Hydraulic loading $= \dfrac{z}{t} = \dfrac{12 \text{ m}}{9.0 \text{ a}} = 1.3 \text{ m/a}$

Using Equation 9-6, the permissible phosphorus loading to maintain oligotrophy is

$$L_c = 0.010 \times 1.3 \, [1 + (9.0)^{0.5}] = 0.010 \times 5.2 = 0.052 \; g/m^2 \cdot a$$

For maintaining mestrophy,

$$L_c = 0.020 \times 5.2 = 0.10 \; g/m^2 \cdot a$$

Phosphorus in local drainage is given as 10 000 kg/a.

Background phosphorus in river flow equals

$$7.1 \; m^3/s \times 31.5 \times 10^6 \; s/a \times 0.02 \; g/m^3 \times 10^{-3} \; kg/g = 4\,500 \; kg/a$$

Phosphorus in the wastewater discharge is

$$4\,000 \; m^3/d \times 365 \; d/a \times 10 \; g/m^3 \times 10^{-3} \; kg/g = 14\,600 \; kg/a$$

Then, the annual phosphorus loading on the lake is calculated as

$$\frac{(14\,600 + 4\,500 + 10\,000)10^3}{168 \times 10^6} = 0.17 \; g/m^2 \cdot a$$

Based on this value, the lake plots in the mesotrophic region of Figure 9-17. Including the additional 4 000 m^3/d of wastewater, resulting from projected population increase, the loading would increase to 0.26 $g/m^2 \cdot a$, which borders on the excessive level.

The amount of phosphorus in the effluent from the expanded treatment plant based on a content of 1.0 mg/l is

$$8\,000 \; m^3/d \times 365 \; d/a \times 1.0 \; g/m^3 \times 10^{-3} \; kg/g = 2\,900 \; kg/a$$

The annual phosphorus loading on the lake would then be

$$\frac{(2\,900 + 4\,500 + 10\,000)10^3}{168 \times 10^6} = 0.10 \; g/m^2 \cdot a$$

This loading level should be sufficiently low to maintain the mestrophic state of the lake.

9-7 Ecological Studies of Impounded Waters

Lake Washington, State of Washington

Located within the metropolitan area of Seattle, this lake is fed by nutrient-poor rivers and drains to Puget Sound through a ship canal (Figure 9-19). The surface area is $110 \times 10^6 \; m^2$, volume $3.6 \times 10^9 \; m^3$, mean depth 33 m, maximum depth 65 m, and average water renewal time 2.9 years.[10] The lake is in full circulation all winter, and stratifies during the summer with an epilimnion approximately 10 m deep. Lake Washington is valued primarily for its esthetics and recreation, notably swimming, boating, and water-skiing. Fishing is a secondary benefit, and use as a drinking water supply ceased in 1965.

Early in the 1900s, the lake received discharges of untreated domestic wastewater that lead to a concern for public health since the lake served as a drinking water

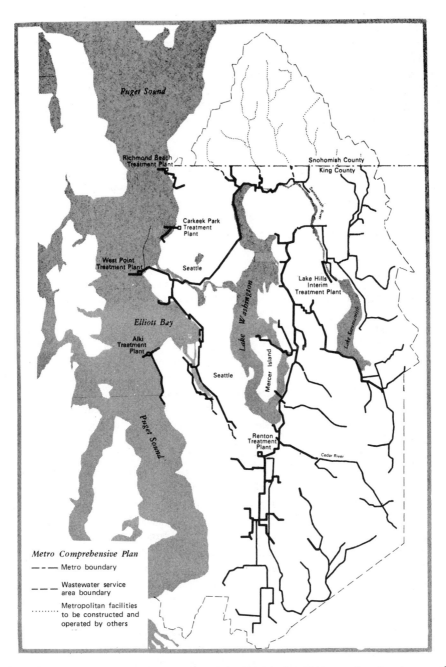

Figure 9-19 Comprehensive wastewater plan of the Municipality of Metropolitan Seattle to prevent pollution of Lake Washington and Puget Sound. Wastewaters are diverted around the lake by collecting sewers and transmission mains extending to treatment plants that discharge processed effluents to Puget Sound.

417

source. In about 1936 to resolve the problem, the untreated domestic wastes were diverted to Puget Sound—at this time nutrient enrichment of Lake Washington was not a concern. However, wastewaters were again discharged to the lake, this time after conventional treatment, as Seattle continued to expand and small towns developed around the lake. The population served by the ten treatment facilities (six activated-sludge and four trickling-filter plants) increased to about 65 000 persons between 1941 and 1957. In addition, creeks flowing into the lake carried septic-tank drainage with an equivalent wastewater from 12 000 persons. Seattle also had combined sewers that overflowed during periods of rainfall adding an estimated population equivalent of 4 500. In 1957, wastewater sources were contributing 49 900 kg of total phosphorus, or 56 percent of the total inflow.[11] The total phosphorus concentration in the lake increased greatly (by a factor of 2.7) during the interval from 1957 to 1963; this was attributed primarily to increased use of household detergents with phosphate builders. By the time corrective action began in the early 1960s, the total phosphorus load on the lake increased approximately threefold with 75 percent coming from wastewater discharges.

A study in 1933 indicated Lake Washington was relatively infertile; however, by the second analysis in 1950, nutrient concentrations had increased and dissolved oxygen content in deep water during the summer decreased. Noticeable eutrophication in the lake accelerated with the nitrogen and phosphorus from wastewater promoting increases in planktonic algae which culminated in a conspicuous bloom of the blue-green alga *Oscillatoria rubescens* in 1955. The following year an advisory committee, appointed by the mayor of Seattle, reviewed the pollution problem and recommended diversion of wastewaters from Lake Washington to Puget Sound. The nutrients added to this saltwater estuary were not expected to cause any problem, thus, the diversion was not considered to be a matter of moving undesirable algal growth from one place to another. Furthermore, the committee recognized that eutrophication could not be prevented by conventional biological treatment. In 1958, the municipality of Metropolitan Seattle (Metro) was formed, upon approval by a public vote, to control wastewaters in Seattle and surrounding areas. Metro currently manages several treatment plants serving approximately one million people in a drainage area of about 800 km^2. The two largest plants are West Point handling the city of Seattle, and Renton serving the east side of Lake Washington and the region to the south (Figure 9-19). Smaller units collect wastes from areas adjacent to Puget Sound.

The first diversion of wastewater took place in March, 1963, five years after organization of Metro, with 99 percent diverted by April, 1967, and the final construction completed in April, 1968. Figure 9-20 relates the reduction of wastewater input to key parameters of phosphorus concentrations, Secchi disk readings, and amounts of chlorophyll in the epilimnion. The lake stopped deteriorating after the first diversion, and noticeable recovery quickly followed. Winter phosphorus concentrations, which had been increasing rapidly, stabilized and began to sharply decrease after some irregular variation. Since the amount of summer phytoplankton followed the winter phosphate trend, chlorophyll in the top 10 m also dropped dramatically and transparency increased. During the summer of 1976, the Secchi disk transparency averaged 5.8 m,

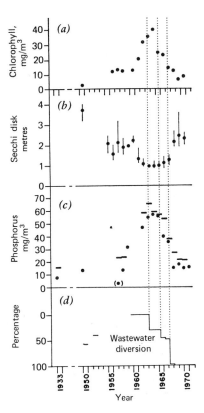

Figure 9-20 Changes in the trophic conditions of Lake Washington resulting from diversion of wastewater discharges into the lake. (a) The mean chlorophyll a in the top 10 m (epilimnion) during July and August. (b) The mean Secchi disk transparency during July and August; the vertical lines show the range, maximum and minimum. (c) Annual means of total phosphorus in the top 10 m are shown as bars, and averages of phosphate phosphorus from January through March as circles. (d) A graph of the relative amount of wastewater draining into the lake with the maximum taken as 100 percent. The vertical dotted lines show the major decreases as effluents were diverted. (From W. T. Edmondson, "Nutrients and Phytoplankton in Lake Washington," *Special Symposia on Nutrients and Eutrophication*, Vol. I, 1972, pp. 172-193, The American Society of Limnology and Oceanography, Inc.)

which is greater than the mean of 3.7 m in 1950. Recovery was enhanced by the flushing action of nutrient-free water. The inflow from tributaries, such as the Cedar River, is greatest when the lake is in full circulation during the winter. The quick recuperation, which took place upon reduction of phosphorus input, slowed during the early 1970s as the ecosystem approached its original condition. Figure 9-21 shows graphs of nutrient and chlorophyll variations for the 12-year period beginning with the first diversion of wastewater; the initial 1963 values are all expressed as 100 percent. Mean winter phosphate, annual average total phosphorus, and summer chlorophyll follow the same downward trend with the magnitudes in 1975 approaching the oligo-

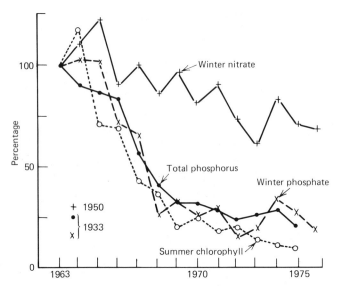

Figure 9-21 Nutrient and chlorophyll variations in Lake Washington beginning with the first wastewater diversion in 1963; all values are expressed as percentages of the initial concentrations. Winter phosphate and nitrate data are average concentrations in the epilimnion (top 10 m) January through March; total phosphorus is the average annual value; and chlorophyll a is the mean in surface phytoplankton during July and August. The absolute values in 1963, plotted as 100 percent, were 55 mg/m³ of winter mean phosphate phosphorus, 425 mg/m³ of winter nitrate nitrogen, and 35 mg/m³ of chlorophyll a. (From W. T. Edmondson, *Trophic Equilibrium of Lake Washington*. EPA-600/3-77-087, August 1977.)

trophic level. In contrast, mean winter nitrate, by decreasing much less than phosphorus, does not relate to summer chlorophyll content of the phytoplankton. This strongly supports the concept that phosphorus is the most important element for plant growth in lakes. The equilibrium trophic level of the lake, of course, cannot be predicted exactly, and certainly the watershed is not immune to further development that can again increase nutrient loading.

Vollenweider[9] plotted phosphorus loading, calculated from Equation 9-5, versus average summer chlorophyll as drawn in Figure 9-22. (Also refer back to Figure 9-18.) During the period from 1957 to 1964, while the phosphorus content of the lake was increasing, summer chlorophyll measurements and corresponding calculated phosphorus concentrations plot within the 99 percent confidence limits. After wastewater diversion was implemented, however, chlorophyll measurements are slightly above the prediction limit until 1971; this may be interpreted as a lag phenomenon. Data from 1972 to 1974 fall very nearly on the chlorophyll-loading line that passed through the 1957 prediversion point.

Successful reversal of cultural eutrophication by wastewater diversion is founded on two fundamental principles: the majority of the phosphorus input is eliminated by diversion of the point sources, and the water renewal time is relatively short. Other considerations include mean water depth, extent of the littoral zone, climate, degree

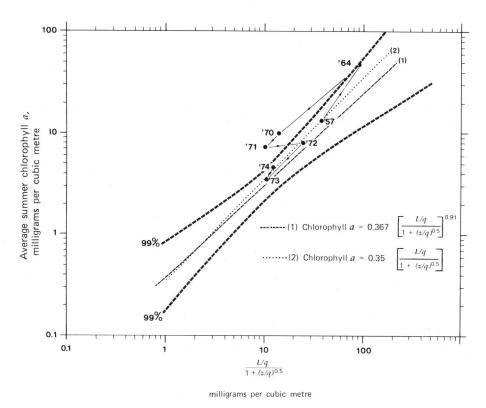

milligrams per cubic metre

Figure 9-22 Application of the phosphorus loading concept to Lake Washington before and after wastewater diversion. (From R. A. Vollenweider, "Advances in Defining Critical Loading Levels for Phosphorus in Lake Eutrophication," *Memorie dell'Instituto Italiano di Idrobiologia*, Vol. 33, 1976.)

of fertilization prior to corrective action, land usage in the watershed, and surrounding population growth. Vollenweider and Dillon[8] summarized the responses of several lakes to reduced phosphorus loading. One historical case is the diversion of wastewater effluents from a chain of lakes (Mendota, Monona, Waukesa, and Kegonsa) near Madison, Wisconsin.[12] Lake Monona, which is situated immediately adjacent to the city, had troublesome algal blooms in the 1890s after untreated domestic discharges had been piped into it for several years. After 1900, the wastes were processed by conventional physical-biological treatment, however, the lakes continued to deteriorate due to high nutrient loadings. Finally, the wastewaters were recognized as the major sources of nitrogen and phosphorus, and in 1936 discharge to Lake Monona was abandoned. Diversion continued until 1958 when all of the effluents were routed around the chain of lakes. Nevertheless, the phosphorus loadings on the lakes remained quite high because of the contribution from surrounding agricultural land and although improvement has not been outstanding, conditions would have become much worse without wastewater diversion. Natural flushing has reduced the soluble phosphorus content. As a result, the trophic levels of the lakes have stabilized, and some indicators reflect the reduction in fertility. For example, the algae have increased in species diversity and created less frequent blue-green blooms.

The Laurentian Great Lakes

Even though their large drainage basins and huge volumes of impounded water provide strong resistance to change, all of the Laurentian Great Lakes have some alterations in environment and biota brought about either directly, or indirectly, by human activities. (Morphometric data for the Great Lakes are given in Table 8-1.) Those most greatly influenced by population growth and concomitant alteration of the natural environment are Lakes Erie, Michigan, and Ontario, with the least affected being Superior. In a little over 200 years, the drainage basin of Lake Erie has been completely altered from wilderness populated by about 100 000 people to a watershed with agriculture and industry supporting a population of approximately 15 million. Associated with the major urban centers are extensive sewer systems collecting wastewater that ultimately discharge to the lake.

Many of the documented changes taking place in these large lakes are similar to those cited as indices of cultural eutrophication in smaller lakes. Limnological observations show: long-term increases in dissolved solids and most major ions (Erie, Huron, Michigan, and Ontario), changes in species composition and numbers of benthic organisms in bays subjected to pollution (western Lake Erie, Saginaw Bay, and southern Green Bay), denser plankton in regions of increased fertility (Erie, Ontario, and southern Lake Michigan), reduction of hypolimnetic dissolved oxygen during thermal stratification (Erie), and shifts in fish populations. However, equating changes in these lakes to moderate-sized bodies of water is an oversimplification, since eutrophication progresses somewhat differently in very large lakes. The concepts of enrichment favoring those algal species requiring high nutrient levels and increased productivity being reflected in hypolimnetic oxygen depletion cannot be applied to the Great Lakes.[13] Their size and diversity of aquatic habitats precludes such an overall response. The initial reaction to nutrient inputs occurs in bays and littoral areas, which can undergo significant alterations in their ecosystems. Comparable changes may eventually take place in open water, but unless the lake is uniformly shallow the effects are different in the offshore areas because of greater water depths. Consequently, morphometric factors are especially important in determining the response of large lakes to nutrient loading. The rate of response to eutrophication is also a function of water renewal time. For an inflow with the same concentration of nutrients, increased plant growth is noticed in a smaller lake more quickly than a lake with greater dilutional capacity. Hence, Lake Erie with a water renewal time of only about 2.5 years has shown the effects of pollution much more rapidly than Michigan with a retention time of about 100 years.

Lake Erie is considered the most eutrophic of the Great Lakes. Pollution was first observed along the shore and in the shallow western basin. Subsequently, the effects spread to the open lake areas of the central and eastern basins as changes in the environment and biota progressed from inshore to offshore waters, and from the western

Table 9-2 Trophic Scheme for the Laurentian Great Lakes

Oligotrophic	Mesotrophic	Secondary[a] Eutrophic	Highly Eutrophic Polluted
Lake Superior			
Lake Huron (offshore)	(inshore)		Saginaw Bay
		Lake Erie	
	Eastern Basin	Central Basin	Western Basin
		Lake Ontario	
	(offshore)	(inshore)	(Bay of Quinte)
	Lake Michigan		
(offshore)		(inshore)	(Green Bay)

[a] "Secondary eutrophic" is used here in the sense of lake regions showing relatively high annual primary production, occurrence of occasional algal blooms, and/or increased growth of periphyton (cladophora) or macrophytes due to local pollution.

Source. R. A. Vollenweider, M. Munawar, and P. Stadelmann, "A Comparative Review of Phytoplankton and Primary Production in the Laurentian Great Lakes," Journal Fisheries Research Board of Canada, Vol. 31, No. 5, 1974.

basin eastward. The morphology of Lake Erie, shown in Figure 9-23, allows separate consideration of the three basins as proposed by the trophic classification in Table 9-2. The eutrophy of Lake Erie increases from the western region, which receives the major sources of nutrient input, to the eastern basin that drains to Lake Ontario.

The effects of human activities have produced obvious changes in fish populations of the Great Lakes. Carp and smelt were purposely introduced, and construction of the Welland Canal in 1829 permitted migration of the alewife and sea lamprey around Niagara Falls. The exact influence of the alewife, carp, and smelt on the populations of native fish is not know, although the decline of lake herring populations in Lakes

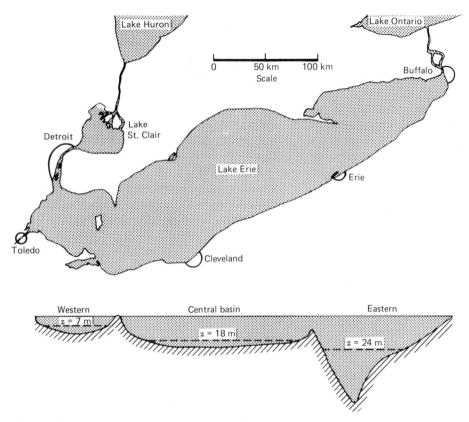

Figure 9-23 Plan and longitudinal cross section of Lake Erie.

Huron and Michigan appear to coincide with the establishment of the alewife in these lakes. The near-extinction of the sturgeon in all the lakes was caused by overfishing, and rapid decline of the lake trout in each of the upper lakes is undoubtedly the result of predation by the sea lamprey. The abundance of this predator was finally reduced by selective chemical treatment in spawning and breeding streams. In the 1960s chinook and coho salmon were introduced in an attempt to restore predator fish that would control the abundant alewife. Lake Erie, being both the shallowest lake and the one receiving the greatest pollutional load, has responded with low oxygen content in the bottom water during stratification. In addition to serious oxygen deficits, the large amounts of organic matter contributed to the sediments have caused major changes in the benthos. Shifts in fish populations of Lake Erie may be related to changes in the sediments, since all of the fish (except sheepshead) have bottom-dwelling eggs and are part of the benthos during a critical period in their life cycles.[14] In conclusion, several combined factors have led to the marked changes in the fish community: intensive selective exploitation, invasion and introduction of marine species, contribution of chemicals as a result of urbanization and industrialization, and adverse modifications of the drainage basin and tributaries used for spawning and natural reproductive success.

River Reservoirs (Tennessee Valley and Ohio River Basins)

The Tennessee Valley Authority (TVA), created as a corporate agency of the federal government in 1933, was directed to provide flood control, navigation, and electric power generation for the Tennessee River Basin. The multiple-purpose development resulted in construction of nine dams varying in height from 12 m to 30.5 m spaced along the 1 050-km stream length (Figure 9-24). Thus, the free-flowing river was transformed into a contiguous series of slack-water pools navigable by vessels of 2.7 m draft. In order to use the storage capacity for both flow control and power, operation involves filling the reservoirs during winter and spring months, with the maximum water levels occurring early summer, followed by drawdown during summer, fall, and early winter. The watershed supports farming, several major urban centers, and substantial industrial development incorporating manufacture of chemicals, textiles, primary metals, food, and paper products. While the highest water quality exists in the headwaters, the river is vulnerable to pollution from industrial cities along the main stem. Major water uses are for municipal supplies, industrial cooling and process waters, recreation (swimming, water-skiing, boating, fishing, camping and picnicking), commercial fishing, navigation, and dilution of domestic and industrial wastewater discharges. The degree of waste treatment is governed by water quality objectives based on the beneficial uses of water supply, recreation, and fish propagation.

Many ecological changes occur when a river is converted into a series of reservoirs. The first environmental challenge was eradication of malaria. The mosquito-borne disease infected many people who inhabited the swampy areas along the original Tennessee River. To prevent creation of new breeding habitats, reservoir basins were cleared of debris and ditches constructed to drain any pools that would form with drawdown of the impounded water. The most important postimpoundment method of controlling mosquitoes is by fluctuating reservoir levels about 0.3 m weekly during the breeding season, followed by a gradual recession later in the year. Other techniques employed include maintenance of drainage, reducing plant growth, and applying larvicides.

A major water quality problem is the low concentration of dissolved oxygen in the water released from deep reservoirs. Since most of the TVA dams were constructed with only low-level outlets, discharges are drawn from the hypolimnion where the water has reduced oxygen content during thermal stratification. For many reservoirs, dissolved oxygen levels below 4 mg/l are common in late fall, and measurements in some drop below 2 mg/l in October and November.[15] Oxygen depletions are attributed to both the organic matter in the river inflow and eutrophication of the impounded water. If influent flow is cooler, and thus denser, polluted river water entering the reservoir mixes with the hypolimnion exerting a biochemical oxygen demand. In contrast, warmer inflow blends organics and nutrients with the epilimnetic water. Oxygen demands on an impoundment, as a result of high productivity in the summer, is more serious in many cases than the contribution of organic matter. An EPA

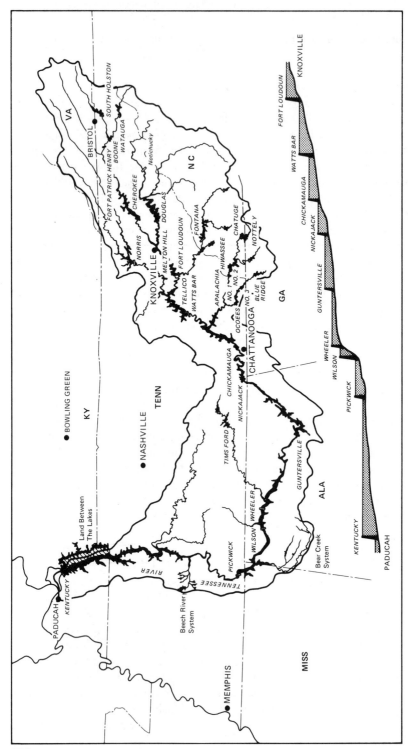

Figure 9-24 Plan of the Tennessee Valley region and profile of the Tennessee River from Paducah to Knoxville. (From *Water Quality in the Tennessee Valley*, TVA, Division of Environmental Planning, Water Quality Branch, Chattanooga, Tenn., 1973.)

national eutrophication survey[16] found the majority of man-made lakes were eutrophic with phosphorus loads above the excessive level. These results are not surprising since phosphorus removal is not usually practiced in wastewater treatment prior to disposal by dilution in major rivers, even if reservoirs are situated on the main stem.

Nutrient enrichment also promotes the growth of aquatic weeds. In TVA lakes, the greatest nuisance is Eurasian water milfoil, a lacy water plant sometimes used to adorn fish bowls or aquariums. Dense growths of this aquatic plant clog coves and block water intakes adversely affecting recreation and creating habitats for mosquito breeding. Milfoil is controlled by dosing with herbicides and manipulation of reservoir water levels. Associated with eutrophication are warm-water discharges from coal and nuclear power plants. Increasing the temperature of river water accelerates biological activity, including plant growth.

In the Ohio River basin, the objectives in developing and managing of water resources are flood control, navigation, water supply, hydropower, flow augmentation, water quality control, recreation, and fish and wildlife.[17] The river extends 1 580 km from Pittsburgh, Pennsylvania, to the Mississippi River at Cairo, Illinois, draining 528 000 km², which supports a population of about 25 million. The watershed is extensively industrialized and approximately one third of the area is used for intensive agriculture. These activities place heavy demands on water resources with one of the most important being reservoir discharge for low-flow augmentation to maintain instream assimilation of domestic, industrial, mining, and other types of wastes. Low-flow augmentation is provided, in part, by the routine operation of the reservoir system in meeting flood control and navigation objectives. Regulated release of summer storm runoff and storage specifically set-aside for flow augmentation can constitute as much as two thirds of the total flow in parts of the main stem. Reduction of reservoir pool levels in late summer and early fall also offsets the most critical problems. In addition to low-flow management, the problem of protecting the quality of reservoir storage and discharge becomes increasingly difficult with rapid commercial development in the basin.[17]

Typically, the reservoirs in the Ohio River basin are thermally stratified resulting in oxygen depletion below the thermocline. The effects of discharges vary depending on the characteristics of the river downstream and quality of the outflow, particularly in relation to oxygen content and temperature. The aquatic environment can be radically changed by discharge of cold water into a previously warm-water stream, and release of a dilution flow low in oxygen content and high in biochemical oxygen demand. Although most dams have low outlets, some were built with bypass arrangements permitting outflow from various pool elevations allowing selective water quality control.

Small Reservoirs

Hundreds of man-made lakes have been constructed throughout the world, most frequently for purposes of water supply, recreation, culturing fish, reducing soil erosion, and flood control.[2] The Great Plains region of the United States does not have a large number of natural lakes; however, many reservoirs have been built in recent years for flood control, soil conservation, and recreation. Facilities for the latter are often boat ramps, bathhouses, sand beaches, and campsites. Unfortunately, while these lakes seemingly alleviate the long-standing need for recreational waters, many existing impoundments are troubled by excessive and rapid eutrophication resulting in deterioration of their water-based uses after a few years of existence. The naturally fertile soils of the region, widespread application of fertilizers to agricultural lands, and livestock feeding can all contribute to the high nutrient content in runoff water leading to naturally productive ecosystems that generate nuisances. These ponds also gradually fill with soil eroded from cultivated fields and organic matter generated in the lake. In the long term, say 20 to 50 years, the problem is likely to be reduction of the pool volume, and ultimate extinction of the lake because of siltation and sedimentation.

The following comments are based on a study of reservoirs in eastern Nebraska.[18] The primary purposes for construction of the dams were flood control and soil conservation with recreation as a secondary benefit. After initial filling over a period of three to five years, discharges are intermittent and generally occur as a result of heavy spring rains. Surface areas of the lakes range from 40 to 700 ha, and mean depths vary from 2 to 4.5 m. The lakes are exposed to wind and continuously mixed throughout their entire depth during most of the year, except under ice cover. Transient stratification can occur occasionally during hot windless periods in the summer, particularly if the impoundment is sheltered by hills and trees. Water temperature, influenced directly by ambient air temperature, averages 25°C during the summer months. The pH remains in the range of 7.5 to 9.0, and soil turbidity varies with the size of reservoir and degree of wind mixing.

Runoff waters entering the lakes contain high concentrations of inorganic nitrogen (0.7 to 1.3 mg/l) and phosphate phosphorus (0.1 to 0.5 mg/l), which result in average concentrations of 1.0 mg/l of inorganic nitrogen and 0.1 mg/l of orthophosphate in the reservoir waters in the spring. These levels of nutrients are sufficient to create excessive growths of phytoplankton and macrophytes. The latter were most abundant during the first few growing seasons after closing the dam. Clarity of the water in late spring permitted sufficient light penetration to stimulate rooted aquatics (*Potamogeton pectinatus, P. americanus*, and *Polygonum*) from water depths to 5 m. However, algal populations were soon established reducing the water transparency and shifting the response of further enrichment from macrophytes to blue-green algal blooms, commonly of the genera *Aphanizomenon, Anabaena*, and *Anacystis*.

Pawnee Lake was one of the reservoirs constructed for flood control and developed as a recreation site near Lincoln, Nebraska. The impoundment at conservation pool elevation has a surface area of 300 ha and mean depth of 3.7 m; the watershed is approximately 9.2 km^2. Facilities are provided in recreational areas for swimming, water skiing, boating, and fishing. After a four-year filling period, the nutrient concentrations in the impounded water during the summer of 1968 averaged 0.16 mg/l of phosphorus as filterable orthophosphate, 0.47 mg/l of phosphorus as filterable acid-hydrolyzable and orthophosphate, 0.35 mg/l of ammonia nitrogen (unfiltered water), and 0.21 mg/l of nitrate nitrogen (unfiltered water).[18] Other physical-chemical measurements during June, July, and August were average pH 8.3, normal temperature range 20 to 25°C, and usual dissolved oxygen concentrations between 3 mg/l and

7 mg/l. The first response to these nearly ideal conditions for growth of plants appeared as extensive beds of rooted aquatics. Suspended soil in spring runoff settled out quickly allowing sunlight penetration. And with the absence of heavy algal growth, transparency of the water in late spring permitted light penetration sufficient to stimulate rooted weed growth from water depths up to 5 m. In 1968 (the second year of full impoundment), submerged and floating leafed aquatics covered over half of the open water area. Even though they persisted for the next few years, this peak growth of macrophytes was not repeated again as blooms of algae in spring increased water turbidity reducing sunlight penetration.

Chlorophyll data for the Pawnee reservoir are plotted in Figures 9-25 and 9-26. Blue-green algae were the predominant group contributing to the chlorophyll content. The impounded water had low algal populations and a mean Secchi disk depth greater than 2 m the first two years after filling. The dam was closed in July 1964, and collected runoff during the fall of that year. During the following spring (1965) the impoundment filled to approximately one-half capacity and remained at that water volume until June 1967. In that month, heavy runoff from rainfall filled the reservoir to overflow. Therefore, the 1968 line on Figure 9-25 represents the fourth season of impoundment. The subsequent growing seasons produced algal blooms in both early and late summer. These intensified so that Secchi disk transparency during the sixth year of impoundment averaged less than 0.5 m during summer months. The plot of mean summer chlorophyll concentrations in Figure 9-26 illustrates the increase in standing crop of algae with age in a fertile-water impoundment.

Lake Volta, Ghana

The primary purpose of the Volta River Project was hydroelectric power for processing aluminum from bauxite and to support other industrial developments since the economy of Ghana was dependent almost entirely on the single crop of cocoa. The artificial lake also created opportunities for lake transportation, a fishery industry, irrigated agriculture, and recreation. Being the largest man-made lake in Africa, it covers 8 500 km^2, which is 3.6 percent of the land area of Ghana, and drains most of its rivers (Figure 9-27). The pool is 400 km long and relatively shallow, averaging less than 20 m; yet, the large water surface results in a capacity of 165 km^3. Although power production has had significant impact on the economy since 1965, the creation of a riverine impoundment of this magnitude causes dramatic changes that interact with the human population, such as resettlement, disease control, and food production.

Most of the 80 000 people in the flooded area of the river basin were subsistence farmers located in 700 villages. The options for resettlement were either to accept compensation for lost property and make personal arrangements, or to be settled by the Volta River Authority. With 85 percent electing the latter, 52 new communities were established with populations between 2 000 and 5 000. Villages from the same areas were consolidated to minimize the social tensions of moving different ethnic groups from their traditional homelands. New town sites were selected with regard to soil conditions, public health, access roads, water supply, and consent of the people.

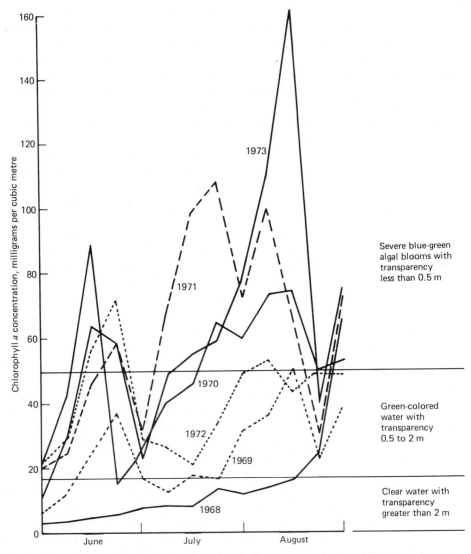

Figure 9-25 Summer chlorophyll concentrations in Pawnee reservoir plotted for successive years after construction. The dam was closed in 1964 and began collecting runoff. The impoundment filled to overflow elevation in 1967. (Unpublished data courtesy of G. L. Hergenrader.)

The typical dwelling provided for the settlers had two rooms with porches, concrete floor, and aluminum roofing. Materials were provided for additional improvements by the owner. After land acquisition by the authority, new farmlands were leased to settlers on long-term agreements that are inheritable and renewable.

Relocation is expected to improve public health by proper site location, better housing, health centers, and educational facilities. Most of the settlements are rela-

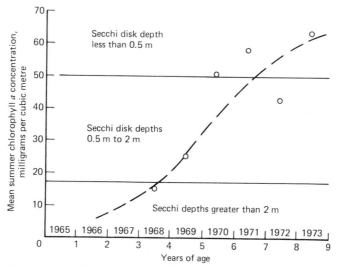

Figure 9-26 Mean summer (June, July, and August) chlorophyll *a* concentrations versus reservoir age from measurements graphed in Figure 9-25. The approximate correlation between chlorophyll concentration and water transparency is delineated by Secchi disk ranges. (Unpublished data courtesy of G. L. Hergenrader.)

tively free from the tsetse and simulium flies, vectors of sleeping sickness and river blindness, respectively. However, incidents of the latter still occur downstream of the dam where *Simulium damnosum* breeds in the rapids of the river. The major new health problems generated by the lake result from growth of aquatic weeds that provide favorable habitats for a number of disease vectors, notably the *Bulinus* snail, which is the vector of urinary schistosomiasis (bilharzia) and the *Mansona africana* mosquito, vector of the yellow fever virus. The prevalence of bilharzia, for which there is no ready control, is high in several localities near the reservoir.

Irrigation has great potential in the Accra plains, which are suitable for mechanized agriculture. Based on soils and climate, the best crops appear to be rice, sugar cane, cotton, grain, vegetables, tree crops, pineapples, and grass and legume mixtures for cattle grazing. This region is capable of supplying almost all the country's present needs in these commodities. Another important agricultural development, associated with the lake, is farming the land exposed by fluctuations in water level. Approximately 80 000 ha are exposed around the lake boundary with a drop in water level of 3 m. Although drought conditions and insects create some problems, flood plain areas near settlements are farmed by cropping vegetables and maize.

Fishing is one of the most significant developments on Lake Volta with the annual catch yielding tens of thousands of tonnes. Residents of over a thousand villages harvest fish from small boats using hooks, lines, traps, and gill nets yielding the greatest catching capacity. Without refrigeration facilities, the fish are processed and preserved by smoking, drying, and salting. Marketing is done either by women from the village or by traders who travel from larger cities by boat.

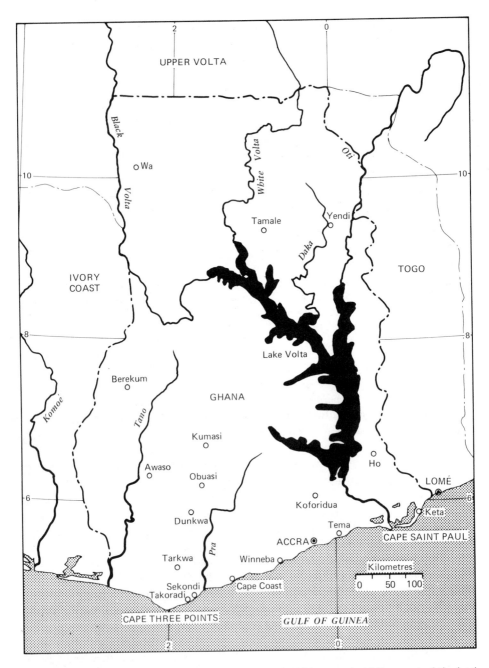

Figure 9-27 The man-made Lake Volta is the largest in Africa covering 3.6 percent of the land area in Ghana. The primary purpose is hydropower for processing bauxite for aluminum; secondary benefits are fisheries, transportation, and irrigated agriculture.

Because of the protein value of fish, a reliable harvest is extremely important to the welfare of the people. Fishery studies include improving methods of processing and preservation, stock assessment, and propagation of desired populations. A major concern is the possible reduction of nutrients, which would reduce yield. In contrast to the problem of unwanted eutrophication in many industrial nations, the reduction of fertility in the food chain resulting from reservoir aging is of great concern to commercial fishing in man-made lakes in tropical climates. The initial postinundation boom in fish yield may decline to a much lower renewable quantity available for harvest. Several alternatives are being evaluated. Perhaps restocking or fishing in deeper waters can be helpful; most of the current catch takes place in the shallow inshore waters. While direct fertilization of a large lake is not economical, fish ponds may be a feasible alternative.

References

1. Lagler, K. F. (editor), *Man-Made Lakes, Planning and Development*, Food and Agriculture Organization of the United Nations, Rome, Italy, 1969.

2. Ackermann, W. C., White, G. F., and Worthington, E. G. (editors), *Man-Made Lakes: Their Problems and Environmental Effects*, Geophysical Monograph 17, American Geophysical Union, Washington, D. C., 1973.

3. *Standard Methods for the Examination of Water and Wastewater*, 14th Edition, American Public Health Association, American Water Works Association, and Water Pollution Control Federation, 1975.

4. Reid, G. K., and Wood, R. D., *Ecology of Inland Waters and Estuaries*, 2nd Edition, Van Nostrand Co., 1976.

5. Lind, O. T., *Handbook of Common Methods in Limnology*, The C. V. Mosby Co., Saint Louis, 1974.

6. Lueschow, L. A., Helm, J. M., Winter, D. R., and Karl, G. W., "Trophic Nature of Selected Wisconsin Lakes," *Wisconsin Academy of Sciences, Arts and Letters*, Vol. 58, 1970, pp. 237-264.

7. Vollenweider, R. A., *Scientific Fundamentals of the Eutrophication of Lakes and Flowing Waters with Particular Reference to Nitrogen and Phosphorus as Factors in Eutrophication*, Organization for Economic Co-operation and Development, Paris, France, 1970.

8. Vollenweider, R. A., and Dillon, P. J., *The Application of the Phosphorus Loading Concept to Eutrophication Research*, National Research Council of Canada, Canada Centre for Inland Waters, Burlington, Ontario, June, 1974.

9. Vollenweider, R. A., "Advances in Defining Critical Loading Levels for Phosphorus in Lake Eutrophication," *Memorie dell'Istituto Italiano di Idrobiologia*, Vol. 33, 1976, pp. 53-83. (Canada Centre for Inland Waters, Box 5050, Burlington, Ontario, Canada.)

10. Edmondson, W. T., "Lake Washington," *Environmental Quality and Water Development,* W. H. Freeman and Co., 1973.

11. Edmondson, W. T., "Nutrients and Phytoplankton in Lake Washington," *Nutrients and Eutrophication, Special Symposia,* Vol. I, 1972, pp. 172-193, The American Society of Limnology and Oceanography, Inc.

12. Sonzogni, W. C., and Lee, G. F., "Diversion of Wastewaters from Madison Lakes," *Journal of the Environmental Engineering Division,* ASCE, Vol. 100, No. EE1, February, 1974, pp. 153-170.

13. Beeton, A. M., and Edmondson, W. T., "The Eutrophication Problem," Journal Fisheries Research Board of Canada, Vol. 29, 1972, pp. 673-682.

14. Beeton, A. M., "Changes in the Environment and Biota of the Great Lakes," *Eutrophication: Causes, Consequences, Correctives,* National Academy of Sciences, Washington, D. C., 1969.

15. Churchill, M. A., and Nicholas, W. R., Effects of Impoundments on Water Quality, *National Symposium on Quality Standards for National Waters Proceedings,* Ann Arbor, Michigan, 1966, pp. 71-84.

16. *EPA National Eutrophication Survey,* U.S. Environmental Protection Agency, Corvallis, Oregon, 1975.

17. Anthony, M., and Drummond, G., Reservoir Water Quality Control, *Man-Made Lakes: Their Problems and Environmental Effects,* Geophysical Monograph 17, American Geophysical Union, Washington, D.C., 1973, pp. 549-551.

18. Hergenrader, G. L., and Hammer, M. J., Eutrophication of Small Reservoirs in the Great Plains, *Man-Made Lakes: Their Problems and Environmental Effects,* Geophysical Monograph 17, American Geophysical Union, Washington, D. C., 1973, pp. 560-566.

Problems

9-1 Comment on the authenticity of the statement: A common feature of natural and man-made lakes is the relatively constant water level.

9-2 List the common water-related human infections associated with man-made lakes.

9-3 Define an oligotrophic lake.

9-4 List the common cations and anions found in inland lake waters.

9-5 What is the principal way in which lake water is oxygenated?

9-6 Compare the dissolved-oxygen profiles in oligotrophic and eutrophic lakes after prolonged thermal stratification.

9-7 What are the sources supplying carbon dioxide to impounded waters?

9-8 Sketch the primary nitrogen cycle in an eutrophic lake.

9-9 Define biologically available phosphorus and identify its position in the classification chart of Figure 9-3.

9-10 What are the major sources of phosphorus in surface waters of populated regions?

9-11 Define the term phytoplankton. What factors determine its abundance in a lake?

9-12 What usually limits the productivity of algae during the growing season?

9-13 Define a copepod.

9-14 What is meant when a fish species is referred to as being tolerant?

9-15 What is the trophogenic zone of a lake? Littoral zone?

9-16 Why is the biomass of primary consumers much less than that of the primary producers, as illustrated in Figure 9-9?

9-17 Describe the method for determining Secchi disk transparency.

9-18 In a lake survey, how are (a) plankton sampled and (b) benthic organisms collected?

9-19 Are primary production and standing crop synonyms?

9-20 Why is phosphorus likely to be the limiting plant nutrient in a fertile lake?

9-21 Discuss the difficulty of controlling nitrogen enrichment of surface waters relative to controlling phosphorus fertilization.

9-22 Why are flowing waters (rivers) less susceptible to the adverse effects of fertilization?

9-23 Outline the key water quality and esthetic problems resulting from cultural eutrophication of a moderately fertile lake.

9-24 How does thermal stratification of an eutrophic lake influence the dissolved oxygen content in the hypolimnion?

9-25 What concentrations of nitrogen and phosphorus at the time of spring overturn are likely to cause undesirable plant growths in lakes during the subsequent growing season?

9-26 List the chemical and biological parameters used as a measure of the trophic level of a lake. What numerical values are normally associated with eutrophy?

9-27 What has been the only successful method of retarding cultural eutrophication?

9-28 List the temporary measures that can be employed to reduce nuisances in small eutrophic reservoirs.

9-29 How was Figure 9-16 developed by Vollenweider?

9-30 What additional factor, not incorporated in Figure 9-16, is accounted for in Figure 9-17? How was it included in the composition of Figure 9-17?

9-31 The mean depth of a lake is 60 m, the water renewal time 20 years, phosphorus loading 0.13 $g/m^2 \cdot a$, and the average epilimnetic chlorophyll 2.0 mg/m^3. Plot the position of this lake on Figures 9-16, 9-17, and 9-18. How is the lake classified and what are the permissible phosphorus loadings? (*Answers* oligotrophic-mesotrophic, 0.28 $g/m^2 \cdot a$ based on depth, 0.16 $g/m^2 \cdot a$ from Equation 9-6)

9-32 The mean depth of a lake is 7.8 m, the water renewal time is 1.2 years, phosphorus loading 2.1 $g/m^2 \cdot a$, and average chlorophyll is 20 mg/m^3. How is this lake classified based on phosphorus loading? What are the values of permissible and excessive loadings?

9-33 A lake with a surface area of 36 km^2 and mean depth of 12 m receives an average streamflow of 1.16 m^3/s. The only significant source of phosphorus input is the stream water that contains an average concentration of 0.15 mg/l. Calculate the phosphorus and hydraulic loadings, and estimate trophic level of the lake based on Figure 9-17. (*Answers* 0.15 $g/m^2 \cdot a$, 1.0 m/a, mesotrophic)

9-34 Major expansion of a resort area near a lake is being planned. You have been asked to give a preliminary recommendation regarding the need for phosphorus removal from the wastewater prior to discharge in a river entering the lake. The lake is classified as mesotrophic and has the following physical characteristics: surface area = 140 km^2, volume = 2.5 × 10^9 m^3, and epilimnion depth between 7 and 10 m during stratification. The river entering the lake has an average annual discharge of 280 × 10^6 m^3 with a mean phosphorus level upstream from the resort of 0.032 mg/l. The projected wastewater after expansion of the resort is 7 600 m^3/d with an average phosphorus content of 10 mg/l prior to treatment. (a) Calculate the separate phosphorus loadings on the lake from the streamflow and projected wastewater flow. (b) Using Equation 9-6, compute the critical loading for a phosphorus concentration of 0.015 g/m^3. (c) What degree of phosphorus removal is needed in wastewater treatment to prevent exceeding this mesotrophic loading? (*Answers* (a) 0.064 g/m^2·a, 0.20 g/m^2·a, (b) 0.12 g/m^2·a, (c) 72 percent)

9-35 A new urban area was planned around the reservoir of a recently constructed hydroelectric plant; the impoundment has a surface area of 40 km^2 and mean depth of 12 m. Siting of the city on land surrounding the artificial lake was for esthetics and to provide nearby water-based recreation. At present, the population is 270 000 people with an ultimate projection at 1.0 million inhabitants. All of the domestic wastewater is treated by conventional physical-biological processing and discharged into the lake. The reservoir has become progressively more eutrophic since its construction 20 years ago. Based on field observations, the average annual total nitrogen and phosphorus concentrations are 0.5 mg/l and 0.06 mg/l, respectively, and the mean Secchi disk depth is 0.8 m. (a) Using data on phosphorus given under "Chemical Factors" in Section 9-5, estimate the phosphorus loading. (b) Are the nutrient concentrations and water transparency representative of an eutrophic lake? (c) What corrective action do you recommend?

9-36 What was the major source of phosphorus entering Lake Washington causing its eutrophication?

9-37 Outline the actions taken to retard the fertilization of Lake Washington. Why were these measures effective?

9-38 What is the present status of Lake Washington? List the present nutrient concentrations, chlorophyll content, and Secchi disk transparency.

9-39 Why were the Madison, Wisconsin, lakes less responsive to the same corrective measures as applied to Lake Washington?

9-40 How does the response of nutrient enrichment in large lakes differ from that of moderate-sized impoundments?

9-41 List the factors that led to the environmental deterioration of the Great Lakes.

9-42 Describe the major water quality problems in the TVA reservoirs.

9-43 Why are small reservoirs in agricultural regions likely to be eutrophic, even though they do not receive domestic or industrial wastewaters?

9-44 Outline the aging process observed in reservoirs in eastern Nebraska.

9-45 How did the formation of Lake Volta in Ghana influence the prevalence of water-related human diseases?

9-46 How is the aging of Lake Volta likely to affect the fisheries?

Chapter 10
Water Resources Management

Under the pressure of population growth and economic expansion, water is appropriated for various uses that either reduce quantity or degrade quality, or both. Water projects sponsored by various special interest groups, both private and public, ultimately result in conflict as resources diminish. In the uncontrolled exploitation of a common resource, each user maximizes his or her benefit at the cost of all others; this is often referred to as the *tragedy of the commons*.* For example, if a water supply is available to many users, the greatest benefit accrues to the biggest consumer; however, if the supply falls short, the depletion is shared by all who have access. The analogy in water quality is pollution of a common lake or river.

Special interest groups also attempt to inhibit other competitors to protect themselves. If a common resource is dwindling, prohibiting increased use by others extends the benefits for current users. For example, attempts to develop new water programs are impeded by conflicts over water rights and agency multiplicity creating discord; each organization fears a loss that might result from the prosperity of others. Under such a stalemate, the participants reluctantly accept the concept of collective planning, which until then had been rejected for self-interest. Perhaps, for this reason, comprehensive management is rarely undertaken until most of the water resources developments in a region have been built, and present water policy emphasizes management and coordination of existing projects more than proposals for undertaking new enterprises.

10-1 Water Quantity Management

The earliest water developments in the United States were single-purpose private enterprises or projects sponsored by local governments, for example, water supplies for towns, construction of canals for transportation, or small dams for hydropower.

---

*"The Tragedy of the Commons" is an essay written by Garrett Hardin in the book *Managing the Commons* published by W. H. Freeman and Company, San Francisco, 1977. The "commons" are the world's common resources. The "tragedy" is that exploitation of a common resource is clearly to an *individual's* advantage; yet, if all individuals follow this strategy the resource would be exhausted—to the detriment of all. This remorseless, inherent logic of freedom in a commons brings ruin to all unless the freedom of the individual to exploit is limited.

The latter are common on small rivers in many regions since water power was the only locally available source of energy. In the beginning of the twentieth century, the federal government undertook projects to regulate major rivers for flood control and to improve navigation. Another major interest was settling the western states, which depended on controlling water in semiarid regions. The federal government extended its powers to protect commerce on navigable streams, manage the use of public lands, and improve the general welfare through the growth of several organizations. The Corps of Engineers, originally involved with only improving navigation and flood control, was authorized in 1927 to prepare studies for all major rivers (except the Colorado) considering the need for flood control and potential for navigation, irrigation, and hydroelectric power. A second extension of authority was given in 1937 to the Bureau of Reclamation in the Department of Interior, which allowed navigation and flood control in addition to irrigation and hydropower in reclamation projects. The third agency designated to design and construct water projects at the federal level was the Soil Conservation Service in the Department of Agriculture. While originally concerned only with erosion control, legislation in 1954 authorized incorporating small reservoirs for flood control; subsequent amendments further expanded the scope to incorporate water supply, irrigation, recreation, and wildlife propagation.

Federally sponsored projects by these three agencies were justified for multiple purposes, for instance, the series of dams on the Missouri River provides for navigation, flood control, hydropower, and irrigation plus the additional benefits of fisheries, recreation, and water supplies. Hoover Dam on the Colorado built in 1935 releases impounded water for downstream irrigation and municipal supplies, as well as providing flood protection and generating electricity. As a result of the economic depression in the 1930s, many major water projects were funded by the federal government to revive the economy while advancing water resources improvements. The Tennessee Valley Authority (TVA) was established as a governmental corporation in 1933 to program resource conservation for the economic development of the valley region. This included management of the Tennessee River and its tributaries for navigation, flood control, and hydropower. TVA was the first multipurpose plan for developing water resources of an entire drainage basin, and the first one sponsored with the clear intent to promote social change.

The federally sponsored multipurpose water ventures were sought by local and state governments in preference to private single-purpose projects, or developments requiring large sums of local tax support. The clientele-oriented structures by the Corps and Bureau designed to expand the benefits of local water resources were built almost entirely with federal monies. However, as the most suitable river sites were dammed and the best western agricultural lands "reclaimed," political support for additional developments diminished and economic justification became more difficult. For example, a proposed reservoir may now be replaced by floodplain zoning that limits flood damages on downstream lands while avoiding inundation of lands behind a dam. Impoundments and canal systems for distributing surface waters may be displaced by installation of center pivot irrigators using groundwater, and selected rivers have been set aside for preservation and recreation precluding future dam construction or channelization. Recently, a major criticism of the so-called construction agencies has been that their proposals do not consider alternatives to building dams even though the landowners being inundated aggressively resisted the proposed construction. Also, reservoirs and channel improvements were oriented heavily toward water quantity considerations, often disregarding quality factors. A dam can block fish migrations, reduce flows needed for downstream wildlife, or release water of poorer quality than the inflow. In 1969, the Environmental Policy Act mandated impact statements for projects sponsored by federal agencies that significantly affect the quality of the environment. Therefore, each proposal has to evaluate both detriments and benefits so that disadvantages cannot be easily ignored. Extension of federal water law, far beyond the original scope for navigation on interstate waterways, has caused concern regarding state rights in water resources. In response, many states have established their own water resources agencies. California is a leader in water enterprises as exemplified by construction of the reservoir-aqueduct system redistributing water from the northern mountains to populated regions extending along the coast to the south.

The extent of water quantity management in the United States can be most dramatically expressed by previous dam construction. The majority of large dams in the United States were built between 1930 and 1960, and currently the main stems of all major rivers are regulated with most of the tributary rivers also controlled. In 1962, the number of reservoirs and controlled natural lakes having an usable capacity of 6 million cubic metres or more was 1 562.[1] The total usable capacity of these reservoirs amounts to about 2 000 m^3 per person in the United States. One third of the total storage volume is allocated for hydropower, one third for flood control, one sixth for irrigation, and one sixth for municipal and industrial water supplies, conservation, and recreation.[1] Very few suitable river sites remain for future large projects. However, smaller water supply reservoirs and soil conservation-recreation impoundments are still projected for construction in the future. In the western states, groundwater irrigation is replacing some of the proposed reservoir and canal projects, and in other regions all the water is allocated, such that, additional reservoirs cannot increase the total area of land under irrigation.

The structural era of water quantity development is ending, leading to greater concern for management of the water resources now under regulation.

10-2 Water Quality Management

Population growth, urbanization, and industrial expansion that accelerated in the 1940s caused a dramatic increase in water pollution. By the 1960s, many municipalities and industries were discharging partially treated or raw wastewaters; brine from oil wells and mining wastes were dumped in freshwater streams; and runoff from feedlots and other agricultural operations drained directly to rivers. Many of the watercourses bordering or flowing through populated states were heavily polluted by these discharges without regard to downstream users, including rivers regulated for flow control by the federal government. (The exceptions were a few river basins with interstate organizations, like the Ohio River Valley Water Sanitation Commission, dedicated to preservation of quality.) The international waters of the Great Lakes were no exception with shoreline cities and rivers from the United States and Canada contributing to eutrophication and industrial pollution. Furthermore, treatment technology had fallen behind the generation of new pollutants. For example, treatment of municipal wastewater was not reducing the phosphate content originating from synthetic laundry detergents. The contamination of surface waters was endangering public water supplies and degrading the environment, which was marked by fish kills and destruction of wildlife habitat.

Quality control became the most important feature in water resources management during the 1970s. The Pollution Control Act amendments of 1972 were directed toward restoration and protection of surface waters, and the Safe Drinking Water regulations of 1974 enacted to protect public supplies. (This legislation is discussed in Sections 3-3 and 3-4.) The unifying force of federal legislation has made substantial progress in water pollution control by instituting: quality criteria for surface waters, effluent standards, tax incentives for industries, federal funding for municipal plants, research and development programs, and, for the first time, authoritative state laws to protect water quality. The program has been effective and is continuing since the goals legislated in the early 1970s have not yet been achieved.

Extensive new construction of water quality control facilities will continue to be a major water resources activity for at least another decade.

10-3 Assessment of Water Policy in the United States

Water resources management affects, directly or indirectly, important domestic problems, such as energy, the environment, food production, regional economic development, and even the balance of international trade. The paper "Scientific and Technological Considerations" (*Transactions, American Geophysical Union*[2]) summarizes a report[3] by the Office of Science and Technology to the President's Policy Committee for Water Resources Policy Study. The following discussion is based on the technical and scientific considerations of water policy presented in this report.

Climate and Water Supply

Existing geological evidence shows that the climate of the earth has changed in the past and is likely to change in the future. In terms of water supply alone, climatic shift can affect both the severity and length of flood or drought periods. Unfortunately, the factors influencing world climate are not well understood today, and our ability to predict future change is extremely limited. Therefore, water resources planning must assess not only the consequences predicted by climatic changes but also evaluate the risks related to the uncertainty of forecasting. Policies of water use should be based on realistic projections of water availability, and the limitations of structural measures (such as dams) in alleviating the impacts of climatic fluctuations must be recognized.

Floods and Droughts

Much of our water resources management is directed toward minimizing the effects of these events. Currently, the weakest component in the program to reduce flood damage is land use management. In response to this deficiency, the National Flood Insurance Program provides incentives for changes in floodplain use. It requires land use controls for insurance eligibility, offers subsidized premiums for existing development, requires insurance coverage for loans from federally regulated lenders, and imposes community insurance eligibility as a condition for federal grants for improvements in the flood hazard zone. Construction of dikes and levees, often justified for flood protection in the past, are not as feasible today because of environmental and economic factors. The new alternative is comprehensive floodplain treatment including floodproofing, flood insurance, tax adjustments, land use control, public education, warning systems, and relocation.

Droughts cannot be forecast, and when they have occurred in the past, management reactions have been poor. Often decisions just prior to the onset of á drought have accentuated the drought damages, and actions during the period of water scarcity have been counterproductive. Drought planning to reduce economic losses and minimize social inconvenience may include establishing water reserves, contingency allocation or reallocation of water supplies, modification of user decisions, and protection of land against wind erosion.

Groundwater

Freshwater supplies are being poorly managed and mined in many parts of the United States. Although not necessarily undesirable, overdraft can result in serious economic repercussions when done recklessly and without considering future impacts. Possible immediate effects include lowering of the water table, degradation of groundwater quality, land surface subsidence, and encroachment of saline water. Economic dislocations can be the long-term result. Mining groundwater from a common aquifer under numerous discreet landowners can be particularly detrimental since normal economics do not consider future consequences without specialized institutional arrangements that are rarely found.

Groundwater pollution has not received proper attention, in fact, it is ignored in many regions. The seriousness of neglect is in the realization that recovery of a contaminated aquifer is impractical and natural purification requires decades. Prevention is the key to groundwater quality management. Knowledge of potential sources and a comprehensive understanding of the hydrogeology of a region are both essential to preventing pollution.

Most state laws do not recognize the interrelation of surface water and groundwater. Realistically, the legal rights to both sources of supply should be integrated, and water management administered conjunctively under a single integrated body of jurisprudence. Benefits of the combined resource can be maximized through laws and regulations that recognize conjunctive use.

Water Conservation in Irrigation

Agriculture in the United States is a major freshwater user accounting for approximately 50 percent of the total water withdrawal and 80 percent of total consumptive use. Owing to this very large consumption, conservation efforts are being focused on irrigation. Also, irrigated agriculture is concentrated in regions of water shortage; future requirements for increased food production require expansion of irrigation; and major savings of water through conservation appear to be possible. The long-established federal and state land and water laws, which provided expansion of irrigation with low-cost water, foster liberal water use and discourage conservation. Current scientific knowledge and technology can evaluate and introduce water-saving measures. Under a carefully formulated future policy, equity among various water users appears to be feasible. With the high value of water for energy, industrial, and municipal uses, water conservation in irrigation can be made profitable to all parties including the irrigator.

Water Quality

Diffuse pollution is a key contributor to the degradation of surface waters, with the major nonpoint sources being runoff from fields, feedlots, urban areas, and waste disposal sites. In addition to heavy metals, organics, and nutrients that lead to stream pollution and eutrophication of lakes, the two contaminants of considerable concern are sediment and dissolved salts. The natural processes of erosion and sedimentation interfere with human use of land and water. A major problem is the gradual reduction of reservoir capacities; a second is the continual need for dredging to maintain navigation channels. These problems and others occur on such vast scales that they defy quick, complete solutions. A practical objective is the control of erosion rates (within limits consistent with a relatively stable watershed and natural stream dynamics) by improving land management practices for soil conservation, such as, crop rotation, tillage methods, terracing, and contouring.

Increased salinity in water is both a natural and man-accelerated problem that can and does severely limit the productivity of agriculture. Importing irrigation water, or groundwater abstractions, in combination with high consumption through evaporation and transpiration increases the concentrations of deleterious sodium and chloride ions. Return flows draining from irrigated fields raises the salt content of surface waters reused downstream, which in turn adds to the increasing salinity. Although salt balance is an essential requirement, salinity is a long-term problem often ignored in many geographical areas until the point of no return is past. This situation, often attributed to neglect, is in reality a problem that defies solution. In most cases, without an unacceptable curtailment of land use, no effective solution exists for managing salt residuals. Hopefully, future water management may be able to provide alternatives for assuring no irreversible consequences resulting from failure to achieve a regional salt balance.

Water for Energy

Water demands are large in the energy processes of mining, on-site processing, site restoration, transportation, refining, conversion of fuels to gases or liquids, and cooling.

Limits on the availability of fresh water can restrict energy production, and increased energy production is expected to compete with other uses of freshwater resources. Unfortunately, water supplies are often scarce near the primary fuels sources of coal and oil. Availability is a serious problem in the western states owing to both limited supply and the need for water in irrigation. Water laws, both prior appropriation and riparian doctrines (Section 2-3), are major institutional factors that determine availability of water for energy production. Environmental damage to land and water resources is a major hazard in accelerated energy production. Energy policies developed must recognize the importance of water and its cost, and encourage conservation in both water use and energy consumption.

New Methods to Increase Water Supply

The classical method of augmenting water supply has been by storage in surface and groundwater reservoirs that hold surplus water when plentiful for use in times of scarcity. Another technique employed to extend the available water in a region is importation from another watershed through an aquifer. Several unconventional sources of freshwater supplies have been suggested, such as, weather modification and desalting seawater. Both of these, and others, have been attempted with claims of some success under relatively limited conditions. Wastewater reuse has not been extensively practiced owing primarily to the problems related to viruses, heavy metals, and dissolved salts. To be realistic, water policy must recognize that methods to substantially increase water supply are not currently known.

Future Demands for Water

The demand for freshwater supplies is not expected to diminish (Section 2-2). Regulation of surface waters, for example, by damming rivers, and exploitation of groundwater have in the past been able to supply inexpensive high-quality water to meet domestic, industrial, and agricultural demands in most regions. With the majority of the available supply now developed, particularly in western states, water conservation is likely to receive widespread attention in the future. Even though droughts are more frequent in the west, several regions throughout the United States have experienced shortages of surface supplies of adequate quality.

For most water uses, the price is too low to encourage efficiency and prevent waste. Although reuse may be beneficial for conservation, many times it is uneconomical compared to low-priced fresh supplies. Also, typical watershed management does not seriously consider conservation; thus, inefficiency by the first consumers can restrict other beneficial uses. For example, the quantity and quality of minimum streamflows for fish and wildlife can needlessly suffer as a result of wasteful practices and pollution of a stream. Energy conservation is expected to accompany water conservation. High power costs are already influencing the application of irrigation water, and rising costs of water treatment and wastewater disposal are expected to reduce use by industries and municipalities. Whether by direct legislation and planning efforts, or out of shortage and economic necessity, conservation is expected to play a significant role in future water resources management.

Summary of Considerations in Water Resources Policy

(1)   Climate and weather fluctuations are inevitable, and water policy, planning, and management procedures must be devised with this fact in mind.

(2)   Flood protection can best be provided by improved short-term forecasting and associated reservoir management and by increased emphasis on nonstructural measures, such as flood insurance and land use management.

(3)   Drought protection can be enhanced by improved advance planning.

(4)   Groundwater is physically related to surface water, and conjunctive management of the two is essential.

(5)   Opportunities exist for substantial conservation of water in agricultural irrigation.

(6)   Greater efforts must be made to control nonpoint sources of pollution, thermal pollution, and salinity.

(7)   Increased efforts are necessary to improve understanding of erosion and sedimentation, and this knowledge should be applied in water planning and management.

(8)   Water may constrain energy production in the future, and energy planners should carefully examine the impact of their plans on other water users.

(9)   No new technologies exist that will substantially increase water supply in the near term.

(10)   Efforts to control demand are an attractive alternative to new investments in water supply. (Reference 2, copyrighted by American Geophysical Union.)

10-4   Regionalization of Water Management in England and Wales

Movement toward adequate water management began with regrouping of water supplies under the Water Act of 1945. Over a decade later, and prodded by a serious drought in the summer of 1959, the Water Resources Act of 1963 created the now nonexistant Water Resources Board, which undertook studies ultimately providing the necessary data for water resources planning. Twenty-nine river authorities, replacing previous river boards, were assigned the tasks of developing water resources and data collection in addition to the original responsibilities of drainage, fisheries, pollution control, and navigation. Under this broader scope, surface and groundwater resources were integrated and withdrawals controlled by licensing, which also served as a means for levying water charges to finance the river authorities. Pollution control was established by issuing discharge permits, monitoring of effluents, and conducting stream surveys.

Regionalization of water management was realized in the Water Act approved by Parliament in 1973 and initiated in 1974: "An Act to make provision for a national policy for water, for the conferring and discharge of functions as to water (including sewerage and sewage disposal, fisheries and land drainage) and as to recreation and amenity in connection with water, for the making of charges by water authorities and

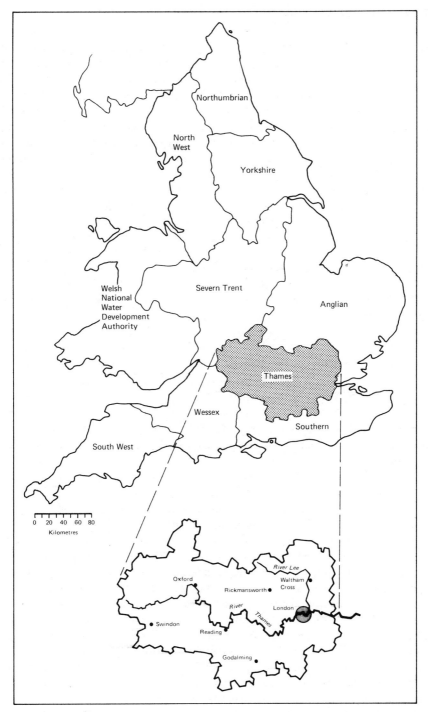

Figure 10-1 The boundaries of the 10 water authorities in England and Wales. Thames Water, shown in detail, encompasses the basins of River Thames and River Lee and serves the major population area of London and surroundings.

other statutory water undertakers, and for connected purposes." The Act consolidated the 29 river authorities, 1 300 local authorities, and water services provided by about 200 separate enterprises into ten Water Authorities defined by river basins. The nine Authorities in England plus the Welsh National Water Development Authority are shown in Figure 10-1. Each Water Authority is headed by a chairman appointed by the Secretary of State for the Environment with the majority of members appointed by local authorities. The National Water Council (NWC) was established consisting of a chairman appointed by the Secretary of State, the 10 chairmen of the Water Authorities, and up to 10 others with special knowledge of water management. The NWC is to advise the government on matters relating to national water policy and to assist the Authorities. The restructured Water Authorities have responsibilities for water conservation, water supply, wastewater collection and disposal, control of river pollution, fisheries, land drainage, recreation, conservation of nature, and esthetics. User charges for various services are to be levied to meet costs.

Water Authorities have considerable freedom since they perform comprehensive river basin planning and control their own financing. Nevertheless, the central government still retains important functions in directing national policy and assisting the Authorities in resolution of common problems. The Water Space Amenity Commission is advisory to all agencies regarding water policy for recreation and esthetics. Moreover, under provisions of the Act, the Authorities must provide for preservation of natural beauty, wildlife, and historic sites. The Water Research Centre, with major financial support from the Authorities, is organized to undertake research and disseminate data encompassing resources, fisheries, pollution control, water quality, and water and wastewater treatment. The Department of the Environment also has the Central Water Planning Unit for multipurpose water management exceeding the scope of regional plans, and the Water Data Unit responsible for collection and dissemination of hydrologic and water quality data.

Thames Water is discussed to illustrate the organization and functions of an Authority. The region, detailed in Figure 10-1, covers the catchment area of River Thames and River Lee and their tributaries incorporating 13 100 km². Including London, the population served is 11.6 million, or about one quarter of the population of England and Wales. The management structures are designed to implement the Authority's policies by combining efficiency with local initiative. Activities are guided by a committee structure, Figure 10-2a, with memberships as small as possible. The General Purposes committee considers matters regarding coordination between committees, procedural and organizational matters, submission of reports and regulations, and so forth. The Finance Sub-Committee advises on drainage rates and charges to be levied, and other financial and economic aspects of operation. Responsibilities of the Personnel Sub-Committee include review and monitoring of the manpower budget, training arrangements, services affecting staff, and negotiations with unions. Water Planning prepares the research and development program, considering the views of the other committees. A key function of the Water Operations Committee is to monitor operations to ensure the standards of performance. The Water Quality Committee surveys water supplies, wastewater discharges, and surface waters, which are compiled

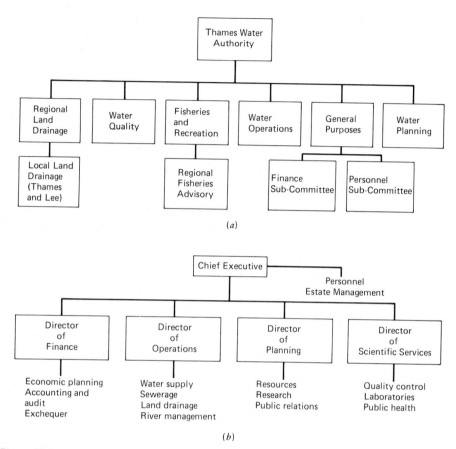

Figure 10-2 The management structures for (a) committees and (b) directors of the Thames Water Authority. (Courtesy of Thames Water.)

in water quality reports. Promotion of sport and recreation is a major function of the Fisheries and Recreation Committee; regional fisheries are advisory to this committee. Land drainage matters are under the Regional Committee, which coordinates the functions of Local Land Drainage Committees.

The chief executive is the leader of four directors—finance, operations, planning, and scientific services. The responsibilities of the directors on this management team are listed in Figure 10-2b. Each director has a small staff, headed by assistant directors, covering the areas for which regional control and coordination are essential.

The nine operating divisions of Thames Water are defined by geographical area, and most are multifunctional organizations providing water supply, wastewater disposal, and other services. Each division is headed by a manager that reports to the Authority's management team through a direct line of command from the Director of Operations. The largest three divisions are the Metropolitan Water District responsible for treatment and distribution to 6.5 million people (Figure 10-3a); the Metropolitan Public Health Division in charge of wastewater collection and disposal for 7.5 million people and industries in the Greater London area (Figure 10-3b); and the Thames Conservancy Division accountable in a 10 000 km² drainage area for flood protection, pollution control, and management of fisheries and navigation on the freshwater River Thames (Figure 10-3c). The other six divisions provide both water and waste-water services with the Lea Division including land drainage. The degree of manage-ment consolidation brought about by the organization of this Water Authority is further exemplified by the incorporation of 115 local planning organizations in the region.

River management stresses flood control and water quality operations. The Author-ity operates 44 locks for navigation on 216 km of the freshwater Thames and is responsible for flood defenses on parts of the lower 42 km of tidal Thames. Routine quality testing monitors wastewater effluents, stream waters, and several points in water treatment and distribution systems. Slightly more than one half of the region's public water supply is drawn from river sources, which is stored in large offstream im-pounding reservoirs. Most of the waterworks and pipe networks are manned by Thames Water; however, about one third of the supply is provided by seven Water Companies as agents for the Authority. Established sewer programs for both storm and sanitary wastes are for maintenance, construction, and rodent control. Wastewater pro-cessing is biological treatment with tertiary filtration and partial denitrification added where necessary to protect water supplies. Most of the waste sludge is spread on agri-cultural land or barged to sea after biological digestion. Facilities for water-based re-creation, such as fishing and boating, are maintained on the rivers and reservoirs. Thus, as with all the Water Authorities, Thames integrates water services for the people in a hydrologically defined region by centralizing financing, operations, scientific services, and water resources planning.

Application of Regionalization in the United States

Recent planning concepts have encouraged regionalization in the United States; how-ever, progress toward organizing multipurpose authorities is proceeding slowly. The Tennessee Valley Authority, established in 1933, is a regional enterprise. While acclaimed by many professionals in water resources, this river basin organization has not been imitated during its nearly half century of existence. Currently, water re-sources management occurs at all governmental levels for control of both quantity and quality. With creation of the Water Resources Council by the Water Resources Planning Act of 1965, river basin commissions were established throughout the United States to coordinate federal, state, interstate, local, and private development plans. However, the success of a final plan relies on resolving diverse and competitive interest of the parties involved. This is difficult under the present organizational structure since the commissions have no strong central authority and major financial control resides with member agencies. Interstate water compacts have been somewhat more successful in establishing regional management. As illustrations, the Colorado River compact allo-cated water rights among the states in the Colorado River basin, and the Delaware

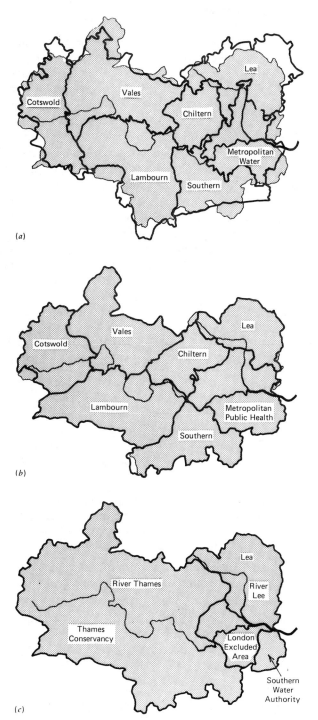

Figure 10-3 Operating divisions of the Thames Water Authority for (a) water supply, (b) wastewater treatment and disposal, and (c) land drainage. (Courtesy of Thames Water.)

River Basin compact commission is empowered to allocate waters and control pollution. Local government planning is usually fragmented among neighboring jurisdictions, consequently metropolitan areas rarely have an established urban water plan. Areawide water quality planning, directed by the Environmental Protection Agency, is segregated from quantity planning. Such division often exists in state organizations with drinking water under a health department, water pollution under a department of environmental control, and planning under a water resources commission.

The uniqueness of water projects requires a regional approach, and economy and efficiency are best achieved by unified management. Okun[4] also stresses that charges for services should reflect actual costs to promote efficiency in water use and allocation of resources, and least-cost solutions in the inevitable conflict between the upstream discharge and the downstream withdrawal are only likely if water supply and pollution control services are regionally integrated. The regionalization of water management in England and Wales, in providing a rational structure for water quantity and quality management, is a model for other countries throughout the world. Few countries, including the United States, are in a position to adopt exactly the same management organization. Nevertheless, for industrialized nations, lessons can be learned from the British process of reorganization, and developing countries in Asia, Africa, and Latin America are in a position to profit from this experience.[4] The primary advantages are regional management rather than remote highly centralized organizations and economy of funds and personnel through self-financing and integration of services.

References

1. Martin, R. O. R., and Hanson, R. L., *Reservoirs in the United States*, Geological Survey Water-Supply Paper 1838, U. S. Government Printing Office, Washington, D. C., 1966.

2. Ackermann, W. C., Allee, D. J., Amorocho, J., Haimes, Y. Y., Hall, W. A., Meserve, R. A., Patrick, R., and Smith, P. M., "Scientific and Technological Considerations in Water Resources Policy," *EOS, Transactions, American Geophysical Union*, Vol. 59, No. 6, June 1978, pp. 516-527.

3. Office of Science and Technology Policy, *Scientific and Technological Aspects of Water Resources Policy*, Executive Office of the President, Washington, D. C., Jan. 19, 1978.

4. Okun, D. A., *Regionalization of Water Management (A Revolution in England and Wales)*, Applied Science Publishers Ltd., London, 1977, p. 337.

Appendix

Common Abbreviations Used in Text

a	year	kN	kilonewton
BOD	biochemical oxygen demand	kP	kilopascal
cm	centimetre	l	litre
°C	degrees Celsius	log	logarithm base 10
d	day	$\log_e$	logarithm base e
DO	dissolved oxygen	m	metre
g	gram	mg	milligram
h	hour	min	minute
ha	hectare	mm	millimetre
kg	kilogram	N	newton
km	kilometre	Pa	pascal
		s	second

Selected SI Units (Systéme International d'Unités)

Unit Type	Quantity	Unit	Symbol	Expression in Other Units
Base Units	Length	metre	m	
	Mass	kilogram[a]	kg	
	Time	second	s	
	Thermodynamic temperature	kelvin[b]	K	
	Amount of substance	mole	mol	
Supplementary Unit	Plane angle	radian	rad	

Selected SI Units—continued

Unit Type	Quantity	Unit	Symbol	Expression in Other Units
Derived Units Having Special Names	Force	newton	N	$kg \cdot m/s^2$
	Pressure	pascal	Pa	N/m^2
	Energy, Work	joule	J	$N \cdot m$
	Power	watt	W	J/s
	Area	hectare	ha	$10^4\,m^2$
	Volume	litre	l	$10^{-3}\,m^3$
Derived Units	Area	square metre		m^2
	Volume	cubic metre		m^3
	Linear velocity	metre per second		m/s
	Linear acceleration	metre per second squared		m/s^2
	Density	kilogram per cubic metre		kg/m^3

[a] The kilogram is the only base unit with a prefix.

[b] The Celsius temperature scale (previously called centigrade) is commonly used for measurements even though it is not part of the SI system. A difference of one degree on the Celsius scale (°C) equals one kelvin (K), and zero on the thermodynamic scale is 273.15 kelvin below zero degrees Celsius.

SI Unit Prefixes

Amount	Multiples and Submultiples	Prefixes	Symbols
1 000 000 000 000	10^{12}	tera	T
1 000 000 000	10^9	giga	G
1 000 000	10^6	mega	M
1 000	10^3	kilo	k
100	10^2	hecto	h
10	10	deka	da

SI Unit Prefixes—continued

Amount	Multiples and Submultiples	Prefixes	Symbols
0.1	10^{-1}	deci	d
0.01	10^{-2}	centi	c
0.001	10^{-3}	milli	m
0.000 001	10^{-6}	micro	μ
0.000 000 001	10^{-9}	nano	n
0.000 000 000 001	10^{-12}	pico	p
0.000 000 000 000 001	10^{-15}	femto	f
0.000 000 000 000 000 001	10^{-18}	atto	a

SI Units in Water Resources

Quantity and Application	Name	Symbol	Permissible Alternate units
Linear Measurement			
Land distances	metre	m	
	kilometre	km	
Pipe diameters	millimetre	mm	
Pipe and channel lengths	metre	m	
Radius of groundwater wells	millimetre	mm	
Aquifer thickness	metre	m	
Drawdown in wells	metre	m	
Height of capillary rise	millimetre	mm	
Depth of rainfall	millimetre	mm	
Depth of irrigation watering	millimetre	mm	
Depth of basins, reservoirs	metre	m	
Piezometric head	metre	m	
Hydraulic head	metre	m	
Level rods, staff gages	metre & 0.01 m		
Area			
Land area	square metre	m^2	
	hectare	ha	

SI Units in Water Resources–continued

Quantity and Application	Name	Symbol	Permissible Alternate units
	square kilometre	km^2	
Irrigation area	hectare	ha	
Catchment area	square metre	m^2	
	square kilometre	km^2	
Surface area of ponds	square metre	m^2	
Surface area of basins	square metre	m^2	
Surface area of lakes	square kilometre	km^2	
Cross sectional area of small pipes	square millimetre	mm^2	
Cross-sectional areas of large pipes, channels	square metre	m^2	
Volume			
Water distribution	cubic metre	m^3	
Wastewater collection	cubic metre	m^3	
Irrigation diversions	cubic metre	m^3	
Storage capacity	cubic metre	m^3	
Time			
	second	s	
	minute	min	
	hour	h	
	day	d	
	year	a	
Velocity			
Pipe flow	metre per second	m/s	
Streamflow	metre per second	m/s	
Acceleration			
Gravity	9.806 7 metres per second squared	m/s^2	
Mass			
	milligram	mg	
	gram	g	
	kilogram	kg	
	tonne	t	
Density			
Material	kilogram per cubic metre	kg/m^3	

SI Units in Water Resources-continued

Quantity and Application	Name	Symbol	Permissible Alternate units
Liquid	gram per litre	g/l	kg/l
Rate of flow			
Water supply	cubic metre per day	m^3/d	
Wastewater discharge	cubic metre per day	m^3/d	
Water consumption per person per day	litre per person per day	l/person · d	
Wastewater production per person per day	litre per person per day	l/person · d	
Pipe flow	litre per second	l/s	
	cubic metre per second	m^3/s	
Streamflow	cubic metre per second	m^3/s	
Channel flow	cubic metre per second	m^3/s	
Pump discharge	litre per second	l/s	
Concentration of material in fluid	milligram per litre	mg/l	
	gram per cubic metre	g/m^3	
Precipitation and Evaporation			
Quantity	millimetre	mm	
Rate	millimetre per hour	mm/h	
Permeability	millimetres per second	mm/s	m/d
Mass loading rate			
Volumetric	grams per cubic metre per day	$g/m^3 · d$	
Surface	grams per square metre per day	$g/m^2 · d$	
	grams per square metre per year	$g/m^2 · a$	
Hydraulic loading rate			
Volumetric	cubic metre per cubic metre per day	$m^3/m^3 · d$	

SI Units in Water Resources–continued

Quantity and Application	Name	Symbol	Permissible Alternate units
Surface	cubic metre per square metre per day	$m^3/m^2 \cdot d$	m/d
	cubic metre per square metre per year	$m^3/m^2 \cdot a$	m/a
Grades and gradients			
	metre per metre	m/m	m/km
Force			
	newton	N	
	kilonewton	kN	
	meganewton	MN	
Pressure			
Piezometric pressure	pascal	Pa	N/m^2
	kilopascal	kPa	kN/m^2
	megapascal	MPa	MN/m^2
Head of water	metre	m	
Temperature			
Thermodynamic	kelvin	K	
Measurement (common)	degree Celsius	°C	
Heat, work or energy			
	joule	J	
	kilojoule	kJ	
	megajoule	MJ	
	kilowatt hour	$kW \cdot h$	
Power			
	watt	W	
	kilowatt	kW	

Conversion Factors SI Metric to U. S. Customary

Multiple	By	To Obtain
Length		
kilometre, km	0.621 4	mile, mi
metre, m	3.281	foot, ft
	1.094	yard, yd
millimetre, mm	0.039 37	inch, in.
Area		
square kilometre, km^2	0.386 1	square mile, sq mi
hectare, ha (10 000 m^2)	2.471	acre, ac
square metre, m^2	10.76	square foot, sq ft
square millimetre, mm^2	0.001 55	square inch, sq in.
Volume		
cubic metre, m^3	264.2	US gallon, gal
	35.31	cubic foot, cu ft
	1.308	cubic yard, cu yd
	0.000 81	acre foot, ac ft
litre, l	0.264 2	US gallon, gal
	0.035 31	cubic foot, cu ft
Velocity		
metre/second, m/s	3.281	foot/second, ft/sec
	196.8	foot/minute, ft/min
Flow		
cubic metre/day, m^3/d	0.183 5	US gallon/minute, gpm
cubic metre/second, m^3/s	35.31	cubic foot/second, cfs
litre/second, l/s	15.85	US gallon/minute, gpm
	0.022 83	million US gallons/day, mgd
Mass		
tonne, t (1 000 kg)	1.102	ton (2 000 lb)
kilogram, kg	2.205	pound, lb
Density		
kilogram/cubic metre, kg/m^3	0.624 2	pound/cubic foot, lb/cu ft
Mass loading rate		
gram/cubic metre · day, g/m^3 · d	0.062 43	pound/1 000 cubic foot/day, lb/1 000 cu ft/day
gram/square metre · day, g/m^2 · d	8.921	pound/acre/day, lb/ac/day

Conversion Factors U.S. Customary to SI Metric–continued

Multiple	By	To Obtain
kilogram/cubic metre · day, kg/m^3 · d	0.062 43	pound/cubic foot/day lb/cu ft/day
kilogram/square metre · day, kg/m^2 · d	0.204 8	pound/square foot/day, lb/sq ft/day
Hydraulic loading rate		
cubic metre/square metre · day m^3/m^2 · d (m/d)	24.54	US gallon/square foot/day, gal/sq ft/day
	1.069	million US gallons/acre/day, mgad
cubic metre/square metre · year m^3/m^2 · a (m/a)	0.304 8	cubic foot/square foot/year cu ft/sq ft/yr
cubic metre/cubic metre · day, m^3/m^3 · d	7.481	US gallon/cubic foot/day, gal/cu ft/day
litre/square metre · second, l/m^2 · s	1.473	US gallon/square foot/minute, gpm/sq ft
Concentration		
milligram/litre, mg/l	8.345	pound/million US gallons, lb/mil gal
Force		
newton, N	0.224 8	pound force, lb
Pressure		
kilopascal, kPa	0.145 0	pound/square inch, psi
Logarithm		
Napierian (base e = 2.718) log$_e$	0.434 3	common (base 10) log

Conversion Factors U. S. Customary to SI Metric

Multiple	By	To Obtain
Length		
mile, mi	1.609	kilometre, km
yard, yd	0.914 4	metre, m
foot, ft	0.304 8	metre, m
inch, in.	25.40	millimetre, mm

Conversion Factors U.S. Customary to SI Metric–continued

Multiple	By	To Obtain
Area		
square mile, sq mi	2.590	square kilometre, km^2
acre, ac	0.404 7	hectare, ha (10 000 m^2)
	4 047.	square metre, m^2
square yard, sq yd	0.836 1	square metre, m^2
square foot, sq ft	0.092 9	square metre, m^2
square inch, sq in.	645.2	square millimetre, mm^2
Volume		
acre foot, ac ft	1 234.	cubic metre, m^3
cubic yard, cu yd	0.764 9	cubic metre, m^3
cubic foot, cu ft	0.028 32	cubic metre, m^3
	28.32	litre, l
US gallon, gal	3.785	litre, l
Velocity		
foot/second, ft/sec	0.304 8	metre/second, m/s
foot/minute, ft/min	0.005 08	metre/second, m/s
Flow		
million US gallons/day, mgd	3 785.	cubic metre/day, m^3/d
	43.81	litre/second, l/s
US gallons/minute, gpm	5.450	cubic metre/day, m^3/d
	0.063 09	litre/second, l/s
cubic foot/second, cfs	0.028 32	cubic metre/second, m^3/s
Mass		
ton (2 000 lb)	0.907 2	tonne, t (1 000 kg)
	907.2	kilogram, kg
pound, lb	0.453 6	kilogram, kg
	453.6	gram, g
Density		
pound/cubic foot, lb/cu ft	16.02	kilogram/cubic metre, kg/m^3
Mass loading rate		
pound/1 000 cubic foot/day, lb/1 000 cu ft/day	16.02	gram/cubic metre · day, $g/m^3 \cdot d$
pound/acre/day, lb/ac/day	0.112 1	gram/square metre · day, $g/m^2 \cdot d$
	1.121	kilogram/hectare · day, kg/ha · d
pound/cubic foot/day, lb/cu ft/day	16.02	kilogram/cubic metre · day, $kg/m^3 \cdot d$

Conversion Factors U.S. Customary to SI Metric–continued

Multiple	By	To Obtain
pound/square foot/day, lb/sq ft/day	4.883	kilogram/square metre · day, kg/m² · d
Hydraulic loading rate		
million US gallons/acre/day, mgad	0.935 3	cubic metre/square metre · day, m³/m² · d
	9 353.	cubic metre/hectare · day, m³/ha · d
US gallon/square foot/day, gal/sq ft/day	0.040 75	cubic metre/square metre · day, m³/m² · d
US gallon/square foot/minute, gpm/sq ft	0.679 0	litre/square metre · second l/m² · s
US gallon/cubic foot/day, gal/cu ft/day	0.133 7	cubic metre/cubic metre · day, m³/m³ · d
Concentration		
pound/million US gallons, lb/mil gal	0.119 8	milligram/litre, mg/l
Force		
pound force, lb	4.448	newton, N
Pressure		
pound/square foot, psf	0.047 88	kilopascal, kPa
pound/square inch, psi	6.895	kilopascal, kPa
Logarithm		
common (base 10) log	2.303	Napierian (base e = 2.718) $\log_e$

Water Pressure

Mass per unit volume is referred to as density of a fluid. The density of water is 998 kg/m³ at a temperature of 20°C and pressure of 101.3 kPa. (Under standard conditions of 4°C and 101.3 kPa, the value is 1 000 kg/m³.) The force exerted by gravity on one cubic metre (specific weight) of water is 9.79 kN/m³, which is equal to the density multiplied by standard acceleration of gravity which is 9.807 m/s².

Pressure is force exerted per unit area. Referring to Figure A-1a, the pressure exerted on the bottom of a one cubic metre container filled with water is equal to 9.79 kPa. (Force in kilonewtons per square metre is numerically equal to pressure in kilopascals.) In engineering hydraulics, water pressure is frequently expressed in terms of metres of

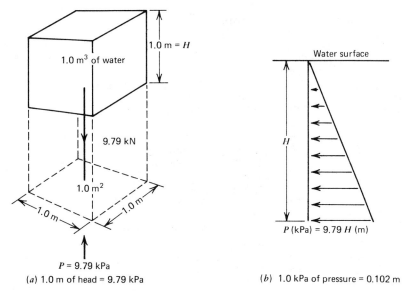

(a) 1.0 m of head = 9.79 kPa

(b) 1.0 kPa of pressure = 0.102 m

Figure A-1 Basic relationships between water pressure in kilopascals and metres of water head.

head, as well as kilopascals. The relationship between these units is visually shown in Figure A-1*a* where a height of 1.0 metre of water head exerts a pressure of 9.79 kPa. Water pressure increases with depth below the surface linearly such that the pressure in kilopascals is equal to 9.79 times the depth in metres. The sketch in Figure A-1*b* shows the pressure acting only horizontally for ease of illustration. In fact, water pressure is exerted equally in all directions.

Table of Chemical Elements

Name	Symbol	Atomic Number	Atomic Mass	Name	Symbol	Atomic Number	Atomic Mass
Actinium	Ac	89	—	Mercury	Hg	80	200.59
Aluminum	Al	13	26.9815	Molybdenum	Mo	42	95.94
Americium	Am	95	—	Neodymium	Nd	60	144.24
Antimony	Sb	51	121.75	Neon	Ne	10	20.183
Argon	Ar	18	39.948	Neptunium	Np	93	—
Arsenic	As	33	74.9216	Nickel	Ni	28	58.71
Astatine	At	85	—	Niobium	Nb	41	92.906
Barium	Ba	56	137.34	Nitrogen	N	7	14.0067
Berkelium	Bk	97	—	Nobelium	No	102	—
Beryllium	Be	4	9.0122	Osmium	Os	76	190.2
Bismuth	Bi	83	208.980	Oxygen	O	8	15.9994
Boron	B	5	10.811	Palladium	Pd	46	106.4
Bromine	Br	35	79.904	Phosphorus	P	15	30.9738

Table of Chemical Elements—continued

Name	Symbol	Atomic Number	Atomic Mass	Name	Symbol	Atomic Number	Atomic Mass
Cadmium	Cd	48	112.40	Platinum	Pt	78	195.09
Calcium	Ca	20	40.08	Plutonium	Pu	94	—
Californium	Cf	98	—	Polonium	Po	84	—
Carbon	C	6	12.01115	Potassium	K	19	39.102
Cerium	Ce	58	140.12	Praseodymium	Pr	59	140.907
Cesium	Cs	55	132.905	Promethium	Pm	61	—
Chlorine	Cl	17	35.453	Protactinium	Pa	91	—
Chromium	Cr	24	51.996	Radium	Ra	88	—
Cobalt	Co	27	58.9332	Radon	Rn	86	—
Copper	Cu	29	63.546	Rhenium	Re	75	186.2
Curium	Cm	96	—	Rhodium	Rh	45	102.905
Dysprosium	Dy	66	162.50	Rubidium	Rb	37	85.47
Einsteinium	Es	99	—	Ruthenium	Ru	44	101.07
Erbium	Er	68	167.26	Samarium	Sm	62	150.35
Europium	Eu	63	151.96	Scandium	Sc	21	44.956
Fermium	Fm	100	—	Selenium	Se	34	78.96
Fluorine	F	9	18.9984	Silicon	Si	14	28.086
Francium	Fr	87	—	Silver	Ag	47	107.868
Gadolinium	Gd	64	157.25	Sodium	Na	11	22.9898
Gallium	Ga	31	69.72	Strontium	Sr	38	87.62
Germanium	Ge	32	72.59	Sulfur	S	16	32.064
Gold	Au	79	196.967	Tantalum	Ta	73	189.948
Hafnium	Hf	72	178.49	Technetium	Tc	43	—
Helium	He	2	4.0026	Tellurium	Te	52	127.60
Holmium	Ho	67	164.930	Terbium	Tb	65	158.924
Hydrogen	H	1	1.00797	Thallium	Tl	81	204.37
Indium	In	49	114.82	Thorium	Th	90	232.038
Iodine	I	53	126.9044	Thulium	Tm	69	168.934
Iridium	Ir	77	192.2	Tin	Sn	50	118.69
Iron	Fe	26	55.847	Titanium	Ti	22	47.90
Krypton	Kr	36	83.80	Tungsten	W	74	183.85
Lanthanum	La	57	138.91	Uranium	U	92	238.03
Lead	Pb	82	207.19	Vanadium	V	23	50.942
Lithium	Li	3	6.939	Xenon	Xe	54	131.30
Lutetium	Lu	71	174.97	Ytterbium	Yb	70	173.04
Magnesium	Mg	12	24.312	Yttrium	Y	39	88.905
Manganese	Mn	25	54.9380	Zinc	Zn	30	65.37
Mendelevium	Md	101	—	Zirconium	Zr	40	91.22

Saturation Values of Dissolved Oxygen in Water Exposed to Water-Saturated Air Containing 20.90 Percent Oxygen Under a Pressure of 760 mm of Mercury[a]

Temperature in °C	Chloride Concentration in Water mg/l			Difference per 100 mg Chloride	Temperature in °C	Vapor Pressure mmHg
	0	5 000	10 000			
	Dissolved Oxygen mg/l					
0	14.6	13.8	13.0	0.017	0	5
1	14.2	13.4	12.6	0.016	1	5
2	13.8	13.1	12.3	0.015	2	5
3	13.5	12.7	12.0	0.015	3	6
4	13.1	12.4	11.7	0.014	4	6
5	12.8	12.1	11.4	0.014	5	7
6	12.5	11.8	11.1	0.014	6	7
7	12.2	11.5	10.9	0.013	7	8
8	11.9	11.2	10.6	0.013	8	8
9	11.6	11.0	10.4	0.012	9	9
10	11.3	10.7	10.1	0.012	10	9
11	11.1	10.5	9.9	0.011	11	10
12	10.8	10.3	9.7	0.011	12	11
13	10.6	10.1	9.5	0.011	13	11
14	10.4	9.9	9.3	0.010	14	12
15	10.2	9.7	9.1	0.010	15	13
16	10.0	9.5	9.0	0.010	16	14
17	9.7	9.3	8.8	0.010	17	15
18	9.5	9.1	8.6	0.009	18	16
19	9.4	8.9	8.5	0.009	19	17
20	9.2	8.7	8.3	0.009	20	18
21	9.0	8.6	8.1	0.009	21	19
22	8.8	8.4	8.0	0.008	22	20
23	8.7	8.3	7.9	0.008	23	21
24	8.5	8.1	7.7	0.008	24	22
25	8.4	8.0	7.6	0.008	25	24

Saturation Values of Dissolved Oxygen in Water Exposed to Water Saturated Air Containing 20.90 Percent Oxygen Under a Pressure of 760 mm of Mercury[a]

Temperature in °C	Chloride Concentration in Water mg/l			Difference per 100 mg Chloride	Temperature in °C	Vapor Pressure mmHg
	0	5 000	10 000			
	Dissolved Oxygen mg/l					
26	8.2	7.8	7.4	0.008	26	25
27	8.1	7.7	7.3	0.008	27	27
28	7.9	7.5	7.1	0.008	28	28
29	7.8	7.4	7.0	0.008	29	30
30	7.6	7.3	6.9	0.008	30	32

[a]Saturation at barometric pressures other than 760 mm, C_s' is related to the corresponding tabulated values, C_s, by the equation:

$$C_s' = C_s \frac{P - p}{760 - p}$$

where C_s' = solubility at barometric pressure P and given temperature, milligrams per litre
$\quad\,\, C_s$ = saturation at given temperature from table, milligrams per litre
$\quad\,\, P$ = barometric pressure, millimetres
$\quad\,\, p$ = pressure of saturated water vapor at temperature of the water selected from table, millimetres

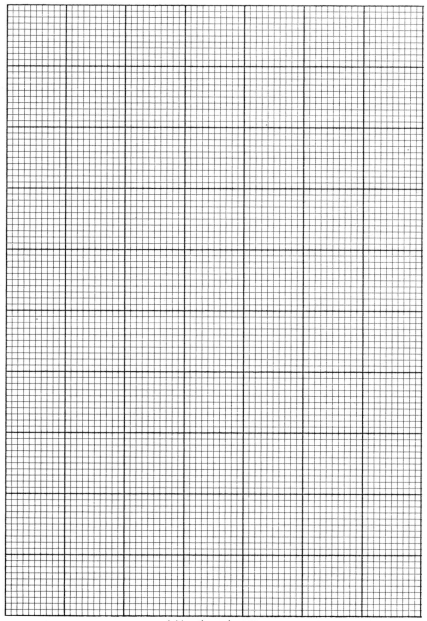

Arithmetic graph paper

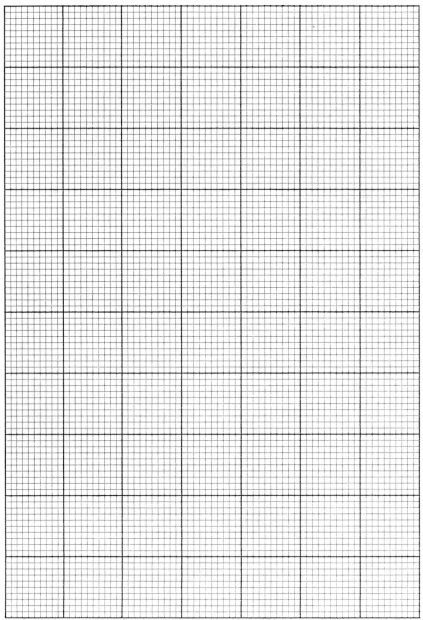

Arithmetic Graph Paper

Two—cycle semilogarithmic paper

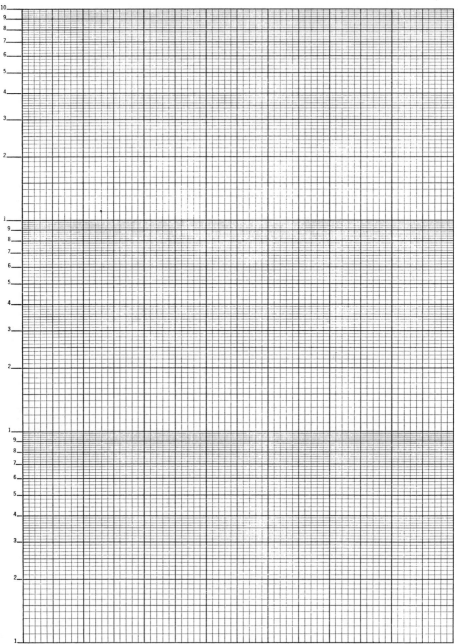

Three—cycle semilogarithmic paper

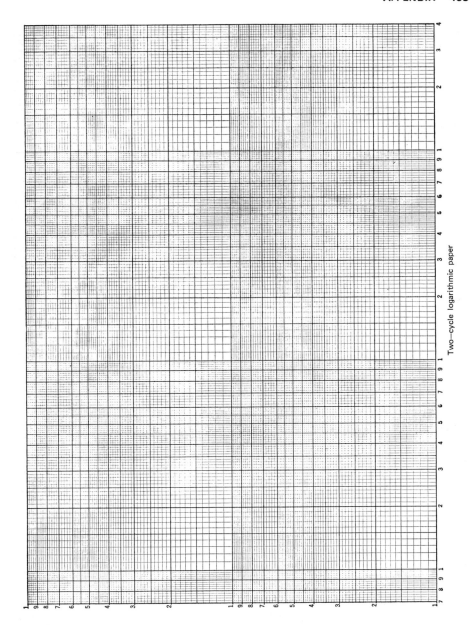

Two—cycle logarithmic paper

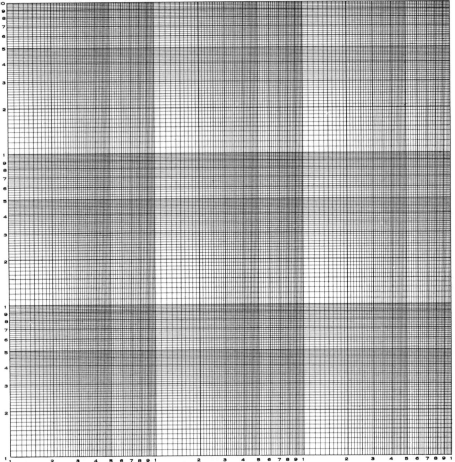

Three—cycle logarithmic paper

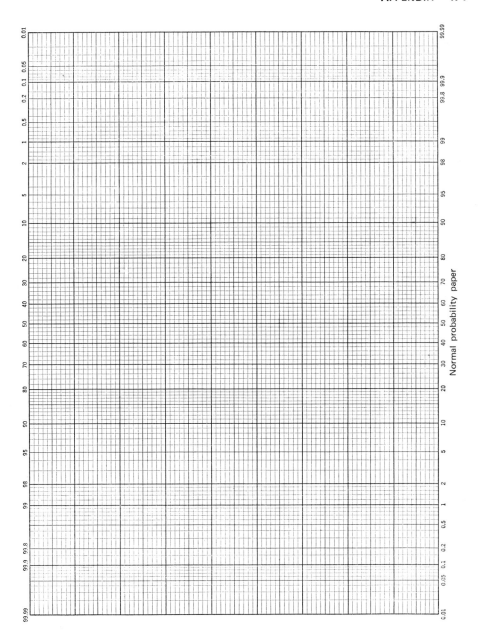

Normal probability paper

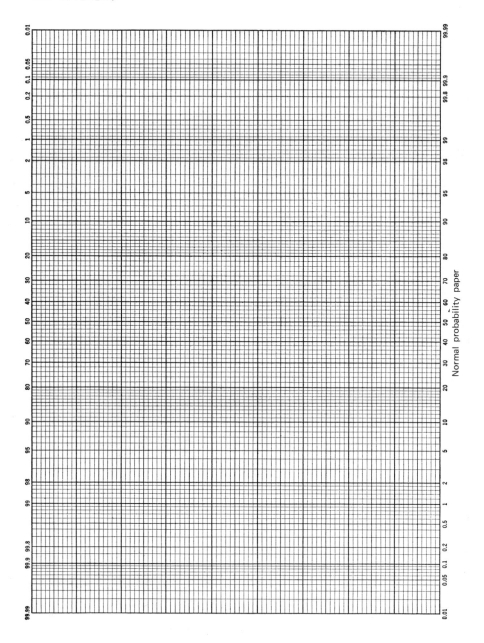

Normal probability paper

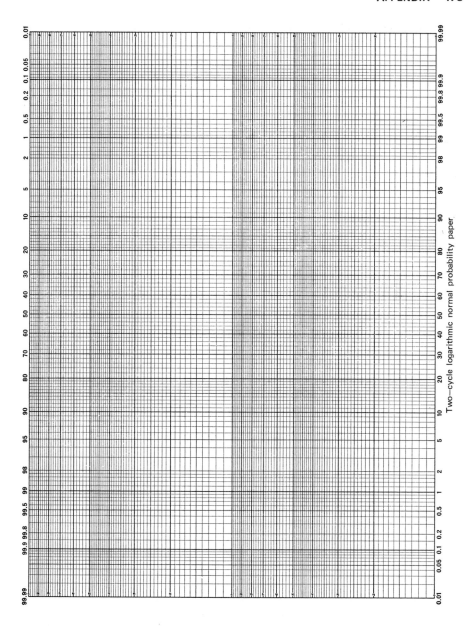

Two–cycle logarithmic normal probability paper.

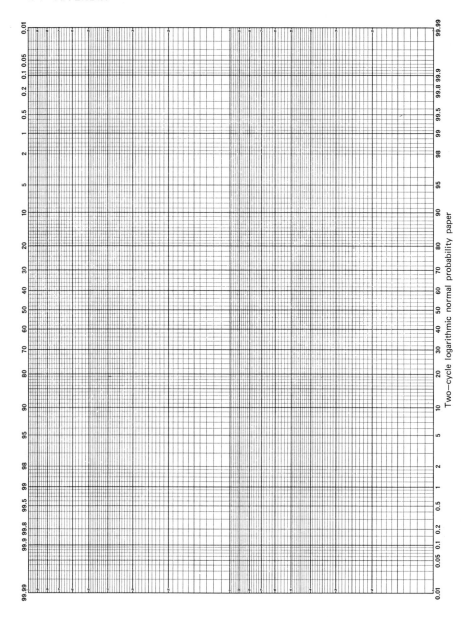

Two—cycle logarithmic normal probability paper

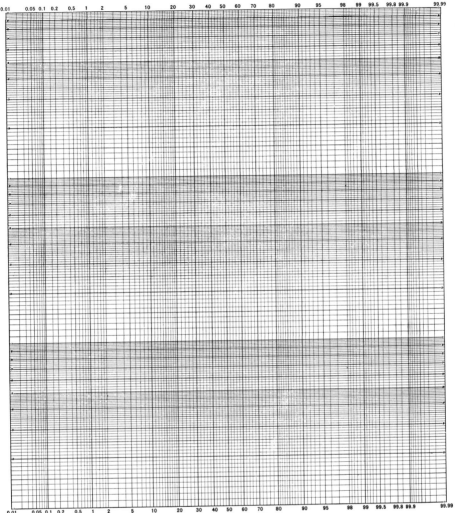

Three—cycle logarithmic normal probability paper

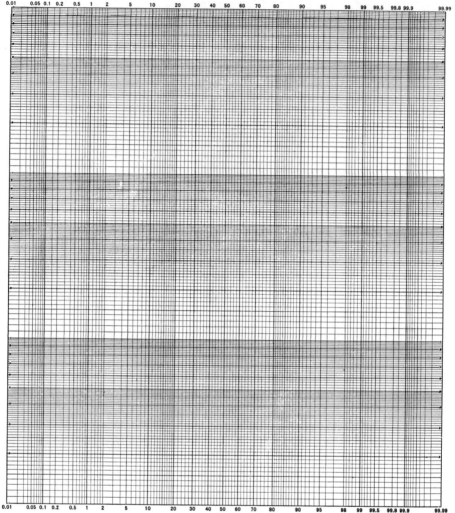

Three—cycle logarithmic normal probability paper

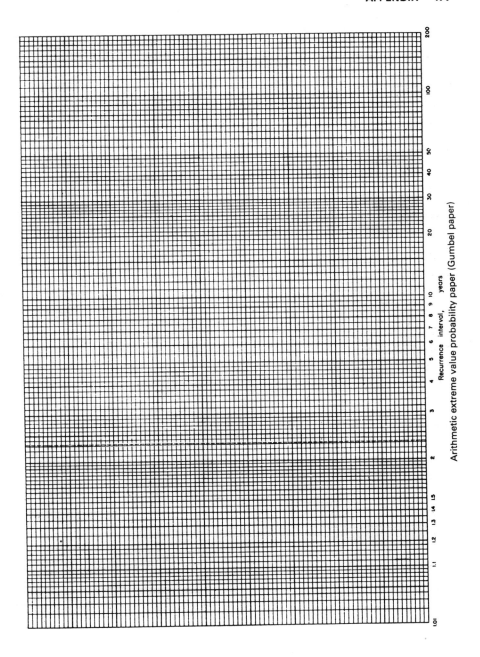

Arithmetic extreme value probability paper (Gumbel paper)

Recurrence interval, years

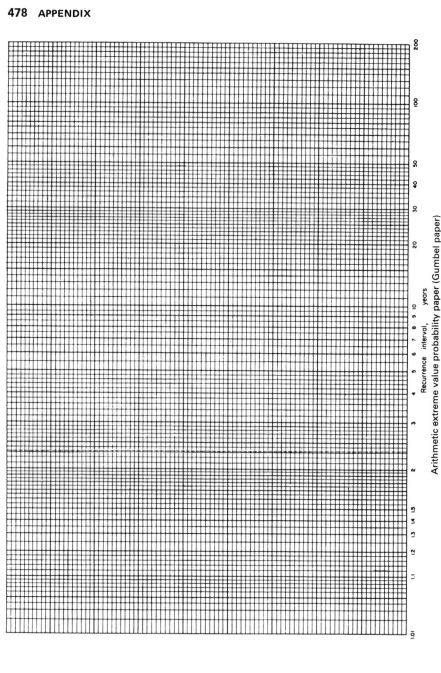

Arithmetic extreme value probability paper (Gumbel paper)

Recurrence interval, years

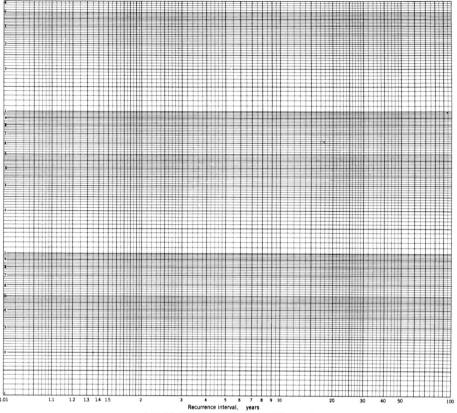

Recurrence interval, years

Logarithmic extreme value probability paper

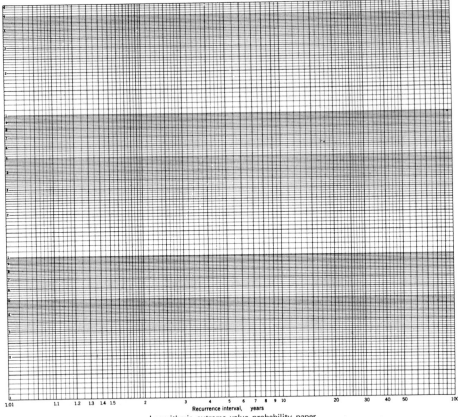

Recurrence interval, years

Logarithmic extreme value probability paper

Index